THE BIOLOGY OF
HUMAN ADAPTABILITY

EDITED BY

PAUL T. BAKER

Professor of Anthropology
Pennsylvania State University, U.S.A.

AND

J. S. WEINER

Professor of Environmental Physiology
University of London

CLARENDON PRESS, OXFORD

1966

Oxford University Press, Ely House, London W.1

GLASGOW NEW YORK TORONTO MELBOURNE WELLINGTON
BOMBAY CALCUTTA MADRAS KARACHI LAHORE DACCA
CAPE TOWN SALISBURY NAIROBI LUSAKA ADDIS ABABA
IBADAN KUALA LUMPUR HONG KONG

PRINTED IN GREAT BRITAIN BY JOHN WRIGHT & SONS LTD.
AT THE STONEBRIDGE PRESS, BRISTOL

FOREWORD

INTERNATIONAL collaboration in science presents two special difficulties. There is an enormous inertial mass to set in motion in the first place, and its motion demands paper as a fuel. But once it is moving it behaves like a breeder reactor and generates paper in increasing volume. The International Biological Programme had its first tentative beginnings as long ago as 1959. It has passed its inertial stages; it has generated a sea of paper, but now, at last, a few rocks and sandbanks of solid achievement are beginning to be visible as the tide retreats. This present volume originated in a symposium organized jointly by the International Biological Programme and the Wenner-Gren Foundation for Anthropological Research, and held in Burg-Wartenstein in 1964. Its primary purpose is to review the present state of knowledge in the general field covered by the studies on Human Adaptability that are being planned under the aegis of the International Biological Programme. What it reveals is, in fact, not knowledge, but a staggering state of ignorance about the human race. Man, like other animal species, is evolving, but evolving under pressures very different from those that have shaped him during the million years of his existence on this planet. And these pressures are becoming every year more intense as movement is facilitated, as races mix, as environment changes with urbanization, and as food supplies dwindle. If the adaptation of man to his environment is to be measured, if we are to predict and eventually forestall, we must have a baseline. This book looks for the existing baseline and finds it to be instead a series of dots and dashes with too few continuous stretches and far too many unfilled gaps. It reveals the really urgent need for man to look at and measure himself. But it shows something else, the immediate good that is accruing from the effort of the International Biological Programme. Geneticists, anthropologists, anatomists, paediatricians, physicians and physiologists, in the small section of activity covered by this book, are crossing not only national boundaries, but the subject barriers that are often higher and more difficult to surmount. It is often easier to talk across a barrier of language to a worker from the other side of the world in one's own

v

subject than to an adjacent colleague whose outlook and technicalities are foreign. This volume represents a collaboration of a mere nine countries and six or so disciplines; thirty countries are now participating in the Human Adaptability Section of the International Biological Programme and the disciplinary mixture must be rich indeed. From all this, no doubt, a few enmities will emerge, a few reputations will be lost, but these eggs will be broken in the making of an omelet of tremendous flavour and high nutritional value.

For me as President of the International Union of Physiological Sciences it is a matter of gratification that this Section of the I.B.P. is moving ahead so well. The few, the very few, catalytic dollars that we were able to supply at an early stage are yielding a fine return. The choice of Professor J. S. Weiner, our representative on I.B.P., as the convener of this section was one we applauded. His energy and enthusiasm have infected others, and the Human Adaptability programme is well launched. But it will need men, money and above all goodwill in abundance if it is to navigate far on its difficult course. We wish it well.

LINDOR BROWN
President, I.U.P.S.

ACKNOWLEDGEMENTS

THE Editors and Participants of the Symposium on "The Biology of Populations of Anthropological Importance", on which the present publication is based, wish to thank the Directors of the Wenner-Gren Foundation for their generous help and hospitality. In particular we wish to thank Mrs. Lita Fejos Osmundsen, Director of Research, and her staff, whose efficient organization made the Symposium such a successful and memorable occasion.

CONTENTS

V AUSTRALIA

VI CIRCUMPOLAR

VII HIGH ALTITUDES

1

MAJOR PROBLEMS IN HUMAN POPULATION BIOLOGY

J. S. WEINER

M.R.C. Environmental Physiology Research Unit, London School of Hygiene and Tropical Medicine, Keppel Street, London, W.C.1

IT IS fitting that the International Biological Programme should include a section aimed at the world-wide comparative study of human adaptability. The IBP as a whole is concerned essentially with the functional relationship of living things to their environments, in the sea, in fresh water, and on the land; it is conceived as the world-wide ecological study of communities of plants and animals—those still existing in relatively natural habitats and those in more disturbed or artificial conditions.

An analogous approach can be made to the ecology of mankind. At this stage of human history vast changes are affecting the distribution, population density, and ways of life of human communities all over the world. The enormous advances in technology make it certain that many communities which have been changing slowly or not at all will relatively soon be totally transformed. We are therefore in a period when the biology of the human race is undergoing continuous change measured in terms of health, fitness, and genetic constitution.

The papers in this volume are intended to be read as a background to the considerations which prompted the formulation of this world programme on 'human adaptability' as one of the main projects of the International Biological Programme. As reviews, even of a limited proportion of the world's area of human habitation, the papers reveal clearly the urgency and cogency of the recommendations agreed on at the IBP assembly of twenty-five nations in Paris in July 1964. These recommendations are based on several years' discussion and consultation with experienced human biologists in over thirty countries, discussion which covered the topics of environmental physiology, population genetics, physiological fitness, growth and physique, including ancillary medical and nutritional aspects. The issues at stake may be conveniently, if not exhaustively, discussed under the four headings that the IBP assembly recommends that research should be planned and carried out.

Category I. Extensive surveys on a world-wide basis

(A) World-wide data collection on genetic polymorphic systems.
(B) World-wide data collection on growth and physique.

Category II. Intensive, multidisciplinary regional studies

These studies based on habitat extremes and on habitat and population contrasts may be listed as follows.

(A) Studies with emphasis on environmental physiology—adaptation to heat and cold.
(B) Studies with emphasis on high-altitude adaptations.
(C) Studies with emphasis on genetic constitution.
(D) Studies with emphasis on nutritional studies.
(E) Studies with emphasis on growth and physique, particularly longitudinal studies.
(F) Studies with emphasis on fitness (working capacity and respiratory function).

Category III. Special investigations on selected populations

(A) Working capacity and fitness of urban, non-urban, and athletic groups.
(B) Socio-demographic factors affecting genetic structure.
(C) Disease as a selective agent.
(D) Special nutritional problems including calorie and protein requirements in different habitats (FAO proposal).
(E) Biological factors in population dynamics.

Category IV. Medical geographical surveys related to current WHO projects

(A) Blood pressure and related studies.
(B) Haematological studies.
(C) Geographical distribution of blood antibodies.
(D) Congenital defects.

These categories were chosen to take account of (i) the need for urgent international action for the rapid accumulation of certain biological data, (ii) the need for a multidisciplinary co-ordinated and sustained approach in certain 'key' habitats for the solution of basic problems, (iii) the great variation in scientific personnel and other resources available in different countries, and (iv) the relevance of the programme to health and well-being. For these reasons the categories have been devised to provide different nations with a maximum choice, and different topics can be combined in many different ways. National contributions can thus take the form of either (a) participation in *extensive* internationally co-ordinated surveys (particularly Categories I, IIIA, IIID, and IV) or (b) *intensive* and usually multi-nationally organized and co-ordinated regional studies (particularly Categories II and III); the latter to a large extent include the objectives of the extensive surveys.

In arriving at the present IBP set of proposals (see *IBP News, No.* 2) the papers and discussions of the Burg Wartenstein symposium were of immense value, not merely because many serious gaps in our knowledge were made so clear; it was possible to examine by reference to progress already made, what was required in terms of hypothesis, design, methodology, and organization, as well as international collaboration, to cope with such fundamental questions of human ecology as fitness, selection, and population balance, with physiological, developmental, polymorphic, and other forms of adaptation, and with problems of genetic and environmental interaction, affinity, and divergency. How actual *field* work should be planned, its design and strategy, as well as the agreed basic methodology, is at the heart of the Human Adaptability Project. In this volume essays bearing on this prime question are those by Harrison, Schull, and Baker. In this first paper the various categories of research under the Human Adaptability Project, as already outlined above, will be examined in the light of the Burg Wartenstein reviews, to give some appreciation of our present ecological insight and to explain what it is hoped to achieve in the years of the International Biological Programme.

Genetic surveys on a world scale (Category 1A)

In two books, 1954 and 1958, following on the earlier publications of Boyd (1939), Mourant and his colleagues assembled and examined as comprehensive a compilation on blood group data as was available at the time. As Mourant himself has stressed, the need to assemble and tabulate the continually accumulating data remains urgent; at the same time there exist a great many gaps in our knowledge. Moreover, while the number of known genetic polymorphic systems has been increasing rapidly, many of the newer systems have been studied in relatively few populations. The great unevenness in our knowledge can easily be illustrated by reference to the Burg Wartenstein papers by Kirk, Hiernaux, Salzano, Tobias, and Edholm. To make an entirely rough guess it would seem that the Kell, Diego, Lutheran, Duffy, and P factors are known for less than one-fifth of the populations for which Rh and MN are known and these in turn are known for less than one-fifth of the ABO data. Hiernaux, for example, points out that on less than 10 per cent of several thousands of sub-Saharan tribes is there any genetic data. Edmondson (1965) assembled data on 24 genetic markers for some 30 'representative' Europeans, 29 Africans, 32 Asians, 25 Caledonians, and 33 American groups. Even this very condensed tabulation reveals complete absence, to the extent of two-thirds, of the desired coverage and even the best of studied groups are less than 75 per cent complete for the traits surveyed.

What purposes would be served by IBP surveys? The distributional pattern of genetic characters has been used of course for a long time, like other anthropological features, to elucidate the degrees of relationship between populations on a local, regional, continental, or world scale. To establish such relations on a secure basis, a knowledge of a large range of genetic markers is necessary. In Laughlin's paper it is shown that much closer affinities exist between the Eskimo-Aleut stock and Asiatic Mongoloids than with their nearer neighbours, the American Indians. This judgement is based on the availability of data on the ABO, MN, Diego, and other blood-group data and by differences in the frequency of non-tasters, in the BAIB excretion rates, and in the frequency of the haptoglobin types. From the data in Tobias' paper it is possible to state that Bushmen and Hottentots are closer together genetically than they are to the Bantu-speaking Africans but that they nevertheless have many characteristics in common with other Africans. Studies of affinity can be carried out to a high degree of discrimination, as Sanghvi's paper explains, and this would be one desirable objective of intensive regional studies (under Category II). There is still, however, much to be learnt on this question even from general genetic surveys.

Another significant outcome of surveys is the uncovering of clines and gradients. The existence of these or of major discontinuities can only be substantiated and made meaningful as more and more gaps between populations are filled in. As Laughlin points out, the accretion of data has revealed the probable occurrence of a *B*-gene frequency cline extending from central Asia into North American Eskimo populations, comparable to that extending westwards into Europe. In the New Guinea region, as Kirk indicates, there may be an altitudinal cline correlated with a decreasing G-6 PD deficiency. Scrutiny of the South African data reveals a gradient of increasing frequency of both A and B blood-group genes (and a decrease in O) as the Bantu populations of the south eastern regions of South Africa are traced into the Cape province so indicating a region of gene flow between Bantu and Hottentot.

The distribution of particular genes in relation to certain geographical features or to climate may suggest the operation of some selective factor. We need many more survey data to provide as complete a geographical picture as possible of those genes with a presumed relation to malarial resistance or sensitivity. The work carried out in New Guinea and described by Kirk in this volume represents a large step in this process of mapping. The past and present distribution of many other diseases, lethal in the reproductive period of life, are known; a more detailed regional mapping of various blood-group genes could well point to the existence of a selective influence.

General surveys may confidently be expected to reveal the existence in high frequency in certain communities of hitherto 'rare' genes or to the discovery of new allelic variations and their modes of inheritance. An example is given in Kirk's paper.

The general genetic survey is an essential first step in all multidisciplinary studies (as proposed under Category II), involving comparison between two or more communities. Some assessment of genetic similarity or dissimilarity is always of significance in such studies, whatever their special purposes might be.

A striking example is provided by Edholm in this volume in the plan he proposes for population research in Israel, where the genetic differences of immigrant groups are superimposed on habitat differences arising from contrasting climatic zones.

What has been said above on the blood-group systems is for the most part applicable to other genetic factors which could be included in surveys if personnel and finance permit. The frequency of non-tasters to PTC for example, has relevance to the existence of goitregenic areas, skin colour to the selective action of ultra-violet light, and colour blindness may be particularly low in still-existing hunting communities. Clearly there are many gradients and clines and other significant types of distribution to be discovered for these and other genetic characteristics.

Surveys of growth and physique on a world scale (Category 1B)

Anthropometric descriptions of samples of adults and children have of course been carried out extensively. In westernized countries standards of weight and height in relation to age are of relevance for insurance purposes, and as a guide to children's health and nutritional status such measurements and standards based on them are of great importance. As a matter of fact the number of well-standardized surveys adequate for specifying the growth and body build of populations on a comprehensive basis is more limited than is generally realized. It is true that anthropologists (of the older schools) have collected data in great abundance but with the avowed aim of making 'racial' or taxonomic comparisons. Consequently (and despite the praiseworthy standardization of technique and the development of statistical method) the data, in their hands, has proved of rather limited biological value. Undue concentration was paid to cranial and facial dimensions; body weight, circumferences, bone, fat, and muscle components were much less often measured. For the assessment of physique, body composition, or growth patterns and their relation to working capacity and to nutritional, climatic, and other environmental factors—in fact on the general questions of selection and adaptation—the older material is badly deficient.

The data on a geographical basis is also extremely uneven. Nevertheless, the information has been just sufficient to indicate that such important ecological generalizations as the Bergmann and Allen 'rules' may (within limits) apply to man. On this and many other questions the available data give no final answer. To give a few examples: Is there a definite effect of climate on the adolescent spurt or on the time of appearance of puberty? Is the secular increase in body height a continuing and world-wide phenomenon and what are its causes? Do nutritional differences affect growth and body composition differently according to the genotype?

What purposes would be served by IBP surveys? In his contribution to this volume J. M. Tanner makes quite clear the contribution co-ordinated international research could make under the IBP. The basic approach to all studies of growth and physique is summarized in his statement: 'We must suppose that in each of the major populations of the world the growth of its members was gradually adjusted, by means of selection, to the environmental conditions in which they evolved. The remnants of this process we should be able to see in modern populations.' In his paper Tanner provides clear guidance on the types of genetic study that are needed. Some of these are clearly a matter for intensive, sustained, and multi-disciplinary research. The scope and value of surveys of growth and physique as explained by Tanner and exemplified in his and other papers may be briefly outlined. As in the case of genetic studies, world-wide anthropometric surveys of body build and growth are urgently needed to fill many gaps in our knowledge of the geographical and climatic distribution of these characters. To give a few examples from the papers in this volume: In the South-East Asian region for few populations outside Israel or Turkey are there any available data. Amongst Negro peoples north of the equator where stature is the best-known measurement, there are data for about 200 populations, about a third of the total. Yet for stature and weight together, which would give some idea of shape, there is information for only twenty-four populations or 4 per cent of the total! The fact is that the growth characteristics of almost every population except the European is so little known that the study of any non-European group if properly carried out would have real scientific value.

Standardized and well-conducted surveys would serve a number of purposes. In many countries it would provide a base-line for measuring progress in health and nutritional programmes, both over a period of time and by comparison as in the results achieved in comparable social and environmental conditions elsewhere. The accumulation of data giving a minimal but adequate assessment of physique could in due course place the investigation of the relation between climate and growth, climate and puberty, climate and physique (i.e. the Bergmann and Allen 'rules') on a secure basis. In many countries as industrialization proceeds the course and cause of a secular trend could be followed and analysed as and when it occurred.

The important studies on growth and physique that should be made as part of multidisciplinary, interhabitat, and interpopulation regional investigations are referred to in a later section.

Intensive multidisciplinary regional studies (Category II)

The general aim is to elucidate physiological and genetic processes involved in adaptation and selection to climatic and other environmental 'stresses'. Numerous forms of stress can be envisaged but of those to which adaptation may occur three appear to be particularly amenable to study, namely heat, cold, and altitude. Various types of malnutrition or modes of life requiring continuous hard work, and above all disease, offer other situations. These are dealt with under Category III. Little is known about the genetic and non-genetic contributions to the array of bio-chemical, morphological, and physiological changes associated with these stresses. Adequate evaluation of these requires intensive regional studies and surveys designed to disclose either intra- or inter-population variability, or both. Particularly valuable in this respect would be investigations which reveal the variability between genetically different groups exposed to the same environment for long as well as short periods of time, or the variability within the same genetic groups when exposed to different environments. Of even greater value will be studies of those occasional situations wherein two or more genetically distinct groups are exposed to the same variety of environments. The investigation of populations actively undergoing adaptation to new surroundings is as important as the study of adapted populations.

Examples of the approach and of the issues involved in intensive regional population studies are given in the papers of the Burg Wartenstein volume. As these examples show, it is always neces-sary, irrespective of the ecological situation or of the question or hypothesis at issue, to obtain a comprehensive 'background' know-ledge of the populations studied. There is always a requirement for a comprehensive, and therefore multidisciplinary, specification of the following components.

(i) A basic socio-demographic assessment of the community (for sampling, genetic, and other purposes).

(ii) A basic assessment of the environment (the terrain, macro-climate &c.).

(iii) A general genetic survey (following Category IA above).

(iv) An assessment of medical status of the subjects.

(v) An assessment of dental condition.

(vi) An assessment of nutritional condition.

(vii) A background description of the daily and seasonal activities.

(viii) A general survey of physique and growth (following Category IB above).

(ix) Some assessment of working capacity as an index of physical fitness.

Because every population chosen is to be studied by this comprehensive approach, the research programme will require preliminary and pilot stages before full-scale study by repeated visits by multidisciplinary teams can be undertaken.

Over and above the 'background' information, the particular problems posed by the ecological situation, the habitat and population contrasts, as well as the research design, will determine which elements are to receive special and sustained attention. The emphasis could fall on climate adjustments (physiological, morphological, or biochemical), on genetic and demographic structure of the community, on intensive studies of growth and physique, on intensive studies of physical fitness or on various aspects of nutrition. As already mentioned one fundamental aim would be to attempt to distinguish between genetic and non-genetic elements in adaptation, and another would be to detect the operation of selection.

Some illustrations of the issues involved may be drawn from the Burg Wartenstein contributions. Baker's report on his work in the high Andes is particularly apposite. Here there is a combination of hypoxia and cold stress. The highland Quechua and Aymara have attained an adaptation to their environment which incoming populations have so far not been able to match! The unravelling of the significant elements contributing to this successful adaptation is a complex task. For cold resistance the Chinchero male 'does not appear to have a body structure particularly adapted to cold stress'; yet as compared to newcomers the natives had greater cold tolerance associated with higher hand and foot temperatures, but how far this superiority is truly genetic remain unclear. At the same time the relatively slight biological differences so far apparent throw into relief the overriding importance of cultural adaptation in the Quechua culture. Baker's preliminary study emphasizes the need to look at the total stress situation and the total adaptive régime—biological and cultural—as well as the considerable difficulties of such a venture

To tackle this kind of problem Harrison in his paper offers a design for a high-altitude (Himalayan) study. He aims at a resolution of three main components—the role of immediate adjustments, the interaction of genetic and non-genetic elements, and the operation of 'on-going' selection. Harrison proposes a fourfold attack: (i) a comparison of two pairs of groups, each pair of similar genetic constitution at low and high altitudes, (ii) a comparison at each altitude of groups of differing genetic structure, (iii) making familial or 'kinship-cluster' analysis of significant and morphological changes to see whether any heritable component exists, and by an extension (following Baker's suggestion), relating the degree of adjustment of characters apparently conferring survival value to fertility, and (iv) looking for the existence, by age group, of a genetic shift, as a non-specific but fairly sensitive criterion of 'on-going' selection. It is true that no field work on man has as yet approached an analysis as elaborate as envisaged by Harrison and perhaps the Human Adaptability Project will stimulate at least a few attempts to do this. The statistical sampling and other methodological problems posed by an ecosystem analysis of this kind are discussed by Schull who suggests alternative approaches for the main issues emphasized by Harrison.

In varying degrees field work, much of it admittedly piecemeal, has provided some insight on these basic questions of adaptation and ecological selection.

The comparison of genetically similar people to different environments has been carried out both in the field and using simulated conditions. The immediate effects of exposure to both 'control' and experimental or stress environments are well known for Europeans subjected to moist heat (Wyndham, Macpherson†),

† Names in brackets refer to contributions in this volume.

dry heat (Wyndham, Metz), and cold (Hildes); for Africans (Wyndham) and Australian aborigines (Wyndham, Macpherson) in extremes of both heat and cold. Thus physiological acclimatization to heat has been shown as broadly similar for these different groups. Comparison of genetically contrasting groups under similar conditions of heat or cold stress does suggest the possibility of significant differences in adaptation. This may be the case in the cold resistance of the Australian aborigine compared to other groups (Macpherson, Hildes, Andersen). Responses to heat may also be quantitatively different as between Europeans and Indians (Malhotra) and Bantu and Europeans (Wyndham). It is interesting to note from the Burg Wartenstein discussion that tolerance to heat has not been studied in equatorial Africa or South America and that the cold tolerance of peoples indigenous to warm climates is almost totally unknown. In his paper on Israel, Edholm proposes a comprehensive and systematic cross-comparison of the physiological responses to both heat and excessive cold of three ethnically distinct communities, each represented by subgroups living in three contrasting habitats. Such a study could be designed to follow many of the lines of analysis propounded by Schull and Harrison.

The possibility of selection acting in these conditions of climate stress have appeared so far only as suggestions from differences of response exhibited by different groups. No investigator has as yet looked for any positive connexion between degrees of heat, cold, or altitude tolerance and reproductive performance as suggested by Baker. Nor has there been any kind of longitudinal study of the kind suggested by Harrison indicating the occurrence of some genetic shift with age under conditions where climatic stress is a major factor. Longitudinal study of genetic constitution and of differential fertility (by genealogical or cohort methods) would appear to be specially applicable to the situation in northern Australia as successive generations of Europeans continue to live in quite severe conditions.

Other aspects of long-term adaptation to extremes of heat and cold are also badly in need of investigation, for example in growth and development (Tanner) and hormonal adjustments in the cold (Hildes) and in heat (Macpherson).

There are many other important questions which only multi-disciplinary, long-term, co-operative investigations can answer.

Some of these are dealt with in the next section (Category III). These and many others are discussed in the papers in this volume, for example, the interaction between training for work and tolerance to cold (Andersen), the salt and water balance achieved in various hot climates and the endocrine basis for such adjustments (Malhotra, Wyndham, Macpherson, Edholm), and the interrelation of cultural and biological adjustments as seen amongst Eskimo (Laughlin), Bushmen (Tobias), or Andean peoples (Baker).

Special topics on selected problems (Category III)

The distinction between the problems discussed in the preceding category and in this category may appear to be hardly more than a matter of emphasis. It would be possible to incorporate most of these 'special topics' within multidisciplinary regional studies but it is equally possible and probably more convenient for certain questions to be isolated for special treatment. On these restricted questions the design appropriate to intrapopulation and intrahabitat comparisons is not necessarily appropriate to the investigation of the questions to be discussed below.

Working capacity and fitness studies (Category IIIA)

Systematic studies of populations in many different kinds of habitat and occupation could be regarded as falling into the category of world-wide surveys planned for the Human Adaptability Project. But the study of fitness as defined for the purposes of the project—'working capacity and pulmonary efficiency'—is technically an exacting matter and not to be undertaken except by well-equipped and well-trained personnel. It is not possible or desirable to advocate that tests of 'fitness' using apparently simple indices of 'strength' and 'endurance' at present in vogue among physical educationalists be carried out on a widespread scale, as it is certain that the lack of standardization, and above all the physiologically limited nature of such tests, would not yield results of a valid scientific character. Indeed the tests proposed for the IBP are not only technically sophisticated but require considerable ancillary information as well as careful sampling. It will be necessary, for any population, to have data on the medical and nutritional background, the daily routine of work and rest, the state of training, and the physique of the subjects. Many investigations in this field have little comparative value because nothing is reported on these important variables. These points are discussed by Andersen.

Under IBP, investigations would be comprehensive, technically standardized, and properly designed. Three groups of subjects are of major interest:

(i) urban groups, drawn from both sedentary and active occupations;

(ii) simple communities where muscular activity is essential for survival;

(iii) athletes, including 'top' athletes.

What purposes would be served by IBP studies? As measures of physical fitness, the working capacity and pulmonary efficiency will vary in relation to many factors—age, sex, environment, heredity, and training. We have little knowledge of the range and variability of physical fitness measured in terms of work capacity and respiratory efficiency, or of the influence of the factors mentioned. Thus we do not know what level of fitness is required for and associated with the life of our ancestors who depended on strength, endurance, physical stamina, and skilled muscular activity for their survival. We do not know how the fitness of peoples still living in subsistence economies compares with that of urbanized workers in occupations which require muscular fitness—dockers or miners, for example. We can fix the range of 'fitness' even wider by looking at the most physically efficient of our population—the athletes—at one end of the scale, and by examining the 'sedentary' groups of our urbanized society at the other.

To delimit the state of 'fitness' in this way would be a considerable achievement; it would serve as a frame of reference for the study of a wide diversity of groups. As Andersen indicates these studies could in fact go further. It would be possible to discover in what ways differences in fitness are brought about. For example, differences in nutrition, daily activity, or climate may be associated with quite different effects on muscle function or in the respiratory or the circulatory systems. It may be that the body build exerts a limitation on the extent and nature of working efficiency. The genetic element in physiological fitness may perhaps be approached through a study of athletes and their close blood-relations. If a high degree of muscular fitness is the prerequisite for survival in hunting communities, it would be interesting to know how this is related to the effort required in the light of studies of trained athletes. Put more generally, we should find, as a result of selection, a noticeably lower variance in work capacity and associated physiological characteristics in primitive groups, along with a very different polymorphic range.

At the present time we have a sketchy knowledge of the topics mentioned above. That work capacity is of significance to productivity is suggested by observation on Eskimos whose maximal oxygen range approaches values well above that of usually active Europeans (Rodahl). Wyndham in his contribution to this symposium records the somewhat surprising finding that the values for Bushmen 'are no better than those for moderately active men of other ethnic groups. Legend has it that they can perform prodigious feats of endurance in tracking the game. . . .' Wyndham's sample was very small—12 individuals—an indication of the difficulties of organizing this kind of research. In his paper Wyndham presents evidence that despite differences in physique, active Europeans and Bantu have similar maximal O_2 usages to Bushmen and Arctic Indians (viz. a mean of about 48 cal/min/kg) with athletes (59–68) and sedentary subjects (39) above and below. Clearly much more data on hunting peoples are required if we are to understand what the 'natural' state of fitness (if there is one) might be. No figures seem to be available for Australian aborigines, or New Guinea natives, tribal Indians, or Africans of Central and North Africa.

There are many good reasons for population studies of pulmonary function using standardized methods.

(a) The function of the lungs depends on their size which is determined by physique. The relationship of lung size to body size in different ethnic groups is at present poorly understood.

(b) Breathlessness is one of the factors which limit exercise in both normal fit subjects at sea level, and, more especially, in subjects taking exercise under conditions of reduced (or increased) barometric pressure, as well as in the elderly and those with diseases of the lungs and heart. Assessment of factors influencing breathlessness, in particular the ventilatory capacity and the ventilation during exercise, should therefore be made at the time of assessment of physical fitness and exercise capacity.

(c) There is evidence for 'racial' differences in pulmonary function in addition to those due to differences in body size;

the underlying reasons for such differences merit investigation. They may turn out to be not racial nor genetic but to be differences in training and strength of the respiratory muscles. This may account for the lower forced expiratory volume of the Indian subjects referred to by Malhotra.

(d) Pulmonary function exhibits diurnal and seasonal variations which are, as yet, poorly documented. Studies in polar regions where there are big differences in the relative lengths of night and day, in particular, provide an opportunity for investigating the underlying mechanisms.

(e) Pulmonary function is influenced by the atmospheric pollution to which the subject is exposed; this may be local and specific to the subject as a result, for example, of smoking a cigarette or living in an igloo, or it may be general as a result of industrial pollution of the atmosphere.

In making comparisons between populations in terms of climate adaptation whether it be to tropical heat, desert conditions, cold, or altitude, the state of physical fitness must be taken into account. Of the few investigations into this subject, that by L. Andersen (see Hildes' paper) suggests that physical fitness plays an important part in tolerance to cold. It is possible that interaction between high cold-resistance and physical fitness accounts for the amazing feats of load carrying by Himalayan peoples as mentioned in Pugh's and Malhotra's papers. Malhotra refers to studies of acclimatization to heat on Indian soldiers carried out in Britain. Interestingly enough, these men when artificially acclimatized did not show the same level of heat tolerance as Europeans similarly treated. The difference could well have been due to a somewhat lower state of fitness, as revealed in exercise and pulmonary tests. Really physically fit Africans exhibit working capacity in the heat the same as or greater than Europeans, as shown by the work of Wyndham and Ladell.

Striking differences in physique have been attributed to differences in diet as for instance among the Tutsi (see Hiernaux) or in comparing peoples of the Punjab with those of Madras (see Malhotra). No exploration of these habitat differences in their effect on working capacity has been made.

Socio-demographic factors affecting genetic structure (*Category* IIIB)

Social and demographic factors influence the genetic structure profoundly, and in the main, by acting as internal or external barriers to gene flow. Amongst human populations there exist groups ranging from virtually closed isolates of various sizes and with varying intensities of inbreeding to groups exposed to every degree of mixing with neighbouring or migrant communities. At this period of history we are witnessing the progressive disappearance of many long-established isolated and inbreeding communities. It is obviously a matter of some urgency to utilize the special opportunities for genetic analysis provided by these communities before they are broken up for ever. This is one reason for a concerted and organized effort in the immediate future such as is planned in the IBP. Reasons for putting special stress on the study of primitive groups are manifold and are given in the WHO memorandum on this subject⁻ (1964). That multi-national resources are needed is clear from the work of expeditions such as those described by Tobias in South Africa, Salzano in Brazil, and Kirk in New Guinea. In this volume Schull presents in detail the requirements for field studies and discusses in particular problems of sampling.

The genetic structure of the isolates and of migrant populations forms the subject of the detailed symposium volume edited by Goldschmidt (1963). Some aspects can also be illustrated by reference to papers in the present volume.

The operation and consequences of socio-demographic factors can be traced in many cases in some detail. Consanguinity studies afford favourable opportunities. There is now quite a good deal of information on degrees of inbreeding for various communities though it is urgently necessary to obtain much more on primitive communities. For example, how far is it generally true for primitive hunting and gathering groups that there was, as Salzano and Neel state, 'a high degree of inbreeding, at least at certain times of their evolution'. Insufficient is known of the consequences of inbreeding or its relaxation in particular on fertility, growth, and physique. If, in sufficient groups, analysis could be made of widely-differing intensities of inbreeding this would throw much needed light on the operation of 'heterosis'. This in turn has a close bearing on the underlying causes of secular trends in body size and development. The influence on height of matings of relatives of varying distance can be seen from a Japanese study (Schull). The study of new crosses needs to be carried beyond the first generation. Such longitudinal approach it is hoped would be instituted through IBP.

In primitive groups socio-sexual selection leading to differential fertility must often be operative. Neel and Salzano give an instance from their Xavante study in which a tribal chief through polygamy is responsible for the genetic endowment of nearly one-third of the next generation. In New Guinea conditions for this to happen are also in evidence (Kirk). In Angmagssalik isolate East Greenland one man who had been married three times had over 100 persons connected to him as a common ancestor. The implications of this are discussed by Laughlin. The fertility differentials within groups have a clear bearing on the 'founder principle'. The endowment of a whole series of populations in a new environment may be predominantly determined by a very closely-related family group. This has often been postulated and Salzano and Neel give an instance which shows how this process may begin. In the view of some it is possible to argue that the entire Australian continent could have obtained its population from one small migrant group. Repeated observations in a given region with detailed recording of the genealogies is quite likely to reveal the operation of fertility differentials in simple subsistence groups.

The intermixing of previously separated groups provides opportunity not merely for validating various hybridization models but may well yield important contributions to human genetics. For example, Haldane suggests that through careful family studies involving that mixture it may be possible to uncover the existence of pleiotropic morphological effects on some of the marker genes. A longitudinal community study in Israel of the kind discussed by Edholm offers a chance of observing effects of this kind. The study of the dynamics and consequences of gene flow between contrasting populations is particularly urgent where representative communities of the parental stocks are still to be found. Brazil (Salzano), Australia (Kirk), and South Africa (Tobias) are specially important in this respect.

One basic issue is the need to establish measures of 'genetic distance' between population groups. An illustration is given by Sanghvi in his paper with reference to caste barriers in India. The difficulties of assessing affinity through descent when it is certain that the frequency of some genes subject to fairly rapid change through selection is referred to both by Kirk and by Schull.

Disease as a selective agent (Category IIIC)

It has been postulated, notably by Haldane, that infectious disease might well have been the most effective agent of natural selection of man in favouring the survival and reproduction of those individuals possessing genes making for resistance. Most chronic or degenerative diseases (e.g. athero-sclerosis) would not be expected to act as selective agents as they kill after reproduction has ceased, unless they are in some way also associated with decreased fertility. That genetic resistance to infectious (and some other) diseases exists is not in doubt, though in only a few cases, so far, has the responsible gene (and its metabolic role in disease protection) been identified.

The subject of genetic differences in susceptibility to disease, infectious and non-infectious, and in determining the manifestation and severity of disease can only be briefly mentioned here; surveys have been made by Motulsky (1958) and Weiner (1964a). It is important however to emphasize the many urgent opportunities that exist for research and that much of this work falls very appropriately within the scope of the Human Adaptability Project of IBP.

What purposes would be served by IBP investigations? It is clear from the experience of field workers that for successful results, well-equipped and manned teams are essential, comprising geneticists, epidemiologists, and specialists in the disease under study. To put a team of this kind into the field would in all but a few cases call for a multi-national effort of the kind that the Human Adaptability Project (and particularly in association with WHO) is designed to stimulate. The ideal would be for several teams to be ready to go to the scene of an epidemic of an infectious disease and to carry out the clinical, pathological, demographic, and genetic comparison of affected and non-affected individuals and families. It was an investigation of this kind that led Vogel and his co-workers (1960) to claim that the ABO polymorphism was related to a differential susceptibility to smallpox.

The general model for research on this topic is provided by the demonstration of a causal relationship between the sickle-cell haemoglobin polymorphism and differential mortality to falciparum malaria. The most convincing evidence for this relationship has come from a study of genetic frequencies by age group. This showed a significantly greater survival of sickle-cell heterozygotes between birth and reproductive age, particularly at the younger age groups. The direct connexion with malaria resistance was provided by the finding that children with the sickling trait harbour significantly fewer malarial parasites. Evidence for 'on-going' selection changes in genetic frequencies by age group is discussed in Harrison's paper. He also deals with comparisons in terms of differential fertility of various matings. It will be recalled that Allison found an increased fertility of women heterozygous for the sickle-cell gene. It always remains essential to show that resistance to a given disease (or stress) is in fact greater for a given genotype.

Malaria still remains a challenging disease for the population geneticist. There is still much controversy over the possible protective effect of other haemoglobin abnormalities and it has been denied that G-6PD deficiency provides any protection against *Plasmodium falciparum* infections.

There remain many other communicable diseases whose geographical distribution or intrapopulation or familial incidence suggests the possibility of a differential genetic effect. Amongst these the enteric and diarrhoeal diseases would seem to carry special significance. They are still an important cause of illness and death in many developing countries—diseases due to enterobacteria are among the main causes of death in infants and small children.

Kirk in his contribution alludes to the interesting suggestion by Curtain and his colleagues of the existence of a genetic selective pressure favouring the Hp gene in lowland areas, as against highland areas, of New Guinea and its relationship to various ecological factors including the presence of arboviruses or of filiaris. Edholm emphasizes the often very sharp demarcation between areas endemic or non-endemic for *Bilharzia* in Iraq. Whether any genetic basis for such differences exists is quite unknown. As there is promise that quicker and reliable skin tests for determining the prevalence and intensity of the infection may be soon available this may open the way to analysis of differential susceptibility from a genetic point of view.

It has been postulated that a genetic, amongst other factors, may enter into the peculiar ecological distribution as well as severity of the eye-lesions associated with onchocerciasis. Transmission is confined to certain tropical areas of the western hemisphere and of the African continent and there are said to be at least 20 million cases. In parts of West Africa 30 per cent of the population has become blind and depopulation of fertile riverine areas has occurred.

If it were possible to organize a few teams under IBP to make 'model' investigations of the relation between certain diseases and genetic constitution, this would have a considerable value in terms of the design and sampling requirements of such studies. For sustained and systematic inquiries the best opportunities appear to lie in forming working associations between genetical and epidemiological teams and units already working in this very large and medically highly important field. WHO is of course a major stimulatory agency for field research and sustains a large programme covering all the main communicable and noncommunicable diseases. Of particular interest to population geneticists are the activities of WHO teams and units concerned with the diarrhoeal and enteric diseases including cholera, virus diseases such as the respiratory and arthropod-borne yellow fever and haemorrhagic fevers, and also measles and smallpox; in the parasitic category, in addition to those already mentioned, are trypanosomiasis, amoebiasis, and ankylostomiasis.

It will be an immediate aim of IBP to try to discover by discussion between virologists, bacteriologists, and parasitologists on the one hand and geneticists and epidemiologists on the other, which of these diseases offer particular encouragement for the genetic approach. A report is now available (Barnicot, 1965).

Special nutritional problems including calorie requirements in different habitats (Category IIID)

In every study of populations, whether in relation to climatic extremes, contrasts in habitat, selective effects of disease, or level of fitness—in fact as an inescapable aspect of human adaptability—account must be taken of the nutritional condition of the population. This underlines the difficulties of field study and the need for a multidisciplinary and intensive approach. The nutritional factor may be considered from two aspects which are not easy to separate. There is first the routine requirement for some form of nutritional assessment of all individuals and groups participating in an investigation. This has been discussed above as one of the aims of any multidisciplinary intensive study. The nutritional factor is in the nature of essential background information. The second aspect is to single out nutritional 'parameters' for particular study as IBP projects. The nutritional factor then becomes the primary aim. The field is of course vast and only a few very tentative suggestions are made here arising from views expressed at discussions on IBP.

(1) *Calorie and protein requirements in different habitats.* If, under Category III, regional studies are launched in a number of the localities singled out as specially suitable and urgent it should be possible to make an assessment of nutritional, particularly of calorie and protein, intakes in a standardized way in a whole series of habitats. FAO has urged the need for this to be done under IBP, and WHO states that there is little factual information for children and adolescents within the period 2–18 years on protein requirements.

It is perfectly clear that the calorie requirements ascertained in a whole series of habitats and populations will be related to several factors, notably differences in climate, in habitual activity, in available food sources, and in average bodily size of the population. The information will be valuable for its own sake, as FAO insists, even if the exact reasons for differences in level may not be easily ascertainable. If, however, reliable assessments can be attached to the factors mentioned, it may turn out that by keeping some relatively constant the influence of the separate items might become apparent. This is an ambitious task and only to be attempted on an international scale.

From references made to nutritional requirements in the papers of this volume it is clear that our knowledge of the calorie, protein, and calcium intake of populations of differing active patterns and in different climates is meagre. It would be interesting, for example, to be able to compare peoples of hot dry areas of South-West Asia with those of northern Africa; or tropical peoples in South America, Africa, India, and South-East Asia. Edholm records that only 5 g of the protein of middle Eastern diets is of animal origin. Macpherson, in his paper on New Guinea natives questions the present assumptions on protein requirements since it has been found that both men and women perform physical feats requiring great stamina on very low protein intakes. This comment draws attention to the need to relate level of work output in different populations to the very variable amounts of protein that we know are consumed. This question could be fruitfully studied in India judging from the data recorded by Malhotra which indicates large regional differences in protein consumption, for example, in the Punjab compared to Madras or Kerala. What the protein intake is of the mountain peoples subject to the physical stress of the terrain (as well as of cold) is not recorded, but these peoples, as described by Baker for the Andes and Pugh and Malhotra for the Himalayas, are capable of moving very large loads.

(2) *Nutritional contrasts and their effects.* In the papers by Hiernaux and Tanner attention is drawn to some of the questions which arise when two groups subsisting on contrasting states of nutrition are compared. The contrast may be in terms of gross nutriture, that is between well-nourished and poorly nourished or semi-starving groups, or in terms of qualitative differences as in protein or fat consumption. The biological effects to be looked for would include such questions as (i) the differences in physiological fitness measured as work capacity between the two groups; (ii) the changes in physique and growth that may have occurred— the birth weight and deposition of fat are of particular interest; and (iii) the effects on fertility and family size, difficulties of labour, pelvic shape, appearance of puberty, etc., which are of special importance. The inquiry could go further and compare the two populations in terms of their heat and cold tolerance and in other performance characteristics.

The significance of the biological effects would be greatly enhanced if it were possible to make similar comparisons on ethnically and genetically different peoples. It is quite likely that the genotype influences the expression of a nutritional defect. Thus the effect of low protein-intake in the Congo groups from Hiernaux's account would seem to be very different from the effects on Indian subjects mentioned by Malhotra. We have unfortunately so far very little information derived from analysis along these lines.

Another question is whether the smaller-sized shorter women in simpler communities are metabolically more efficient and suffer the disabilities of reproduction to a lesser degree than deprived females in the lower socio-economic classes of industrialized communities. Is it true that despite much lower protein and calorie intakes the birth rates are not diversely affected? It does seem to be the case that even women of poor physique and of general ill-nourishment in many developing countries appear to be able to sustain adequate lactations.

Supplementary feeding. As a further development of intensive regional studies involving comparisons of communities or villages at markedly differing protein levels the effect of introduction of such preparations as UNICEF dried milk or INCAP'S incaparina should be followed on a long-term basis.

Medico-geographical topics related to current WHO projects (Category IV)

In the course of IBP surveys and regional studies opportunities will almost certainly arise for collecting data and material of medico-geographical interest. There would always be a 'background' medical examination of the subjects with recording of personal and social data. In the genetic surveys (Category IA) and in the regional studies (Category II) and in many of the special studies on selected populations (Category III) there would be collection of blood. If agreed and standardized procedures are carefully followed field work under the Human Adaptability Project could be made to yield, on a wide variety of populations and habitats, urbanized communities, preliterate groups, and industrialized and underdeveloped regions, data which are already being sought for through international action. Under HAP the information on the following topics could conveniently be obtained:

(a) measurements of blood pressure and allied data, e.g. blood cholesterol levels,
(b) haematological data,
(c) blood antibodies,
(d) congenital defects.

The International Biological Programme provides a great opportunity to take stock of human adaptability, as it is manifested at the present time in a wide variety of terrains, climates, and social groups, to deepen our knowledge of its biological basis and to apply this knowledge to problems of health and welfare. To do all this satisfactorily, for communities ranging from the very simple to the highly industrialized, requires an integrated approach (Weiner, 1964) and an application of methods drawn from many fields, particularly those of human environmental physiology, population genetics, and developmental biology, aided by auxiliary disciplines, for example in medicine, anthropology, ecology, and demography. The papers in this book point the way to the realization of these exciting objectives.

REFERENCES

BARNICOT, N. A., 1965. 'Natural Selection and Transmissable Disease', *Nature* **208**, 535–536.

BOYD, W. C., 1939. 'Blood groups', *Tabul. Biol.* **17**, 113–240.

EDMONDSON, M. S., 1965. 'A measurement of racial difference', *Curr. Anthrop.* **6**, 167–198.

GOLDSCHMIDT, E. (ed.), 1963. *The Genetics of Migrant and Isolate Populations*. Williams and Wilkins, Baltimore.

MOTULSKY, A. G., 1958. 'Metabolic polymorphisms and the role of infectious diseases in human evolution', *Hum. Biol.* **30**, 43–72.

MOURANT, A. E., 1954. *The Distribution of the Human Blood Groups*. Blackwell, Oxford.

—— KOPEC, A., and DOMANIEWSKA-SOBCZAK, K., 1958. *The ABO Blood Groups, Comprehensive Tables and Maps of World Distribution*. Blackwell, Oxford.

VOGEL, F., PETTENKOFER, H. S., and HUMBOLD, W., 1960. 'Über die populations genetik der ABO-Blutgruppen', *Acta genet. Statist. med.* **10**, 267.

WEINER, J. S., 1964a. 'Human ecology', *Human Biology* (HARRISON *et al.*), Chap. V. Clarendon Press, Oxford.

—— 1964b. 'The biology of social man' *Jl. R. anthrop. Inst.* **94**, 230–240.

W.H.O. SCIENTIFIC GROUP, 1964. 'Research in population genetics of primitive groups', *Tech. Rep. Ser. Wld Hlth Org. No.* 279.

2

SOME CONSIDERATIONS IN THE DESIGN OF GENETIC SURVEYS

WILLIAM J. SCHULL

Department of Human Genetics, University of Michigan Medical School, Ann Arbor, Michigan

POPULATION genetics seeks to explain the origin and maintenance of genetic diversity. It attempts to accomplish this through the formulation of hypotheses and models, and the estimation of parameters which are functionally related to the persistence and spread of mutant genes. These estimates may be generated from observations made routinely for demographic or vital statistical purposes, but more frequently are derived from the data of a census or survey designed not only to serve this end but possibly other ends as well. Patently, such surveys will differ as a result of differences in their objectives, the state of the art, the manpower and funds available, and so on. However, if they are to provide for any population or community a fundamental assessment upon which more intensive studies may be based, they must be alike in a number of respects. At the very least, each survey must attempt to enumerate exhaustively the elements of interest in the population, for without such an enumeration, probability sampling at a subsequent stage in the study would be impossible. But there are other necessary similarities which become apparent when considering the tasks which confront one in the planning and execution of a survey.

The orderly design of a survey obliges one to:

(1) formulate a set of objectives or purposes,
(2) define the population to be examined,
(3) determine the information to be collected,
(4) choose, when possible, the methods of measurement,
(5) designate the sampling units, if the entire population is not to be studied,
(6) select, where appropriate, a sample,
(7) organize the fieldwork, and, finally,
(8) analyse the data and present the results.

While most of these aspects of survey design warrant more measured consideration than can be given here, possibly some of the more dangerous pitfalls and limitations of the survey technique will emerge from the presentation to follow, though, of course, some distortion may accompany the brevity.

To provide a focus let us assume that our charge is to expose a few of the general principles and problems in the design of surveys of a particular kind, namely those whose objectives are to provide 'background' knowledge on certain primitive and migrant populations. Insofar as primitive populations are concerned, our interest will centre chiefly on studies more akin to censuses than to sampling surveys, for the latter require an enumeration of the population, i.e. the sampling frame, and presumably it is to furnish just such an enumeration that is one of the aims of the studies under discussion. Surveys in migrant populations may, of course, be quite different, for on some of these, as in Israel for example, data already exist from which a variety of sampling frames may be derived. Under these circumstances, true sampling surveys can be undertaken, and more sophisticated experimental designs used (see Harrison, this volume).

Objectives or purposes of the surveys

Scattered across the world are groups of individuals who have in common cultures based upon the most simple of economies. They lead existences founded upon hunting-and-gathering, a simple pastoral life, or a digging-stick-and-hoe type of agriculture. The genetic structure of these groups and the biological and sociological parameters pertinent to this structure are virtually unknown. These aggregations of individuals are, by definition, the primitive populations of which we speak. What, now, are to be the aims of surveys of some or all of such groups ?

Broadly, we seek to collect, in an ecological and sociological context, data of several kinds which will contribute to an understanding of the roles of genetic and physiological factors in the birth and death process, and which will simultaneously provide a number of sampling frames pertinent to a variety of problems of genetic or physiologic interest. At a minimum, therefore, we are interested in a complete enumeration of the population; the best possible assessment of fertility and survival; a careful description of the social, biological, and physiological environments; and, quite possibly, the collection of genetic and/or physiological and/or growth and development data that are not conspicuously related to birth and death.

Further definition of the populations to be studied, and problems associated with the enumeration of these populations

As noted above, the populations we are interested in have characteristically primitive economies. They are, furthermore, generally isolated, often highly inbred, and usually small. Moreover, most of the individuals in these populations will be illiterate, and have a poorly developed notion of time. In this or any other context, the ideal census is one which describes a fixed and readily definable population. Unfortunately, human populations can be viewed as fixed only if the interval between the initiation and the completion of a census is infinitesimally small; if this is not true, migration and the birth-death process itself result in a steady flux of individuals into and out of the 'population'. To minimize the effects of this flux one generally attempts to complete a census as expeditiously as possible. Clearly the enumeration of many primitive or migrant populations may require weeks if not longer, and, as a consequence, the individuals enumerated cannot be said to constitute a fixed population. This may not be too important, however, if the flux is small relative to the size of the population. Of greater moment is the question of whether one should attempt to enumerate the population actually residing in a given place at the time of the census (the so-called *de facto* population) or the population of individuals 'usually residing' in the place (the *de jure* population). Admittedly the difference between the *de facto* and the *de jure* population of a primitive but agrarian community must be small and quite possibly negligible, but it is moot whether this would be so for a hunting-and-gathering group. This is neither here nor there, however, for our main purpose in introducing these notions is to call attention to a much larger issue, that of the definition and location of the population to be studied. This latter definition is not always self-evident, and in support of this statement consider the following illustrations: The Birhor of India are hunters-and-gatherers of a type; they number in the hundreds. Through most of the year they wander through their territories in small bands which differ in size with the seasons, and the difference between a band's largest and smallest size may involve a factor of 2. Wives are exchanged between bands in a characteristic manner and residence is patrilocal (Williams, 1965). Under these circumstances what constitutes the most appropriate unit of study? The band? The connubium? The totality of Birhor?

A second illustration concerns the Xavante recently studied by Neel and his colleagues (Neel, Salzano, Junqueira, Keiter, and Maybury-Lewis, 1964). At the time of their study some 110 individuals were to be found in Apewe's village whereas but a few years earlier the village numbered 200 to 220. This reduction was due to a schism within the village which these authors conjecture may be healed upon the death of the present chief, Apewe. Whether this does or does not occur is immaterial, for it is now evident that this fission-fusion process is common, and we know little about the effect upon disease experience, mate selection, &c., of these purposive perturbations in the *de facto* population— short-term though they may be. It is of obvious importance that the aggregate of individuals studied be drawn from the population about which information is wanted, and it is equally important to bear in mind that neither geographic proximity nor cultural affinity necessarily assures this.

Determination of the information to be collected

It is well to recall at this juncture that demographic and vital statistical data in modern societies are derived from elaborate and continuing systems of record-keeping which, in many respects, are not over-sensitive to the fallibility of the human mind. In primitive societies, however, such information is dependent upon the recall of a short-lived and illiterate people, prone to certain exaggerations and predictable lapses of memory. Since these latter biases may differ as a function of an informant's age, sex, place, or status in the family, clan, or village, they may be offset to some extent by seeking the same information from several individuals. Helpful though this may be, the observations which are sought must be constantly monitored, and evaluated against the biases and inadequacies of the informants. But what data might one seek in order to describe in genetic terms the birth-death process, say, and what shortcomings might such data have?

At a minimum it would seem possible, even mandatory, to obtain the following:

(1) the name or names of each individual, and the names of his spouse or spouses; these names should, of course, include social group affiliation;

(2) sex;

(3) the individual's age or age-set and position therein;

(4) place of birth;

(5) names of parents and all siblings;

(6) names and sex of all children, live or stillborn; for those children still alive, the present age, and for those dead, the age at death along with some indication of the cause, if possible;

(7) place of birth of all members of the family whether currently residing in the village or not; and

(8) age at marriage or beginning of cohabitation; preferably the latter if these ages differ markedly as in the Xavante, for example (see Neel, Salzano, Junqueira, Keiter, and Maybury-Lewis, 1964).

It would be possible with the data thus far outlined to describe the breeding structure of the population with respect to age and sex, degree of endogamy, frequency of consanguineous or affinal marriages of various kinds, &c. It would be further possible to specify some of the changes in this structure over a short time interval. One could also describe to an extent age-specific patterns of mortality and reproduction, and, to a more limited degree, changes in these patterns. To interpret differences between groups within the population or between populations with respect to any of these measures certain additional information would be necessary. It must be borne in mind that meaningful comparisons within the population or between two or more populations require the comparison groups to be alike in all respects save the one under consideration. This implies, of course, adequate allowance for all extraneous sources of variation either through the choice of the comparison groups or through the estimation procedure used, for instance covariance analysis. One of the more formidable tasks in the design and implementation of a survey is the identification of possible sources of extraneous variation, the evaluation of their probable importance, and the initiation of steps to control or minimize their effects.

We know that the number of extraneous variables, or more properly, variables of but incidental interest which impinge, for example, upon the birth and death process, are numerous. They range from nutritional habits, to cultural practices that may favour the survival of one sex as contrasted with the other, to endemic disease and the relationship to it of population size. There is no prior basis for believing that these factors will be uniformly distributed with respect to other variables of greater genetic interest, for instance to inbreeding. In fact, and with specific reference to inbreeding, there is a basis for suspecting that important 'socio-economic' differences will probably exist (Dronamraju, 1963; Furusho, 1964; Schull and Neel, 1965).

Among the factors of potential importance where data could be obtained the following have been suggested (WHO Scientific Group on Research in Population Genetics of Primitive Groups, 1963):

(9) non-paternity or non-maternity;
(10) attitudes which favour assortative mating;
(11) hazards of war, hunting, leadership, &c.;
(12) practices related to parturition, social activities, &c., which may affect sexual intercourse;
(13) practices related to infant feeding;
(14) differential nutrition between, as well as within, families;
(15) occurrence of disease or forms of self-mutilation which might influence fertility and survival; and
(16) attempts to control population size through infanticide, the use of abortifacients, &c.

Other factors can undoubtedly be added to this list, and some of these will be of general importance while some will, of course, have importance only in specific instances.

Two admonitions about the data to be collected now seem in order. First, care must be taken to ensure that every observation is, in fact, relevant to one or more of the objectives of the survey, and that no essential observations are omitted. Second, care must be taken not to over-measure. Alternatively stated, since resources are finite, there must be some number of measurements in a survey that will give maximum returns, both in terms of quantity and quality of information. To exceed this number may be to invite disaster.

Choice, when possible, of the methods of measurement

It is generally less taxing to think of variables to measure than of the methods of measurement of these variables that will lend themselves to statistical analysis. Several of the variables in the list just enumerated serve to illustrate the problem. For example, there is general agreement that nutrition affects fertility and mortality, and, therefore, that nutrition must be measured with a view towards possible differences which may obtain between individuals, families, &c., within a population. What choices of measurement exist? First, one might merely note that males are given larger portions than females, the young larger portions than the old, the strong larger portions than the weak. Under these circumstances, differences in nutrition are categorical, and some of the analytic possibilities are immediately compromised. Second, one might attempt to replace assignment to categories by a quantitative measurement. Where this is possible, it opens the way to the use of more powerful statistical techniques, principally regression analysis. It seems unrealistic to believe that nutritional measurements on primitive groups undertaken as part of a many-faceted study would ever satisfy a nutrition specialist. That is to say, reliable estimates of caloric intake are not likely to be obtainable on the basis of a few days or even weeks of observation. Granted this, and granted also that the aim of the nutritional studies is primarily to control extraneous variation, one is tempted to settle for a more 'rough and ready' form of measurement. This may consist of designating arbitrarily some small number of staples of the diet, and then crudely reckoning the intake of these. As an illustration, we are presently engaged in a survey in Japan, one objective of which is to ascertain the effect of inbreeding upon fertility. There is evidence that systematic socio-economic differences may obtain among consanguinity classes, and that these may be reflected in nutrition. Some 8200 households are involved which clearly precludes detailed dietary studies. We have, therefore, selected six staples of the diet—fish, meat, milk, potatoes, rice, and *mugi* (wheat or barley). The units in which these staples are to be measured are of the simplest kind—number of times eaten per day or week, or, in the case of the cereals, *go* per day, a unit of measure known to every Japanese housewife. These simple measures are ultimately to be put together into a linear compound, a nutritional score so to speak, which, other experience suggests, will have the attributes of a normal variate (or nearly so) and will therefore admit of covariance analysis.

Similar mensurational problems exist for other variables on the list previously enumerated. Thoughtful consideration of every variable to be measured in each survey, and the phenomenon one is attempting to elucidate with a given measurement, will unquestionably improve the method of measurement in many, though possibly not in all, instances.

Sampling problems

Presumably most primitive populations will be of a size such that, at any given time, every member of the population can and will be examined. It is conceivable, however, that some groups may be too large, or spread over too great an area, to make it feasible to examine everyone, so that some form of selection of the individuals to be examined must be devised. Two general alternatives present themselves. First, one might strive, but without system, to examine as many individuals as possible. The justification for this approach might be its convenience, and the presumption that if the 'chunk' of the population studied is sufficiently large the biases which may be introduced by a failure to assure representative sampling must be small. This is a tempting but dangerous point of view. It can, in fact, lead to results which may be actively misleading if, for example, the frequency of the event under consideration is less than the proportion of the population not examined, however small the latter may be. Second, one might invoke some form of probability selection, the justification for which has been carefully detailed in numerous books on sampling theory (Cochran, 1953; Deming, 1950; Hansen, Hurwitz, and Madow, 1953; Yates, 1960). If this is chosen to be the wiser course, as in fact it is, then three questions immediately arise. What is to be the sampling unit? What is to be the sample size? What is to be the sample structure, the method of sample selection? An answer to the first of these is generally to be found in the objectives of the survey, but practical considerations are apt to determine one's responses to the other two questions. Among such considerations will be the cost of a particular observation, the time it requires, its difficulty, the effect of a particular measure or group of measurements upon the response rate, the precision desired for the estimate, &c. A general discussion of these matters is likely to prove profitless, for they are often uniquely determined by the population and the problem.

All of the numerous forms of sample selection which may be employed have in common one requirement, that every element or sampling unit in the population (or sampling frame) must be known, and each must have a non-zero probability of selection. While it is not mandatory, selection usually proceeds in such a way that all elements have an equal probability of being chosen. The simplest form of sampling is the so-called unrestricted random sample. This admits with equal probability all of the possible ways that a sample of n elements can be drawn from a population of N. Though it is widely used, this form of sampling does not provide, as a general rule, the most precise, nor the most economical solution to a given sampling problem. It is basic, however, to all other selection methods that seek to introduce some control over the probabilities associated with the various possible sample combinations.

One of the more frequently used alternatives to unrestricted random sampling is the stratified sample. In this the population is divided into groups or strata so that every element appears in one stratum and an unrestricted random sample is then drawn from each stratum. When the sampling fraction is the same for all strata, sampling is said to be proportionate, but there are situations in which it is advantageous to vary the sampling fraction, that is, for sampling to be disproportionate. This is particularly true when one's resources are limited, and some 'optimum allocation' seems desirable. The possibilities for stratified sampling in the study of human populations are virtually limitless. For example, if one were interested in attempting, through antibody studies, to determine the array of diseases to which a primitive or migrant population had been exposed, stratification on sex and age would be mandatory. In this case, it might be desirable to stratify on certain other variables such as size of family, occupation, and socio-economic class if differences with respect to these exist within the population.

Implicit in our remarks thus far are two assumptions, namely, that element sampling is to occur, i.e. that the basic elements of the population are also the sampling units, and that the choice of each sample unit is random. There are alternatives to both of these situations. Thus, the choice of the sampling unit may be systematic rather than random. This implies the selection of sample units k elements apart on a list after a random start in the interval 1 to k. Sampling would be systematic if, for example, all individuals within a population were assigned unique numbers and a sample selected by the random choice of a terminal digit in these registration numbers. The alternative to element selection is cluster sampling, and instances of this would be the selection of entire families within a village, or a specific village among a group of villages. This form of sampling may be highly economical, particularly when time or difficulty of travel is important, but cluster sampling often increases the variance of the sample estimate and its economic advantage may thereby be vitiated. If this seems likely, it may be advantageous to turn to sub-sampling wherein two or more stages are involved in the selection of the sample. The objective is to subselect a final sample from a larger one in such manner as to improve the final selection. Most screening procedures are, in effect, the first stage in a multi-stage sampling design.

Among other useful sampling procedures are multi-phase sampling and the use of interpenetrating samples. In the former, one selects a sample and then a subsample. Certain observations are made upon all elements in the sample and others are made only on the elements within the subsample. The objective is to obtain some experience upon the subsample, to tie this functionally to some more readily obtained observation in the large sample, and thereby to predict some parameter in the population. The following example may serve to illustrate the technique. A comprehensive examination of the stool for helminthic parasites is time-consuming and must be repeated several times if there is to be reasonable probability of determining the nature and extent of these parasites that any individual harbours. Most helminthic infestations that are demonstrable by stool examination are accompanied by a marked rise in number of the circulating eosinophils. The determination of the number of eosinophils in the peripheral blood is a relatively straightforward and simple procedure, and thus, to determine the frequency and nature of helminthic infestations in a population, one might draw a large sample of individuals and determine the degree of eosinophilia in each, whilst upon a smaller, random subsample, stool examinations might be carried out. With the aid of these two types of observations, and of the relationship of the subsample to the main one, the frequency of worm infestations could be estimated more reliably than either sample alone would permit. Notice that had attention at the second step been confined to individuals found to have eosinophilia in the first step we would have had a multi-stage sample rather than an instance of multi-phase sampling.

'Interpenetrating subsamples' is a technique largely developed by Mahalanbois (1946, 1960) and his students. One draws an unrestricted random sample of size n; this sample is randomly divided into m subsamples. Work is then planned so that there is no correlation between the errors of measurement associated with any two observations in different subsamples. For example, suppose physical examinations were to be performed on a sample of individuals. This sample is randomly divided into m subsets. An individual within a given group is then randomly assigned to one of a number of examining physicians; the physicians associated with each group of individuals are different. This design would be one of interpenetrating subsamples. Its merit rests upon the unbiased estimate of error (diagnostic in this case) which it affords, and the insight into the effects of correlations in the errors of measurement in different groups.

Whatever the sample structure the objectives are, of course, the same, namely, to provide an estimate (estimates) of some parameter(s) of the population together with an appraisal of its (their) accuracy. The various procedures here described differ primarily in the precision and cost with which these estimates and their variances are obtained.

Analysis of data and presentation of results

An investigator's moment of truth comes when, armed with a question (or a population to be described) and data presumed pertinent to the occasion, he begins the analysis of his observations to determine what deeper insight into his problem they afford. Clearly, these manipulations and the presentation of the results of the survey must serve, first and foremost, the objectives of the investigation. There are, of course, restrictions on the form of the analysis; these are set by the questions to be answered, the model(s) to be fitted to the data, and the method of sample selection that has been used. Since these vary from survey to survey, a meaningful account of the specifics of data analysis and presentation is precluded. Accordingly, this section will be devoted to a brief mention of certain advances in data processing and statistics which should find application in many surveys.

One of the more important technological advances of this century has been the development of the digital computer, for this machine has revolutionized methods of data processing. Advances in only data storage and retrieval and their applicability to studies of primitive or migrant peoples could well be the topic of a special symposium. Briefly, one is no longer restricted to the eighty columns of an IBM card, or the equally limited capacity of a McBee card. Magnetic tapes or disks can store more than a million words of information, and each word may involve as much as 2^{36} bits of information. Present machines can read and process this information with a speed that is truly staggering. Moreover, digital computers are now so widely available that inaccessibility of a machine is no longer a valid argument for their non-use. Automatic programming and 'canned' programs for storage, retrieval, and screening put an extremely sophisticated data processing capability at the elbow of virtually every investigator.

The large-scale digital computer has also revolutionized numerical analysis. Out of this revolution have come new statistical techniques, but more important, perhaps, a broader use of a variety of analytic possibilities previously denied the investigator. Parts of multivariate theory, for example, are more than thirty years old, yet so formidable have been viewed the calculations involved in their application, that these procedures have seen only limited use. Psychology, and to a lesser extent anthropometry, have attempted to incorporate some of these advances into their methodologies, but even here, the arithmetic required in component or factor analysis led to the development of numerous methods, for instance, the centroid method, whose object was to avoid as far as possible the labour involved in the solution of the characteristic equation, the cornerstone of so many multivariate techniques. Today, the solution of a characteristic or determinantal equation is no longer viewed as challenging even when thirty, forty, or more roots may be involved. It seems appropriate, therefore, to consider briefly some of the analytic opportunities which these developments have made possible.

We have earlier stated that many, if not all, of the primitive populations of concern to us are in imminent danger of extinction or absorption. It will be tempting to incorporate into studies of these groups too many observations, and to attempt to make each study an omnibus for all manner of biologic observations. Most investigators will succumb to this temptation. The error of this will become apparent only when they are faced with the analysis of their data. It will then become patent that to relate many observations such as those on growth and development to another variable poses rather knotty problems, as a consequence of the number and interdependence of the former variables. One could, of course, deny the existence of a problem and analyse each variable separately, and this is, in fact, commonly done. Alternatively, the investigator may seek some means of reducing the number of variables that he feels obliged to consider. A given set of variables may be reduced, of course, by the arbitrary exclusion of those one thinks are unimportant, but there are less subjective means. These involve examination of the dependences as well as the interdependences among the variates and two techniques are particularly useful in this regard. One of them attempts to identify important dependences by what is now termed stepwise regression. The general argument proceeds somewhat as follows.

The classical multiple regression model asserts that some observed variate, y, is a function of p variables X, that is

$$y = \sum_{j=0}^{p} \beta_j X_j + \varepsilon,$$

where ε is a random variable usually assumed, without loss of generality, to have a mean of zero. It is important to note that the X's are not regarded as random variables, and, therefore, the model though multivariable is not multivariate. Solution of the equation above gives the least squares 'best' estimates of the coefficients, β_j, for a particular set of observations. These coefficients are, of course, measures of the dependence of y on the various variables, X. Normally in the solution of this equation one does not solve intermediate equations; that is to say, one does not investigate equations where the limits of j are less than p. In the stepwise procedure this is precisely what is done. The intermediate equations which are solved are obtained by adding one variable at a time to the regression equation. The variable which is added is that one which makes the greatest improvement in the 'goodness of fit', i.e. reduces the residual sums of squares by the greatest amount. The importance of the stepwise procedure here rests on the fact that the final regression equation includes only significant variables. Insignificant ones are removed in the course of the analysis. A recent experience will serve to illustrate the usefulness of this method as a means of reducing the number of variables in a multivariable situation. An orthodontist interested in malocclusion studied some twenty-nine measurements which can be made on a lateral cephalogram. He chose one measurement, the so-called A–B distance, as 'dependent' variable, and attempted to determine the degree of dependence of this variable on the remaining twenty-eight. Stepwise regression revealed that only twelve of these measurements were significantly related to this distance. Presumably in future studies the remaining sixteen can and will be discarded.

The second technique attempts to reduce the number of variables through a consideration of their interdependences, that is, through a consideration of their interrelatedness when no one is viewed as dependent upon the others. Thus one could, for example, attempt to describe anthropometric differences in terms of size and shape where each of these is some linear function of the k measurements which are presumed to be available, or some subset thereof. Or, without necessary reference to size and shape, one could restrict attention to those linear combinations of the measurements with large variance since it is variation between individuals itself which concerns us, and not the means by which that variation is necessarily expressed. We assume, of course, that the number of such linear combinations does not exceed k. The method of principal components to which we now turn provides, from a matrix of observations, new sets of linearly combined measures with certain desirable variance properties. The argument, largely due to Hotelling (1933), which underlies the use of principal components, proceeds somewhat as follows.

Suppose we have observations on N individuals where each observation consists of k measurements, say, $y_1, y_2, ..., y_k$. Let us assume that these variables have a common multivariate normal distribution characterized by mean vector $\mu = 0$, and variance-covariance matrix Σ. Now our interests lie in the sources of the variation which exists between individuals with respect to some phenomenon, for example, growth. A vector of simple anthropometric observations may not necessarily be the best measure of this variation. As an illustration, in the case of inbreeding, we are not overly concerned with what inbreeding does to a specific anthropometric but rather with its overall effect on growth and development. The yardstick which most effectively measures the latter could readily be some combination of the measurements other than the simple sum. We can profitably ask, therefore, is some new variable, L, where

$$L = w_1 y_1 + w_2 y_2 + \ldots + w_k y_k,$$

a better metric than the original vector of observations ? We judge L to be better if, ideally, the variance of L is equal to the generalized variances of the y's, that is, the determinant of Σ, for under these circumstances all of the variation in the y's can be subsumed under a single variable, L. Rarely, however, will this situation obtain; one more frequently finds that a single linear combination does not describe all of the variation, but that often some small number of combinations will describe the bulk of the variation. Mathematically, the task is to generate a series of uncorrelated linear combinations L_r ($r = 1, 2, \ldots, k$) which collectively account for all of the variation in the original vector variables. A full account of the theory whereby this is accomplished is to be found in Kendall (1957) and Anderson (1958).

Some notion of the usefulness of principal components is to be gained from the following. Several years ago, we (Schull and Neel, 1963) had occasion to examine 853 young girls whose parents were first cousins. We were interested in the extent to which growth in childhood might reflect the existence of polygenic systems to which the X-chromosome contributed disproportionately either in terms of number of genes or through the presence of one or more 'major modifiers' of the basic system(s). Observations on these children consisted of

weight,	head length,
height,	head breadth,
head girth,	head height,
chest girth,	sitting height,
calf girth,	knee height.

There are, of course, ten eigen vectors or principal components associated with this matrix of observations. It is possible to show that within these children the first eight components account for some 98·5 per cent of the variation, the first three for some 75·5, and the first component alone for slightly more than 50 per cent. Thus, if one restricts his attention to just the first three components, one is, in effect, still studying the bulk of the variation which exists between these children.

The nature of these components is also interesting, for they reveal a surprising similarity between 5- to 11-year-old Japanese girls and British adult males (for data on the latter see Burt and Banks, 1947). This may be regarded as evidence that these components are largely invariant from one group of individuals to the next. Whether this proves to be true or not, the technique here illustrated can be used to reduce the number of variables under scrutiny, and in that very process may reveal new and fundamental relationships between these variables. A further illustration of this is to be found in the attempts of Cavalli-Sforza and Edwards (1965) to analyse human evolution.

Lest the future of multivariate analysis appear too rosy it should be borne in mind that these procedures are dependent upon certain assumptions regarding normality of distributions, homogeneity of variance-covariance matrices, &c. There is evidence, however, that many multivariate as well as multivariable methods of analysis are robust, that is to say, small departures from the basic assumptions do not jeopardize the meaningfulness of the tests (see, for example, Ito and Schull, 1964).

No consideration, no matter how brief, of the role to be played by digital computers in studies of primitive groups would be complete without some mention of the uses of these machines for Monte Carlo simulation and in the calculation of certain descriptive statistics of a kind not previously mentioned. Specifically, I have in mind the calculation of coefficients of inbreeding for individuals who are members of highly inbred communities. Such computations are notoriously tedious and error-prone. One method of calculating these coefficients which can be readily programmed was set out many years ago by Sewall Wright (see Wright and McPhee, 1925). This method yields an approximation to the 'true coefficient' and is based upon analysing random lines of ancestry through father and mother for common individuals. More recently, Kudo (1962; see also Kudo and Sakaguchi, 1963) has suggested an exact method for calculating coefficients of inbreeding which lends itself readily to machine programming, and, in fact, has already been programmed (MacCluer, unpublished). The program exists in MAD (Michigan Algorithm Decoder) and FORTRAN, but the former appears somewhat more efficient. The time to compute a given coefficient of inbreeding varies, of course, but some notion of the rapidity with which the calculations can be carried out can be gained from the following. In a pedigree of 330 persons and 6 consanguineous marriages, the coefficients of inbreeding for the 6 consanguineous marriages were computed on the average in 1·6 seconds.

Finally, since one of the avowed purposes of studies of primitive groups is to provide some new insight into the factors which may have shaped contemporary man, mention should be made of the use of computers to advance our knowledge in this sphere. It is generally agreed that current evolutionary models incorporate too few stochastic elements. Efforts to remedy this have been largely unsuccessful because the equations which arise have proven analytically intractable (for a more complete discussion the reader is referred to Moran, 1962). This has encouraged a number of individuals to explore the applicability of Monte Carlo methods to a variety of problems in population genetics (Brues, 1963; Kundstadter, Buhler, Stephan and Westoff, 1963; Schull and Levin, 1964). The worth of these latter studies is, of course, directly proportional to the reality of the values assigned to the various parameters which constitute part of the input data. If these values are realistic, and only further studies of primitive groups can provide some guidance in this respect, then the consequence of altering singly or in concert any of the numerous forces which shape the genetic structure of a population can be examined. Complex genetic models can be investigated which envisage, for example, selection operating simultaneously upon a number of loci, some linked and some not linked (see for example Fraser and Hausche, 1965). The ultimate impact of investigations of this kind upon population genetics cannot now be foreseen. Some individuals hold, however, that our concern should be directed solely toward a description of average behaviour, and that an overweaning concern with stochastic elements serves only to obscure the central problems of population genetics. Even if this is true, the computer would still have an important function, namely, the numerical evaluation of equations too complex for more traditional analysis (as an illustration of this use of the computer see Lewontin, 1964; or Nei, 1964).

REFERENCES

ANDERSON, T. W., 1958. *Introduction to Multivariate Statistical Analysis*. Wiley, New York.

BRUES, A. M., 1963. 'Further contributions to the problem of the ABO blood group polymorphism.' Paper delivered at the meeting of the American Association of Physical Anthropologists, Boulder, Colorado, 4 May, 1963.

BURT, C. and BANKS, C., 1947. 'A factor analysis of body measurements for British adult males', *Ann. Eugen.* **13**, 238–256.

CAVALLI-SFORZA, L. L. and EDWARDS, A. W. F., 1965. 'Analysis of human evolution', *Genetics Today* (ed. S. J. GEERTS), Vol. 3. Pergamon Press, London.

COCHRAN, W. G., 1953. *Sampling Techniques*. Wiley, New York.

DEMING, W. E., 1950. *Some Theory of Sampling*. Wiley, New York.

DRONAMRAJU, K. R., 1963. 'Genetic studies of the Andhra Pradesh population', *The Genetics of Migrant and Isolate Populations* (ed. E. GOLDSCHMIDT). Williams and Wilkins, Baltimore, Maryland.

FRASER, A. S. and HAUSCHE, P. E., 1965. 'Simulation of genetic systems. Major and minor loci', *Genetics Today* (ed. S. J. GEERTS), Vol. 3. Pergamon Press, London.

FURUSHO, T., 1964. 'Relationship of stature to infertility, miscarriages, and fetal deaths. A preliminary report', *Jap. J. hum. Genet.* **9**, 100–109.

HANSEN, M. H., HURWITZ, W. N., and MADOW, W. G., 1953. *Sample Survey Methods and Theory*. Wiley, New York.

HOTELLING, H., 1933. 'Analysis of a complex of statistical variables into principal components', *J. educ. Psychol.* **24**, 417–441, 498–520.

ITO, P. K. and SCHULL, W. J., 1964. 'On the robustness of the T_0^2 test in multivariate analysis of variance when variance-covariance matrices are not equal', *Biometrika* **51**, 71–82.

KENDALL, M. G., 1957. *A Course in Multivariate Analysis*. Griffin, London.

KUDO, A., 1962. 'A method for calculating the inbreeding coefficient', *Am. J. hum. Genet.* **14**, 426–432.

—— and SAKAGUCHI, K., 1963. 'A method for calculating the inbreeding coefficient. II. Sex-linked genes', *Am. J. hum. Genet.* **15**, 476–480.

KUNDSTADTER, P., BUHLER, R., STEPHAN, F. F., and WESTOFF, C. F., 1963. 'Demographic variability and preferential marriage patterns', *Am. J. phys. Anthrop.* **21**, 511–519.

LEWONTIN, R. C., 1964. 'The interaction of selection and linkage. I. General considerations; heterotic models', *Genetics* **49**, 49–67.

MAHALANOBIS, P. C., 1946. 'Recent experiments in statistical sampling in the Indian Statistical Institute', *J. R. statist. Soc.* **109**, 325–370.

——and LAHIRI, D. B., 1961. 'Analysis of errors in censuses and surveys with special reference to experience in India', *Bull. Inst. int. Statist.* **38**(2), 401–433.

MORAN, P. A. P., 1962. *The Statistical Processes of Evolutionary Theory*. Clarendon Press, Oxford.

NEEL, J. V., SALZANO, F. M., JUNQUEIRA, P. C., KEITER, F., and MAYBURY-LEWIS, D., 1964. 'Studies on the Xavante Indians of the Brazilian Mato Grosso', *Am. J. hum. Genet.* **16**, 52–140.

NEI, M., 1964. 'Effects of linkage and epistasis on the equilibrium frequencies of lethal genes. II. Numerical solutions', *Jap. J. Genet.* **39**, 7–25.

SCHULL, W. J. and LEVIN, B. R., 1964. 'Monte Carlo simulation: some uses in the genetic study of primitive man', *Stochastic Models in Medicine and Biology* (ed. J. GURLAND). University of Wisconsin Press, Madison, Wisconsin.

—— and NEEL, J. V., 1963. 'Sex linkage, inbreeding, and growth in childhood', *Am. J. hum. Genet.* **15**, 106–114.

—— —— 1965. *The Effects of Inbreeding on Japanese Children.* Harper and Row, New York.

WHO, 1964. 'Research in population genetics of primitive groups', *Technical Report No.* 279, p. 26.

WILLIAMS, B. J., 1965. 'A model of hunting-gathering society and some genetic consequences'. Unpublished Ph.D. dissertation, University of Michigan.

WRIGHT, S. and McPHEE, H. C., 1925. 'An approximate method of calculating coefficients of inbreeding and relationship from livestock pedigrees', *J. agric. Res.* **31**, 377–384.

YATES, F., 1960. *Sampling Methods for Censuses and Surveys*, 3rd ed. Griffin, London.

3

GROWTH AND PHYSIQUE IN DIFFERENT POPULATIONS OF MANKIND

A PROPOSAL FOR THE ESTABLISHMENT OF AN INTERNATIONAL BUREAU FOR GROWTH STUDIES

J. M. TANNER

*Department of Growth and Development, Institute of Child Health,
University of London*

I. *Introduction*

THE physique of a population—whether its members are tall or short, long- or short-limbed, broad or slender, muscular or slight, fat or lean, round-headed or long-nosed—depends on the distribution in it of numerous genes, on the mutual interaction of the products of these genes during development, and on the further interaction of these products with a wide variety of continuously changing environmental stimuli during the whole process of growth.

Such a system can respond very flexibly to alterations in the environment. Short-term alterations, such as a transient period of starvation, are met by homeorrhetic responses on the part of individuals; long-term alterations, such as an increase in solar radiation, by selective or evolutionary responses on the part of the population as a whole. These two types of response are not entirely separable, for they interact on each other. During a period of starvation a child may slow down in growth, and promptly catch up onto his previous growth curve when food again becomes freely available. This represents the individual homeorrhetic response. However, children whose growth regulation in the face of transient starvation is poor will be selected against. Such selection may occur either by a higher mortality at the time or by more subtle mechanisms such as reaching breeding age later, having narrower pelves (females, at risk in childbirth), or being smaller and less powerful (males, at disadvantage in competitive mating). The general ability to regulate growth in the face of a variety of environmental difficulties will be selected for in all populations. All children everywhere must be able to depart from and return to the lines of growth that characterize them.

The lines of growth themselves differ, however, from one population to another. We must suppose that in each of the major populations of the world the growth of its members was gradually adjusted, by means of selection, to the environmental conditions in which they evolved. The remnants of this process we should be able to see in modern populations—the remnants only, because relatively recent migrations have much altered the distributions of peoples, so that many no longer live in the areas in which they evolved.

These two aspects, the response of the individual and the response of the population, each have their separate counterpart in the study of growth. The first takes us into medical, social, and economic studies; the second into ecological physiology, human evolution, and history. Both have their place in the International Biological Programme, and both need continuing study and co-ordination, as I shall argue later, in some permanent International Bureau for Growth Studies.

In regard to the first aspect, growth is one of the best indices of child health that we have, and a continuous monitoring of the growth and development of children in under- and over-nourished populations is, or should be, a major concern of all public health authorities and governments. If we compare the growth of members of a single population under differing social, nutritional, and medical conditions we can see to what extent their present environment falls short of supplying those stimuli and substrates which are necessary if all members of the population are to fulfil the potentialities of their gene complex. If we continue to study different social groups in the population as social and economic development or regression occurs we can see clearly whether or not we have really advanced and whether we have favoured one social group at the expense of others.

As for the second aspect; if we study healthy, fully developed children and adults, or as near to them as we can find, in a variety of populations, we can arrive at some notion as to the elements in physique which have been adaptive and we can obtain a more informed view of the great biological variability of our species.

In other words, we can advance the scientific study of man and the understanding of his evolution. It is true that only family studies will throw light on the genetic mechanisms concerned in the control of growth, but the physiological mechanisms can be investigated in populations, and so too can the effects of selection. In all that follows population, rather than family, studies are considered. Wherever possible, however, family studies should be made concurrently.

II. *The effect of starvation and disease on growth and physique*

To begin with, we must get as clear a notion as we can of the effects of starvation and disease upon growth and physique. These are the environmental stimuli we hope to reduce or eliminate, in contrast to other more permanent aspects of the environment, such as climate and altitude.

It is convenient to distinguish clearly between effects on (1) rate of growth, (2) growth in size, (3) growth in skeletal shape, and (4) growth in tissue composition. These four effects may all occur together, or they may occur separately. If a child suffers an overall reduction in rate of growth at age 5, then clearly his size at age 5·5 must be affected, but not necessarily his size at 20 or adulthood. His shape and tissue composition may or may not be affected at 5·5 depending on whether the rate change is an overall one or peculiar to certain areas. It is perfectly possible for growth in size to be affected at all ages without the rate of maturation being slowed down; puberty and cessation of growth would occur at the usual age but at a smaller size than usual. Growth in skeletal shape could be affected without growth in size being changed, provided we took care that our definitions of skeletal size and shape were made so that the two were independently measured; and growth in tissue composition could, of course, be affected without growth in size or skeletal shape being necessarily involved.

In fact starvation seems usually to cause effects in a certain order, so that shape changes seldom, if ever, occur before size and rate changes are far advanced. Differences in gene complex on the other hand seem most frequently to affect shape and tissue composition. Thus we have already some guide as to the likelihood of a given population difference being due mostly to gene differences or to starvation and disease.

Besides distinguishing possible effects in this way, we must also clearly distinguish different causes. The effects of acute temporary, and chronic persistent, starvation may be very different. We must also remember that all the effects depend upon the age of the child, and all or many may depend also upon sex, boys in general being more easily affected than girls.

Acute temporary starvation occurs from time to time in many populations. It may be associated with war, or temporary economic collapse, or physical disaster. In some populations it may occur fairly regularly at a certain time of year, so that the condition is a sort of half-way house between acute temporary and chronic persistent starvation. We can observe individual children from time to time with acute starvation due to psychological or medical causes. Unless the starvation is severe, all that happens is that the child's growth and development slow down, and when food is again available speed up to a rate above normal until the child has quite caught up again to its previous growth curve. Mild temporary starvation has clearly no lasting effect. But we do not know exactly how severe and how long-lasting starvation has to be before it produces a permanent effect, that is, a reduction in size of the adult. Probably this depends on the age at which it occurs, permanent effects being more rapidly produced in young children and possibly adolescents than in children in the mid-growth years. Possibly for a given degree of malnutrition, the critical time is proportional to the natural velocity of growth. One can imagine a sort of metabolic debt signifying 'unsatisfied growth potential' being built up as time passes and no growth occurs; I have elaborated elsewhere a hypothesis of how such a mechanism might operate (Tanner, 1963).

If rats are partially starved from birth to 21 days and then allowed to eat as much as they like, they at once have a catch-up spurt of growth, but it is insufficient to restore them to the normal curve of their litter-mates and they remain small all their lives (Widdowson and McCance, 1960; McCance, 1962). If rats are partially starved from 14 to 21 days they catch up better but still not entirely; if they are partially starved from 21 days to 40 days they are capable then of catching up completely. The rat is born at a much earlier stage of development than man, so that the birth-to-21 day period corresponds to the latter part of the foetal period in man. Malnutrition of the foetus is probably quite rare in man, but the rat experiments do show that, if we are seeking to explain some of the differences in size between populations as due to malnutrition, we should scrutinize most carefully the first two or three years, for it is influences at that time which are mostly likely to produce manifest and persistent effects.

Both temporary and permanent effects of periods of malnutrition are much less upon skeletal shape than on size. The answer to the question 'Are Nilotics linear because they eat too little at some particular time or throughout growth?' is clearly in the negative. At one time it was thought that acute or chronic malnutrition could change body proportions, and by analogy with some early results in cattle, it was suggested that short legs relative to the trunk length was a sign of malnutrition at an early age, as it may be in calves. Later work on rats and pigs has shown that the cattle results are not of general application and indeed the early results have not been uniformly repeated even in cattle. Widdowson's starved small rats had the same proportions of tail to body length, and of femur length to femur breadth, as the well-nourished larger rats, and also the same bone composition at each age. Apart from fat (and hence body weight) the only difference in shape seems to have been in the relation of head size to body length. As the head was much nearer adult size than the body at birth to 21 days, when starvation occurred, it remained relatively large in the starved small animals.

One good piece of evidence on this point in man comes from Greulich's (1957) study of Japanese children reared in California compared with those reared in the worse environment of Japan. The California-reared children were bigger at all ages, but the relationship of sitting height to leg length was practically the same throughout growth under both conditions (as shown by plotting Greulich's data on standard sitting height/stature charts). In general the proportion of limb to trunk, which varies so much from one population to another, is strongly regulated by genetic programming, in a way that overall body size is certainly not. This regulation can be seen very clearly in children who are severely dwarfed due to lack of growth hormone. They maintain normal proportions of limbs to trunk not only while they are dwarfed but even while they are catching up at four times the normal rate of growth when given human growth hormone (Tanner, unpublished). Similarly, there are recorded a number of cases of identical twins, one of whom has been malnourished or has had a chronic disease. This one has always been smaller than the healthy twin, but of the same skeletal proportions.

An exception to this rule may occur in hypothyroidism. Hypothyroid children are said to have legs which are relatively shorter than their trunks, even for their small overall size. This does not seem to be true of juvenile hypothyroids, whose disease starts after age 3 or 4. But in children who are hypothyroid at birth this disproportion may well exist, and may even be persistent, especially if therapy is not begun immediately after birth. Here again we see that it is disturbances in the early stages of growth which are least readily put right. A recent paper (Stock and Smythe, 1963) has in fact suggested that undernutrition during infancy may cause decreased brain growth and subsequent intellectual damage. Twenty-one very undernourished children in South Africa were followed, from 1 year of age to about 5 years, and the growth of their head circumference was compared with that of a control group whose parents had the same head circumference as the parents of malnourished children, but who lived in good circumstances. It appears that the head circumference of the malnourished was indeed less than that of the controls even at the time when the growth in both groups was nearing completion. The malnourished children also scored less in tests of mental ability, but this means very little since their homes were appalling and their parents non-existent or hopelessly improvident: in these circumstances the stimuli necessary for the development of mental ability are well known to be lacking. However, it is clear that research should be concentrated upon the early growth of the brain, particularly in areas where undernutrition is rife.

Whether growth of tissues, such as muscle, may be differentially affected by starvation or disease is not known. Here again we need data, and particularly data in the early years, and at adolescence when a new spurt of muscular growth occurs. The technical means of measuring widths of fat and muscle and bone in the limbs is at hand in simple X-rays (see Tanner, 1962) which can be used even in remote field conditions. Until this is done we cannot really be sure how much of the characteristically slender muscles of some East African Negroes are due to inheritance or to starvation. We do know, however, that the amount of muscle in Europeans is largely governed by inheritance, just as is bone (Hewitt, 1958; and see Osborne and De George, 1959). It seems likely that the shape of the muscle covering the bones and also the shape of the fat covering the muscle are both chiefly gene-determined. However, the amount of the muscle is governed, to some extent, by exercise, and the amount of fat is governed, to a far greater extent, by diet and sloth.

As for chronic malnutrition, there is little in practice that we can say to distinguish its effects from those of acute food shortage, although the distinction is of much theoretical importance, and will certainly be of practical importance when our data are better. In this respect it is important, for the IBP and later, to collect data on the best nourished and most healthy children in the population in underdeveloped countries so as to determine their growth potential. Knott (1963) has recently given figures for well-off Puerto Rican children which shows them to be as large as Middle-West Americans from 7 years onwards and larger than the Spaniards from whom they are chiefly descended. Burgess and Burgess (1964) have likewise given 'healthy' figures for East Africans, and Tanner and O'Keefe (1962) for Nigerian girls from 12 years onwards.

Acheson and others have maintained that the trend towards greater height that has occurred in the adult, as well as the child, population of Europe, America, and Japan during the last 80 to 100 years reflects better nutrition and less disease. He asserts that even relatively mild disease or subnutrition will cause chondrogenesis to stop while permitting osteogenesis—the turning of cartilage to bone—to continue. If this did occur it would certainly cause ultimate stunting. However, the evidence for such dissociation is very poor, since in most illnesses it seems that the two processes are retarded or advanced together. A degree of special pleading has tended to enter this discussion. Recently Acheson and Fowler (1964) have estimated that the sons of well-off men in London would, when fully grown, exceed their father's height by 1·9 inches; the sons of miners in the Rhondda Valley whose fathers grew up in conditions of unemployment and often misery were estimated to exceed their fathers by 2·3 inches. The hypothesis to be tested is that the differences between the circumstances of fathers and sons during the growing period—small for the London group, large for the Rhondda—have brought about a differential effect on growth. This the authors declare to be shown, despite themselves saying that the difference of 0·4 inch between

the means is far from significant. But the facts are in themselves very interesting and remind us that we have at present no sure explanation of the secular trend. Probably in certain areas it is chiefly due to better nutrition and less disease; probably in others chiefly to heterosis and the breaking of isolates. We lack data on this from tropical and underdeveloped countries and it is much to be hoped that the IBP will lay the foundation on which continuing studies of the trend may be built (see Tanner, 1962, p. 143; Milicer, 1962; Craig, 1963).

There is also a well-defined social class difference in European countries, the children of well-off parents being larger at all ages, and as adults, than children of poorly-off ones. The better-off also appear to have a lower weight for the same height. They seem to be a little more linear, less squat, and less muscular. This may be due to their being better nourished, but it could also be due to some inherent relation between size and/or shape and ability to rise in a European-type society, combined with assortative mating. Children with many siblings are significantly less in height and weight at each age and have a later puberty than children with few, presumably for similar nutritional-care reasons (see Tanner, 1962, p. 142; Valšik et al., 1963). These social class differences are a good example on a microscale of the differences between populations that we are trying to explain. They may be due to environment, and chiefly nutrition; but there may be also a genetic differential involved. The two interact inextricably.

Disease and growth. All that has been said about malnutrition applies equally to the effects of disease. A short and mild disease in a well-nourished child produces such a transient effect that if it exists it cannot be detected (see Tanner, 1962, pp. 130–134; Meredith and Knott, 1962). More severe diseases cause slowing of growth followed by a catch-up if the disease is cured. Probably critical periods for the effects of disease on growth exist, as they do for malnutrition, and certainly disease and undernutrition interact, not necessarily in an additive fashion.

Chronic disease, however, is our chief concern, and we are just beginning to have reports on the effects on growth due to eradicating malaria or hookworm or other similar diseases in areas in Africa and South America. In general the effects seem to be not spectacular. Thus reduction of the incidence of malaria in a heavily parasitized population in Tanganyika did not result in any significant increase in the weights of children during the first 18 months after birth (Draper and Draper, 1960); and children with repeated heavy malarial infections in the Gambia were no smaller by age $3\frac{1}{2}$ than those protected by chloroquine (McGregor *et al.*, 1956). Similarly being heterozygous for sickling haemoglobin S, even in malarious areas where its possession is supposed to confer an advantage in mortality, does not affect growth in height or weight (Garlick and Barnicot, 1957; Roberts, 1960). Diseases which cause a large reduction in regular haemoglobin content of the blood have a larger effect.

Neither disease nor malnutrition should be accepted uncritically as the cause of differences in growth between, for example, African and European populations. McGregor, Billewicz, and Thomson (1961) studied the growth of 187 children in rural Gambia from 9 months onwards. Though 43 per cent died before age 7, the heights and weights of these in the year previous to death were no different from the heights and weights of survivors. Growth was similar to that of Europeans in the first 6 months, then slowed until 2 years, when it resumed at the European rate. The authors say this slowing is not nutritional in origin in this area of rural Africa and think that undernutrition in certain children more likely follows disease than is the cause of it. They lay the chief blame on the inefficient development of active immunity.

III. *Differences between populations in growth and physique*

Anthropologists have documented some of the physical differences between populations with a zeal that approaches the excessive; but other aspects of physique such as muscle width have been less well studied, and the all-important question of how members of each population grew during childhood so as to attain their characteristic size and shape has been studied least of all. This is the field in which studies, internationally planned but nationally conducted, could contribute immensely to an understanding of the genesis of human variation.

What follows is not an exhaustive catalogue of studies of growth and physique in non-European populations—useful though that would be at the present time—but a selection and discussion of a number of the chief attempts to explain adult differences in physique by reference to differential growth rates.

One of the best of such studies is that of Hiernaux (1964) on the growth of the Tutsi and Hutu peoples of Rwanda. The Tutsi are tall, linear people, with an average adult male height and weight of 176 cm and 57 kg. The Hutu are shorter and stockier, with averages of 167 cm and 58 kg. There are two ways by which the Tutsi could grow to be taller. Either they may be longer at birth or shortly after and grow slightly more in length throughout their childhood; or they could grow at the same rate, but for a longer period, adding their extra 9 cm after the Hutu had stopped growing. The former is in fact the case. Both Tutsi and Hutu grow slowly compared with European children, probably because their nutrition is suboptimal, but both cease growth at about the same age (being 93–94 per cent of mature height at age 17), have menarche at the same age (about 16·5 years) and show the reversal of boys-taller to girls-taller at the same age (14 years). Hiernaux's data start at age 6 only, so we cannot tell exactly when the characteristic height-weight differences first were obvious. They are clear enough at age 6, however, Tutsi averaging 4 cm taller than Hutu, with almost identical weights. They probably start immediately after birth and reflect genetic differences of the same sort as those which cause boys' forearms to grow, from birth onwards, relatively a little faster than girls' (see Tanner, 1962). Tutsi and Hutu were growing up in a similar environment (the survey was made in 1957–8) but the Tutsi were better nourished, being the ruling caste. Despite this the Tutsi weight for given height was considerably lower than that of the Hutu. In the same paper Hiernaux gives figures for a group of Hutu reared from birth in Congo mining camps, where they were somewhat better nourished than in Rwanda. Only boys aged 6 to 9 are adequately represented and these are taller, by 2 to 2½ cm, than the Rwanda Hutu. They are also about 4 kg heavier.

This study raises virtually all the problems that we need to discuss in planning the IBP studies. They are as follows.

1. *Chronological age.* In this study age was known. When age is unknown, differentiation between the growing-faster and the growing-for-longer hypotheses is impossible. Except in special circumstances, there seems to be virtually no way out of this impasse. Certain pairs of measurements change their relationship during growth; for example the head circumference, which is relatively advanced at birth and grows little later, and the leg length, which is relatively retarded at birth and grows much later.

Hence the ratio, leg length/head circumference, increases as the child gets older; or, better, the figure for leg length adjusted to head circumference by a regression increases as the child grows. This ratio, or the position in the regression chart, could therefore be used to estimate the child's age, but only within a given population under given conditions. If we have to compare two populations we would have first to be sure that in whatever other aspects of physique they differed, in the relation of leg length and head circumference they were the same at all ages. This seems virtually impossible even if both populations are equally well nourished. If one population's growth is retarded in all respects, perhaps by malnutrition, then the argument breaks down completely. A more accurate estimate of age can be made from combining a whole series of measurements—this is called 'shape age' and is currently under statistical investigation in my laboratory and others—but again this only works within, not between, populations.

Given a single population under stable environmental circumstances, the chronological age of the children could be 'reconstructed' at the end of a 5-year longitudinal study perhaps, starting with groups at birth, 5, 10, and 15 years. Either through measurement ratios or perhaps better by taking hand and wrist X-rays for skeletal age the appearance of known 1-, 2-, 3-, 4-, and 5-year-olds is secured and then those children who were, on this criterion, 4, 5, &c., five years ago located. The skeletal ages of the whole child population could be reconstructed in this way, but no allowance could be made for the variation between skeletal and chronological age in individual children older than 5 years. Reconstruction by reference to tooth eruption has the same difficulties but perhaps to a lesser degree.

We need to find something which is entirely unaffected by malnutrition and disease, and absolutely the same for all populations. Only age satisfies this criterion. Perhaps amongst physical measurements the one which most nearly approaches the criterion is the number of erupted teeth. The eruption of teeth seems to be less affected by malnutrition than maturation of the skeleton or physical growth. This is particularly the case for the primary dentition (Voors, 1957; Voors and Metselaar, 1958) which also seems, in our relatively scanty data, to vary less from one population to another than does the secondary. In eruption of secondary dentition East African and South African Bantu and Dutch New Guinea children are ahead of Europeans; in primary dentition this is not the case, but American Negroes are somewhat ahead of American Whites (see Tanner, 1962, p. 71).

We may say, then, that in IBP surveys so far as possible only children of known age should be included and much ingenuity and time may have to be expended getting parents to date their children's birth accurately by reference to remembered local events. Secondly, so that we may investigate further the possibilities for the future, tooth eruption should be recorded on all children, particularly those in the stage of primary dentition. If X-rays are available more sophisticated methods for dental maturity should also be used. Radiographs of the mandibular teeth will give a dental maturity rating at all ages.

2. *Cross-sectional and longitudinal studies.* Hiernaux's study is cross-sectional and this has not been detrimental for the purposes for which the study was designed. We have to keep in mind, however, exactly what cross-sectional studies will and will not do. They tell us the attained heights, weights, &c., at each age. They tell us, up to but not during adolescence, the mean velocity of growth from year to year in each measurement. They enable us to compare two populations for size and shape at a given age. They enable us to say something about differences in rate of change of size and shape before adolescence, though we cannot make a significance test of population differences since we do not know the standard errors of the mean velocities. However, we can approximate them by a general knowledge of the results of longitudinal studies. Cross-sectional studies do not tell us how much a population varies in growth rate. They give us an idea of the average age at which the adolescent acceleration reaches its peak (though a slightly biased one) but little idea of the magnitude of the average peak velocity. They do not give a true figure for the average age at which growth ceases, since the latest-finishing subjects affect the height-achieved averages. We may wish to know whether two populations which differ in some measurement as adults were the same before adolescence, one having a greater adolescent spurt in the measurement; or if the differences arose before adolescence, the quantities added in the spurt being the same. A general notion of which has occurred may be obtained from cross-sectional studies, but not a precise answer. If menarcheal

age is available as a guide to when adolescence occurs, this improves the tentative answer; the same is true of skeletal age.

Thus in the IBP cross-sectional studies are useful, but should be supplemented where possible by longitudinal studies particularly of infancy and adolescence. These longitudinal studies should extend over a minimum of 5 years.

3. *Ages represented.* In Hiernaux's study the first age represented is 6 years. For this reason we cannot say whether the increased rate of growth in height of the Hutu begins at birth or later. In the IBP all ages from birth to maturity, i.e. at least 25, should be represented. For the first year 3-monthly groups should be used and from 1 to 2 years 6-monthly groups. This implies that there should be three or four times as many 0- to 1-year-olds and twice as many 1- to 2-year-olds measured as 3- to 4-, 4- to 5-year-olds, &c.

4. *Boys and girls.* In Hiernaux's study both boys and girls are represented. Hence we can see at what age girls' height begins to exceed boys', which is a valuable guide to the age of beginning of the girls' adolescent spurt. The same is true of the age at which this trend reverses. Secondly we can see whether there is any significant sex-population interaction. This may be important. The response of girls to a variety of environmental disturbances is less than that of boys; girls seem to be better canalized (see Tanner, 1962, p. 127). Hence a lesser growth of boys in one population compared with another, in the presence of equal growth of girls in both, points to an environmental difference between the populations (as for example in Graffer, Asiel, and Emery-Hanzer, 1961). This is not an absolute criterion since sex-limited genes may differ between the two populations, but less usually.

For the IBP then, girls and boys should be studied simultaneously.

5. *Measurements of developmental age.* Without some measure of developmental age we cannot answer accurately the basic question as to whether the Tutsi grow for longer—whether they are the same height as the Hutu at each skeletal age, for example, but have a lower skeletal age for each chronological age—or grow more. Hiernaux answered this in his paper by reference to menarcheal age, which was known, and by reference to the percentage of adult height reached by his oldest age groups, that is 17-year-olds. Both methods are useful; obtaining figures for menarche may be easier than obtaining a sample of healthy

25- to 30-year-olds for the adult mature measurement. Neither technique tells us whether the situation in height relative to stage of development changed between 6 and 17. It might be that at 6 the Tutsi had a more advanced skeletal age than the Hutu and that their superiority of height at that age corresponded simply to faster growth and development; the height of the two groups for skeletal age might be the same. This might have gone on till adolescence was approached. Then the Hutu might have had a more rapid advance during adolescence, catching up to the Tutsi in skeletal age by the time of menarche, without having a correspondingly greater increase in their adolescent height spurt. Such would be the picture of population-age interaction for rate of growth. Admittedly such a thing is less likely than the more simple situation, and it probably does not occur in the Tutsi-Hutu comparison. But as between Chinese and Europeans (see below) it seems to be present, just as the analogous interaction takes place between different individuals in the same population.

Thus in IBP studies some measure of developmental age should be included. Menarche is by far the easiest. All that is necessary is to ask a large sample of girls of known age from about 9 to 17 whether or not they have yet begun to menstruate and fit the resulting percentage incidence curve by logits or probits (see Burrell, Healy, and Tanner, 1961). The presence of secondary sex characters such as pubic hair, breasts, and male external genitalia can be dealt with in the same way, though less accurately. (Good examples are the papers of Lee, Chang, and Chan (1963) on the maturation of Chinese girls in Hong Kong as related to social class and of Bottyán and associates (1963) in Hungary.) Pictorial standards for judging development are given in Tanner (1962). Skeletal ages should be done where possible also, using the left hand and wrist and either the Greulich-Pyle or the Tanner-Whitehouse assessments.

In the IBP therefore menarcheal age should always be investigated, and secondary sex character age and skeletal age where possible.

In passing it may be noted that menarche may not occur at the same place on the height curve in all populations. Its position is rather constant in European groups, but in Nigerians it may perhaps occur later, that is nearer the point of cessation of height growth (see Tanner and O'Keefe, 1962). Hong Kong girls mature early, but have the same relation of menarche and mature height as Europeans. However, in Hong Kong girls the relative timing of appearance of breasts and pubic hair differs from that observed in Europeans and white Americans; pubic hair appears relatively later in the Chinese (Lee, Chang, and Chan, 1963).

Chinese-European differences. Another interesting difference of rate occurs in Hong Kong children. From 6 to 15 years in boys and 6 to 12 years in girls, the skeletal maturity of Hong Kong children is retarded relative to the American Greulich-Pyle standards. However, at adolescence a change occurs and the Chinese pass more rapidly through the standards than the Americans, so that they are advanced after 12 in girls and 15 in boys (Low, Chan, Chang, and Lee, 1963). Here then is our example of the population-age interaction in rate of growth (or non-parallelism, to use another biometrical analogy) discussed above. It is not possible to tell from the cross-sectional studies whether this rapid adolescent skeletal development is accompanied by a stature spurt with a higher peak velocity than in Europeans; the figures suggest it may be so in boys. When plotted on the 1954 standard British charts the Hong Kong girls' average height lies at the 25th percentile from 9 to 11, reaches the 30th at 13 and 14, and drops to the 10th at 15, 16, and 17. It seems here that the adolescent spurt was of average European intensity, occurred early, and finished more rapidly than in Europeans. The best-off members of the Hong Kong population showed similar timings, though a different size level. The girls were at the British 50th percentile for height at 9 to 11, rose to the 65th at 12, had menarche at 12.5 compared with the British 13·1, and fell to the British 15th percentile by age 15. Well-off boys were at the 40th percentile at 9–11, 50th at 12 rising to 60th at 14, and dropping back to the 20th at 17. Clearly there are many interesting timing differences, but their full extent can only be elucidated by longitudinal study.

Negro-White differences. There are, of course, many differences in build between Negroes and Whites. The Negro has long legs and arms relative to the trunk length, narrow hips, less muscular calves, and heavier bones. Not only is this true of the average American Negro student compared with Whites, but it even holds in Olympic athletes, amongst competitors at each type of sport (Tanner, 1964). Hurdlers, for example, have long legs, but Negro hurdlers have longer legs than White hurdlers. Weight-lifters, both White and

Negro, have short legs, but the White lifters are shorter than the Negro.

We know very little of how these differences come about. One very well attested difference, however, is in the rate of maturing. Negroes, whether in America, West or East Africa, are ahead of Whites at birth in skeletal ossification, even compared with Whites living in better economic circumstances. This probably reflects an inherited difference in hormone secretion during the late foetal period, for their permanent teeth also erupt earlier, and the basis of these teeth is laid down in the uterus, though later than the laying down of the primary teeth, whose eruption date differs less between the races (see Tanner, 1962, pp. 66 and 77; Massé and Hunt, 1963). The Negro child maintains his advancement for about 2 to 3 years if living in good economic circumstances; it is reflected in a greater rate of growth in length and weight and a greater maturity of motor development and behavioural milestones. But after this age even in good circumstances the African child appears to decelerate in growth and development. This may well be a natural occurrence, the velocity curve of the two races having a different shape, just as do the velocity curves of males and females, in both races. The same thing is seen between members of the same population. Hewitt (1958) has shown that sibs resemble each other in having either a rapid growth of calf muscle from 6 months to 3 years followed by a relatively slower growth from 3 to 5 years, or the reverse pattern. This is a fairly complicated problem in growth velocities, and can only be satisfactorily solved by longitudinal studies on various populations living under good nutritional circumstances.

Indian-Asian differences. Berry and Deshmukh (1964) have recently shown that the somatotype distribution of Indian students differs greatly from that of European ones and probably even more from Asians (Heath, Hopkins, and Miller, 1961). Indians are less mesomorphic and more ectomorphic. This difference has also a genetic component, and starts early in childhood. In Singapore, Indian children had a lower weight for height than Chinese and Malayan children living in similar circumstances at all ages from 3 months to 5 years (the oldest studied), though by 5 years they were actually taller (Millis, 1957, 1958). More studies of children of different ethnic groups living in a similar environment are very desirable.

Primitive populations. None of what has been said so far refers to primitive populations, and one of the avowed tasks of the IBP is to study these so as to have records of them before they disappear or are assimilated. Few primitive populations have been adequately studied from the point of view of either physique or growth. There is little on the Eskimo or the Andean, little on the Pygmy or the Australian Aboriginal. We have heights and weights, but no chronological ages, on Shilluk and Dinka in the Sudan (Roberts, 1961), but this has actually led to a probably incorrect interpretation of the genesis of their linearity (see Hiernaux, 1964). A few studies on American Indians have been done (see Kraus, 1954), but nothing on Tibetans or dwellers in Himalaya. Yet we know there are vast differences between these populations, not only in adult physique but in childhood. Margaret Mead, Tony Schwartz, and I studied somatotype pictures of all members, adults and children, in a Sepik River village community in New Guinea. Both men and women were strikingly mesomorphic compared with Europeans, and the children seemed to show the same type of build. Certainly between many primitive communities there is no overlap at all in physique. It takes no great anthropologist to distinguish any one Dinka from any one Manus even if the facial features, skull contour, and skin colour are all obliterated. The techniques developed in the study of more advanced cultures are mostly quite easily applicable to these groups, and we must hope that in the IBP their children's growth will be studied now before it is too late.

Climate and altitude. We do not at present know to what extent the differences between populations are due to climate and altitude. We must presume that these geographical features originally governed the selection of growth-controlling genes and hence led to the emergence of the differences we see now. The adaptive significance of the various features can only be assessed by physiological studies, and at least some of these should if possible be carried out on children as well as adults, for the adaptation may be relevant to the growing period rather than adult life. Most selection takes place before the reproductive age is reached. It seems less likely that many of the differences in growth pattern are directly due to the action of climate and altitude on the growing child, except in such instances as emphysematous chests in very high altitude dwellers. A test of this is provided by people of one race who grow up in the area mostly inhabited by another. Europeans reared in the Sudan do not grow up with the Dinka physique, nor do Africans reared in Liverpool grow thick European-type calves. Englishmen who pass their youth in Japan are not, so far as we know, characteristically short-legged. Nevertheless a study of persons reared in a *milieu* very different from that of their parents would be a very desirable addition to the IBP programme. Italian migrants to Boston are being studied intensively by Boutourline Young. Few results have yet been published. Greulich's (1957) excellent study of Japanese migrants to California has already been mentioned. Two great difficulties are presented by all migrant studies, however: first migrant parents seem never to be a random sample of the nation they leave, being usually larger and more intelligent than the stay-at-homes (even if they only migrate from one English county to another); and secondly food habits and opportunities are very seldom the same for migrants as for sedentes. Thus the effects of climate and altitude are hard to assess by this means. A similar difficulty beset Wurst's (1961) study of the growth of Austrian children in relation to altitude. The higher the villages, the poorer were the people, the worse was the food and the greater the calories expended on walking to school. Thus though the high-altitude children were smaller at all ages, the reasons for this cannot be disentangled.

IV. *Proposals*

Proposals for the IBP fall under two headings:

1. Studies of the growth of children in a series of populations, with attention paid to different socio-economic and nutritional groups within the populations. These to be a base-line for continuing studies as a guide to public health, particularly in impoverished and emergent countries.

2. Comparisons of the growth of children in primitive and other communities, equated so far as possible for nutritional circumstances. This would supply biological knowledge about human variability and should be related to the differences in adult physique, work capacity, and physical adaptation to the environment.

In both types of study, proper and precise methods of sampling must be used. The ages of the children should be known or obtained by appropriate questioning; all ages and both sexes should be studied; and measures of developmental age included if possible. Menarche and dental eruption data should always be included, secondary sex characters and skeletal age where possible. The number of physical measurements recommended has been given elsewhere at two levels, one more detailed than the other (see *IBP Handbook*). Cross-sectional studies should always be made first, but if possible 5-year longitudinal studies, particularly over infancy and adolescence, should be begun at the same time on smaller groups.

3. These studies need a co-ordinating centre if maximum usefulness is to be derived from them. I suggest this should be called the International Bureau of Growth Studies or IBGS (or, if you prefer evolution by simple substitutions in a triplet code, IBG as evolving from IBP). Its duties should be to co-ordinate studies of human growth throughout the world, to serve as a repository of data and a source of technical aid, and, where necessary, training. Though it would not itself undertake growth studies, it would endeavour to help those who do, particularly in underdeveloped countries, by technical advice and by arranging computing facilities where necessary. It might organize occasional courses, and would certainly bring doctors and scientists for periods of instruction in advanced countries. Conversely it might from time to time send out experts into field areas, to give help to local investigators. I envisage the Bureau as having some of the qualities of the International Bureau for Communicable Disease of WHO, the Nuffield Blood Group Centre, and the International Children's Centre. The last has in fact shown that co-ordination of growth studies is possible; but the Bureau would be different from the ICC in that it would have a far wider international coverage, and be a small permanent organization rather than a club consisting of members of a limited number of small longitudinal studies. The Bureau might initially be staffed by only one experienced graduate and one secretary if it is adequately backed by the facilities of a department concerned with growth and able to supply, on contract, such facilities as programming and computing.

Summary

1. A summary is given of present knowledge of the effects of malnutrition and disease on growth and physique. Disturbances of the environment affect first rate of growth, then, if prolonged,

final size. Only very severe disturbances affect shape. It is likely that malnutrition in the early years has a more lasting effect than malnutrition later.

2. Differences in patterns of growth between different populations are then considered, an attempt being made to distinguish those which are inherited from those which occur as a result of malnutrition or disease. A comparison of two African populations is cited and used as an example for the development of a list of guiding principles to be observed when making growth studies in the IBP. The limitations of cross-sectional and longitudinal studies are discussed and the usefulness of such landmarks as menarche, whose mean and variability can be assessed even on cross-sectional data.

3. It is proposed that a small International Bureau for Growth Studies be set up, to co-ordinate present and future knowledge, which at the moment is widely scattered and collected with little reference to existing work. The function of such a Bureau would be somewhat similar to those of the International Blood Group Centre.

REFERENCES

ACHESON, R. M. and FOWLER, G. B., 1964. 'Sex, socio-economic status and secular increase in stature', Br. J. prev. soc. Med. **18**, 25–34.

BERRY, J. N. and DESHMUKH, P. Y., 1964. 'Somatotypes of male college students in Nagpur, India', Hum. Biol. **36**, 157–176.

BOTTYAN, O., DEZSO, GY, EIBEN, O., FARKAS, GY, RAJKAI, T., THOMA, A., and VELI, GY, 1963. 'Age at menarche in Hungarian girls', Annls hist. nat. Mus. natn. hung. **55**, 561–571.

BURGESS, A. P. and BURGESS, H. K. L., 1964. 'The growth patterns of East African schoolgirls', Hum. Biol. **36**, 177–193.

BURRELL, R. J. W., HEALY, M. J. R., and TANNER, J. M., 1961. 'Age at menarche in South African Bantu girls living in the Transkei reserve', Hum. Biol. **33**, 250–261.

CHANG, K. S. F., LEE, M. M. C., LOW, W. D., and KVAN, E., 1963. 'Height and weight of southern Chinese children', Am. J. phys. Anthrop. **21**, 497–509.

CRAIG, J. O., 1963. 'The heights of Glasgow boys: secular and social influences', Hum. Biol. **35**, 524–539.

DRAPER, K. C. and DRAPER, C. C., 1960. 'Observations on the growth of African infants with special reference to the effects of malaria control', J. trop. med. Hyg. **63**, 167–171.

GARLICK, J. P. and BARNICOT, N. A., 1957. 'Blood groups and haemoglobin variants in Nigerian (Yoruba) schoolchildren', Ann. hum. Genet. **21**, 420–425.

GRAFFAR, M., ASIEL, M., and EMERY-HAUZEUR, C., 1961. 'La taille et le périmetre cephalique pendant la première année de la vie', Acta paediat. belg. **15**, 61–74.

GREULICH, W. W., 1957. 'A comparison of the physical growth and development of American-born and native Japanese children', *Am. J. phys. Anthrop.* **15**, 489–515.
HEATH, B. H., HOPKINS, C. E., and MILLER, C. D., 1961. 'Physique of Hawai-born young men and women of Japanese ancestry, compared with college men and women of the United States and England', *Am. J. phys. Anthrop.* **19**, 173–184.
HEWITT, D., 1958. 'Sib resemblance in bone, muscle and fat measurements of the human calf', *Ann. hum. Genet.* **22**, 26–35.
HIERNAUX, J., 1964. 'Weight/height relationship during growth in Africans and Europeans', *Hum. Biol.* **36**, 273–293.
KNOTT, V. B., 1963. 'Stature, leg girth and body weight of Puerto Rican private school children measured in 1962', *Growth* **27**, 157–174.
KRAUS, B. S., 1954. *Indian Health in Arizona.* University of Arizona Press, Tucson.
LEE, M. M. C., CHANG, K. S. F., and CHAN, M. M. C., 1963. 'Sexual maturation of Chinese girls in Hong Kong', *Pediatrics* **32**, 389–398.
LOW, W. D., CHAN, S. T., CHANG, K. S. F., and LEE, M. M. C., 1964. 'Skeletal maturation of southern Chinese children in Hong Kong', *Child Develpm.* **35**, 1313–1336.
MCCANCE, R. A., 1962. 'Food, growth and time', *Lancet* **2**, 621–626.
MCGREGOR, I. A. and BILLEWICZ, W. Z., 1961. 'Growth and mortality in children in an African village', *Br. med. J.* **2**, 1661–1666.
—— GILLES, H. M., WALTERS, J. H., DAVIES, A. H., and PEARSON, F. A., 956. 'Effects of heavy and repeated malarial infections on Gambian infants and children', *Trans. R. Soc. trop. Med. Hyg.* **2**, 686–692.
MASSÉ, G. and HUNT, E. E., 1963. 'Skeletal maturation of the hand and wrist in West African children', *Hum. Biol.* **35**, 3–25.
MEREDITH, H. V. and KNOTT, V. B., 1962. 'Illness history and physical growth III. Comparative anatomic status and rate of change for schoolchildren in different long-term health categories', *Am. J. Dis. Child.* **103**, 146–151.
MILICER, H., 1962. 'Investigations on the physical development of youth', *Physical Education in School* (Eds. W. MISSIURO and J. SADOWSKA). Institute of Physical Culture, Warsaw.
MILLIS, J., 1957. 'Growth of pre-school Malay infants in Singapore', *Med. J. Malaya* **12**, 416–422.
—— 1958. 'Growth of pre-school Chinese and Southern Indian children in Singapore', *Med. J. Malaya* **12**, 531–539.
ROBERTS, D. F., 1961. 'Körperhöhe und Gewicht nilotiden Kinder', *Homo* **12**, 33–41.
STOCK, M. B. and SMYTH, P. M., 1963. 'Does undernutrition during infancy inhibit brain growth and subsequent intellectual development'? *Archs Dis. Childh.* **38**, 546–552.
TANNER, J. M., 1962. *Growth at Adolescence*, 2nd ed. Blackwell, Oxford.
—— 1963. 'Regulation of growth in size in mammals', *Nature, Lond.* **199**, 845–850.
—— 1964. *Physique of the Olympic Athlete.* Allen and Unwin, London.
—— and O'KEEFE, B., 1962. 'Age at menarche in Nigerian schoolgirls, with a note on their height and weights from age 12 to 19', *Hum. Biol.* **34**, 187–196.

VALŠIK, J. A., ŠTUKOVSKY, R., and BERNATOVA, L., 1963. 'Quelques facteurs geographiques et sociaux ayant une influence sur l'âge de la puberté', *Biotypologie* **24**, 109–123.

VOORS, A. W., 1957. 'The use of dental age in studies of nutrition in children', *Documenta Med. geogr. trop.* **9**, 137–148.

—— and METSELAAR, D., 1958. 'The reliability of dental age as a yardstick to assess the unknown calendar age', *Trop. geogr. Med.* **10**, 175–180.

WIDDOWSON, E. M. and MCCANCE, R. A., 1964. 'Some effects of accelerating growth, I. General somatic development', *Proc. roy. Soc.* B **152**, 188–206.

WURST, F., WASSERTHEURER, H., and KINNESWENGER, K., 1961. *Entwicklung und Umwelt des Landkindes.* Osterreichicher Bundesverlag, Vienna.

4

WORK CAPACITY OF SELECTED POPULATIONS

K. Lange Andersen

Institute of Physiology, University of Bergen

Introduction

Man's ability to perform his daily round of work is a complex function and involves so many factors that the term 'work capacity' cannot be precisely defined without limiting the scope to one or a few separate aspects. In any society manpower serves an important function in production and subsequently in creating favourable living conditions. The demand for physical work varies, depending upon climate and the cultural and social structure of the society, and is greatly influenced by the degree of industrialization and technical 'know-how'. For a man of the primitive hunting community, the tasks associated with locating game, killing, and bringing the meat home are essential features; skill in target shooting and endurance in walking, running, or paddling a canoe are highly important. Men of modern industries are faced with other problems. Their jobs require skills in using specialized tools and the understanding for handling complicated machinery; the work usually requires little energy expenditure above the normal resting value, and is associated with negligible use of muscle power. Fatigue may mainly be related to sustained static work and monotonously high rates of rhythmic exercises, often exaggerated by unfavourable climatic and environmental conditions, psychological factors, and social stress.

Capacity for work may be assessed by measurement of performance exercises, e.g. the maximal work output under appropriate conditions. This may involve tests as simple as measuring how fast a subject is able to run a mile, a 100-m dash, the weight he can lift, or in terms of production output, e.g. how much timber a lumberjack can fell per day. This approach is scientifically not very valid, because the results depend on many factors which can seldom be specified and never completely controlled. Psychological factors, such as motivation to do one's best, are highly important, but also extremely changeable in the individual. The ability to run fast may be important for a hunter, a soldier, and possibly for a waiter, but this quality is of little, if of any, significance for successful performance of most jobs in any society. There are few—if any at all—muscular skills which have sufficient general interest to make them important enough to measure when dealing with an overall evaluation of capacity for manual work. For this purpose it becomes necessary to deal with more basic measurements, giving insight into the body composition and the physiological status of the body as a whole, as well as of relevant organ systems. This is the only approach which may yield results of basic scientific interest, and which subsequently may be of significance in handling problems related to productivity and human welfare.

Broadly speaking, the underlying morphological and physiological factors may be evaluated through measurements which fall in four categories:

1. size, shape, and composition of the body;
2. energy mechanisms,
   (i) the aerobic capacity,
   (ii) the anaerobic capacities;
3. the functioning of the muscles in static and dynamic work;
4. circulatory and respiratory functions.

Exercise performances engage the muscles in static or dynamic work. All daily activity is maintained by a continuous shift or a combination of these types of muscular performances. In static effort the maximal tension that a muscle group can produce and the time it can be maintained measure aspects of the functional capacity. In dynamic work, the total kinetic energy that can be produced in a single movement measures another functional output. This depends on neuro-muscular co-ordination, skill, and on the strength of the muscles. Again, the maximal tension a muscle group can exert involves an important aspect of the function.

The reloading of the contractile muscle mechanism demands energy. The capacity to deliver energy for muscle contraction is therefore a fundamental characteristic of fitness for work. Energy can only be liberated for muscle contraction by the splitting of the energy-rich phosphate compounds, mainly ATP and creatine phosphate. These have to be rebuilt at the expense of some exergonic process, this being the dissimilation of restricted stores of glycogen in the muscles themselves and of foodstuffs carried to the muscles by the blood. The high energy phosphate process is, therefore, only a temporary one, as the final energy comes from oxidation. The capacity of the high energy phosphate process is very small, about 200 cal/kg body weight, while the amount (total energy liberated) of energy coming from the oxidation processes is almost unlimited. On the other hand, the amount of energy which can be given off by the high energy phosphate process per time unit (the power) is much higher than that from the oxidation process. The power of high energy phosphate is related to the amount of the phosphate compound and to the speed of splitting, while the velocity of the oxidative processes is related mainly to the capacity for carrying oxygen from the ambient air to the muscles, and subsequently to the speed of the oxidative processes in the muscles.

At the beginning of muscular exercise the oxidative processes are slow to enter into play, so that a very short exercise—no matter how heavy—is accomplished only or substantially at the expense of the high energy phosphate breakdown.

If the exercise is too heavy for the energy being supplied by the oxidative processes, an emergency exergonic mechanism is available. This is the breakdown of glycogen into pyruvate/lactate. The energy liberated by the high energy phosphate and by the lactate formation, is referred to as the oxygen-debt contraction, or the anaerobic capacity, the first being the alactacid component, the latter the lactate component.

All these mechanisms, the oxidative, the alactacid, and the lactacid, can be measured in an integrated organism. The capacity of the oxidative mechanism is named the aerobic work capacity, and is assessed by measuring the maximal oxygen uptake during exhaustive work. Since the oxidation mechanism is the normal energy delivering process, the aerobic capacity is a most important determinant for muscular work. The capacity of the anaerobic mechanism is seldom fully utilized, except in athletics, where this characteristic determines their fitness for many events.

Maximal oxygen uptake as a function of body size

Interspecies differences. The functional relationship between body size and basal metabolic rate was elucidated when the comparative aspects had been established. The basal metabolic rate in adult mammals is exponentially related to body size, and the relationship is mathematically expressed by the equation $BMR = k.W^b$, or $\log BMR = b.\log W + \log k$. BMR is the metabolic rate (in kcal/min or O_2 ml/min) and W is body weight in kilograms. By plotting the data on a double logarithmic graph paper the constant b gives the slope of the curve which expresses the relationship (Benedict's mouse to elephant curve). The value of b for mammals is 0·73 or close to three-quarters. This law becomes meaningful when interpreted in relation to the evolutionary process. When a species, as a result of natural selection, becomes larger, Nature is likely to favour the animals with the lowest standard metabolic rate, because of their lower food requirement. Since metabolism also serves an important function in temperature regulation, there must be a lower limit best associated with fitness for survival. These two demands probably balance each other, resulting in an animal kingdom where the standard metabolism of the individual species is a ¾-power function of body weight.

A similar approach may yield insight into the relationship between maximal working metabolism and the body size. The capacity to raise the metabolic rate during muscular exercise may be expected to be of significance for survival in two aspects. First, a high ability to deliver energy for muscle contraction will make an animal more fit for the inter- and intra-species struggle for life. Second, a high power in raising the metabolic rate during work would also be expected to be associated with a greater ability to resist cold exposure, because of the greater capacity to furnish body

TABLE 1

Resting metabolism and maximal working metabolism in three homeothermic species of various body size

Species	Weight (kg)	Rest. O_2-uptake (ml/min/kg)	Max. O_2-uptake ml/min/kg	Met.*
Mouse†	0·023	50·0	200	4
Rat‡	0·256	16·0	107	7
Man§	70·000	3·7	48	13

* Met=Times above BMR.
† Unpublished data by Hart and Segrem.
‡ Unpublished data by Segrem and Lange Andersen.
§ Hermansen and Lange Andersen, *J. appl. Physiol.*, **20**, 425–431, 1965.

· heat, and this would make the animal more fit to live in temperate
and cold regions, which occupy the largest part of the globe.
The maximal working metabolism of three species of mammals
of various size are listed in Table 1.
When plotted on a double logarithmic graph paper the data
falls on a straight line which parallels but is somewhat steeper than
the line representing the basal metabolism. Consequently, the maximal metabolism is exponentially related to body weight (Fig. 1).

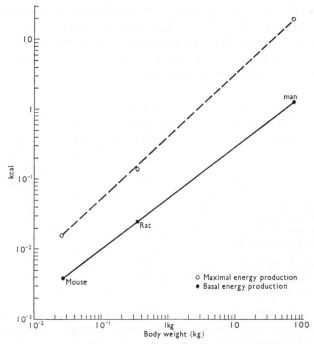

FIG. 1. The relationship between body weight and basal and maximal
metabolic rate. Data plotted on double logarithmic graph paper.

The mouse is only able to raise the resting metabolism by a
factor of 3–5, the rat by 5–7, and the man by 12–15. Thus, as well as
the phylogenetically induced decrease in resting standard metabolism per unit of body weight, Nature also tends to favour larger
animals with an increased ability to raise their metabolic rate.
However, much more experimental data are needed for a full understanding of this problem.

These considerations may lead us to propose that the evolutionary process brings about animals with larger body size which have adapted their standard resting metabolism to a $\frac{3}{4}$-power of body weight, and predominantly selects those for survival which have the greatest capacity to deliver oxidative energy for external work.

Humans of the same age and sex. There are considerable individual differences with regard to the aerobic work capacity of humans of the same age and sex, even when normalizing the values on basis of body size. The variability coefficient for maximal oxygen uptake becomes reduced when expressing the data on basis of body weight, and even more when the data are on the normalized basis of fat-free body weight, which was expected since the fat tissue does not contribute to the elevation of metabolism during work (Table 2).

TABLE 2

Maximal oxygen uptake of young sedentary men
(after Buskirk and Taylor, J. appl. Physiol. **11**, 72–78, 1957)

	Mean	S.D.	Variability coefficient
Age (y)	22·5	2·8	—
Height (cm)	177·4	6·2	—
Weight (kg)	78·6	16·9	—
Max. O$_2$-uptake			
l./min	3·44	0·46	13·4
ml/min/kg body weight	44·6	5·5	12·3
ml/min/kg fat-free weight	53·1	3·6	6·8

When a group of extremely fit men are compared with a group of sedentary men considerable differences appear with regard to maximal oxygen uptake. These differences actually become greater when the values are expressed on the basis of body weight, and even more marked on the basis of fat-free body weight, because fit men in general are leaner (Fig. 2). The amount of muscle mass which a well-trained and a sedentary man of the same fat-free body weight can activate in running or similar exercises is probably different with larger values for the former. However, the differences are unlikely to be great enough to account for the large differences in maximal oxygen uptake, as is apparent from Fig. 2. Consequently we are forced to accept that each unit of muscle mass of the fit man

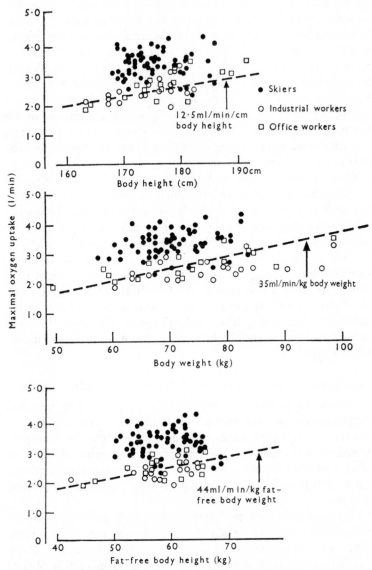

FIG. 2. The relationship between maximal oxygen uptake and indices of body size in middle-aged men (50–60 y). A group of fit men (skiers) are compared with sedentary men (industrial and office workers).

is able to consume oxygen at a higher maximal rate than in the sedentary man. This must be due to a mechanism which involves the capacity of the circulatory organs, the oxygen-transporting capacity of the blood, and possibly the diffusion capacity, lung/ blood and blood/tissue, and the biochemical oxidative machinery in the cells themselves. Sjöstrand (1953) and Åstrand (1952) have proposed that individual differences in maximal oxygen uptake can be explained in terms of differences in total haemoglobin. Other reports on this problem do not support this concept (Buskirk and Taylor, 1957; Lange Andersen, unpublished). Differences in the functional status of the cardio-respiratory system probably exert a major influence in producing differences in aerobic capacity in subjects of the same age and sex.

These considerations make it clear that if one wishes to examine the capacity of an individual to perform external work in which he has to move the body along the ground, the appropriate criterion to take is his maximal oxygen uptake per kilogram body weight, since this describes the maximum quantity of oxidative energy available for the purpose. In subjects of ordinary leanness, maximal oxygen uptake per kilogram body weight may also be taken as a criterion of the functional status of the combined circulatory-respiratory system. Caution should, however, be exercised when using it for this purpose. The data therefore become more meaningful when expressed on the basis of fat-free body weight.

Variation in maximal oxygen uptake within a life-cycle

Growth. In addition to the interspecies changes in maximal oxygen uptake as a function of increasing size, there are changes which occur in the same individual during the life-cycle. A graphic presentation of maximal oxygen uptake in growing children in relation to body weight is given in Fig. 3. Clearly, the functional status develops in close and linear relation to morphological growth.

Girls and boys have the same aerobic work capacity up to the beginning of puberty. Then the girls' fitness (as O_2 ml/min/kg body weight) becomes lower and diverges from the boys'. Much speculation has been devoted to the explanation of this phenomenon. Von Döbeln (1956) related maximal uptake to 'fat free' body weight, and on this basis he found that the sex differences disappeared. This finding suggests that the sex differences are brought about by differences in body composition, with a higher ratio of adipose muscle tissue in women during the fertile period, The possibility, however, cannot be excluded that the sex differences and the decrease in the girls' fitness are due to differences

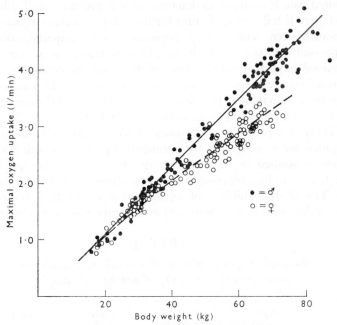

FIG. 3. The relationship between maximal oxygen uptake and body weight in growing children (from Åstrand, 1952).

in the functional capacity of the circulatory-respiratory system, brought about, for instance, by training and physical activity. Girls usually become less active at the beginning of puberty. Since, however, a similar sex difference at puberty is also found in primitive people, the phenomenon is likely to be of a biological nature rather than a reflection of the cultural and social environment.

Although the maximal O_2-uptake per kg body weight is the same in 10-year-old and 20-year-old males, the young boys' fitness for muscular exercise may be inferior to the older men. This is because the resting metabolic rate is greater in children than in adults. If maximal working metabolism is expressed in terms of resting metabolism, the 7- to 9-year-old boys in Åstrand's material raised their metabolism by a factor of 9–10 while the adult men were able to increase theirs by a factor of 15–16.

The relationship between functional development and morphological growth may be influenced by many factors, and differences between populations are expected to be found. Only limited data is available to demonstrate this problem. In Tables 3 and 4 are listed average figures for the maximal oxygen uptake of schoolchildren, and various populations are compared. When expressed on basis of body weight it is readily seen that the maximal oxygen uptake of boys of the same population is unaffected by age in the age range from 10 to 18 years. This suggests that the age increase in functional status takes place at the same rate as the morphological growth in most populations.

There are probably differences between children's fitness in populations as suggested by published reports. The Stockholm children studied in 1952 are superior to any other groups, but the Lapp children are close to the same fitness level (Tables 3 and 4). The Boston children of 1938 are lower, but they compare favourably with Köln (Germany) and Bergen (Norway) children.

TABLE 3

Maximal oxygen uptake of schoolchildren. Figures are average values ($max\ O_2\ ml/min/kg$ body weight)

Age (y)	1938† Boston		1952‡ Stockholm		1960§ Köln		1961‖ Lapps	
	♂	♀	♂	♀	♂	♀	♂	♀
10–11	52	—	56	52	—	—	53	51
12–13	—	—	56	50	45	—	53	48
14–15	47	—	59	46	48	—	55	44
16–18	53	—	57	47	45	—	53	42

† S. Robinson, *Arbeitsphysiologia*, **10**, 251–323, 1938.

‡ P. O. Åstrand, *Experimental Studies of Working Capacity in Relation to Sex and Age.* Munksgaard, Copenhagen, 1952.

§ W. Hollmann, *Höchst- und Dauerleistungsfähigkeit der Sportler.* Barth, München, 1963.

‖ K. Lange Andersen, R. Elsner, B. Saltin, and L. Hermansen, 'Physical fitness in terms of maximal oxygen uptake of nomadic Lapps', Report to U.S.A.F., 1961.

Data for German schoolchildren reported by König et al. (1961) and for American schoolchildren (Rodahl et al., 1961)) are so much lower that one must doubt if these values represent true maximal levels.

TABLE 4
Maximal oxygen uptake of schoolboys, age 14–15 years
(average values)

Subjects	Number of subjects	Max. O₂-uptake l./min	ml/min/kg	Maximal HR	Blood lactate
1938 Boston (Robinson)	9	2·63	47	210	62
1952 Stockholm (Åstrand)	10	3·53	59	203	90
1960 Köln (Hollman)	51	2·39	48	192	—
1961 Lapps (Lange Andersen)	14	2·37	55	198	85
1965† Bergen (Lange Andersen)	20	2·23	48	192	82

† Unpublished data.

The difference between the Stockholm children of 1952 and the Köln and Bergen children measured a decade later may merely be due to the fact that the tested Stockholm children were so few in number that they probably represent a selected group drawn from a physically better part of the population. The tested Bergen children represent a randomized sample; about 10 per cent of the total population (boys age 14–15 years) were initially studied with a simple bicycle test (Table 5), and then 20–25 per cent of these were randomly selected for the direct measurement of maximal O₂-uptake. The results of this study should thus yield a fairly true picture of the fitness standard of Bergen schoolchildren (age 14–15 years) in 1965.

The heart rate response to a fixed ergometer load is closely

related to the maximal oxygen uptake, and the former may, therefore, be used as an index of the latter. The technique of measuring
heart rate while riding a bicycle ergometer is so simple that this
procedure can be used as a fitness test on a large-scale basis. In
Table 5 is listed an extract of the available information on heart

TABLE 5

*Heart rate during bicycle riding. Schoolchildren 14–15 years.
Figures are averages*

Subjects	n	Height (cm)	Weight (kg)	Skinfold thickness	HR 300 kpm/min	HR 600 kpm/min
Boys						
Stockholm	54	163	49	—	128	160
Göteborg	62	167	53	—	—	150
Philadelphia	50	165	56	—	133	166
New York	76	169	62	121	129	146
Halden	90	173	61	89	120	150
Bergen	77	167	61	—	124	154
Hernes	11	160	50	—	—	155
Girls						
Stockholm	51	161	48	—	137	176
Philadelphia	50	159	49	—	154	186
Hernes	9	163	56	—	—	174

rate response in 14- to 15-year-old children while riding a bicycle
ergometer. It is quite obvious that there are considerable differences
within each country. Thus, in Sweden, Stockholm children are
inferior to any other city children. In Norway, country children
seem to be inferior to city children, which is the opposite of what
was expected. Philadelphia children are inferior to Scandinavian
children, but data from a New York school (Brewster High School)
suggest no differences between Scandinavian and American boys.
All these differences tend to show that great caution must be exercised when using this indirect method as a basis for comparing
populations.

Adults. Ageing exerts a strong influence on the major functions
that determine the total exercise performance capacity. The decline
with increasing age may start as early as 25–30 years for some
functions, while others are delayed. In adults, males average better
than females, and this sex differentiation starts at puberty. In old

age the functional status of the two sexes seems to come closer (K. Lange Andersen, 1959).

In his classical paper on age differences with regard to respiratory and circulatory functions during exercise, Robinson (1938) describes the capacity of the aerobic muscle metabolism. He investigated 95 males ranging in age from 6 to 91 years, representing more or less the whole life-span. He found that the highest oxygen uptake during exhaustive muscular exercise increased in parallel to the increase in body size up to the age of 20 years. A decline started at the age of 30 years, and then there was a consistent trend of continuous decrease in aerobic capacity with age. In relation to body weight the average figures ranged between 47 and 53 ml/min/kg body weight up to the age of 30 years. The 50-year-old men averaged 39 ml/min/kg body weight and the 70-year-old men 26 ml/min/kg.

P. O. Åstrand (1952) published an extensive study of children's and young people's (up to 30 years) aerobic work capacity. For all the male subjects the maximal oxygen uptake per kilogram body weight was fairly constant, with average values ranging from 56 to 59 ml/min/kg body weight. The girls averaged the same as the boys up to an age of 11–12 years, corresponding to the beginning of puberty. Then the oxygen uptake per kilogram body weight became less by about 20 per cent. Aastrand reviewed in 1956 human fitness in relation to age and sex, and this paper should be consulted for details.

I. Åstrand (1960) has provided data showing that adult females follow a similar age-dependent fitness curve to that described for males, but that the values for women are 40 per cent lower. Women aged 20–29 years averaged 40 ml/min/kg body weight at the age of 50–65. Hermansen (1964) studied sedentary Oslo women, and found, in contrast to Aastrand, that the maximal oxygen uptake remained fairly constant during the fertile part of adult life, and that the age deterioration started at the beginning of the climacterium. The same tendency is also suggested from studies of female Lapps (K. Lange Andersen et al., 1961). The weight increased with age in these women due to increased fatness. Thus, the fitness in relation to the body weight became gradually reduced from the age of 20 to the age of 50.

Age and sex differences have recently been the subject of many studies and some results from investigations that used the same

direct method technique of measuring maximal oxygen uptake
are listed in Tables 6 and 7. Except for German men and women,
the similarity in average figures are striking. This suggests that a
variety of patterns of living in different habitats and exposure to
different climates do not exert any appreciable influence on the
level of fitness in people of the same ethnic origin (in this case
Caucasians of the northern European stock). Again, we lack data
so this statement can only be tentative. The lower values for the

TABLE 6

Maximal O₂-uptake (l./min) of Caucasian men.
Figures are averages

Age (y)	1938† Boston	1960‡ Stockholm	1963§ Köln	1964 Oslo
20–29	3·56	—	—	3·20
30–39	3·42	3·01	2·97	3·20
40–49	2·92	2·99	2·68	2·90
50–59	2·63	2·99	2·68	2·90
60–69	2·35	2·23	1·79	—
70–79	1·71	1·99	1·52	1·95
80 and over	—	1·50	—	1·63

† Ref. Table 3.
‡ I. Åstrand, *Acta physiol. scand.* Vol. 49, Suppl. 169, 1960.
§ Strandell: Ref. Table 3.
‖ L. Hermansen, Unpublished data. A. Benestad, K. Lange Andersen,
Unpublished data.

TABLE 7

Maximal oxygen uptake (l./min) of Caucasian women.
Figures are averages

Age (y)	1960 Stockholm	1963 Köln	1964 Oslo
20–29	2·23	2·20	2·10
30–39	2·13	1·89	2·00
40–49	2·01	1·87	2·00
50–59	1·85	1·67	1·80
60–69	—	—	—
70 and over	—	—	1·08

Same reference as in Table 6.

Germans may reflect technical rather than biological differences, because another measuring technique was used.

For American men of today values have been published that are considerably lower than those referred to above. Ninety-six policemen (average age 38 years) in Philadelphia, studied by Hettinger *et al.* (1960), averaged only 2·22 l./min, which is the same as found in sedentary Scandinavian women of the age of 20, and only little above that found for Scandinavian men older than 70 years. In relation to body weight (the average weight for the policemen was 81 kg) the Philadelphia policemen were even less fit than the Norwegian girls or the Norwegian old men. These reported fitness values for present-day American men are so much lower than those found elsewhere that it raises doubts as to whether these values are truly maximal. These and other conflicting results suggest that great care must be taken to standardize technique and experimental procedures for fitness testing.

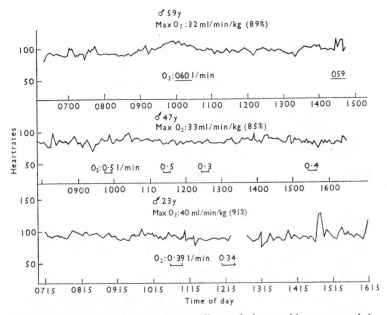

FIG. 4. Continuous heart rate recordings of three subjects engaged in sedentary work. Oxygen uptake measurements are given together with data for maximal oxygen uptake, the latter also given in per cent of average for office workers.

7

Maximal oxygen uptake in relation to occupational activity

The physical activity associated with the daily round of work may exert an influence on the level of aerobic work capacity. A study of the pattern of activity involved in performing various jobs, together with information about the work capacity of the workers, might be expected to throw some light on this problem. A group of Oslo physiologists over the last three years has undertaken a programme of research devoted to this task. Data from three occupations are at present available: office work, representing a sedentary profession; lumbering, regarded as the heaviest manual work in the country; and industrial work which might occupy an intermediate position.

The pattern of energy expenditure during a working day has been evaluated by continuous heart rate recordings (which roughly indicate the level of oxygen uptake), supplemented by spot sampling of oxygen uptake. A miniature radio-transmitter has been constructed for the use of telemetering heart activity so that this

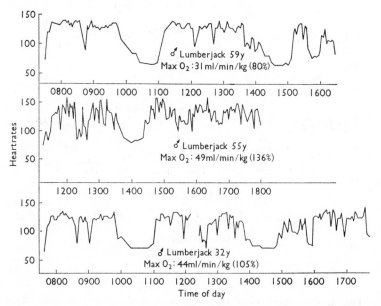

FIG. 5. Heart rate recordings of three subjects engaged in lumbering. Data for maximal oxygen uptake are given, also in per cent of average for office workers.

could be recorded without disturbing the subjects. The oxygen uptake measurements are performed by using a conventional open respiratory circuit system, collecting and metering the expired air by means of a gasometer with subsequent analysis of the expired gas. Sedentary office work is characterized by an energy expenditure elevated 50–100 per cent above the resting level, and heart rates fluctuating between 80 and 90, with occasional peaks up to 100 (Fig. 4). It is typical that the peaks represent rest pauses where the subjects stood up for a smoke or went to the toilet. The daily pattern of energy expenditure associated with lumbering is quite different (Fig. 5). An oxygen uptake of up to 2·0–2·5 l./min, or 8 to 10 times above the normal resting level, is found. The heart rate fluctuates more than in sedentary work, and may reach values up to 150. The lumberjacks usually take two long rest pauses during a working day, which are shown by periods of resting heart rates.

Work in modern industries is quite variable with regard to physical efforts. With increasing mechanization comes a reduced

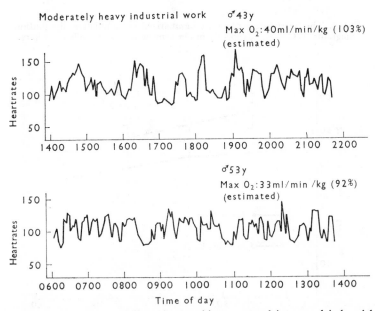

FIG. 6. Heart rate recording of two subjects engaged in manual industrial work. Data of estimated maximal oxygen uptake based on sub-maximal work tests are given (also expressed in per cent of average for office workers).

need for manual work, and many industrial jobs are today as
sedentary as office work. In Fig. 6 data are presented on men
occupied by what is regarded as moderately heavy industrial work,
involving transportation activities.

The heart rates of a working day are summarized in cumulative
distribution diagrams (Fig. 7). The heart rate is given as the
abscissa, ranging from the approximate basal level to the maximum.
The diagram square thus represents the total capacity of the
individual, and the area to the left of the distribution curve

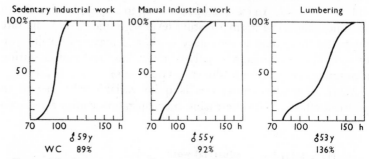

FIG. 7. The heart rate recordings summarized in cumulative distribution
diagrams. WC = work capacity in per cent of average for office workers.

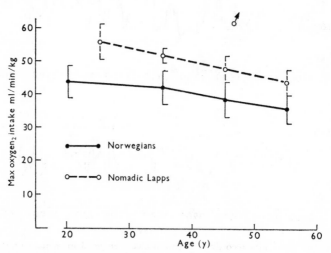

FIG. 8. Maximal oxygen uptake of nomadic Lapps compared with office
workers. Vertical lines denote one S.D.

indicates the fraction of the total capacity utilized by the work. Clearly, sedentary work utilizes only 10–15 per cent but lumbering 50 per cent of the total capacity.

The aerobic work capacity of representative samples of the three professions is listed in Table 8. Lumberjacks average a slightly higher maximal oxygen uptake expressed as l./min. Expressing the

TABLE 8

Maximal oxygen uptake of Norwegian lumberjacks, industrial and office workers. Figures are averages. Unpublished data from Institute of Work Physiology, Oslo

Age (y)	Lumberjacks		Industrial workers		Office workers	
	l./min	ml/min/kg	l./min	ml/min/kg	l./min	ml/min/kg
Under 30	3·4	45	—	—	3·2	44
30–39	3·3	46	3·1	44	3·2	42
40–49	3·1	44	2·9	38	2·9	39
50–59	2·8	39	2·5	34	2·6	36

maximal oxygen on a basis of body weight brings out a 10 per cent superiority for industrial and office workers, who are closely similar. In general, and on a basis of great differences in the habitual physical activity of these people, the differences in aerobic work capacity were remarkably and unexpectedly small. There is no doubt that the lumberjacks possess a greater ability to perform manual work with less fatigue than the differences in aerobic capacity suggest. The lumberjacks have apparently a better ability to utilize this capacity than sedentary subjects. How this is brought about is an open question worth further investigation.

Maximal oxygen uptake of athletes of international standard

The athletes form a group of subjects who, besides being drawn from the physically fittest part of the population, have trained their performance capacity to the limits of its adaptability. Their fitness in terms of physiology and body composition will represent the upper end of the scale.

Åstrand (1956) lists data for the maximal oxygen uptake of the world's best 1500-metre runners and of five of the most outstanding cross-country skiers. Oxygen uptake ranges from 4·81 l./min to 5·88 l./min or from 67 to 81 ml/min/kg body weight. Other investigations have shown maximal oxygen uptake of the same order. Table 9 lists average figures for successful Norwegian cross-country skiers who are compared with sedentary subjects of the

TABLE 9

Maximal O₂-uptake of Norwegians, age 20–30 y. Average values.
L. Hermansen og K. Lange Andersen, J. appl. Physiol., 1965

		Maximal O₂-uptake			Times above	Highest
Subjects	n	l./min	ml/min/kg	ml/min/kg	B.M.R.	HR
Athletes	14	4·8	71	28	20	178
Students	12	3·2	44	18	12	189
Athletes	5	3·3	55	20	15	186
Students	12	2·3	38	14	11	203

same age. Male athletes average 60 per cent higher in maximal values than sedentary men. Female athletes average 45 per cent higher than sedentary women.

Middle-aged cross-country skiers also have a higher maximal oxygen uptake than sedentary men of same age (Table 10). This

TABLE 10

Aerobic work capacity of Norwegian men, age 50–60 y
(mean and S.D.). K. Lange Andersen and L. Hermansen,
J. appl. Physiol., 1965

		Maximal O₂-uptake			Times above	Highest
Subjects	n	l./min	ml/min/kg	ml/min/cm	B.M.R.	HR
Skiers	66	3·2	47	19	15	164
Nomadic Lapps	6	2·8	44	17	14	167
Office workers	17	2·1	36	15	11	177
Industrial workers	21	2·5	34	14	11	164
Students 20–30 y	12	3·2	44	18	12	189

finding raises the question of whether the normal age decline in work capacity is due to inevitable morphological and/or functional changes, or whether it is related to reduced habitual physical activity. This problem cannot be conclusively answered, but the superiority of the middle-aged skiers suggests that training may delay the functional age deterioration.

Maximal oxygen uptake of inhabitants of primitive communities

People who base their living upon a simple hunting-and-gathering economy are to a larger extent dependent upon muscular strength and endurance for survival and successful adaptation to their habitat than are members of the technically advanced societies, who are protected from hazardous environmental influences and who no longer need to train their physical abilities in order to make a comfortable living.

The maximal oxygen uptake of nomadic Lapps who inhabit the northern Scandinavian Peninsula is given in Table 11 and

TABLE 11

Aerobic work capacity of primitive men, age 20–40 y (mean ± S.E.). Data for Norwegian students and athletes are given for comparison

Subjects	n	Max O_2 ml/min/kg	Highest HR
Bantu negroes	23	$48 \pm 1 \cdot 96$	180
Kalihar bushmen	3	$47 \pm 6 \cdot 98$	—
Eskimoes	8	$44 \pm 1 \cdot 81$	173
Arctic Indians	8	$49 \pm 1 \cdot 71$	—
Nomadic Lapps	16	$54 \pm 1 \cdot 27$	191
Alucaluf Indians	4	38 ± 0	—
Norwegian students	12	$44 \pm 1 \cdot 10$	189
Norwegian athletes	14	$71 \pm 1 \cdot 80$	178

Fig. 8. These results are based on measurements of a representative sample of the total population. Clearly, the adult Lapps' higher aerobic capacity is demonstrated in all ages and both sexes. This observation is in keeping with studies undertaken on other people living on a subsistence economy, such as the Bantu Negroes and Kalahari bushmen investigated by Wyndham et al. (1964) and the Arctic Indians studied by K. Lange Andersen et al. (1960).

However, Arctic Eskimoes (1963) and Alucaluf Indians of the Southern Chilean Pelagos (1962) do not seem to be characterized by a high level of aerobic work capacity. Primitive people's higher aerobic capacity may reflect a high level of physical activity. No doubt the pattern of living of these people involves strenuous exercise, although never recorded by acceptable physiological technique. These people are also genetically different from those they are compared with, and the differences in aerobic capacity may, therefore, demonstrate inherited differences. That such differences may exist is suggested by a comparative study of Czechoslovakian and Vietnamese medical doctors (Skranc and Havel, 1964). It was found that the Czechoslovakian men at the age of 37 averaged 40 ml/min/kg body weight O_2-uptake, which is similar to values for sedentary men reported from other European laboratories, but that the Vietnamese men of the same age average 33 ml/min/kg body weight, which is 18 per cent lower.

Deficiencies in knowledge

All our knowledge regarding aerobic work capacity stems from studies of a small number of restricted samples of selected humans, drawn mainly from limited social and occupational groups of people, representing industrialized and urbanized societies. While the results of this work undoubtedly have given some insight into basic physiological problems and have yielded some ideas as to which general factors influence the level of physical fitness in a population, such as that described in this paper, they must be considered rather as examples that population surveys can be undertaken, than as forming a firm basis for a knowledge of the working capacity of populations. The presented data suggest that there may be differences between populations, but many more studies need to be undertaken in order to understand this problem fully. This will primarily be a descriptive task, investigating representative samples of all ages and both sexes.

The more dynamic aspects will include elucidations of the many biological and ecological factors influencing the functional status, and this undertaking will certainly require the utilization of a variety of descriptive data in addition to those purporting to measure the morphology and the physiological capacities. Much remains to be done in order to gain a better understanding of the importance of the forces at work and of their interrelations. It is not at all clear that we today have formulated precisely the scientific problems or even that we can do so. But the research diverted toward these problems will certainly have to include investigations of such factors as the physical environment, the state of nutrition, and the cultural and social patterns of living. including habitual physical activity, genetics, and diseases.

Provided that the nutritional status is optimal, the habitual physical activity seems to be the most powerful factor influencing the work capacity of a healthy subject. It is not known to what extent this can be achieved by training. Young subjects are possibly able to increase their functional status more than elderly people; results of recent research certainly suggest this.

The industrialization and urbanization which take place with an ever-increasing rate in all countries have reduced the need for vigorous muscular exercise in the process of earning a living. Since modern technology has provided motorized transport to almost everybody, it is now possible for an individual to spend almost his entire life at an energy level close to the resting state. The effect upon the functional work capacity of the body of this reduction in the load of all of life's daily activities may be a deleterious one. It remains to be seen scientifically what such a decreased functional capacity may mean for man's health, in terms of his resistance to diseases, longevity, adaptive capability, and so on, and for the well-being of the individual.

REFERENCES

ÅSTRAND, I., 1960. 'Aerobic work capacity in men and women', *Acta physiol. scand.* **49**, Suppl. 149.

ÅSTRAND, P. O., 1952. *Experimental Studies of Physical Working Capacity in Relation to Sex and Age.* Munksgaard, Copenhagen.

ANDERSEN, K. LANGE, 1960. 'Den aerobe arbeidskapasitet', *Tidskr. norske Lægeforen,* **22**, 1087–1091.

—— 1959. *Respiratory Recovery from Muscular Exercise of Short Exercise.* Oslo University Press.

—— BOLSTAD, ATLE, LÖYNING, YNGVE, and IRVING, L., 1960. 'Physical fitness of Arctic Indians', *J. appl. Physiol.* **15**, 645–648.

—— and HART, J. S., 1963. 'Aerobic working capacity of Eskimoes', *J. appl. Physiol.* **18**, 764–768.

—— and HERMANSEN, L., 1965. 'Aerobic work capacity of middle aged Norwegian men', *J. appl. Physiol.* **20**, 432–436, 1965.

—— ELSNER, R., SALTIN, BENGT, and HERMANSEN, L., 1961. 'Physical fitness in terms of maximal oxygen intake of nomadic Lapps. Report to USAF under grant AF-EOARDS.

BUZKIRK, E. and TAYLOR, HENRY LONGSTREET, 1957. 'Maximal oxygen intake and its relation to body composition, with special reference to chronic physical activity and obesity', *J. appl. Physiol.* **11**, 72–78.

DÖBELN, W. VON, 1956. 'Human standard and maximal metabolic rate in relation to fat free body mass', *Acta physiol. scand.* **37**, Suppl. 126.

HERMANSEN, L. and ANDERSEN, K. LANGE, 1956. 'Aerobic work capacity of young Norwegians', *J. appl. Physiol.* **20**, 425–431, 1965.

—— *Aerob arbeidskapasitet i relasjon til alder og kjönn*, Hovedfagsoppgave i zoofysiologi. Oslo University, 1964.

HETTINGER, T., BIRKHEAD, N. C., HORWARTH, S. M., ISSEKUTZ, B., and RODAHL, K., 1961. 'Assessment of physical work capacity', *J. appl. Physiol.* **16**, 153–156.

HOLLMAN, W., 1963. *Höchst und Dauerleistungsfähigkeit des Sportlers.* Barth, München.

KÖNIG, G., REINDELL, H., KEUL, J., and ROSKAM, H., 1961. 'Untersuchungen über des Verhalten von Atmung und Kreislauf im Belastungsversuch bei Kindern und Jugendlichen in Alter von 10–19 Jahren', *Int. Z. angew. Physiol.* **18**, 393–434.

ROBINSON, S., 1938. 'Experimental studies of physical fitness in relation to age', *Arbeitsphysiologie* **10**, 251–323.

RODAHL, K., ÅSTRAND, P. O., BIRKHEAD, N. C., HETTINGER, T., ISSEKUTZ, B., JONES, D. M., and WEAVER, R., 1961. 'Physical work capacity', *Archs envir. Hlth* **2**, 499–510.

SJÖSTRAND, T., 1953. 'Volume and distribution of blood and their significance in regulating circulation', *Physiol. Rev.* **33**, 202–228.

SKRANC, O. and HAVEL, V., 1964. 'Fitness of Czechoslovakian and Vietnamese physicians under graded workload', *Int. Z. angew. Physiol.* **20**, 412–419.

STRANDELL, T., 1963. 'Heart rate, blood lactate and oxygen uptake during exercise in old men', *Acta med. scand.* **174**, 479–499.

WYNDHAM, C. H., STRYDOM, N. B., STRYDOM, J. F., MORRISON, J. F., PETER, J., WILLIAMS, C. S., BREDELL, S. A. S., and JOFFE, A., 1963. 'Differences in physical working capacity', *J. appl. Physiol.* **18**, 361–366.

5

PEOPLES OF AFRICA FROM 22°N TO THE EQUATOR

CURRENT KNOWLEDGE AND SUGGESTIONS FOR FUTURE RESEARCH

J. HIERNAUX

Laboratoire d'Anthropologie de la Faculté des Sciences, Paris

Introduction

THIS chapter is an attempt to appraise our current knowledge on questions pertinent to the 'Human Adaptability' section of IBP in the strip of Africa that the author had to cover at the Burg Wartenstein meeting. Examples have been chosen mainly from his own experience. The bibliography is therefore overloaded with references to his own papers. This should not be interpreted as complacency for his own work, but by his restriction, at the level of examples, to what he knows best.

References and values (samples, means, standard deviations, and frequencies) relative to the next section will be published later.

Current knowledge on the distribution of gene frequencies, metrical means, and phenotype frequencies

In any survey of the distribution of anthropological characters, the unit of investigation is the breeding population. Means or frequencies for a nation, or a city, known to be inhabited by a mosaic of several breeding populations, are of little interest for problems of population genetics. For appraising the amount of data published in this field, only samples representing well-defined ethnic groups may therefore be considered. Even for a crude approximation, this requires accurate ethnic maps of the area covered. The map used in this attempt is that of Murdoch (1959). It shows 603 names of ethnic groups in Africa from 22° N to the equator.

Most of the literature has been screened; a few still unanalysed papers are known of, and other ones undoubtedly escaped attention. A minimum sample of forty for quantitative characters and dermatoglyphics, and of 100 for qualitative characters has been required. Only male series were considered for metrical characters, dermatoglyphics, and sex-linked traits. The characters considered were the ones whose study in extensive surveys has been recommended by various IBP subcommittees: in document HA 23 for serological and biochemical hereditary traits, colour-blindness, taste-blindness to PTC, and dermatoglyphics; in document HA 22 for a minimum list of metrical characters. Data on growth will be considered separately.

From the data so collected, maps have been drawn which locate the populations on which one or several specified measurements or tests have been performed, and the extent and gaps of our current knowledge can be estimated by comparing these maps to that of Fig. 1, which shows all 603 ethnic groups. (Maps for separate data are given in Figs. 2–13.) Data that meet the above-cited requirements have been published on 267 ethnic groups. Fifty-five per cent of the populations in the area covered remain unstudied for any character. Much higher percentages of unknown are observed for particular characters or combinations of characters, as exemplified by the maps contained in Figs. 2–13:

Map 2. ABO (Fig. 2)

Owing to its importance for blood transfusion, this is the most widely determined monofactorial genetical system. Data exist on 70 populations (11 per cent of the total number of ethnic groups).

Map 3. ABO + Rh (including surveys with anti-D only) (Fig. 3)

Despite the importance of Rh groups for transfusion, data on ABO and Rh concern 28 populations only (4·6 per cent).

Map 4. Sickle-cell trait (slide test) (Fig. 4)

An extensively investigated trait, owing to its importance for medicine and anthropology, and its easy determination: 83 populations (13 per cent).

Map 5. Abnormal haemoglobins (studied by electrophoresis) (Fig. 5)

Much more limited distribution: 47 populations (7·8 per cent), despite their medical interest: laboratories equipped for their determination are rare in Africa, and rapid transport overseas implies personnel, time, planning, and budget.

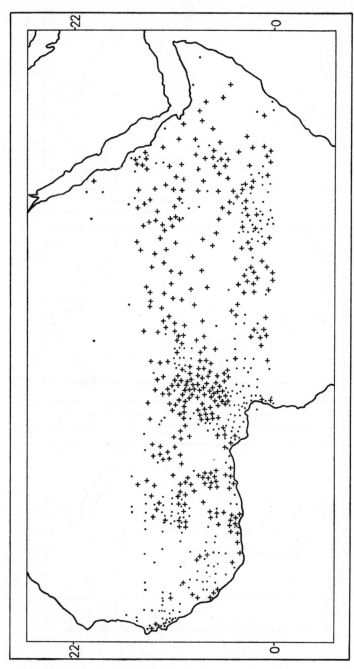

FIG. 1. Location of ethnic groups north of equator; · : data available, + : no published data.

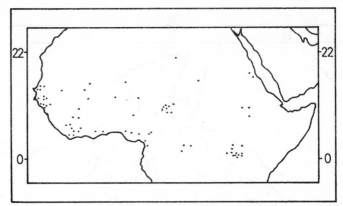

FIG. 2. Data available on the ABO system.

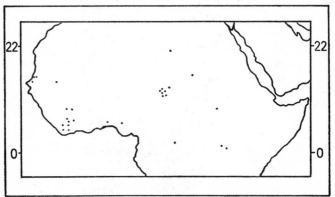

FIG. 3. Data available on both ABO and Rh systems.

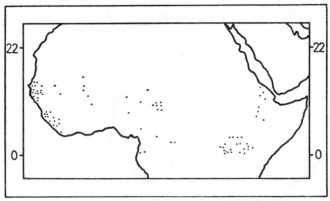

FIG. 4. Data available on sickle-cell trait (slide test).

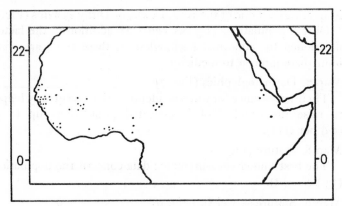

FIG. 5. Data available on abnormal haemoglobins (by electrophoresis).

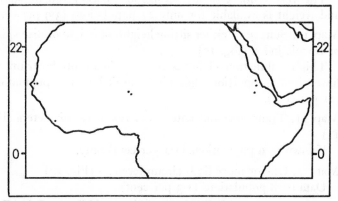

FIG. 6. Data available on at least one of Kell, Lewis, or Duffy systems.

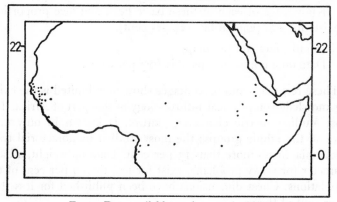

FIG. 7. Data available on dermatoglyphics.

Map 6. At least one of the Kell, Lewis, or Duffy systems (Fig. 6)

Only 8 populations (1·3 per cent). In addition to the factors mentioned for abnormal haemoglobins, these traits are of no immediate interest to medicine.

Map 7. Dermatoglyphics (Fig. 7)

Their importance for forensic identification has greatly helped to raise the number of investigated populations up to 36 (5·9 per cent).

Map 8. Stature (Fig. 8)

The best-known measurement: data concern 199 populations (33 per cent).

Map 9. Stature + weight (Fig. 9)

The very crude estimate of size and mass given by stature and weight is available for only 24 populations (3·9 per cent).

Map 10. Stature + either sitting height, or height of iliac spine, or cormic index (Fig. 10)

This combination giving a crude estimate of the trunk vs. lower limb proportions has been studied in 127 populations (21 per cent).

Map 11. Transverse and anteroposterior chest diameters (Fig. 11)

Known in 9 populations (1·4 per cent) only.

Map 12. One or more limb circumferences (Fig. 12)

Data on 8 populations (1·3 per cent).

Map 13. Cephalic, facial, and nasal indices (Fig. 13)

Knowledge of each of these basic head and face proportions exists for 150 populations (24 per cent).

Skinfolds, any site (no map)

Data on 2 ethnic groups only (0·3 per cent).

These few maps and percentages show how limited is the existing knowledge on physical anthropology of this part of Africa. The most studied metric character, stature, is known in only one-third of the ethnic groups: the most studied monofactorial trait, sicklaemia, in no more than 13 per cent. Data on weight, a basic character for many problems, exist for less than 4 per cent of the populations. Chest dimensions have been published for less than 2 per cent of them.

FIG. 8. Data available on stature.

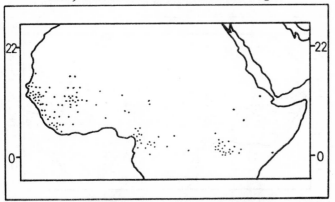

FIG. 9. Data available on both stature and weight.

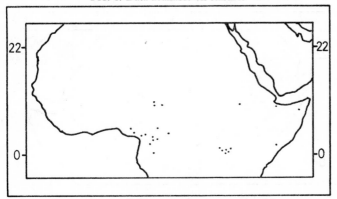

FIG. 10. Data available on stature and either sitting height, or height of iliac spine, or cormic index.

8

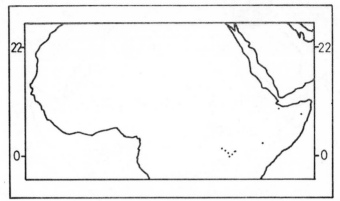

FIG. 11. Data available on transverse and anteroposterior chest diameters.

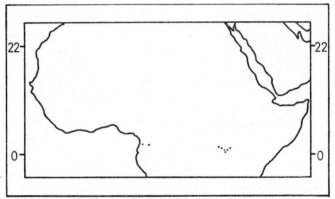

FIG. 12. Data available on one or more limb circumferences.

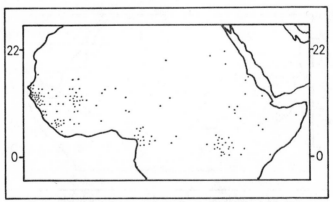

FIG. 13. Data available on cephalic, facial, and nasal indices.

Current knowledge on growth

Even less is known about growth than about adult morphology. Cross-sectional data have been published on growth in height and weight in a few ethnic groups. Longitudinal surveys have been started in Dakar and Kampala, using the set of characters common to all centres of the Centre International de l'Enfance, but only as yet fragmentary results have been published.

Suggestions for extensive surveys on genetic polymorphic systems, growth, and adult physique

The purposes that extensive surveys could serve have been listed and exemplified by Weiner in Chapter 1. For any of these purposes, the ideal would consist of having available accurate data on every breeding population. The two preceding sections have stressed how far away we are from this ideal for the part of Africa considered here.

Is extrapolation permissible from the small percentage of the known to the much vaster unknown? Clearly not. Human mobility, variety of interpopulational breeding, occurrence of genetic drift, of the founder effect, and lack of concordance in the variation of independent traits make the predictability of the characters of any population from those of others geographically near very poor. The fact that a population has been assigned by some to a taxon on the basis of a few traits and/or historical or linguistic arguments does not much increase the predictability of the value of another trait in this population from its knowledge in some members of the taxon. For example, the frequencies of dermatoglyphic whorls and loops within the group called 'African Pygmies' show nearly the same range of interpopulational variation as that displayed by the gamut of African populations south of the Sahara (Hiernaux, 1964a). The relation between stature and limb segments varies interpopulationally within a geographically restricted group of Bantu-speaking tribes of Eastern Congo nearly as much as between British and Ugandese groups (Hiernaux, unpublished). On the basis of morphological features, Twa populations of central and southern Congo are usually grouped as 'Pygmoids' with the Pygmies or considered as hybrids between Pygmies and taller Bantu populations; their ABO gene frequencies are nevertheless drastically different from those of the Bambuti Pygmies and are not intermediary between these and those of their Bantu landlords

(Hiernaux, 1962). While it is unrealistic to hope that IBP, however great its effort, could cover a majority of the African breeding populations by extensive surveys, it must be realized that any hypothesis based on the known variability of a trait is highly tentative as long as this variability is known for only a small minority of human groups.

Moreover, what is needed for many of the purposes that extensive surveys can serve is the combined distribution of different traits. For monofactorial genetic ones, we need data not only on the different alleles at a given locus, but also on other loci which can interact with the former or respond to the same selective forces (see for example Livingstone (1964) on genes S, C, and T at the Hb locus and the sex-linked G-6-P D deficiency gene). Morphology varies and reacts to the environment not through the individual measurements that we usually take but in so complex a way that it is necessary for any morphological survey (be it on the adult stage or on growth) to include measurements representing the most various aspects of the physique. It is rewarding to collect data on both multifactorial and monofactorial traits, in order to have material available on an array of characters displaying the widest range of sensitivity to various selective forces and to genetic drift. For example, the Bantu ethnic groups which moved from the savannah into the forest of Eastern Congo a few centuries ago differ morphologically from the present savannah-dwelling, closely related groups in the direction of the Pygmies' means, but are similar for blood group frequencies. This substantiates the hypothesis that convergent morphological evolution in the equatorial forest is the main cause of the observed similarities of the forest groups, and minimizes the importance of the influence of hybridization (Hiernaux, 1956). In a general way, the interpretation of any difference found between populations will require consideration of all known mechanisms of evolution and differentiation: direct influence of the environment on the phenotype, adaptive evolution, mutations, drift, hybridization, and inbreeding. The hope to reach a valid conclusion for any one trait is meagre if we do not have available data on other traits showing a large variety of ecosensitiveness, susceptibility to drift, and differences between the possible contributors to the gene pools.

The preceding considerations emphasize the need for data on many human traits in the same populations. It can be seen on the maps published here that as soon as we increase the number of traits, the number of populations represented sharply falls. It falls to nearly zero for any combination of characters approaching the list of traits whose recording is recommended by the IBP sub-committees. Owing to this nearly complete lack of adequate knowledge, the study of any human group in sub-Saharan Africa north of the equator will be of value.

It must be stressed again that such studies have to be on well-specified breeding populations, or else they run a strong risk of representing a great loss of time, money, and human effort. Any extensive survey must start with a careful study of the mating patterns in the area covered. This will require at least the reading of the ethnological literature, and most often the co-operation of an ethnologist. Two examples will illustrate this point. First, several papers published within the last decade give frequencies or means for a group called 'Banyarwanda'. It is known, however, since the work of Czekanowski (1922), and has been confirmed several times, that this term designates the residents of Rwanda, a country inhabited by three breeding populations which differ largely in their gene pool and in their morphology. Second, a few papers on anthropometry and dermatoglyphics refer to the Sara, in the southern part of Tchad. This term, however, designates, in a loose way that varies with time and with its user, a number of breeding populations whose degree of differentiation is still unknown.

Delineation of the breeding populations, in terms of geography or of sociology, is often difficult. Generally speaking, it is easier in sub-Saharan Africa than in many other parts of the world, since the African tribe or caste is usually highly endogamous, and of modest territorial size. Large ethnic groups may, however, show some internal differentiation due to isolation by distance or to marked local endogamy; the accurate unit of study may sometimes be the chiefdom or even a subdivision of the chiefdom, as Livingstone (1960) indicates for the distribution of the sickle-cell gene among the Bassa of Liberia.

One of the potentially most fruitful uses that we shall be able to make of a large body of data from extensive surveys is the research on associations between a human trait or combination of traits and a feature of the environment. This will be possible only if we have available quantified data on the environment as well as on man. Data on the physical environment will be needed by any section of IBP; it may be hoped that this need will promote their systematic recording. They should concern a wide variety of aspects of the physical environment, to permit the enlargement of the range of associations that can be tested. That this field is promising is shown by the conclusions of Weiner (1954) that nasal index has its highest correlation with absolute humidity, while previous studies using temperature and relative humidity only concluded that temperature is more determinant than humidity.

Man's environment results in an important part from his specifically human, or cultural, activities. Heat load depends not only on the climate, but also on clothing and on the type and organization of work. Nutrition depends only partly on soil fertility and resources in game and fish: agricultural and pastoral practices, food habits and taboos, modalities of sharing food in respect to age, class, and sex are all-important. Pathological load is largely dependent on cultural factors: not only on the efficiency of hygiene and medicine, but also on the impact of human activities on the life-cycle of parasites (see for example Livingstone (1958) on the influence of agriculture on proliferation of malaria-transmitting mosquitoes). For interpreting human variability, data on the cultural factors of man's environment are as indispensable as on climatic variables or soil composition and fertility. The two kinds of factors probably always interact, as Brace (1964) points out.

Since genetic adaptation to new environmental conditions requires a number of generations to reach an equilibrium, the length of time during which the populations have lived in their current environment is a datum of prime importance for interpreting man-*milieu* associations. Historical data are also necessary for appraising the probability of genetic drift or of founder effect in the past, and for indicating the modalities of cross-breeding.

All this shows that extensive surveys need to be carefully planned to be of use. Even for the aim of elucidating the degree of biological similitude between populations, these surveys require, in the planning stage, the co-operation of an ethnologist, or at least a good knowledge of the ethnological literature when available, for defining the units of study. Interpretation of clines and associations between anthropological characters and environmental variables requires data from many disciplines: ethnohistory, cultural anthropology, demography, human geography, climatology, geology, epidemiology, and nutrition.

Sub-Saharan Africa shows a large variety of human environments. The potential yield of extensive surveys on genetic polymorphic systems, growth, and adult physique depends on their covering the largest range possible of every environmental variable. The international co-operation in planning implied by IBP will, it is hoped, assure that the array of ethnic groups that will be surveyed in the near future fulfils this requirement. The environmental factors most obviously displaying a large variation in this part of the world are atmospheric humidity (ranging from very low to very high), altitude (though the total range of human habitats for this variable is lower than in Asia or South America), diet (from the viewpoint of both total calorie intake and specific nutrients: African diets vary from moderately high to very low protein, or fat and liposoluble vitamin intakes; proportion of vegetal to animal proteins also largely varies), pathology (for example, from nil to heavy infestation by malaria or schistosomiasis), ways of life (hunting-gathering, different levels of agriculture, pastoralism, city-dwelling). Population density, size and degree of isolation, all factors of importance in population genetics, also vary widely. The time during which the population has lived in its present environment is rarely known in years, but in some cases populations may be contrasted for this factor in terms of long and short time. All the cited variables should be considered in a planning of extensive surveys on a pan-African basis, or in counselling individual, institutional, or national efforts. Any set of populations surveyed in the part of the world considered here would fall short of any requirement of representativity if it did not include data on each of the following regions: the southern Sahara, the Sudanic (in a geographical sense) savannah, the Upper Nile, the Ethiopian highlands, the Somali lowland, the Guinean forest, the equatorial low forest, and the equatorial highlands. Populations displaying extremes of morphological differentiation, like the pygmy groups of the equatorial forest and the ethnic groups of the Sudan's Upper Nile, should be represented in the set.

The very little we know about clines and associations in sub-Saharan Africa promises much for future research based on more substantial data.

The haemoglobin genetic polymorphism, probably the most elucidated one today, seems to respond to differences in malarial load, and this in turn has been tentatively linked, for a part of West Africa, with the time elapsed since the introduction of agriculture (Livingstone, 1958). The frequency of the Hb^S gene shows a correlation of -0.73 with altitude in the Rwanda-Burundi-Kivu area (Livingstone, Gershowitz, Neel, Zuelzer, and Solomon, 1960), probably through differences in malarial infestation.

In the polymorphic system of fingerprints, the frequency of whorls correlates with location along a north–south scale by a value of 0.49 among 56 populations of sub-Saharan Africa, a finding that might reflect the long-term population pressure in this direction evidenced by the ethnohistorians (Hiernaux, 1964).

On a world-wide scale, adult body weight and body weight to surface ratio correlate with latitude (Schreider, 1950 and 1953; Roberts, 1953), but large deviations from the correlation axis can be found in Africa (Schreider, 1963).

The high world correlation between nasal index and absolute humidity has already been cited. It has not been computed yet for sub-Saharan Africa alone. An approximation to this end is sought here by dividing the area in three main climatic zones—arid zone, savannah, and wet forest—and computing the mean nasal index in each of them from all the data considered in the appraisal of knowledge given above (with a further screening for identical technique). This analysis is extended to stature, facial index, and cephalic index. Only preliminary values are given here; a more refined analysis will be published later together with the basic data. Pygmies, the most ancient forest-dwellers, have not been joined to the corresponding climatic group in order to isolate the time factor in the action of the wet forest environment (Table 1).

TABLE 1

Means of four characters in the three main climatic zones of sub-Saharan Africa and in the Mbuti Pygmies

	Stature (cm)	Nasal index	Facial index	Cephalic index
Arid zone	171	85·0	89·7	74·8
Savannah	169	85·9	85·8	75·3
Wet forest	164	94·0	81·9	76·1
Mbuti Pygmies	144	103·8	78·3	77·0

All four characters vary concordantly with increasing humidity; for all of them the Mbuti Pygmies show an extreme differentiation in keeping with their longer submission to the most humid conditions. The association between climate and morphology is clearly evidenced, and strongly suggests genetic adaptation.

The list of clines and associations here considered is not at all exhaustive; especially patent cases have been chosen in order to show the potential yield of data from extensive surveys, hence the need, owing to the indigence of current knowledge, for more data on more breeding populations.

Suggestions for intensive multidisciplinary regional studies

Interpretation of extensive survey data can lead only to hypotheses, many of which involve processes of adaptation. As Weiner points out in Chapter 1, elucidation of the processes involved in adaptation to environmental stresses requires 'intensive regional studies and surveys designed to disclose either intra- or interpopulation variability, or both'. Two fundamental aims for these studies would be 'to attempt to distinguish between genetic and non-genetic elements in adaptation, and . . . to detect the operation of selection'. He indicates as particularly valuable in this respect investigations bearing on 'genetically different groups exposed to the same environment for long as well as short periods of time, or the variability within the same genetic groups when exposed to different environments'; or 'of even greater value, studies of those occasional situations wherein two or more genetically distinct groups are exposed to the same variety of environments'. These points will be illustrated here by the author's studies on regional situations approximating to some of the ones indicated above (Hiernaux, 1956, 1963, 1964a, b). The data on which they are based suffer by representing a smaller variety than the array recommended by IBP; the studies would have reached much more fundamental conclusions if they could have included data on environmental physiology, physical fitness, and working capacity, and if the growth survey had covered the first five years of life.

In Rwanda, two main breeding populations, the Tutsi and Hutu, live side by side in relatively similar environmental conditions (or, more accurately, lived thus at the time of the investigation, deep social changes have occurred since then); they are submitted to the same climate and the same endemic diseases, their diets differ moderately, mainly by a slight superiority of the Tutsi's intake in animal proteins and fat during childhood. Their gene pools are largely dissimilar, as can be judged from monofactorial genetic traits and descriptive and metrical features. The Tutsi, a minority, are relative newcomers to the country and maintain their genetic differentiation from the Hutu, the bulk of the country's population, through a high rate of endogamy socially based on a caste system. This situation is therefore that of two genetically different populations living in a relatively similar environment for different lengths of time (a few centuries for the Tutsi, and an undetermined, but surely much longer time for the Hutu). On the other hand, the Hutu could be subdivided into ecological subgroups: a study on adults considered two subgroups differing mainly in their nutrition and in the incidence of malaria, while a growth study compared the rural Rwanda's Hutu children with the offspring of the same ethnic group born in mine camps in the Congo and raised there in better nutritional, hygienic, and medical conditions (the latter group unfortunately did not include children older than 13 years). These studies concern different environments acting since conception on similar gene pools. Better nutrition and hygiene result in accelerated growth and to a change in adult physique. They increase head dimensions, body laterality, relative weight, and muscle mass. Their differentiating action on body proportions takes place before the age of 6; after this age they only maintain the differentiation acquired. The influence of heredity on the last three cited characters is evidenced by the fact that the Tutsi, though slightly better fed during childhood on calories, proteins, and fat, are more linear than the Hutu and show a lower relative weight and a poorer muscular development; all these differences are already established at the age of 6. The four characters in Table 1 all differentiate the Tutsi from the Hutu in the direction of the means for the arid zone, and even surpass these; the Tutsi's average stature is 176 cm, their nasal index 69·4, their facial index 92·8, and their cephalic index 74·4. Hence the hypothesis that their physique evolved in a dry environment is put forth, based also on its fair conforming to the model or 'ideal' man for tolerance of desert heat constructed by Baker (1958) from experimental and actuarial data.

It is clear that one of the major problems of human adaptability, for the attack on which Africa is especially suited, is that of genetic adaptation to various levels of air moisture in generally hot conditions. From the desert plains and mountains of southern Sahara to the wet equatorial forest, a number of populations should be submitted to the full range of investigations planned by IBP. Their comparative responses to experimental stresses ranging from hot and dry to hot and wet would be especially interesting to know, as well as the variability and associations with particulars of the morphology that these responses show within each population. Such data are, it must be noted, not apt to disprove adaptive selection. Lack of significant differentiation between populations for physiological tests does not disprove adaptive genetical differences, because the experimental conditions may not duplicate, at least in quantity, the stresses that lead to death of a proportion of individuals. It is not easy to prove selection either. In the field of monofactorial genetics, differences in gene frequencies between age classes are highly suggestive of selection; differences in means between age classes or between populations for age- and environment-dependent variables are much more difficult to interpret. Direct evidence of selection at work can only be obtained from following cohorts of individuals during one generation. It is hoped that the long-term effort and the development of human biology implied by IBP will help to start such longitudinal studies in a few African populations contrasted by their environments and the length of time during which they have lived in them.

Probably many situations in sub-Saharan Africa could be found meeting Weiner's conditions for efficiency. Ethiopia probably offers suitable opportunities for the study of adaptation to altitude. The author knows of two regions north of the Equator presenting most favourable conditions for the study of adaptation to moist heat. Both are in the Congo-Léopoldville; similar situations are likely to be found in other countries where forest and savannah meet.

One area is in the northern part of the Congo; it is cut by the savannah-forest border. In both the Bantu and the Sudanic linguistic classes can be found similar agricultural tribes living, the ones in the savannah, the others in the forest. Occupation of the forest by such populations does not seem to be very ancient; much more ancient forest-dwellers in the area are the Pygmies. It has been already stated that the Pygmies' morphology is consistent with the hypothesis of its resulting from the long-term action of selective forces linked with the wet equatorial forest, whatever these forces may be. The Pygmies in themselves are worth an intensive multidisciplinary study, but comparing them with their agricultural landlords and these with the related groups in the savannah is still much more promising. Moreover, some agriculturalist groups have access to large rivers and are skilful in fishing; their diet contrasts by its protein content with that of related populations which rely on cassava as a staple food and badly lack proteins.

Farther south, near to the Equator, the Lake Tumba area is inhabited side by side by agriculturalists of the Mongo group of tribes and by predominantly hunting-gathering Twa, who morphologically are intermediary between the Pygmies and the non-pygmy forest agriculturalists, and are therefore usually called 'Pygmoids'. During the last decades the Mongo declined in number while the Twa increased, to the point of outnumbering their landlords in some places. The study of the determinants of this situation is worth a multidisciplinary effort.

Combining both areas, the comparison of Pygmies, Twa groups, other peoples living in the equatorial forest, and related populations in the savannah would no doubt shed some light on the phenomenon of convergence.

Possible selective agents cited in this paper fall into three groups: climate, nutrition, and disease. They usually interact, which makes the isolation of their specific action difficult from interpopulational comparisons. For example, Pygmy morphology has been interpreted as a genetic adaptation to hyponutrition by Brace (1964) rather than to climatic conditions of the wet forest. Low mean weight in the tropics, if not due only to the effect of malnutrition on the phenotype and therefore really involving a difference in gene pools, could be interpreted as a genetic adaptation to malnutrition as well as to thermoregulatory requirements. Only multidisciplinary studies performed on a variety of cases can hope to solve such questions.

Within a breeding population, selective action of a factor can be isolated if it varies independently of other possible selective agents. There are many opportunities for such studies in Africa, especially in the field of selective role of disease, owing to the high rate of infantile mortality still suffered by many rural populations.

Relation between malaria and abnormal haemoglobins has been widely investigated, and a few papers deal with the association between the same genetical polymorphism and other diseases, like that of André and André-Gadras (1957) on the relation between sickle-cell trait and leprosy. The probable importance of disease as a selective agent in the poor conditions of hygiene and medicine that have been general during most of man's evolution justifies detailed studies wherever such conditions still prevail.

REFERENCES

ANDRÉ, L. J. and ANDRÉ-GADRAS, E., 1957. 'Étude des rapports entre la sicklémie et la lèpre', *Annls Soc. belge Méd. trop.* **17**, 596–599.

BAKER, P. T., 1958. *A Theoretical Model for Desert Heat Tolerance*, U.S. Army, Technical Report EP-96, Natick, Mass.

BRACE, L. C., 1964. 'A nonracial approach towards the understanding of human diversity', *The Concept of Race* (Ed. A. MONTAGU), pp. 103–152. Free Press of Glencoe, New York.

CZEKANOWSKI, J., 1922. 'Anthropologische Beobachtungen', *Wissenschaftliche Ergebnisse der Deutschen Zentral-Afrika-Expedition* 1907–1908. Klinkhardt und Biermann, Leipzig.

HIERNAUX, J., 1956. 'Analyse de la variation des caractères physiques humains en une région de l'Afrique centrale: Ruanda-Urundi et Kivu', *Annls Mus. r. Congo belge*, Sciences de l'homme, **3**, 1–131.

—— 1962. 'Données génétiques sur six populations de la République du Congo (groupes sanguins ABO et Rh, et taux de sicklémie)', *Annls Soc. belge Méd. trop.* **42**, 145–174.

—— 1963. 'Heredity and environment: their influence on human morphology. A comparison of two independent lines of study', *Am. J. phys. Anthrop.* **21**, 575–590.

—— 1964a. 'Les dermatoglyphes digitaux des Tutsi du Rwanda et des Shi du Congo', *Bull. Mém. Soc. Anthrop. Paris*, **6**, 369–385.

—— 1964b. 'Weight/height relationship during growth in Africans and Europeans', *Hum. Biol.* **36**, 273–293.

—— 1965a. 'La croissance des écoliers rwandais,' Académie Royale des Sciences d'Outre-Mer, Classe des Sciences Naturelles et Médicales, Bruxelles, n.s., **16–2**, 1–204.

—— 1965b. 'Hérédité, milieu et morphologie', *Biotypologie*, **26**, 1–36.

—— 1965c. 'Variabilité de la régression de la stature en la longueur des segments de membres en Afrique centrale', unpublished.

LIVINGSTONE, F. B., 1958. 'Anthropological implications of sickle cell gene distribution in West Africa', *Am. Anthrop.* **60**, 533–562.

—— 1960. 'The wave of advance of an advantageous gene: the sickle-cell gene in Liberia', *Hum. Biol.* **32**, 197–202.

—— 1964. 'Aspects of the population dynamics of the abnormal hemoglobin and glucose-6-phosphate dehydrogenase deficiency genes', *Am. J. hum. Genet.* **4**, 435–450.

LIVINGSTONE, F. B., GERSHOWITZ, H., NEEL, J. V., ZUELZER, W. W., and SOLOMON, M. D., 1960. 'The distribution of several blood group genes in Liberia, the Ivory Coast and Upper Volta', *Am. J. phys. Anthrop.* **18**, 161–178.

MURDOCH, G. P., 1959. *Africa. Its Peoples and Their Culture History.* McGraw-Hill, New York.

ROBERTS, D. F., 1953. 'Body weight, race and climate', *Am. J. phys. Anthrop.* **11**, 533–558.

SCHREIDER, E., 1950. 'Geographical distribution of the body-weight/body-surface ratio', *Nature, Lond.* **165**, 286.

—— 1953. 'Régulation thermique et évolution humaine. Recherches statistiques et expérimentales', *Bull. Mém. Soc. Anthrop. Paris* **4**, 138–148.

—— 1963. 'Anthropologie physiologique et variations climatiques', *Physiologie et Psychologie en Milieu Aride—Compte-rendu de Recherches,* pp. 39–76. UNESCO, Paris.

WEINER, J. S., 1954. 'Nose shape and climate', *Am. J. phys. Anthrop.* **12**, 615–618.

6

THE PEOPLES OF AFRICA
SOUTH OF THE SAHARA

PHILLIP V. TOBIAS

Department of Anatomy, University of the Witwatersrand, Johannesburg

THE genetic and ecological diversity of African populations south of the Equator provides a number of situations of potential value in the study of human adaptability, biological as well as cultural. As a first approach to the problem, this chapter aims to explore our present knowledge of the genetic diversity of peoples living in this area.

Although a fairly comprehensive picture is given, there is no pretence of this being an exhaustive analysis. It is intended as the starting-point for a programme of research, rather than as a synthesis of work accomplished. In keeping with the aims of the Burg Wartenstein Symposium on the Biology of Human Adaptability, it is hoped that this chapter may provide a rough working basis for the planning of IBP activities on human biology in this area. It will emerge from the ensuing pages that the systematic collection of far more data and their arrangement and interpretation according to a conceptual framework are necessary before a synthesis can confidently be attempted.

A brief survey is given of the nature, numbers, and distribution of population groups. This is followed by tables and summaries of phenotype and, in some cases, genotype frequencies for a number of genetic and other traits. Deficiencies in our knowledge of the distribution of particular genetic markers, as well as of the genetic constitution of individual populations, are specified.

A provisional characterization of the sub-Saharan African genotype is put forward. Special attention is given to the Bushmen and an attempt is made to show how this group provides admirable material for the kind of human adaptability survey envisaged by the IBP. Furthermore, the correlation of genetic studies with the results of prehistoric skeletal studies may—through the long archaeological record of Bushman skeletons available—help to confirm or disprove Mourant's (1961) suggestion:

'It is tempting to regard the various genetical systems . . . as providing us with a series of probes reaching varying distances into the past, the haemoglobins some hundreds of years, the ABO blood-groups one or two thousand years, the Rh and MNSs blood-groups and perhaps most of the others several thousand years.'

Preliminaries

Africa's 250 million people, representing only about 8 per cent of the world's total population, occupy 23 per cent of the world's land area. Both the land surface and its population may be divided roughly into a smaller northern moiety, essentially the Saharan region and Africa north of the Sahara, and a larger tropical and southern African part. The northern part has an area of some 10 million square kilometres and a population of about 80 million; the sub-Saharan part has an area of 20 million square kilometres and a population of some 160 million. That is, for both the northern and the sub-Saharan parts of the continent, the population density is 8/km², compared with a world average of about 23.

These figures are not accurate since large areas of the continent have never experienced an adequate census. In areas which have fairly reliable population figures over some length of time, it has been shown that the population is growing rapidly. Since rapid or explosive growth of the population will influence the rate of diffusion of alleles, it would be well to elaborate on this point. The available records of Bantu and other groups show that the population trend is ascending markedly among the Southern Bantu and especially steeply in Bechuanaland and Rhodesia (Cappieri, 1950). The average yearly increase may be calculated

on the formula $i = \left(\dfrac{P_n}{P}\right)^{1/n} - 1$, where n is the period of time in

years considered; P is the population at the beginning of the period; and P_n is the population at the end of the n period. The

following are a selection of average yearly increases for southern
Africa and several other areas:

Southern and Eastern Bantu	1·82
South Africa	1·99
Basutoland	1·11
Swaziland	1·75
Bechuanaland	2·33
South-West Africa	1·68
Rhodesia (formerly Southern Rhodesia)	2·72
American Indians	0·59
Maori	1·30
Lapps	0·23
Australian Aborigines	0·42

This rapid growth of the African population is based partly upon
fairly high fertility. For example in a Dinka village of the
southern Sudan, the main demographic features were found to be
'a low average age, a high proportion of children, and a conjugal
situation in which all women (and all men after a rather later age)
are married, and very few of these fail to reproduce. Reproduction of the community is shared by the maximum number of
women and is spread over the whole of their reproductive span,
fertility being fairly high but not excessively so' (Roberts, 1956).

Badenhorst (1951) predicted that rapid population growth
would continue, not only because of high fertility, but because
mortality is gradually being brought under control. If the recent
rate of increase were to continue, the population of Africa would
be at least 290 million by 1980.

Broadly speaking, one-third of the peoples of Africa belong to
the Mediterranean world; linguistically, they are predominantly
Hamites and Semites; racially, they have traditionally been
classified as members of the Mediterranean or Brown race of the
Caucasiform racial constellation (Trevor, 1955). The remaining
two-thirds of the African population belong to sub-Saharan
Africa; the two major linguistic components are the Sudanic- and
Bantu-speakers; racially, they comprise essentially the Negriform
racial constellation together with certain anthropologically important minority groups of uncertain affinities.

This chapter is concerned with Africa south of the Equator,
that is, for the most part south of the 'Bantu line', a linguistic
boundary running across Africa from the Gulf of Guinea to the

9

region of Mombasa (Seligman, 1957). North of this line are an estimated 60–65 million Negroes speaking one or another of the Sudanic family of languages. To the south lie about the same number of Bantu-speaking Africans, with a few small enclaves of Nilo-Hamites, Pygmies, Hadza, Sandawe, Hottentots, Bushmen, Kwadi, and Bergdama. On physical grounds, the Bushmen and Hottentots, and sometimes also the Sandawe, have been regarded as comprising another major racial constellation, the Khoisaniform (Trevor, 1955): genetical surveys over the past decade, however, have brought to light a number of serological and other genetic resemblances between the Bushmen and Hottentots, on the one hand, and Negriform Africans on the other. It has therefore been questioned whether the genetic distance between the two groups is sufficient to regard them as belonging to separate racial constellations.

Available data

Tables 1–20 summarize most of the available published data for sub-equatorial African groups, as well as many bodies of unpublished data, either collected by the author and members of his Department (Drs. Blecher and Jenkins) or made available from other sources. The geographical distribution of the tribes is shown in Fig. 1.

The tables convey the following information:
(1) ABO (pp. 138–146),
(2) Rh (pp. 147–152),
(3) MN (pp. 153–154),
(4) other blood groups (Kell-Cellano, Diego, Henshaw, Lutheran, Duffy, P, V$^+$, and Js$^+$) (pp. 154–159),
(5) sickle-cell haemoglobin (pp. 159–165),
(6) haemoglobin C (pp. 166–167),
(7) haemoglobin K (p. 167),
(8) haptoglobins (pp. 168–169),
(9) transferrins (p. 170),
(10) serum cholinesterase (p. 170),
(11) glucose-6-phosphate dehydrogenase deficiency (pp. 171–172),
(12) group specific component (p. 173),
(13) colour-blindness (pp. 173–174),
(14) PTC state sensitivity (pp. 174–175),

(15) dermatoglyphs (digital pattern frequency) (pp. 175–177),
(16) Cummins Index (pp. 178–179),
(17) palmar pattern frequency (pp. 179–180),
(18) anthropometric surveys (pp. 181–185),
(19) dental characteristics (pp. 186–187),
(20) serum proteins (Bushmen only) (p. 188),
(21) percentages of serum protein fractions (Bushmen and Bantu) (p. 189),
(22) cholesterols (Bushmen only) (p. 190).

The *availability of data* for each genetic marker may be summarized as follows:

ABO groups: all sub-equatorial groups except Sandawe, Hadza, Kwadi, and Bergdama.

A_1A_2: all except Sandawe, Hadza, Kwadi, Bergdama, and Cape Coloured.

Rh/MN: Bushmen, Hottentots, Pygmoid, other non-Bantu and Bantu groups, but apparently not Sandawe, Hadza, Kwadi, Bergdama, and Cape Coloured.

Kell-Cellano: Bushmen, Hottentots, Southern and Eastern Bantu, but apparently not Western Bantu, nor Sandawe, Hadza, Kwadi, Bergdama, Cape Coloured, and Pygmy.

Diego: only Bushmen, Hottentots, Cape Coloured, Southern and Eastern Bantu.

Henshaw: Bushmen, Hottentots, Cape Coloured, Cape Malay, Pygmoid and other non-Bantu, Southern and Eastern Bantu.

Lutheran: only Bushmen, Hottentots, and Southern Bantu.

Duffy: only Bushmen, Hottentots, Southern and Eastern Bantu.

P: apparently only Bushmen, Hottentots, Southern and Eastern Bantu.

V^+/Js^+: apparently only Bushmen, Hottentots, and Southern Bantu.

Sickling trait: all except Sandawe, Hadza, Kwadi, and Bergdama.

Haemoglobin C: Bushmen, Cape Coloured, and the three Bantu sub-groups.

Haemoglobin K: apparently only Western Bantu (Angolan).

Haptoglobins: all except Sandawe, Hadza, Bergdama, Kwadi, and Eastern Bantu.

Transferrins: all except Hottentots, Sandawe, Hadza, Kwadi, Bergdama, and Pygmy groups.

Serum cholinesterase: only Cape Coloured and Southern Bantu.

G-6-P D deficiency: Bushmen, Cape Coloured, Cape Malay, Pygmoid, and the three Bantu groups.

Group-specific component: few determinations have thus far been made on sub-equatorial populations.

Colour-blindness: apparently only Bushmen and the three Bantu groups have been tested.

PTC sensitivity: apparently only Bushmen, Cape Coloured, and samples of the three Bantu groups.

Dermatoglyphs: all groups, except Sandawe, Hadza, Kwadi, Bergdama, and Eastern Bantu.

Anthropometric data are available for all groups except Hadza, Kwadi, Bergdama, and Cape Coloured; while data on many *anthroposcopic* features, including such probably genetic dental traits as median upper diastema, shovel-shaped incisors, and Carabelli cusps, are available for relatively few population groups, mainly Bushmen and the Tonga group of Southern Bantu.

As concerns populations, we have most information about the Southern Bantu, Bushmen, Eastern Bantu, and Hottentots; only a relatively modest amount is known about the Cape Coloured and Western Bantu; still less about the Pygmies; and virtually nothing at all about four anthropologically important populations, namely the Sandawe, Hadza, Kwadi, and Bergdama. The following is a summary of the *data still required* for each of the population groups in this survey:

Bushmen: serum cholinesterase, haemoglobin K.

Hottentots: PTC taste-testing; colour-blindness; G-6-P D D; sickling; haemoglobin C and K; serum cholinesterase; Gc and transferrins.

Sandawe, Hadza, Bergdama, Kwadi: all blood groups† and all other genetic markers considered here.

Cape Coloured: A_1A_2; detailed MNS and Rh analysis; also Kell-Cellano, Lutheran, Duffy, P, V+, and Js+; haemoglobin K; Gc; colour-blindness.

† However, according to the *W.H.O. Technical Report No.* 29 on 'Research in population genetics of primitive groups', p. 17, some preliminary blood-group studies have been made on the "Bergdamara" (1964).

Pygmy: Kell, Diego, Henshaw, Lutheran, Duffy, P, V^+, and
Js^+; haemoglobin C and K; transferrins; serum cholinesterase;
Gc; colour-blindness and PTC sensitivity.

Southern Bantu: Haemoglobin K.

Eastern Bantu: Lutheran, V^+, and Js^+; Gc; haptoglobins;
serum cholinesterase; dermatoglyphs.

Western Bantu: A_1A_2; Kell, Diego, Lutheran, Duffy, P, V^+,
and Js^+; Gc; serum cholinesterase.

In addition, anthropometric data are lacking on the Hadza,
Cape Coloured, Kwadi, and Bergdama, while some dental and
other anthroposcopic studies are still required on all population
groups, except Bushmen and Southern Bantu.

The International Biological Programme provides an opportunity to fill systematically the deficiencies enumerated here, as
well as to collect supplementary information, such as demographic,
ecological, and growth data.

THE CHARACTERISTICS OF THE SUB-SAHARAN AFRICAN GENOTYPE

Sufficient data are on record to enable one to piece together a
tentative overall picture of the African genotype, south of the
Sahara.

Blood groups

ABO. The ABO groups vary widely, with phenotype A ranging
from 6·0 in 50 Pygmoid Boni of Somaliland to 54·5 in 22 Bantu
Himba of Angola and 53·4 in 73 Kun Bushmen of Bechuanaland;
while the B phenotype ranges from 0 in the Bantu Nyungwe and
the small Angolan Himba sample, to 46 in a sample of Kenyan
Swahili and 50 in the Pygmoid Boni of southern Somaliland. A_1 is
more frequent than A_2 the latter occasionally being absent.

Rh. The high frequency of Rh_0 (*ccDee*) is absolutely characteristic of African populations: it ranges in those considered here
from 45·3 per cent to 80·5 per cent (excluding Rh_0-*ccD^{u}ee*). In
all except a few populations, *rh* (*cde*) is present, its frequency
ranging up to 27·5; in Bushmen and Hottentots it is almost
completely absent except in a group of hybridized Bushmen
(5·6 per cent). Rh_z is rare, not rising above 4·4 per cent.

MNSs. M and N are about equal in frequency, but S is relatively
uncommon. According to Mourant (1954), MS is only slightly
commoner than NS. Hottentots have the highest African

frequency of M; it is also high in Bushmen, as well as in certain East African tribes (Tutsi, Iraqw).

The *Henshaw* antigen is present in all populations tested: its frequency varies from 2·0 per cent in 107 Cape Malays and 2·7 in 188 S.W.A. Bushmen, to 10·5 in 201 Hottentots and 11·8 in 93 Tanganyikan Iraqw. New highest values have been obtained on samples of Kalahari Bushmen, namely 16·4 ($n=122$), 17·9 ($n=112$) and 18·7 ($n=80$).

Kell-Cellano. The K+ antigen occurs in low percentages in most Africans, but may reach as high as 10·4 (Bushmen) and 10·6 (Southern Bantu).

Diego. The Di[a] antigen has been found in only a single Cape Coloured individual (Zoutendyk, personal communication): there is a small Malay component in the Coloured population and the isolated instance of the Diego antigen may have resulted from this source. Thereapart, no single Diego-positive individual has been reported in Africans.

Lutheran. This antigen occurs generally in low frequency, with values comparable with those of Caucasiforms; the antigen is completely absent in Bushmen and Hottentots.

Duffy. The Fy[a] antigen occurs in low frequency, ranging down to 0 per cent in parts of East and West Africa. On the other hand, in some Bushmen and Hottentots it rises to 31·2 and 27·9 respectively. The Fy[a] antigen has thus far been reported only in Africa (Mourant, 1962).

P. The P+ antigen is present in very high frequency in Africa, the values ranging from about 87 to 99 per cent. Zoutendyk (1955) has, however, reported that Hottentots have a low frequency of P (24·4 per cent), while in three samples of Bushmen we have found values as low as 50·0, 54·1, and 63·1.

V+. Relatively few data are as yet available: Bushmen gave values of 4·2, 5·3, 10·8, and 12·9, Hottentots 9, and a Southern Bantu group (unpublished) one of 36·4 per cent.

Js+. Among the scanty data available are phenotype figures of 0, 4·2, and 5·3 per cent for Bushmen, 7·0 for Hottentots, and 0·0 for Southern Bantu (unpublished).

Sickling trait

Haemoglobin S is widespread in Africa, reaching the high frequency of 45 per cent among the Amba of Uganda and 44 in a sample of Bangala in Angola. However, variability is great and in the southernmost parts of the subcontinent the frequency drops to o per cent among the Bushmen, Hottentots, and some Southern Bantu tribes.

Haemoglobin C

This abnormal haemoglobin is extremely restricted in distribution, there being a high focus in West Africa (up to 10·5 per cent) and a zero frequency for most of the rest of the subcontinent, save for isolated individual cases among the Valley Tonga of Zambia (Jenkins and Anderson, 1963, unpublished) and among a sample of 219 Cape Coloured.

Haemoglobin K

A few isolated cases have been reported in Bantu populations of Angola.

Haptoglobins

In contrast with most peoples of Europe, Asia, and Oceania, most Africans have a higher incidence of the gene Hp^1 than of Hp^2. Hp^1 reaches its highest values in West Africa, where its frequency attains the figure of 0·87 among the Yoruba of Nigeria. Nearly as high is the frequency of 0·77 among a sample of Congolese Bantu at Léopoldville. However, the frequencies of Hp^1 and Hp^2 approach equality elsewhere, as among Zulus (0·53, 0·47), Xhosa and Sotho (0·55, 0·45), and Hottentots (0·51, 0·49). The Ibo, too, have an approximately equal frequency of the two genes (0·49, 0·51). In a few peripheral or morphologically diversified populations, the frequency is reversed: as among Cape Coloured (0·47, 0·53 in a sample of 88, 0·39, 0·61 in a sample of 100, and 0·28, 0·72 in a sample of 75), Congo Pygmies (0·40, 0·60), and Bushmen (0·29, 0·71). The extraordinarily low frequency of the Hp^1 in Bushmen finds a parallel in several other hunting and herding groups (Swedish Lapps—0·28; Alaskan Eskimos—0·29; Australian Aborigines—0·17), as well as in several Indian and Mongoloid groups. Ahaptoglobinaemia (Hp^0) reaches high frequencies in Africa, but the relative participation of genetic and disease factors in the etiology remains obscure (Singer, 1961).

Transferrins

A slow transferrin variant occurs in Africa and is fairly common among Bushmen (6·6) and some Southern Bantu (Tswana—4·9). It was absent in a sample of 100 Cape Coloured.

Glucose-6-phosphate dehydrogenase deficiency

This enzyme deficiency occurs in low frequencies in Southern Bantu, Bushmen, Pygmies, and Cape Coloureds ($\pm$1·5 to $\pm$10) and higher frequencies in Eastern Bantu (3 to 28). Furthermore, Zail, Charlton, and Bothwell (1962) have demonstrated that the form of G-6-P D deficiency in Southern Bantu produces a pattern of drug sensitivity somewhat similar to that of affected American Negroes, but not so severe as that of affected Caucasiforms. Motulsky (1960) has found a good correlation between this enzyme deficiency and the frequency of sickling in a number of African populations. He has suggested that a common selective agent—malaria—has favoured carriers of both of these independent mutations. The Ituri Forest Pygmies seem to be the only exception, with 31 per cent of sickling but an enzyme deficiency rate of only 4 per cent.

Colour-blindness

Frequencies in Eastern Bantu range from 1·7 to 2·7 per cent, whereas in Southern Bantu samples the incidence is 2·8 to 4·6 per cent. The incidence in Bushmen—2·7 per cent of 75 males tested—falls between these two ranges of frequencies.

PTC taste-sensitivity

Very few sub-equatorial African groups have been tested. In seven Bantu groups, the incidence of non-tasters ranges from 0 to 13·3 per cent. The figure for 85 Bushmen is 7·1 and for 103 Cape Coloured 10·7 per cent.

Dermatoglyphs

The general African pattern seems to be a moderately high frequency of whorls ($\pm$20 to $\pm$40) with a low frequency of arches ($\pm$3 to $\pm$10), giving an overall Cummins Index of Pattern Intensity of about 12·0. No sub-equatorial African group has a Cummins Index above 13·5, save for 100 Western Pygmy Yaka females with 14·02. Two groups depart from this pattern, namely Bushmen (especially Northern Bushmen) and Eastern Pygmies, both of whom have fewer whorls and more arches, giving Cummins Indices of about 9–9·5. Further analyses, including Poll's Index of Pattern Intensity for each finger and Poll's triangular co-ordinate systems, are at present being worked out by Professor W. E.

Adams on the author's data. The provisional graphs by Adams show that deltadiagrams cannot be completed for Northern Bushmen, as for Maoris (personal communication). Fewer data are available for palmar patterns.

Other traits

Other probably or certainly gene-determined morphological traits, for which data have been collected on Southern Bantu and Bushmen, are skin reflectance readings with an E.E.L. reflectance spectrophotometer; hair-colour, -form, and -distribution; eye-colour; eye-folds; ear-form; shovel-shaped incisors; missing teeth; median upper diastemata—which we have found in a fairly high percentage of Bantu, but which occur hardly at all among Bushmen; Carabelli cusp, groove or pit; supernumerary teeth; mid-digital (mid-phalangeal) hair; prehelicine or pre-auricular fistulae; supernumerary nipples, etc.

In addition, biochemical variables are being investigated: these are of more complex determination, being subject to strong environmental influences but possibly having a genetic component as well. These include serum proteins, urinary oestrogens, cholesterols, blood electrolytes, salivary amylase (ptyalin) secretion, for all of which we now have data for Bushmen. Furthermore, the studies have included the determination of blood-pressure, caries incidence, and parasite infestation rates.

THE POSITION OF FRINGE POPULATIONS, WITH SPECIAL REFERENCE TO THE BUSHMEN

A number of African populations occupy a fringe position amid the major present-day population groups: either numerically, culturally, linguistically, or in physical appearance, or in a combination of two or more of these features. Examples north of the Equator are Nilo-Hamites and Nilotes; others south of the Equator are the Sandawe and Hadza of Tanzania, the various groups of peoples known as BaTwa in Ruanda, Burundi, Zambia, and elsewhere; Eastern and Western Pygmies; Bergdama of South West Africa; the Kwadi and other non-Bantu tribes of southern Angola; Bushmen; Hottentots; and hybrid groups such as Cape Coloureds, the Dunn community, Griquas, and Basters.

Among the urgent tasks of the International Biological Programme must be the systematic study of these fringe groups.

Some are changing from a hunting-and-food-gathering economy to a food-producing economy, or from simple hoe-culture to more complex forms of agriculture, or again from a purely agricultural society to one in various stages of industrialization. A twofold opportunity is thereby provided: firstly, the chance of studying the populations before and after change-over, and secondly, the opportunity of studying the mechanics and genetic, demographic and other consequences of the change. One such group, about which most data have been amassed is the Bushman people living in the Kalahari Desert and the areas fringing it.

The Bushmen

South of the Equator, the Bushmen are one of the last surviving hunter-gatherer peoples, although probably fewer than half of the estimated 50,000 survivors still pursue a subsistence way of life (Tobias, 1956, 1964). They provide an invaluable starting-point for studies on human adaptability in this area, for a number of reasons.

(1) They are distributed mainly in hot, dry, semi-desert terrain, with small groups living in inland deltaic areas (the 'River Bushmen' of the Okavango) and others in somewhat heavily wooded areas such as southern Angola (De Almeida, 1965). Thus, a people which is genetically more or less homogeneous is distributed mainly in an extreme environment, but also in a range of more genial ecological niches.

(2) Morphologically, they are highly distinctive, even among the diverse peoples of Africa, and it is legitimate to enquire (a) to what extent their distinctive morphology is a feature of their present environment, as has often been asserted; (b) whether their extreme morphology has any bearing whatever on their adjustment to their present ecological situation, or their hunter-gatherer mode of life with its periodic shortages of first-class protein and of water (Tobias, 1964).

(3) Large numbers of Bushmen share their territory with Bantu-speaking negriform peoples. Thus, two peoples with differing genomes occupy the same range of environments.

(4) Many Bushmen are hybridizing with Bantu-speakers, thus bringing new gene combinations into existence in essentially the same territory.

(5) Numbers of Bushmen are acquiring more settled habits, with pastoral and agricultural pursuits borrowed from their Bantu neighbours. This 'agrarian revolution' is being actively expedited by the Administration of South-West Africa, and this is likely to be true as well of the Bechuanaland Administration, following the recommendations of G. B. Silberbauer (1965). Thus, for the time being, it is possible to study genetically similar populations pursuing different modes of existence in similar territories. Furthermore, the genetic, demographic, and other biological consequences of the transition may be pursued in both cross-sectional and longitudinal studies over the next decade. By the end of that time, it may be expected that the overwhelming majority of Bushmen will have become food-producers.

(6) For nearly a decade, Bushmen have been the object of intensive multidisciplinary studies by the Kalahari Research Committee of the University of the Witwatersrand and of the Institute for the Study of Man in Africa (Tobias, 1959, 1961a). In a rudimentary way, these studies by physical anthropologists and human geneticists, applied physiologists, odontologists, psychologists, and others have adumbrated the pattern of multidisciplinary study now envisaged for the Human Adaptability Project of the IBP.

For all these reasons, the Bushmen and their Kalahari neighbours must constitute a major IBP objective in sub-equatorial Africa. The following somewhat more detailed account is therefore provided, to serve as a baseline for the planning of such a project.

Formerly occupying large areas of southern Africa, Bushmen are to-day confined mainly to Bechuanaland, South-West Africa, and Angola. Their language-family is distinct from Bantu, Hottentot, and other African languages and is characterized among other features by clicks (Westphal, 1962; Cole, 1963). Morphologically, they show distinctive features: light yellowish-brown skin, short stature (although it has been shown that their average stature has increased by about an inch in the last three generations—Tobias, 1962), tufted ('peppercorn') hair, very small ears with over-rolled helix and commonly lobeless, medial epicanthic eye-folds, broad flat noses, small faces, other distinctive features of skull and head, macronympha (enlargement of the labia minora), steatopygia, and steatomeria—features which in varying degrees they share with the Hottentots, ichthyphallus in the males, sparse facial and bodily hair. In many anatomical features, the Bushman is closest to the Hottentot, both differing in a number of respects from Bantu and other Africans. Their culture and language also set them apart, whilst archaeological and skeletal evidence supports the belief that Bushmen have been distinct for a long time. For these reasons, they had come to be recognized by some as the remnant of a major racial constellation known as the Khoisaniform (from the Hottentot names for themselves and the Bushmen). Trevor, for instance, classifies them as one of five major racial constellations, the others being the Caucasiform, Mongoliform, Negriform, and Australiform (1955).

Genetical studies, however, have shown that the Bushmen share a number of allelic patterns with other sub-Saharan Africans. This led Singer and Weiner (1963) to propose that the definition of the Negro should now be extended to include light-skinned peoples, namely the Hottentots and Bushmen.

Let us examine the resemblances and differences of monogenic and oligogenic characters among Bushmen, Hottentots, and other Africans.

Blood-groups of the Bushmen

In general, Bushmen agree with other African populations in blood group frequencies and especially resemble or surpass them in many respects in which Africans generally differ from non-Africans (Zoutendyk, Kopec, and Mourant, 1953; Weiner and Zoutendyk, 1959). These results are confirmed by a new series of 144 blood-group determinations on Northern and Central Bushmen (Zoutendyk and Tobias, unpublished data). Most striking is the very high incidence of Rh_0 ($ccDee$); the lowest Bushman value for this phenotype is 50·0 in our new series of 114, while the highest value is 78·8 in a S.W.A. series of 446 Bushmen. However, rh (cde), which has a general African frequency of 20 per cent, is absent in all save three individuals in two of our latest series and totally absent in all previous series, i.e. it has been present in three out of 1100 Bushmen. Rh_1 ($CcDee$) is of fairly high frequency, ranging from 17·2 in 232 S.W.A. Bushmen to 46·0 in the latest series. V^+ occurs to the frequency of 5·3 and 10·8 per cent in our two most recent series; while

Js+ occurs in 5·3 per cent in one recent series and 0 in another (in contrast with 20·0 per cent in Negroes (Giblett and Chase, 1959)). Diego has still not been found in a single case. Group A varies from 21·9 to 53·4 per cent in different series; group B from 2·4 to 14·9 per cent; and group O from 37·0 to 73·2 per cent. The ratio of A_1 to A_2 varies from 3·2 to 3·7.

The Henshaw antigen occurs in the S.W.A. series in only 3·3 per cent of 120 individuals. However, in our 1958 and 1959 Bushman groups, it occurs in as many as 16·4 per cent of 122 subjects, 17·9 per cent of 112 subjects, and 18·7 per cent of 80 subjects. These are believed to be the highest Henshaw values yet recorded. This gene is considered to be linked to the MNS system (Shapiro, 1956) and is found almost exclusively in Negroids. In Nigerians, it is almost invariably accompanied by N and frequently by NS (Zoutendyk, Kopek, and Mourant, 1955), whereas in the latest Bushman series, only 9 out of 20 Henshaw-positive subjects have N, although 14 out of 20 have S and only 4 out of 20 have NS. The association instead is with M and S, as in the Congolese, Hottentot, and Iraqw, which previously had the highest frequency of Henshaw-positives.

In the latest Bushman series, M is more than twice as frequent as N (39·2 as against 17·7 per cent). The corresponding values in the S.W.A. series were 37·8 as against 19·7 per cent. Most African populations have approximately equal frequencies of M and N genes.

P+ Bushmen have been found in both our 1958 and 1959 series, the frequencies being 54·1 and 63·1 per cent. These are low by general African standards.

The Duffy (Fy^a) antigen is of lower frequency in Africans than other tested populations (except the Brazilian Indians). The frequency in S.W.A. Bushmen was 15·7; while our recent series of Central and mixed Kalahari Bushmen yielded the high values of 27·9 and 31·2.

In sum, most Bushman groups tested differ from most other African groups in possessing:

high A and low B;
highest Rh_0 frequency (although *one* Bushman group has one of the *lowest* among sub-Saharan populations);
virtual absence of *rh*;
high M and low N;

high He+, rising in two population groups to the highest on
    record;
high K+;
absence of Lu^a;
high Fy^a;
relatively low P+;
fairly low V+.

A break-down of the blood-group data among Bleek's major
linguistic subdivisions shows that the Northern Bushmen tend to
differ from Central and Southern Bushmen in possessing rather
less O and more B; higher incidence of Rh_0 but lower Rh_1;
fewer Henshaw positives, the Central-Southern Bushmen having
the highest values in the world; lower incidence of Duffy-
positive individuals, the Central-Southern group having twice
the frequency of the Northern group. These data point to a degree
of genetic differentiation among Bushmen; in some respects the
Northern Bushmen show extreme frequencies; in others the
Central-Southern group do.

Other gene markers in Bushmen

Low Hp^1 further distinguishes Bushmen from other Africans;
on the other hand, the apparently very low rate of G-6-P D
deficiency in Bushmen correlates with the absence of sickling,
as Motulsky (1960) found for other parts of Africa. Dermato-
glyph frequencies support the idea of internal genetic differentiation among Bushmen. Thus, from our own data (Tobias, 1961b),
as well as those of Weninger (1926), Cummins (1955), and Fleish-
hacker (1934), it has been possible to subdivide the Bushman and
Hottentot populations into three broad groups:

Northern Bush, characterized by low whorls and moderate to
high arches; high pattern frequency in thenar/1st interdigital,
2nd interdigital, and 4th interdigital areas, and medium values
in 3rd interdigital and hypothenar areas;

Central and Southern Bush, characterized by high whorls and
low to moderate arches; and at least in Central Bushmen, high
patterns in 2nd and 4th interdigital areas; and medium to high
values in the remaining three areas;

Hottentots, characterized by moderate whorls and very low
arches; very low pattern intensity in 2nd and 4th interdigital areas
and in the hypothenar area; and a medium value in 3rd interspace.

The dermatoglyphs of Hottentots and South-Central Bushmen approximate to the general African negroid pattern, as exemplified by my data on 441 male and 343 female Zambezi Tonga. The Tonga show fairly high whorls and low arches, similar to Hottentots and South-Central Bushmen (Tobias, 1961b). In contrast, Northern Bushmen can be matched with only one other group in Africa, namely the Eastern Pygmies, such as the Efé Pygmies studied by Dankmeijer (1934) and Valsik (1938) and the Ituri Pygmies (Geipel 1948). (Western Pygmies, such as Bakola and Bayaka, have much higher whorl frequencies and generally lower arch frequencies (Dankmeijer, 1947).)

Serum proteins of Bushmen

Total protein values are high in all three groups of Bushmen (Table 20). The values of 8·24, 8·0, and 7·9 compare with Bantu means of 7·96 (males only—on the Okavango in S.W.A.) and 8·24 (males and females—in Cape Town), and a figure of 6·92 for male White South Africans (Cape Town). This high total protein is due largely to the high serum γ-globulin values (2·68, 2·59, 2·16), as compared with a male Bantu mean of 1·72 (Cape Town) and a value for White South Africans of 1·57 (Witwatersrand). However, Okavango Bantu living in approximately the same area as the S.W.A. Bushman sample have a γ-globulin of 2·34, i.e. of the same order as the Bushmen. De Meillon (1951) found the highest malarial endemicity within the 20-mile zone from the river, and, because Brock and Bronte-Stewart found a high percentage of splenomegaly within 20 miles of the river, they have broken down their sample into three sub-samples, one living within 20 miles of the river, one living 20 miles away, and one within 50 miles of the river. The river group has the highest total protein (although the difference is not significant); but it shows, too, significantly lower α_2-globulin and β-globulin and significantly higher γ-globulin (Table 21), the value reaching 3·08 in the riverine sample of 20. Brock and Bronte-Stewart felt they could not ascribe the bio-chemical abnormalities of their Bushmen to chronic malnutrition; however, the possibility of dietetic differences (rather than gross undernourishment) influencing the serum protein picture cannot be excluded. Thus, our own series of nomadic Bushmen, with their relatively poor diet, show higher γ-globulins than do our better nourished farm Bushmen (2·59 as against 2·16); likewise the nomads' albumin values are very low (2·80), the lowest in all the Bushman series.

Urinary oestrogens in Bushmen

With the co-operation of Dr I. Bersohn and the South African Institute for Medical Research, urinary oestrogens were determined on two small samples of 24-hour urine specimens.

Strikingly high values have been found in Bushman males, the mean for the first group of 7 being no less than 30·12 μg total oestrogens (S.D. 13·0). This contrasts with a Bantu mean of 11·5 μg total oestrogens for men aged 20–45 years (Bersohn and Oelofse, 1957). None of the 21 men in the Bantu series has a total oestrogen as high as the Bushman mean, the highest Bantu value being 21·0 μg. Corresponding values for South African Whites are 8·0 μg for a sample with a mean age of 30·5 years (op. cit.) and 14·4 for a sample of mean age of 55 years (Bersohn and Oelofse, 1958). Thus, the Bushman values are far higher than the highest values in Bantu and European series.

The very potent oestradiol fraction averages 7·69 μg, many times the value in South African Whites (1·1 μg at mean age 30·5 and 2·1 μg at mean age 55) and Bantu-speaking Africans (2·5 μg) (Bersohn and Oelofse, 1957, 1958).

Oestrone averages 8·12 μg in the Bushmen, in comparison with 5·5 in Bantu, 6·3 in older South African Whites, and 4·3 in younger Whites. Finally, oestriol averages 14·32 μg, in contrast with 3·5 in Bantu, and 6·0 in older and 2·6 in younger South African Whites.

Thus Bushmen show a very marked absolute increase in total oestrogen, as a result of a striking absolute increase in both oestradiol and oestriol. The value for oestrone is only slightly raised.

The mean ratio of the most potent fraction, oestradiol, to the least active fraction, oestriol, is 0·54. This lies intermediately between the values for the young urbanized Bantu group (0·71) and the young European group (0·43) (Bersohn and Oelofse, 1958), suggesting that in Bushmen the rate of breakdown of oestradiol is retarded as compared with the European group, but occurs more rapidly than in the Bantu group.

On the other hand, the level of production of total urinary oestrogen is highest in Bushmen. In this regard, diet plays a definite role in regulating the level of oestrogens, as Gillman and Gillman (1951) have demonstrated in rats fed on various experimental diets. Bersohn (1959) has been able to show similar effects by modifying the diet of European and Bantu prisoner-volunteers. If Bantu prisoners are fed on a poor 'rural' diet—with high caloric and low fat intake—their oestrogen levels rise even higher than those of urban Bantu, though never as high as some Bushmen in our small sample. Likewise, when Europeans are fed a similar diet over a long period, their oestrogens rise to levels indistinguishable from those of Bantu. It is likely that the high level of oestrogens in Bushmen reflects their mode of life and especially their diet. A most important practical requirement for the immediate future is for larger samples of urine to be obtained from groups of both nomadic and farm Bushmen.

It is well known that the level of oestrogen affects lipid metabolism. It has even been suggested that it is the hormonal level that spares the Bantu from arterial disease and accounts for their low incidence of coronary disease (Bersohn and Oelofse, 1958). In this event, diet would act not directly, but indirectly through its effect on oestrogen levels.

The other effects of over-oestrogenization are interesting to contemplate. Davies (1949), formerly of Kampala, suggested that it may account for feminizing morphological features shown by East Africans. It may well be enquired to what degree the small stature and infantile (pedomorphic) anatomy of Bushmen are a feminizing response to extreme over-oestrogenization. The possibility of a carcinogenic effect of the high oestrogen levels has been stressed by Davies and it would be useful to find out whether the incidence of primary carcinoma of the liver is as high in Bushmen as in other Africans. We have seen no evidence of it and Bronte-Stewart and Brock in their studies of Kun Bushmen found hepatomegaly only infrequently.

The possibility that much of the characteristic morphology of Bushmen is hormonal in basis has long been pondered (e.g. Marrett, 1936; Tobias, 1957): our results on the urinary oestrogens have provided the first evidence that the endocrine make-up of Bushmen is different. To what extent such differences are genetically determined, and to what extent environmental and especially dietetic, is one of the challenging problems for our future investigations.

10

Salivary amylase (ptyalin) secretion in Bushmen

Further evidence of the influence of changing diet on body chemistry was provided by Squires (1953). In a group of 10 nomadic Bushmen on a very low carbohydrate diet, he found amylase activity which, in every case, fell below 50 units, with a mean of 22. This contrasted with a sample of 32 South African Whites whose mean value was 101 units and with a sample of 90 Tswana (Bantu) on a high carbohydrate diet, where the mean value was 248 units.

When five Bushmen were attending as court witnesses, an opportunity was provided to study their amylase activity after they had lived for three months on a fairly high carbohydrate diet. Their mean amylase activity at the end of this time was 95 units, almost the same as the European value.

Cholesterols in Bushmen

The mean total cholesterol in 66 farm Bushmen is appreciably higher than in 22 nomadic Bushmen (Table 22). The figure of 121·0 is lower than the lowest cholesterol mean for Bantu series: 136 for the age group 21–30 years (Bersohn, personal communication). (The Bushman values have not yet been broken down into age groups.) The Bushman value is also appreciably lower than the values for 24 nomadic Australian aborigines (212 mg per cent) (Charnock *et al.*, 1959).

On the other hand, the value of 145 in farm Bushmen compares well with the figures of 136 and 150 in urban Bantu Africans in the age groups 21–30 and 31–40 respectively (Bersohn, personal communication). Urbanized Australian Aborigines, however, have values as high as 231 and 234 (op. cit.).

Despite the differences in total cholesterol between farm and nomadic Bushmen, the relative concentration of β-cholesterol A and B is almost identical between these two groups. The lipoprotein readings are too few to permit valid conclusions to be drawn.

The different diets of the two groups of Bushmen have apparently influenced the total cholesterol levels, since there is little difference in age distribution between the two groups.

Blood pressure in Bushmen

Blood-pressure readings were taken on 224 Bushmen (123 males and 101 females). An analysis has been made by Kaminer and Lutz (1960).

The average systolic pressures for nomadic Bushmen are 108·4 mm Hg (S.D. 11·4) for males and 112·8 mm Hg (S.D. 14·6) for females.

The mean diastolic pressures are 66·0 mm (S.D. 6·9) and 69·6 (S.D. 8·0) for males and females respectively.

Among the highest pressures obtained were 140 systolic, 78 diastolic, in an old woman, and 134 systolic, 80 diastolic, in a young adult.

As it is not possible to ascertain precise chronological ages in Bushmen, Kaminer and Lutz have classified subjects as adolescents (c. 12–17 years), young adults (c. 18–23), middle-aged (c. 40–55) and old-aged (60+). When the blood pressures are classified in these categories, the systolic blood-pressure of the men shows no tendency to rise with age. In women, there is a slight rise towards middle age, with a subsequent decrease in old age, but the differences are not statistically significant. Likewise, diastolic pressure and pulse pressure do not increase with age.

The absence of an increase in blood pressure with age distinguishes the Bushman sharply from European and American populations, where blood pressure is a 'graded characteristic' continuously increasing with age. This finding in the Bushman has a parallel in studies on some African, Chinese, and Ceylonese people. In the light of these results, a rise in mean blood-pressure need not be considered an inevitable concomitant of ageing in all populations of *Homo sapiens*.

The evidence suggests that the systolic and diastolic pressures of women are 3 to 4 units higher than those of men. The analysis of a larger body of Bushman data now available confirms that the difference is significant. The difference exists in spite of the women being on the average lighter than the men, as determined by the weight/height ratio.

Farm labourer and prisoner Bushmen show a significantly higher blood-pressure than nomads. Their mean systolic pressure is 122·0 and diastolic 70·7, as compared with 108·4 and 66·0 in the nomads.

The mean blood pressure of Bushmen, including the values 'corrected' for arm girth, are lower than those reported for other Africans. Kaminer has suggested that the small stature and lightness of Bushmen may contribute to their low blood-pressure.

Parasites of Bushmen

Dr. H. J. Heinz, a member of our Kalahari team, has examined stool specimens from about 200 subjects and urine specimens from about 150 subjects. Gum and tooth scrapings, as well as blood smears and blood samples, have also been examined. The following results are taken from his reports (1961*a*, *b*) with his permission. The intestinal flora is much the same as that of any other society of rural Africans. Thus he has observed *Chilomastix mesnilii*, *Iodamoeba butschlii*, *Endolimax nana*, *Entamoeba coli* with *Entamoeba histolytica* in the cystic form in two cases and an amoeba closely resembling *Entamoeba hartmanni* in one case.

A surprisingly high incidence of *Trichomonas vaginalis* has been detected: it occurs in the urine of 24·7 per cent of women examined, though accompanied by low numbers of leucocytes.

Only one Bushman—who migrated southwards from the Okavango swamps—has shown bilharzial ova, namely those of *Schistosoma haematobium*.

Ascaris ova occur in the stools of farm Bushmen, but not in those of nomadic Bushmen.

The most startling finding was a high incidence of infestation with hookworm, *Necator americanus*. Heinz quotes Levy that hookworm incidence among S.W.A. Kun Bushmen is high. Ova of these worms have been found in farm Bushmen, partly nomadic and nomadic Bushmen in frequencies of 22·4, 35·5, and 26·0 per cent respectively. Thus, in one series of 19 Bushmen, only 2 were free of hookworm. It is difficult to reconcile this finding with what is known of the ecology of the hookworm, since the Ghanzi District of Bechuanaland is semi-desert with a rainfall of about 13 inches per year, concentrated in a very short rainy period of 2–3 months. Heinz feels that boreholes are not to be incriminated as places of infection and has suggested that the capillarity of the Kalahari soil, overlying the desert limestone, may be a contributory factor in the survival of the parasites. He finds that, during the wet months, the infestation seems to increase greatly.

Bushmen and Hottentots in relation to other African peoples

Enough has been said to show that Bushmen and Hottentots belong to the same major gene constellation as other sub-Saharan Africans, but that morphological and genetic markers strongly point to a lengthy period of differentiation in relative isolation. Singer and Weiner (1963) have accordingly suggested that Bushmen and Hottentots should be regarded as Negroid peoples.

Several lines of evidence point to an alternative way of looking at these data. Archaeological evidence suggests that the Bushman as a skeletal type has a long history, possibly longer even than might be uncovered by the genetic markers we have used. The earliest Bushman skeletons can probably be traced to the Second Intermediate Period, about 12,000–14,000 years before the present. Furthermore, Bushman-like skeletons are known from a far wider area than the present restricted distribution of Bushmen; it is likely that a large part of Central and East Africa, if not also northeast Africa, was inhabited in the earlier parts of the Holocene Period by people skeletally similar to the Bushmen (Schapera, 1930; Tobias, 1961c). On the other hand, little is known of the skeletal ancestry of the Negro; probably the earliest recognizable Negriform material is that excavated at Khartoum and dated to about 6000 years ago. On this prehistoric evidence, it is possible that the Bushman skeletal type represents the ancestral form. Perhaps from this form, with selective pressures and hybridization, the Negroid peoples have differentiated; in this event, we should have to regard the Negro as an offshoot of the Khoisaniform racial stock rather than the other way around! Or perhaps we may once more have to re-open Haddon's old proposal that the Negro, or at least a significant contribution to the Negroid gene-pool, had an Asian origin.

Of course, we do not know that the ancestral Bush skeletal type was accompanied by a genic make-up comparable with that of modern Bushmen; but it is at least of interest that, in a number of respects, Bushmen with their characteristic morphology show extreme frequencies of various marker genes, as compared with other Africans. To produce the Bushman gene-pattern from the Negriform, one would need to postulate that selective agencies have operated on a number of widely different polymorphisms— including, for instance, the Rh_0 and Henshaw genotypes, haptoglobins, and dermatoglyphic patterns—selecting each of these to a maximum (or minimum) frequency. Clearly this is not impossible, when one considers the variety of potential selective agencies operating in Africa. But it is probably more likely that the Bushman genome represents an approximation to the ancestral

African genome. This ancestral genome could have been modified in different parts of Africa by mutation and selection pressures, as well as by external increments to the gene-pool, following hybridization with the numerous streamings of people into and across Africa, testified to by prehistoric and historic records. Two factors render the analysis of the Bushmen particularly favourable for intensive further study along these lines: firstly, their skeletal morphology is distinctive and different from that of Bantu and other African groups—thus, their features can be recognized in prehistoric skeletal material. Secondly, a large number of prehistoric remains is available. This means that we have a skeletal control against which to assess the patterns of affinity and divergency inferred from blood groups and other genetic markers.

A careful reappraisal of all archaeological skeletal material, as well as the filling of many gaps in gene frequency data, may help towards a valuable synthesis. This should not only clarify the Bushman-Hottentot problem, but, through the skeletal control, might contribute to the methodology of using genetic markers as probes into the past.

Acknowledgements

The studies, results of which have been drawn upon in this report, were made possible by the Nuffield Foundation, the University of the Witwatersrand, the Institute for the Study of Man in Africa, the South African C.S.I.R., the South African Institute for Medical Research, the Livingstone Museum (Zambia), and the Bechuanaland Administration.

I thank my research assistant, Miss J. Soussi, who has been largely responsible for the preparation of the comparative tables. My thanks are due as well to Dr. S. R. Blecher, Dr. T. Jenkins, Dr. R. Plotkin, Dr. M. Bobrow, Dr. I. Bersohn, Dr. H. J. Heinz, Dr. J. Hiernaux, Dr. A. Zoutendyk, Mrs. R. W. Levine, Mrs. L. V. Hitchings, as well as research students and staff of the Anatomy Department, University of the Witwatersrand, Johannesburg.

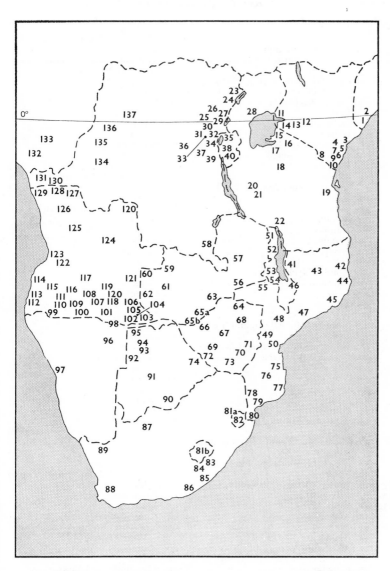

FIG. 1. Tribes for which serological data are available in sub-equatorial Africa. The Key to the numbers on this map is given on pp. 136–137.

Key to Numbers on Fig. 1

1. Boni
2. Bajun
3. Sanya and Swahili
4. Kamba, Kauma, Rabai, and Ribe
5. Digo
6. Chonyi, Duruma, Giryama, and Pokomo
7. Taita and Taveta
8. Pare
9. Galla and Luo
10. Chagga
11. Kakamega, Kitosh, Nyore, Marama, Ragoli, and Wanga
12. Kikuyu
13. Masai
14. Amba, Konjo, Nyoro, and Toro
15. Kisii
16. Ikoma
17. Sukuma
18. Iraqw
19. Zaramo
20. Nyamwezi
21. Gogo and Ha
22. Konde (Nyakyusa)
23. Alur and Bira
24. Gisu
25. Mbuba
26. Ituri pygmies Binga, Efé, Mbuti, and Twa
27. Budu
28. Hima, Ganda, Iru, and Nyanga
29. Humu and Mbuba
30. Shu and Swaga
31. Mamvu
32. Hema
33. Nyanga
34. Hunde
35. Tutsi and Hutu
36. Rega
37. Havu, Shi, Tembo, Kumu, and Rumbi
38. Twa (of Rwanda and Burundi)
39. Fulero
40. Imbo, Mosso, Rwanda, and Rundi
41. Erati
42. Makonda
43. Maravia
44. Makua
45. Manhaua
46. Nguru (Lomwe) and Nyanja
47. Chuabo
48. Tachaua
49. Sena
50. Shangaan
51. Nyakyusa

52. Tumbuka
53. Chewa and Ngoni
54. Yao
55. Mntumba and Nyungwe
56. Lala and Nsenga
57. Bemba
58. Luba
59. Kasempa and Lunda
60. Lubale (Lovale)
61. Mbala
62. Ngongo
63. Korekore
64. Cikunda
65. (a) Tonga (Valley)
    (b) Tonga (Plateau)
66. Dombe and Nambya
67. Rotse (Lozi)
68. Bujga, Koni, and Zezuru
69. Ndebele
70. Manyika and Ndau
71. Shona
72. Kalanga
73. Karanga
74. Mangwato
75. Tswa
76. Chopi
77. Inyambane
78. Mungone
79. Thonga
80. Ronga
81. (a) Northern Sotho
    (b) Southern Sotho
82. Swazi
83. Bacha
84. Pondo
85. Zulu
86. Xhosa
87. Korana Hottentots
88. Nama Hottentots (Richtersveld)
89. Cape Coloured and Cape Malay
90. Tswana
91. Magon Bushmen
92. Auen, Heikum, and Naron Bushmen
93. Barakwengo
94. Mpukushu
95. Kun Bushmen
96. Northern Bushmen of South-West Africa
97. Hottentots
98. Dirico
99. Mundimba and Mutwa
100. Kwamato and Kwanyama
101. Zama and Sekele
102. Mbukushu
103. Kafue

Key to Numbers on Fig. 1 (cont.)

104. Kwangare
105. Nyengo
106. Maxi
107. Ncangala
108. Kwankala, Kwede, and Kwepe
109. Evale
110. Himba
111. Gambwe and Kubale (Mucubai)
112. Kwanyoka
113. Mucuisse
114. Kwandu
115. Muila, Mutxibugue, and Quissange
116. Tshipungo
117. Nyemba
118. Mbwela
119. Lundo
120. Tshokwe and Shinji

121. Mbundu
122. Quibala
123. Amboin (Huambo) and Apinda
124. Songo and Nungo
125. Kalandula and Ngola
126. Mucusso Damba and Sosso
127. Mukaba and Zombo
128. Muchikongo
129. Mussurongo
130. Kongo (Kakongo)
131. Yombe
132. Bembe and Lali
133. Bulia
134. Lesa, Suku, and Yanzi
135. Ngbaka, Ngbundu (North and South), Nkundu, and Ntomba
136. Ekonda
137. Bushong, Bondjo, and Mongo

It should be noted that in cases where two or more tribes are represented by a single number, the grouping has been arbitrarily determined for convenience, and more by geographical proximity of the peoples concerned than for any other reason.

TABLE 1

Distribution of the ABO blood groups in sub-equatorial
African populations

Population	n	O	A	B	AB	Reference
			% Frequency			

Population	n	O	A	B	AB	Reference
NON-BANTU			SOMALILAND			
PYGMOID						
Boni	50	34·0	6·0	50·0	10·0	Foy et al. (1954)†
BANTU						
Bajun	37	51·3	29·7	16·2	2·7	Foy et al. (1954)†
NON-BANTU			KENYA			
HAMITIC						
Luo	449	54·6	28·3	15·8	1·3	Elsdon-Dew (1939)
	128	45·3	25·0	27·3	2·3	Allison et al. (1952)
Masai	233	48·1	20·2	30·5	1·3	Allison et al. (1952)
	86	44·2	23·2	27·9	4·7	After Buettner-Janusch et al. (1960)
PYGMOID						
Tswa	33	36·4	42·4	15·1	6·1	Allison et al. (1954)
BANTU						
Chonyi	55	72·7	21·8	5·5	—	Foy et al. (1954)†
Duruma	37	43·2	24·3	16·2	16·2	Foy et al. (1954)†
Giryama	100	50·0	22·0	26·0	2·0	Foy et al. (1954)†
Jibana	72	47·2	22·2	28·8	2·8	Foy et al. (1954)†
Kamba	450	53·3	31·8	12·9	2·0	Elsdon-Dew (1939)
	77	57·1	24·7	15·6	2·6	Foy et al. (1954)†
	50	42·0	24·0	32·0	2·0	After Buettner-Janusch et al. (1960)
Kauma	27	55·5	7·4	37·0	—	Foy et al. (1954)†
Kikuyu	449	60·4	18·7	19·8	1·1	Elsdon-Dew (1939)
	124	46·8	28·2	21·0	4·0	Allison et al. (1952)
Kisii	448	68·3	17·6	13·6	0·4	Elsdon-Dew (1939)
Pokomo	42	38·1	28·6	26·2	7·1	Foy et al. (1954)†
Pokomo and Giryama	42	50·0	19·1	26·2	4·8	After Buettner-Janusch et al. (1960)
Rabai	50	60·0	14·0	20·0	6·0	Foy et al. (1954)†
Ribe	50	78·0	10·0	10·0	2·0	Foy et al. (1954)†
Sanya (at Adu)	65	36·9	23·1	30·8	9·2	Foy et al. (1954)†
Sanya (at Witu)	61	34·4	63·9	1·6	—	Foy et al. (1954)†
Swahili (Ganda division)	98	35·0	10·0	46·0	8·0	Foy et al. (1954)†
Taita	27	44·4	40·7	7·4	7·4	Foy et al. (1954)†
Taveta	56	44·6	30·4	21·4	3·6	Foy et al. (1954)†

TABLE 1 (cont.)

Population	n	O	A	B	AB	Reference
		% Frequency				
		UGANDA				
NON-BANTU						
HAMITIC						
Hima	328	66·2	20·1	12·5	1·2	Elsdon-Dew (1939)
	117	66·7	14·5	15·4	3·4	Allison et al. (1954)
BANTU						
Ganda	450	68·7	18·7	12·0	0·7	Elsdon-Dew (1939)
		CONGO (LÉOPOLDVILLE)				
NON-BANTU						
PYGMY AND PYGMOID						
Binga	100	28·0	32·0	30·0	10·0	Miletto (1951)
	1015	27·0	35·9	28·3	8·9	Julien (1935)
Mbuti (Eastern Nomadic)	1032	30·6	30·3	29·1	10·0	Jadin (1935)
Mbuti (Western)	474	36·7	37·8	17·9	7·6	Jadin (1935)
	1015	27·0	35·9	28·3	8·9	Julien (1935)
Mbuti	100	27·0	41·0	25·0	7·0	Gusinde (1936)
Twa (of Ntomba)	1508	58·5	21·2	18·2	2·1	Jadin (1940)
	94	62·7	21·3	12·8	3·2	Snoeck and Hubinont (1949)
Twa (of Nkundo)	1000	71·5	14·5	12·1	1·9	Jadin (1940)
Twa	547	43·5	38·0	14·3	4·2	Jadin and Bruynoghe (1952)
Twa (of Kuba)	295	58·0	28·1	11·5	2·4	After Hiernaux (1956)
Twa (of Lia and Iyembe)	104	69·2	20·2	9·6	1·0	Hiernaux (1962)
NEGRO AND PYGMY HYBRIDS						
at Ituri	143	38·5	43·4	13·3	4·9	Jadin (1935)
BANTU						
Alur	512	40·6	38·5	17·0	3·9	Jadin (1935)
Bira	273	53·1	26·0	18·7	2·2	Jadin (1935)
Budu	150	50·0	35·3	12·0	2·7	Dubois (1935, quoted by Jadin (1940)
Bulia	192	55·7	22·9	21·3	—	After Hiernaux (1962)
Bushong	388	51·3	24·7	19·6	14·4	After Hiernaux (1962)
Ekonda Boliassa	505	63·8	18·6	15·8	1·8	Jadin (1940)
Fulero	300	45·7	27·3	20·7	6·3	After Hiernaux (1956)
Havu	300	46·0	32·3	17·7	4·0	After Hiernaux (1956)
Hema	197	43·1	25·4	26·4	5·1	Julien (1935)
Humu (Hamu)	248	55·2	26·6	14·1	4·1	After Hiernaux (1956)
Hunde	300	45·7	33·3	14·7	6·3	After Hiernaux (1956)
Kongo	335	52·8	23·6	20·6	3·0	Lambotte-Legrand (1950)
	494	47·0	25·3	19·2	8·5	Ronse (1952)

TABLE 1 (cont.)

Population	n	% Frequency				Reference
		O	A	B	AB	

CONGO (LÉOPOLDVILLE) (cont.)

BANTU (cont.)

Population	n	O	A	B	AB	Reference
Bantu (mainly Kongo)	8000	51·7	25·0	19·7	3·7	Van Ros and Jourdain (1956)
Lesa	507	48·5	30·8	16·4	4·3	Jadin (1935)
Luba	284	48·6	21·8	26·1	3·5	After Hiernaux (1962)
Luba and Lulua	3000	50·5	25·2	19·8	4·5	Resseler (1962)
Mbuba	300	53·3	23·7	18·0	5·0	After Hiernaux (1956)
Ngbaka	500	32·4	33·2	25·4	9·0	Jadin (1940)
Ngbundu (N)	500	40·0	32·8	19·2	8·0	Jadin (1940)
(S)	500	24·4	36·2	24·4	15·0	Jadin (1940)
Nkundu (Mongo)	1914	59·1	23·7	15·6	1·7	Jadin (1940)
Ntomba (Ekonda)	1025	61·4	19·4	17·5	1·8	Jadin (1940)
Ntomba (Yeli)	560	64·8	13·6	18·6	3·0	Jadin (1940)
Ntomba (Nkole)	520	59·0	20·2	17·1	1·7	Jadin (1940)
Nyanga	300	47·3	31·7	17·7	3·3	After Hiernaux (1956)
Rega	300	53·7	23·3	19·7	3·3	After Hiernaux (1956)
Shi	800	48·0	30·7	19·3	2·0	Lambillon and Denisoff (1940)
	200	45·0	30·5	21·0	3·5	After Hiernaux (1956)
Shu	300	48·7	32·3	13·3	5·7	After Hiernaux (1956)
Swaga	300	41·0	38·7	16·3	4·0	After Hiernaux (1956)
Tembo	300	40·7	36·3	18·3	4·7	After Hiernaux (1956)
Tutsi (at Itombwe)	203	56·6	28·6	12·3	2·5	After Hiernaux (1962)
Tribe unspecified						
In Elizabethville district	500	45·6	22·2	24·2	8·0	Bruynoghe and Walravens (1926)
In Kibali-Ituri district (Mamvu and Lesa)	776	38·8	33·6	21·4	6·2	Julien (1935)
Léopoldville district	327	55·1	26·0	16·8	2·1	Lambotte-Legrand (1950)
Léopoldville district	150	46·8	26·2	21·2	5·8	Sonnet and Michaux (1960)
Soldiers (of Katanga)	242	52·9	19·0	24·0	4·1	Resseler (1962)
Soldiers (of Kasai)	695	47·6	27·1	20·9	4·5	Resseler (1962)
Soldiers (of Léopoldville)	638	55·3	23·5	18·3	2·8	Resseler (1962)

CONGO (BRAZZAVILLE)

BANTU

Population	n	O	A	B	AB	Reference
Bembe	74	50·0	25·7	20·3	4·1	Ceccaldi et al. (1946)
Lali	99	53·5	21·2	22·2	3·0	Ceccaldi et al. (1946)

TABLE 1 (*cont.*)

Population	n	% Frequency O	A	B	AB	Reference
			GABON			
BANTU						
Miscellaneous	400	41·0	27·0	26·0	6·0	Liodt and Pojarski (1929)
			TANZANIA (formerly Tanganyika and Zanzibar)			
NON-BANTU						
Iraqw	93	57·0	15·3	24·9	2·9	Allison *et al.* (1954)
PYGMOID						
Tswa	33	36·4	42·4	15·1	6·1	Allison *et al.* (1954)
BANTU						
Gogo	449	73·1	19·6	5·8	1·6	Elsdon-Dew (1939)
Ha	448	68·3	19·2	11·6	0·9	Elsdon-Dew (1939)
Ikoma	435	45·7	30·1	17·9	6·2	Elsdon-Dew (1939)
Nyamwesi	450	66·0	22·0	11·1	0·9	Eldson-Dew (1939)
Sukuma	450	63·8	24·2	11·1	0·9	Elsdon-Dew (1939)
Zaramo	425	61·6	14·8	23·1	0·7	Elsdon-Dew (1939)
Miscellaneous	130	52·3	22·3	23·9	1·5	Rife (1956b)
			RWANDA and BURUNDI (formerly Ruanda-Urundi)			
BANTU						
Hutu	1156	53·8	22·1	19·0	5·0	Jadin and Bruynoghe (1952)
	267	48·3	27·6	21·3	2·5	Hiernaux (1954)
Tutsi	861	65·0	16·6	17·2	1·2	Jadin and Bruynoghe (1952)
	127	66·1	22·0	9·4	2·2	Hiernaux (1954)
			MOZAMBIQUE			
BANTU						
Chopi	500	64·2	17·8	16·4	1·6	Elsdon-Dew (1936)
Inyambane	500	63·2	16·4	17·4	3·0	Elsdon-Dew (1936)
Makua (Macoua)	141	48·9	23·4	24·1	3·5	Alberto and Barreto (1955)
Mntumba	28	78·6	14·3	3·6	3·6	Dos Santos (1937)
Nyungwe (Nhungué)	110	92·7	7·3	—	—	Dos Santos (1937)
Shangaan	500	54·0	26·6	18·6	0·8	Elsdon-Dew (1936)
	530	66·4	19·6	9·6	4·3	Zoutendyk (1955a)
Shangaan-Thonga	218	58·3	24·3	14·2	3·2	Alberto (1953)
Shangaan and Chopi	151	49·7	25·8	21·9	2·7	Zoutendyk (1955a)
Ronga, Thonga, and Chopi	576	57·6	24·1	15·3	3·0	Alberto and Barreto (1955)

TABLE 1 (cont.)

Population	n	% Frequency				Reference
		O	A	B	AB	

MOZAMBIQUE (cont.)

BANTU (cont.)

Population	n	O	A	B	AB	Reference
'Negro'	94	60·6	16·0	20·2	3·2	Dos Santos (1934)
	155	60·6	16·1	20·0	3·2	Dos Santos (1937)
	4383	56·8	23·7	17·1	2·4	Rebelo (1955)
'Central Bantu'	1064	50·2	21·4	22·0	6·4	Alberto (1961)
'Southern Bantu'	10,790	58·8	22·6	16·4	2·2	Alberto (1961)
'Eastern Bantu'	5468	49·9	24·3	22·0	3·8	Alberto (1961)
'Western Bantu'	735	54·0	23·4	19·2	3·4	Alberto (1961)
From North of Zambesi	6111	49·3	24·4	22·4	3·9	Alberto (1961)
From South of Zambesi	11,946	58·5	22·4	16·6	2·5	Alberto (1961)

MALAWI
(formerly Nyasaland)

BANTU

Population	n	O	A	B	AB	Reference
Chewa	574	50·7	20·9	26·0	2·4	Elsdon-Dew (1939)
Konde	297	51·2	16·8	31·3	0·7	Elsdon-Dew (1939)
Ngoni	476	49·8	24·0	22·9	3·4	Elsdon-Dew (1939)
Nguru	458	46·5	22·7	24·7	6·1	Elsdon-Dew (1939)
Nyanja	231	51·1	24·2	19·9	4·8	Elsdon-Dew (1939)
Tonga	456	60·3	18·6	20·0	1·1	Elsdon-Dew (1939)
Tumbuka	123	43·9	26·0	22·8	7·3	Elsdon-Dew (1939)
Yao	576	53·6	21·5	22·2	2·6	Elsdon-Dew (1939)

ZAMBIA
(formerly Northern Rhodesia)

BANTU

Population	n	O	A	B	AB	Reference
Tonga (Valley)	184	44·0	27·2	23·9	4·9	Blecher and Zoutendyk (1962, unpublished)
Tonga (Plateau)	150	46·5	22·2	30·7	0·7	Jenkins and Zoutendyk (1963, unpublished)

ANGOLA

NON-BANTU
BUSHMAN

Population	n	O	A	B	AB	Reference
Kwankhala	814	47·5	33·3	6·9	12·3	Almeida (1954)
(Cuancala)	621	59·7	25·6	11·6	3·1	Almeida and Basto (1957)
Kwede (Muquéde)	62	43·5	37·1	6·5	12·9	Almeida (1954)
Kwépe (Mucuépe)	45	26·7	42·2	4·4	26·7	Almeida (1954)
Sekele (Cassequéle)	605	57·9	33·4	4·3	4·5	Almeida (1954)
Zama (Cazama)	239	55·2	31·8	8·4	4·6	Almeida (1954)
MULATTO	190	47·9	32·1	14·7	5·3	Sarmento (1953)

TABLE 1 (*cont.*)

Population	n	O	A	B	AB	Reference
BANTU						
Amboin	99	47·5	35·3	10·1	7·1	Almeida (1954)
(Huambo)	373	48·8	21·5	24·7	5·1	Sarmento (1953)
Apinda	112	56·3	25·9	8·0	9·8	Almeida (1954)
Bieno	53	64·1	15·1	20·7	—	Sarmento (1953)
Dirico	34	50·0	29·4	20·6	—	Almeida (1954)
Evale	217	47·0	26·3	19·3	7·4	Almeida (1954)
Gambue	202	37·6	34·7	14·9	12·9	Almeida (1954)
Ganda	76	44·7	27·6	21·1	6·6	Sarmento (1953)
Himba	22	31·8	54·5	—	13·6	Almeida (1954)
Kafue	45	31·1	40·0	28·9[1]	—	Almeida (1954)
Kakonda	41	58·5	21·9	17·1	2·4	Sarmento (1953)
Kakongo	201	49·3	29·9	15·9	5·0	Almeida (1954)
Kabinda (= Kakongo)	208	54·3	24·0	11·1	10·6	Almeida (1954)
Kalandula	106	45·3	22·6	26·4	5·7	Almeida (1954)
Kubale (Mucubai)	198	32·8	29·8	24·7[2]	12·6	Almeida (1954)
Kwamato (Cuamato)	200	51·5	25·5	21·5	1·5	Almeida (1954)
Kwandu (Mucuando)	119	37·0	46·2	8·4	8·4	Almeida (1954)
Kwangare (Cuangare)	212	45·3	28·3	19·8	6·6	Almeida (1954)
Kwanyama (Cuanhama)	202	58·9	24·3	10·4	6·4	Almeida (1954)
Kwanyoka (Mucuanhoca)	60	35·0	31·7	8·3	25·0	Almeida (1954)
Lundo	108	50·0	27·8	17·6	4·6	Sarmento (1953)
Maxi (Camáxi)	176	42·0	31·8	20·5	5·7	Almeida (1954)
Mbwela	160	50·6	21·9	24·4	3·1	Almeida (1954)
Mbukushu (Cambucusso)	194	38·1	30·9	26·3	4·6	Almeida (1954)
Mbundu	968	49·6	23·3	22·6	4·4	Sarmento (1953)
Mucusso Damba	105	50·5	25·7	13·3	10·5	Almeida (1954)
Muchicongo	200	54·5	18·0	19·0	8·5	Almeida (1954)
Mucuisse	179	35·7	43·6	11·7	8·9	Almeida (1954)
Muila	200	47·5	25·0	14·5	13·0	Almeida (1954)
Mukaba	208	57·7	14·4	18·7	9·1	Almeida (1954)
Mundimba	36	30·6	41·7	11·1	16·7	Almeida (1954)
Mussorongo	180	50·6	16·7	23·9[3]	8·9	Almeida (1954)
Mutua (? Twa)	120	56·6	31·7	1·7	10·0	Almeida (1954)
Mutchibugwe (Mutxibugue)	200	54·0	22·5	19·5	4·0	Almeida (1954)
Ncangala (? Ngangela)	60	55·0	25·0	16·7	3·3	Almeida (1954)
Ngola	163	57·7	19·0	20·3	3·1	Almeida (1954)

TABLE 1 *(cont.)*

Population	*n*	O	A	B	AB	Reference
			% *Frequency*			

ANGOLA *(cont.)*

Population	*n*	O	A	B	AB	Reference
BANTU *(cont.)*						
Nyemba (Canhemba)	173	55·5	26·0	17·3	1·2	Almeida (1954)
Nyengo (Canhengo)	85	49·4	23·5	23·5	3·5	Almeida (1954)
Quibala	129	50·4	20·9	13·9	14·7	Almeida (1954)
Quissange	200	43·0	24·0	21·5	11·5	Almeida (1954)
Sambo	318	47·8	25·2	23·0	4·1	Sarmento (1953)
Songo	630[4]	51·1	23·5	23·7	1·7	David (1949)
	201	44·8	21·9[5]	18·4	14·9	Almeida (1954)
Sosso	200	62·0	23·5	12·0	2·5	Almeida (1954)
Tshokwe (N)	81	45·7	23·5	18·5	12·3	Almeida (1954)
(S)	112	54·6	19·5	21·0	4·9	Almeida (1954)
(Lunda)	722	51·0	27·8	19·4	1·8	David (1949)
Tshipungo (Txipungo)	200	39·5	30·0	14·0	16·5	Almeida (1954)
Yombe	204	52·0	22·5	19·6	5·9	Almeida (1954)
Zombo	204	63·2	23·0	11·8	2·0	Almeida (1954)
'Native'	2000	48·6	23·3	24·5	3·5	Teixeira (1946)
'Bantu'	892	44·4	27·6	23·1	4·9	Lessa (1953)
	8000	47·9	24·3	24·7	3·1	Mayor (1954)

RHODESIA
(formerly Southern Rhodesia)

Population	*n*	O	A	B	AB	Reference
BANTU						
Bujga	298	53·7	26·2	19·8	0·3	Elsdon-Dew (1939)
Kalanga	414	67·4	18·6	12·3	1·7	Elsdon-Dew (1939)
Karanga	522	65·5	15·7	17·6	1·1	Elsdon-Dew (1939)
Koni	421	56·8	24·9	15·9	2·4	Elsdon-Dew (1939)
Korekore	425	48·7	26·4	20·5	4·5	Elsdon-Dew (1939)
Mangwato	485	58·1	17·4	22·9	1·6	Elsdon-Dew (1939)
Manyika	449	51·0	28·1	17·4	3·6	Elsdon-Dew (1939)
Ndau	433	74·4	13·4	10·4	1·8	Elsdon-Dew (1939)
Ndebele	218	61·9	24·8	11·0	2·3	Elsdon-Dew (1939)
Rotse	506	52·8	17·8	27·1	2·4	Elsdon-Dew (1939)
Shona	478	49·2	25·9	22·0	2·9	Barker *et al.* (1953)
Tonga	450	53·8	21·8	21·6	2·9	Elsdon-Dew (1939)
Zezuru	450	58·4	20·0	20·0	1·6	Elsdon-Dew (1939)

BECHUANALAND

Population	*n*	O	A	B	AB	Reference
NON-BANTU						
BUSHMAN						
Northern Bushman						
Kun	73	37·0	53·4	5·5	4·1	Blecher, Jenkins and Zoutendyk (1963, unpublished)

TABLE 1 (*cont.*)

Population	n	O	A	B	AB	Reference
			% Frequency			

BECHUANALAND (*cont.*)

Population	n	O	A	B	AB	Reference
NON-BANTU (*cont.*)						
Central Bushman						
Miscellaneous (mainly Naron)	82	73·2	21·9	2·4	2·4	Tobias and Zoutendyk (1959, unpublished)
Miscellaneous	114	61·4	35·1	3·5	—	Weiner and Zoutendyk (1959)
Southern Bushman						
Magon	72	61·1	34·7	4·2	—	Weiner and Zoutendyk (1959)
Pooled	122	61·5	35·2	3·3	—	Tobias and Zoutendyk (1958, unpublished)
Northern,Central, and Southern	114	70·2	25·5	2·6	1·7	Tobias and Zoutendyk (1959, unpublished)
Kwai River hybrid Bushmen	41	34·1	24·4	36·6	4·8	Blecher, Jenkins, and Zoutendyk (1963, unpublished)
BANTU						
Tswana	500	49·4	24·8	24·0	1·8	Elsdon-Dew (1936)
	292	40·7	32·2	21·6	5·5	Zoutendyk (1955a)
	500	53·2	18·6	24·6	3·6	Wohlgemuth (quoted by Mourant *et al.*, 1958)

SOUTH-WEST AFRICA

Population	n	O	A	B	AB	Reference
NON-BANTU						
BUSHMAN						
Northern Bushman	446	56·1	33·9	8·5	1·6	Zoutendyk *et al.* (1953)
Auen	280	53·9	31·1	5·4	9·6	Pijper (1932)
Kun	268	60·4	28·0	7·8	3·8	Pijper (1932)
Heikum	67	47·7	29·9	14·9	7·5	Pijper (1932)
HOTTENTOT	506	34·8	30·6	29·2	5·3	Pijper (1935)
	213	37·1	32·4	24·4	6·1	Zoutendyk *et al.* (1955)

REPUBLIC OF SOUTH AFRICA

Population	n	O	A	B	AB	Reference
NON-BANTU						
HOTTENTOT						
Nama (Richtersveld)	44	27·0	34·0	25·0	13·0	Singer *et al.* (1961)
Korana (Vaal River)	174	26·4	44·8	24·7	4·0	Grobbelaar (1955)

TABLE 1 (cont.)

Population	n	% Frequency				Reference
		O	A	B	AB	

REPUBLIC OF SOUTH AFRICA (cont.)

NON-BANTU (cont.)

Korana	203	18·2	35·5	37·4	8·9	Grobbelaar (1955)
(Orange River)						
CAPE COLOURED	135	33·3	40·7	20·7	5·2	Zoutendyk (1955a)

BANTU

Bacha (Bacca)	357	38·1	37·3	20·7	3·9	Zoutendyk (1955a)
Pondo	500	42·6	33·2	22·8	1·4	Elsdon-Dew (1936)
	315	42·5	23·2	28·6	5·7	Zoutendyk (1955a)
Sotho	705	52·2	26·5	19·1	2·1	Pijper (1930)
	481	37·2	33·5	23·3	6·0	Zoutendyk (1955a)
	127	40·2	29·9	21·3	8·7	Zoutendyk (1955a)
N. Sotho	500	58·8	19·0	19·6	2·6	Elsdon-Dew (1936)
S. Sotho	500	53·8	25·0	17·4	3·8	Elsdon-Dew (1936)
Swazi	500	61·6	19·8	17·4	1·2	Elsdon-Dew (1936)
Xhosa	500	45·6	28·4	22·2	3·8	Elsdon-Dew (1936)
	893	37·4	34·9	23·1	4·6	Zoutendyk (1955a)
'Makossa'	100	43·0	37·0	13·0	7·0	Wohlgemuth (quoted by Mourant et al., 1958)
Zulu	500	51·8	24·6	21·6	2·0	Elsdon-Dew (1936)
	322	37·6	33·5	23·3	5·6	Zoutendyk (1955a)
East Coast Bantu	100	56·0	24·0	17·0	3·0	Wohlgemuth (quoted by Mourant et al., 1958)
Miscellaneous	250	52·0	27·2	19·2	1·6	Pirie (1921)
Bantu	880	53·2	25·3	19·2	2·3	Pijper (1935)
	4000	46·1	29·9	19·3	4·7	Shapiro (1951a)
	820	46·2	27·3	21·1	5·4	Shapiro (1951a)
	1200	47·4	29·3	18·7	4·6	Shapiro (1951b)
	858	50·2	28·2	17·4	4·2	Shapiro (1953)
	1094	45·9	31·9	19·2	3·0	Zoutendyk (1955a)
	4205	42·9	30·8	21·3	4·9	Zoutendyk (1955a)
	20,170	46·9	30·3	18·6	4·2	Zoutendyk (1955b)

† Foy et al. (1954): Per cent rounded off to nearest whole number in original paper. In present Table 1, figures are given to one decimal place, after Mourant et al. (1958), the numbers in the latter work having been calculated from the published frequencies.
 (1) Erroneously given as 23·89 in Almeida (1954).
 (2) Erroneously given as 23·74 in Almeida (1954).
 (3) Erroneously given as 28·89 in Almeida (1954).
 (4) Quoted as n=603 by Hiernaux (1964).
 (5) Erroneously given as 28·89 in Almeida (1954).

TABLE 2

Distribution of Rh(CDE) blood groups in sub-equatorial African populations

Population	n	% Frequency		Reference

KENYA

NON-BANTU

Luo	128	$ccDee(RoRo)$	80·5	Allison *et al.* (1952)
		$CcDee(RoR')$	8·6	
		$ccDEe(RoR'')$	8·6	
		$ccD^uee(Ro^ur)$	0·8	
		$ccddEe(R''r)$	0·8	
		$ccD^uEe(Ro^uR'')$	0	
		$ccddee(rr)$	0	
		$Ccddee(R'r)$	0	
		$CCddee(R'R')$	0	
		$CcddEe(R'R'')$	0	
		$ccddEE(R''R'')$	0	
Masai	86	$ccDee$	72·1	After Buettner-
		$CcDee$	11·6	Janusch *et al.* (1960)
		$ccDEe$	10·5	
	(?)	$\dagger ccDee$	2·3	
		$Ccddee$	1·2	
		$CcDEe$	1·2	
		$CCDee$	1·2	
		$ccddee$	0	

BANTU

Kamba	50	$ccDee$	74·0	After Buettner-
		$CcDee$	14·0	Janusch *et al.* (1960)
		$ccDEe$	10·0	
		ccD^uee	2·0	
		$Ccddee$	0	
		$CcDEe$	0	
	(?)	$\dagger ccDee$	0	
		$CCDee$	0	
		$ccddee$	0	
Kikuyu	124	$ccDee(RoRo)$	63·7	Allison *et al.* (1952)
		$CcDee(R_1Ro)$	17·7	
		$ccDEe(R_2Ro)$	12·1	
		$ccD^uee(Ro^ur)$	3·2	
		$ccddee(rr)$	1·6	
		$CcDEe(R_1R_2)$	0·8	
		$Ccddee(R'r)$	0·8	
		$CCDee(R_1R_1)$	0	
		$CcD^uee(R_0{}^uR')$	0	
		$CCdee(R'R')$	0	
		$ccDEE(R_2R_2)$	0	

TABLE 2 (*cont.*)

Population	n		% Frequency	Reference
		KENYA (*cont.*)		
BANTU (*cont.*)				
Pokomo and	42	*ccDee*	64·3	After Buettner-
Giryama		*ccDEe*	16·7	Janusch *et al.* (1960)
		CcDee	9·5	
		CcDEe	4·8	
		ccddee	4·8	
		ccD^uee	0	
		Ccddee	0	
	(?)	†*ccDee*	0	
		CCDee	0	
		UGANDA		
NON-BANTU				
Hima	117	*ccDee*	45·3	Allison *et al.* (1954)
		ccD^uee	17·1	
		ccDEe	15·4	
		CcDee	12·0	
		ccddee	7·7	
		CcDEe	1·7	
		ccDEE	0·9	
		CCDee	0	
		CCD^uee	0	
		CcD^uee	0	
		TANZANIA		
		(formerly Tanganyika and Zanzibar)		
NON-BANTU				
Iraqw	93	*ccDee*	52·7	Allison *et al.* (1954)
		CcDee	19·3	
		ccDEe	12·9	
		ccD^uee	6·5	
		ccddee	4·3	
		CCDee	2·1	
		CcDEe	1·1	
		CcD^uee	1·1	
		ccDEE	0	
		CCD^uee	0	
PYGMOID				
Tswa	33	*ccDee*	69·7	Allison *et al.* (1954)
		ccDEe	30·3	
		CONGO (LÉOPOLDVILLE)		
NON-BANTU				
PYGMY and PYGMOID				
Twa (of Kuba)	295	*cDe*	63·8	Hiernaux (1962)
		cde	15·3	
		cD^ue	9·2	
		CDe	5·6	
		cDE	5·4	
		Cde	0·7	

TABLE 2 *(cont.)*

Population	n	% Frequency		Reference
		CONGO (LÉOPOLDVILLE) *(cont.)*		
NON-BANTU *(cont.)*				
Twa (of	94	cDe	58·8	Snoeck and Hubinont
Ntomba)		cDE	19·4	(1949)
		cde	10·1	
		$cD^u e$	4·2	
		CDe	3·7	
		Cde	0	
BANTU				
Bushong	388	cDe	55·4	Hiernaux (1962)
		cde	22·5	
		$cD^u e$	8·9	
		cDE	6·5	
		CDe	5·7	
		Cde	0·8	
Hunde	300	cDe	63·3	Hiernaux (1956)
		cde	16·3	
		cDE	8·0	
		$cD^u e$	6·8	
		CDe	5·7	
		Cde	0	
Rega	300	cDe	63·7	Hiernaux (1956)
		cde	15·2	
		cDE	8·5	
		$cD^u e$	6·3	
		Cde	3·9	
		CDe	2·5	
Swaga	300	cDe	58·6	Hiernaux (1956)
		cde	16·3	
		CDe	9·2	
		cDE	8·2	
		$cD^u e$	6·7	
		Cde	1·0	
Congo (at	252	cDe	61·2	Resseler and Legros
Bukavu)		cde	27·5	(1957)
		ccDE	6·8	
		$C^N cDe$	4·6	
Congo (at	150	D	94·0	Sonnet and Michaux
Léopoldville)		D^u	2·6	(1960)
		d	3·3	
		RWANDA and BURUNDI		
		(formerly Ruanda-Urundi)		
BANTU				
Hutu	267	cDe	58·3	Hubinont *et al.* (1953)
		cde	19·2	
		$cD^u e$	9·3	
		cDE	5·6	
		CDe	5·2	
		Cde	2·5	

TABLE 2 (*cont.*)

Population	*n*	% *Frequency*	*Reference*
		RWANDA and BURUNDI (*cont.*)	
BANTU (*cont.*)			
Tutsi	127	cDe 52·7	Hubinont *et al.* (1953)
		cde 21·6	
		$cD^u e$ 10·2	
		CDe 8·3	
		cDE 5·7	
		Cde 1·6	
		ZAMBIA (formerly Northern Rhodesia)	
BANTU			
Tonga	184	cDe 63·0	Blecher and
(Valley)		$C^N cDe$ 23·8	Zoutendyk (1962,
		$ccDE$ 7·0	unpublished)
		$CcDE$ 4·3	
		$cD^u e$ 0·5	
		$CCDe$ 0·5	
		$C^N De$ 0·5	
		cde 0·5	
Tonga	150	6% *Rh*-negative	Jenkins and
(Plateau)			Zoutendyk (1963,
			unpublished)
		RHODESIA (formerly Southern Rhodesia)	
BANTU			
Shona	106	$ccDee$ 72	Quoted by Singer *et*
		CDe 9	*al.*, 1961
		$ccDE$ 9	
		$ccddee$ 6	
	(?)	$\ddagger CcDE$ 4	
		BECHUANALAND	
NON-BANTU			
BUSHMAN			
Central	114	$ccDee$ 67·5	Weiner and
Kalahari		$CcDe$ 28·1	Zoutendyk (1959)
		$ccDE$ 4·4	
		C^W 0	
		$ccddee$ 0	
Kun	72	cDe 62·5	Blecher, Jenkins, and
		$CcDe$ 34·7	Zoutendyk (1963,
		cde 2·8	unpublished)
		$cD^u e$ 0	
		cDE 0	
		$CcDE$ 0	
		Cde 0	

TABLE 2 (cont.)

Population	n	% Frequency		Reference

BECHUANALAND (cont.)

NON-BANTU (cont.)
BUSHMAN (cont.)

Population	n		% Frequency	Reference
Pooled	122	cDe	65·6	Tobias and Zoutendyk
Northern,		CDe	30·3	(1958, unpublished)
Central, and		$CcDE$	4·1	
Southern		cD^ue	0	
		$CCDee$	0	
		cde	0	
	114	cDe	50·0	Tobias and Zoutendyk
		CDe	45·6	(1959, unpublished)
		cD^ue	0·9	
		$CCDee$	0·9	
		$CcDE$	0·9	
		cde	0·9	
Kwai River	36	cDe	50·0	Blecher, Jenkins, and
hybrids		$CcDe$	25·0	Zoutendyk (1963,
		cDE	11·1	unpublished)
		cde	5·6	
		cD^ue	2·8	
		$CcDE$	2·8	
		Cde	2·8	

SOUTH-WEST AFRICA

NON-BANTU
BUSHMAN

Population	n		% Frequency	Reference
South-West	232	$ccDee$	78·0	Zoutendyk et al.
Africa		$CDee$	17·2	(1953)
		$ccDE$	3·9	
		ccD^uee	1·0	
		CDE	0	
	446	$ccDee$	78·8	Weiner and
		$CcDe$	17·2	Zoutendyk (1959)
		$ccDE$	3·9	
		$ccddee$	0	

HOTTENTOT

Population	n		% Frequency	Reference
South-West	210	$ccDee$	58·1	Zoutendyk et al.
Africa		$CcDee$	26·7	(1955)
		$ccDE$	6·7	
		$CcDE$	4·8	
		$CCDee$	3·3	
		$ccddee$	0·5	

TABLE 2 (*cont.*)

Population	n	% Frequency		Reference

REPUBLIC OF SOUTH AFRICA

NON-BANTU

Population	n	% Frequency		Reference
HOTTENTOT	44	*ccDee*	54	Singer *et al.* (1961)
Richtersveld		*CDe*	32	
		ccDE	11	
	(?)	‡*CcDE*	3	
		ccddee	0	

BANTU

Population	n	% Frequency		Reference
Miscellaneous	300	*cDe*	64·3	Zoutendyk (1947)
Bantu (mainly		*CDe*	27·0	
Zulu and Sotho)		*cde*	5·3	
		CDE	2·3	
		Cde	1·0	
		cDE	0	
		cdE	0	
		CdE	0	
Miscellaneous	1200	*cDe(Rho)*	66·2	Shapiro (1951a)§
		$CDe(Rh_1)$	16·9	
		$cDE(Rh_2)$	10·2	
		$CDE(Rh_1Rh_2)$	4·4	
		cde(rh)	1·4	
		Cde(rh′)	0·8	
	644	*Rho*	69·1	Shapiro (1953)
		Rh_1rh	14·4	
		Rh_2rh	6·9	
		Rho	3·0	
		Rh_1rh	2·2	
		rh	1·4	
		Rh_1Rh_2	1·2	
		rh′	0·8	
		Rh_1Rh_1	0·3	
		$Rh_1{}^WRh_2$	0·3	
		$Rh_1{}^Wrh$	0·3	
		$Rh_1{}^WRh_1$	0	
		Rh_2Rh_2	0	
		rh″	0	

Note: *Rh* and *CDE* notations are given as quoted by each individual author. Per cent frequency of phenotypes is given in decreasing order of size.

† *ccDee* is quoted twice by Buettner-Janusch *et al.* (1960). The second one, with the low percentages, is obviously incorrect.

‡ Given as *ccDE* in Singer *et al.* (1961).

§ Figures given include D^u as D. If D^u is included as d, the following frequencies apply:
cDe(Rho): 64·1; $CDe(Rh_1)$: 15·3; $cDE(Rh_2)$: 10·2.
$CDE(Rh_1 Rh_2)$: 4·4; *cde(rh)*: 3·6; *Cde(rh′)*: 2·3.

TABLE 3

Distribution of the MN *blood groups in sub-equatorial African populations*

Population	n	% Frequency			Reference
		M	N	MN	
KENYA					
NON-BANTU					
Hima	117	23·9	25·6	50·4	Allison *et al.* (1954)
Luo	128	23·4	21·9	54·7	Allison *et al.* (1952)
BANTU					
Kamba	50	28·0	16·0	56·0	After Buettner-Janusch *et al.* (1960)
Kikuyu	124	33·1	15·3	51·6	Allison *et al.* (1952)
Pokomo and Giryama	42	26·2	21·4	52·4	After Buettner-Janusch *et al.* (1960)
TANZANIA (formerly Tanganyika and Zanzibar)					
NON-BANTU					
Iraqw	93	46·2	10·8	43·0	Allison *et al.* (1954)
PYGMOID					
Tswa	33	9·1	36·4	55·5	Allison *et al.* (1954)
CONGO (LÉOPOLDVILLE)					
BANTU					
Fulero	300	29·7	26·0	44·3	After Hiernaux (1956)
Havu	300	22·0	26·7	51·3	After Hiernaux (1956)
Humu	248	27·8	24·2	48·0	After Hiernaux (1956)
Hunde	300	26·3	29·3	44·3	After Hiernaux (1956)
Mbuba	300	26·7	21·7	51·7	After Hiernaux (1956)
Nyanga	300	22·3	29·3	48·3	After Hiernaux (1956)
Rega	300	20·3	24·3	55·3	After Hiernaux (1956)
Shu	300	21·0	30·7	48·3	After Hiernaux (1956)
Swaga	300	23·7	27·0	49·3	After Hiernaux (1956)
Tembo	300	26·3	20·7	53·0	After Hiernaux (1956)
RWANDA and BURUNDI (formerly Ruanda-Urundi)					
BANTU					
Hutu	267	28·0	25·4	46·4	Hiernaux (1954)
Tutsi	127	40·1	18·8	40·9	Hiernaux (1954)
ZAMBIA (formerly Northern Rhodesia)					
BANTU					
Tonga (Valley)	184	30·4	19·2	50·4	Blecher and Zoutendyk (1962, unpublished)

TABLE 3 (*cont.*)

Population	n	M	N	MN	Reference
		% Frequency			

BECHUANALAND

NON-BANTU
BUSHMAN

Population	n	M	N	MN	Reference
Central	79	39·2	17·7	43·0	Tobias and Zoutendyk (1958, unpublished)
Pooled Northern, Central, and Southern	112	39·3	17·9	42·9	Tobias and Zoutendyk (1959, unpublished)

SOUTH-WEST AFRICA

NON-BANTU

Population	n	M	N	MN	Reference
BUSHMAN	188	37·8	19·7	42·6	Zoutendyk *et al.* (1953)
HOTTENTOT	201	56·2	9·0	34·8	Zoutendyk *et al.* (1955)

REPUBLIC OF SOUTH AFRICA

BANTU

Population	n	M	N	MN	Reference
Miscellaneous	500	27·0	22·0	51·0	After Shapiro (1951*a*)
	205	33·7	17·5	48·8	Shapiro (1953)
	?	28·0	20·0	52·0	Zoutendyk (1954)

TABLE 4

Distribution of various blood groups in sub-equatorial
African populations

(Kell-Cellano, Diego, Henshaw, Lutheran, Duffy, P, V+, Js+)

Population	n	% Frequency	Reference

Kell-Cellano (K-k) system

KENYA

BANTU

Population	n	% Frequency	Reference
Kamba	50	K+=0	After Buettner-Janusch *et al.* (1960)
Pokomo and Giryama	42	K+=4·8	After Buettner-Janusch *et al.* (1960)

SOUTH-WEST AFRICA

NON-BANTU

Population	n	% Frequency	Reference
BUSHMAN	106	K+=10·4	After Zoutendyk *et al.* (1953)
HOTTENTOT	201	K+=5·0	After Zoutendyk *et al.* (1955)

TABLE 4 (cont.)

Population	n	% Frequency	Reference

REPUBLIC OF SOUTH AFRICA
BANTU
Miscellaneous	500	$K^+ = 10.6$	Shapiro (1952)

Diego system
KENYA
BANTU
Kamba	50	$Di^a = 0$	After Buettner-Janusch et al. (1960)
Pokomo and Giryama	42	$Di^a = 0$	After Buettner-Janusch et al. (1960)

ZAMBIA
(formerly Northern Rhodesia)
BANTU
Tonga (Plateau)	180	$Di^a = 0$	Blecher and Zoutendyk (1963, unpublished)
Tonga (Valley)	105	$Di^a = 0$	Blecher and Zoutendyk (1962, unpublished)

BECHUANALAND
NON-BANTU
BUSHMAN
Central Bushman	31	$Di^a = 0$	Tobias and Zoutendyk (1959, unpublished)
	114	$Di^a = 0$	Weiner and Zoutendyk (1959)
Southern Bushman (Magon)	72	$Di^a = 0$	Tobias and Zoutendyk (1959, unpublished)
Pooled Northern, Central, and Southern	37	$Di^a = 0$	Tobias and Zoutendyk (1959, unpublished)

SOUTH-WEST AFRICA
NON-BANTU
HOTTENTOT	60	$Di^a = 0$	Zoutendyk et al. (1955)

REPUBLIC OF SOUTH AFRICA
NON-BANTU
HOTTENTOT
Richtersveld	44	$Di^a = 0$	Singer et al. (1961)
CAPE COLOURED	?	$Di^a = 1$ case	Zoutendyk (unpublished)

BANTU
Miscellaneous	60	$Di^a = 0$	Weiner and Zoutendyk (1959)

TABLE 4 (cont.)

Population	n	% Frequency	Reference
		Henshaw system	
		UGANDA	
NON-BANTU			
Hima	117	$He^+ = 3\cdot4$	Allison et al. (1954)
		TANZANIA (formerly Tanganyika and Zanzibar)	
NON-BANTU			
PYGMOID			
Tswa	33	$He^+ = 3\cdot0$	Allison et al. (1954)
HAMITIC			
Iraqw	93	$He^+ = 11\cdot8$	Allison et al. (1954)
		ZAMBIA (formerly Northern Rhodesia)	
BANTU			
Tonga (Valley)	184	$He^+ = 6\cdot0$	Blecher and Zoutendyk (1963, unpublished)
		BECHUANALAND	
NON-BANTU			
BUSHMAN			
Central	80	$He^+ = 18\cdot7$	Tobias and Zoutendyk (1958, unpublished)
Pooled Northern, Central, and	122	$He^+ = 16\cdot4$	Tobias and Zoutendyk (1958, unpublished)
Southern	112	$He^+ = 17\cdot9$	Tobias and Zoutendyk (1959, unpublished)
		SOUTH-WEST AFRICA	
NON-BANTU			
BUSHMAN	120	$He^+ = 3\cdot3$	Zoutendyk et al. (1953)
	188	$He^+ = 2\cdot7$	Zoutendyk (1955b)
HOTTENTOT	201	$He^+ = 10\cdot5$	Zoutendyk (1955b)
		REPUBLIC OF SOUTH AFRICA	
NON-BANTU			
Cape Coloured	1000	$He^+ = 4\cdot7$	Shapiro (1956)
Cape Malay	107	$He^+ = 2\cdot0$	Shapiro (1956)
BANTU			
Miscellaneous	4000	$He^+ = 6\cdot2$	Shapiro (1956)

TABLE 4 (*cont.*)

Population	n	% Frequency	Reference
		Lutheran system	
		SOUTH-WEST AFRICA	
NON-BANTU			
BUSHMAN	89	Lu(a+)=0	Zoutendyk *et al.* (1953)
HOTTENTOT	201	Lu(a+)=0	Zoutendyk *et al.* (1955)
		REPUBLIC OF SOUTH AFRICA	
BANTU			
Miscellaneous	205	Lu(a+)=5·4	Shapiro (1953)

Population	n	% Frequency	Reference
		Duffy system	
		KENYA	
BANTU			
Kamba	50	Fy(a+)=0	After Buettner-Janusch *et al.* (1960)
Pokomo and Giryama	42	Fy(a+)=9·5	After Buettner-Janusch *et al.* (1960)
		BECHUANALAND	
NON-BANTU			
BUSHMAN			
Central	68	Fy(a+)=27·9	Tobias and Zoutendyk (1958, unpublished)
Pooled Northern, Central, and Southern	77	Fy(a+)=31·2	Tobias and Zoutendyk (1959, unpublished)
		SOUTH-WEST AFRICA	
NON-BANTU			
BUSHMAN	108	Fy(a+)=15·7	Zoutendyk *et al.* (1953)
HOTTENTOT	201	Fy(a+)=27·9	Zoutendyk *et al.* (1955)
		REPUBLIC OF SOUTH AFRICA	
BANTU			
Miscellaneous	365	Fy(a+)=11·8	Shapiro (1953)

Population	n	% Frequency	Reference
		P system	
		KENYA	
BANTU			
Kamba	50	P+ =96·0	After Buettner-Janusch *et al.* (1960)
Kikuyu	?	P+ =97·0	Henningsen (1950)
	124	P+ =97·0	Allison *et al.* (1952)
Pokomo and Giryama	42	P+ =95·2	After Buettner-Janusch *et al.* (1960)

TABLE 4 (*cont.*)

Population	n	% Frequency	Reference
		BECHUANALAND	
NON-BANTU			
BUSHMAN			
Central	68	$P+ = 50 \cdot 0$	Tobias and Zoutendyk (1958, unpublished)
Pooled Northern,	122	$P+ = 54 \cdot 1$	Tobias and Zoutendyk (1958, unpublished)
Central, and			
Southern	77	$P+ = 63 \cdot 1$	Tobias and Zoutendyk (1959, unpublished)
		SOUTH-WEST AFRICA	
NON-BANTU			
HOTTENTOT	201	$P+ = 24 \cdot 4$	Zoutendyk *et al.* (1955)
		REPUBLIC OF SOUTH AFRICA	
BANTU			
Miscellaneous	500	$P+ = 86 \cdot 8$	Shapiro (1951*a*)
	400	$P+ = 92 \cdot 0$	Shapiro (1953)
		V^+ system	
		ZAMBIA	
BANTU			
Tonga (Valley)	184	$V^+ = 36 \cdot 4$	Blecher and Zoutendyk (1963, unpublished)
Tonga (Plateau)	24	$V^+ = 16 \cdot 7$	Jenkins and Zoutendyk (1963, unpublished)
		BECHUANALAND	
NON-BANTU			
BUSHMAN			
Central	31	$V^+ = 12 \cdot 9$	Tobias and Zoutendyk (1959, unpublished)
	114	$V^+ = 5 \cdot 3$	Weiner and Zoutendyk (1959)
	37	$V^+ = 10 \cdot 8$	Blecher and Zoutendyk (1962, unpublished)
Southern	72	$V^+ = 4 \cdot 2$	Tobias and Zoutendyk (1959, unpublished)
(Magon)			
		REPUBLIC OF SOUTH AFRICA	
NON-BANTU			
HOTTENTOT			
Richtersveld	44	$V^+ = 9$	Singer *et al.* (1961)

TABLE 4 (*cont.*)

Population	n	% *Frequency*	Reference
		Js+ system	
		ZAMBIA	
BANTU			
Tonga (Valley)	92	Js+ =0	Blecher and Zoutendyk (1962, unpublished)
		BECHUANALAND	
NON-BANTU			
BUSHMAN			
Central	114	Js+ =5·3	Weiner and Zoutendyk (1959)
	31	Js+ =0	Tobias and Zoutendyk (1959, unpublished)
	37	Js+ =0	Blecher and Zoutendyk (1962, unpublished)
Southern (Magon)	72	Js+ =4·2	Tobias and Zoutendyk (1959, unpublished)
		REPUBLIC OF SOUTH AFRICA	
NON-BANTU			
HOTTENTOT			
Richtersveld	44	Js+ =7	Singer *et al.* (1961)

TABLE 5

Distribution of sickle-cell haemoglobin in sub-equatorial African populations

Population	n	% *Sicklers*	Reference
		SOMALILAND	
NON-BANTU			
PYGMOID			
Boni	81	0	Foy *et al.* (1954)
		KENYA	
NON-BANTU			
Galla	30	0	Foy *et al.* (1954)
Kipsigi	100	2	Foy *et al.* (1954)
Luo	100	28	Foy *et al.* (1954)
	482	18–20	Foy *et al.* (1955)
	294	20·4	Trowell *et al.* (1957)
	196	20·9	Trowell *et al.* (1957)

TABLE 5 (cont.)

Population	n	% Sicklers	Reference
BANTU			
Chagga	75	0	Foy et al. (1954)
Chonyi	90	26	Foy et al. (1954)
Digo	50	22	Foy et al. (1954)
Duruma	68	10	Foy et al. (1954)
	302	10	Moore et al. (1954)
Giryama	150	11	Foy et al. (1954)
Jibana	119	13	Foy et al. (1954)
Kakamega	96	12	Foy et al. (1954)
Kamba	134	1	Foy et al. (1954)
Kamba (Kambe)	78	35	Foy et al. (1954)
	220	34	Moore et al. (1954)
Kauma	39	10	Foy et al. (1954)
Kikuyu	67	2	Foy et al. (1954)
	227	0·44	Allison (1954)
Kisii	100	3	Foy et al. (1954)
Kitosh	100	21	Foy et al. (1954)
Marama	100	10	Foy et al. (1954)
Nyore (Bunyori)	100	6	Foy et al. (1954)
Pare	40	5	Foy et al. (1954)
Pokomo	102	27	Foy et al. (1954)
Rabai	48	10	Foy et al. (1954)
Ragoli (Maragoli)	100	9	Foy et al. (1954)
Ribe	50	26	Foy et al. (1954)
Sanya (Witu)	61	0	Foy et al. (1954)
(Adu)	68	12	Foy et al. (1954)
Taveta	154	24	Foy et al. (1954)
Teita	127	0	Foy et al. (1954)
Wanga	96	20	Foy et al. (1954)

UGANDA

	n	% Sicklers	Reference
NON-BANTU			
Luo	130	28	Lehmann (1954)
PYGMOID			
Twa	33	0	Allison (1954)
BANTU			
Amba	140	45	Lehmann and Raper (1949)
	623	39	Lehmann and Raper (1956)
Ganda	740	19	Lehmann and Raper (1949)
	3362	16·2	Jacob (1957)
	953	16·3	Trowell et al. (1957)
	758	17·2	Trowell et al. (1957)
Gisu (Gishu)	207	30	Lehmann and Raper (1949)
Hima	166	2·4	Lehmann and Raper (1949)
Hutu	496	8	Lehmann and Raper (1949)
Iru	139	2	Lehmann and Raper (1949)

TABLE 5 (cont.)

Population	n	% Sicklers	Reference
	UGANDA (cont.)		
BANTU (cont.)			
Kenyi	88	26	Lehmann and Raper (1949)
Konjo	102	18	Lehmann and Raper (1949)
Nyoro	91	12	Lehmann and Raper (1949)
Toro	120	12·5	Lehmann and Raper (1949)
	CONGO (LÉOPOLDVILLE)		
NON-BANTU			
PYGMY and PYGMOID			
Binga	327	6·8	Ravisse (1952), quoted by Heuse, 1957
Efé	456	25·9	Van den Berghe and Janssen (1950)
Twa (of Bulia)	104	13·4	Hiernaux (1955a)
(of Kuba)	295	19·0	Hiernaux (1955a)
BANTU			
Bulia (Bolia)	213	16·4	Hiernaux (1955a)
Bondjo	221	25·3	Ravisse (1952), quoted by Heuse, 1957
Bushong(o)	388	21·4	Hiernaux (1955a)
Fulero	300	18·3	Hiernaux (1956)
Havu	300	5·0	Hiernaux (1956)
Humu	273	36·3	Hiernaux (1956)
Hunde (of Kasai)	300	4·3	Hiernaux (1955a)
Hungana	449	22·9	Burke et al. (1958)
Kongo	395	24·6	Lambotte-Legrand (1951)
	1195	25·3	Vandepitte (1954)
Kumu and Rumbi	552	5·6	Van den Berghe and Janssen (1950)
Luba (of Kasai)	1020	20·1	Van den Berghe and Janssen (1950)
(of Katanga)	280	15·3	Hiernaux (1962)
Mamvu	217	22·1	Van den Berghe and Janssen (1950)
Mbala	7602	26·3	Burke et al. (1958)
Mbuba (Mvuba)	334	34·4	Hiernaux (1955a)
	300	36·0	Hiernaux (1956)
Mongo	3366	22·7	Allard (1955)
	11,288	24·2	Delbrouck (1958)
Ngongo	416	28·1	Burke et al. (1958)
Nyanga	300	7·3	Hiernaux (1956)
Rega	150	12·0	Hiernaux (1955a)
	300	22·3	Hiernaux (1956)
Shi	375	4·2	Hiernaux (1952)
	301	4·0	Neel et al. (1956)
Shu	300	9·0	Hiernaux (1956)

TABLE 5 (cont.)

Population	n	% Sicklers	Reference
	CONGO (LÉOPOLDVILLE) (cont.)		
BANTU (cont.)			
Suku	464	13·4	Lejeune (1952)
Suku and Luba	655	14·2	Lejeune (1952)
Swaga	300	7·7	Hiernaux (1956)
Tembo	300	5·3	Hiernaux (1956)
Yanzi (Yans)	16,878	30·0	Burke et al. (1958)
Léopoldville area	510	25·5	Vandepitte (1952), quoted by Heuse (1957)
	501	25·7	Shapiro and Vandepitte (1954)
	151	21·8	Sonnet and Michaux (1950)
Jadotville area	1004	30·4	Parent (1950), quoted by Heuse (1957)
Elizabethville area	649	22·0	Stijns and Delville (1952) as in Jadin (1963)
	515	24·9	Stijns and Delville (1952)
Stanleyville area	1000	27·9	Vandepitte (1959)
Miscellaneous	400	±20	Vandepitte (unpublished), quoted by Neel (1956)
	TANZANIA (formerly Tanganyika and Zanzibar)		
BANTU			
At Dar-es-Salaam	1036	19·4	Mackay (1949)
	RWANDA and BURUNDI (formerly Ruanda-Urundi)		
NON-BANTU			
PYGMOID			
Twa	141	2·8	Hiernaux (1952)
BANTU			
Hutu	496	8	Lehmann and Raper (1949)
(of Rwanda)	403	5·2	Hiernaux (1952)
(of Burundi)	395	11·8	Hiernaux (1952)
	1000	2·5	Van den Berghe and Janssen (1950)
Imbo	?	22·0	Hiernaux (1955a)
	269	18·6	Hiernaux et al. (unpublished) quoted by Neel (1956)
	328	18·8	Neel et al. (1956)
Mosso	233	27·3	Hiernaux (1952)
	478	25·9	Hiernaux (1952), as quoted by Hiernaux (1962)
Rwanda	496	8·0	Lehmann (1954)
Rundi	108	19·0	Lehmann and Raper (1949)

TABLE 5 (cont.)

Population	n	% Sicklers	Reference

RWANDA and BURUNDI (cont.)

BANTU (cont.)

Tutsi (of Rwanda)	294	1·3	Hiernaux (1952)
(of Burundi)	264	1·6	Hiernaux (1952), as quoted in Hiernaux (1962)
	306	0·65	Neel et al. (1956)
(of Itombwe)	191	1·1	Hiernaux (1962)
Miscellaneous	135	3·7	Trowell et al. (1957)
	136	5·1	Trowell et al. (1957)

MOZAMBIQUE

BANTU

Chope (Muchope)	100	2	Foy et al. (1952)
Chuabo	100	3	Foy et al. (1952)
Erati	25	0	Foy et al. (1952)
Lomwe	100	4	Foy et al. (1952)
(=Nguru)	101	0	Brain (1953)
Makonda (at Porto Amelia)	100	40	Foy et al. (1952)
Makonda (at Vipinco)	50	4	Foy et al. (1952)
Makua	110	38	Foy et al. (1952)
Manhaua	50	4	Foy et al. (1952)
Maravia	25	0	Foy et al. (1952)
Mungone	50	1	Foy et al. (1952)
Ronga	100	1	Foy et al. (1952)
Sena	50	1	Foy et al. (1952)
	142	6·3	Brain (1953)
Shangaan	150	2	Foy et al. (1952)
	136	0	Brain (1953)
Tachana	50	2	Foy et al. (1952)
Thonga	100	1	Foy et al. (1952)
Tswa	100	2	Foy et al. (1952)

MALAWI
(formerly Nyasaland)

BANTU

Ngoni	359	9·2	Beet (1949)
	108	6·5	Brain (1952)
Nyanja	118	3·4	Brain (1953)
Yao	186	3·2	Brain (1953)

ZAMBIA
(formerly Northern Rhodesia)

BANTU

Angoni	359	9·2	Beet (1947)
	226	6·2	Brain (1953)
Bemba-Bisa	37	27·0	Brain (1953)

TABLE 5 *(cont.)*

Population	n	% Sicklers	Reference
		ZAMBIA *(cont.)*	
BANTU *(cont.)*			
Chewa	522	12·5	Beet (1947)
	110	9·0	Brain (1952)
	275	9·5	Brain (1953)
Cikunda	54	13·0	Brain (1953)
Karanga	956	0·6	Brain (1953)
Kasempa	25	16·0	Beet (1946)
Lala	308	13·6	Beet (1949)
Lubale (Lovale)	86	3·5	Beet (1946)
	815	12·9	Beet (1947)
Lunda	53	17·0	Beet (1946)
	220	15·5	Beet (1949)
Nsenga	169	18·9	Beet (1947)
	82	22·0	Brain (1953)
Nyakyusa	108	18·5	Brain (1953)
Shona	120	o	Seymour and Gelfand (1960)
Tonga	100	1	Foy *et al.* (1952)
(Valley)	401	0	Jenkins (1963)
	253	3·9	Jenkins (1963, unpublished)
(Plateau)	84	5·9	Jenkins (1963, unpublished)
Tumbuka	50	12·0	Beet (1947)
Fort Jameson area	1289	11·9	Beet (1947)
Miscellaneous	349	13·5	Beet (1946)
	38	13·2	Beet (1946)
	140	12·8	Beet (1946)
	41	14·6	Beet (1946)
Mixed Copperbelt population	717	17·5	English (1945)
		ANGOLA	
BANTU			
Bangala	98	43·9	David (1960)
	600	33·5	David *et al.* (1962)
Chokwe (Quioco)	1709	17·0	David (1960)
	600	17·5	David *et al.* (1962)
Lubale (Lovale)	44	11·4	Beet (1946)
Lunda	?	27·0	Teixeira (1944)
	605	19·2	David (1960)
	600	18·2	David *et al.* (1962)
Nungo (Minungo)	280	20·7	David (1960)
	485	18·1	David *et al.* (1962)
Shinji (Xinje)	290	21·4	David (1960)
	600	25·5	David *et al.* (1962)
Songo	542	24·7	David (1960)
	600	26·6	David *et al.* (1962)

TABLE 5 (*cont.*)

Population	*n*	% *Sicklers*	*Reference*
RHODESIA (formerly Southern Rhodesia)			
BANTU			
Dombe	60	11·6	Jenkins (1963)
Lozi	298	6·0	Jenkins (1963)
Nambya	571	2·1	Jenkins (1963)
Miscellaneous	500	±8·0	Gelfand (1946)
BECHUANALAND			
NON-BANTU			
BUSHMAN			
Northern Bushman			
Kun	79	0	Jenkins and Blecher (1963, unpublished)
River Bushmen	58	0	Jenkins and Blecher (1963, unpublished)
Central Bushman			
Barakwengo	58	0	Griffiths (1953)
South of Okavango	60	0	Griffiths (1953)
Miscellaneous	118	0	Griffiths (1953)
	500	0	Zoutendyk *et al* (1953)
BANTU			
Francistown-Maun district	252	5	After Griffiths (1954)
SOUTH-WEST AFRICA			
BANTU			
Mpukushu	119	0	Griffiths (1953)
REPUBLIC OF SOUTH AFRICA			
NON-BANTU			
CAPE COLOURED	1555	0·58	Esrachowitz *et al.* (1952)
	219	0·6	Brain (1955)
BANTU			
Transvaal Bantu	354	0·85	After Griffiths (1954)
Zululand Bantu (North of Eshowe)	421	0	After Griffiths (1954)
Miscellaneous	403	0·25	Altmann (1945)
	660	0·33	Griffiths (1952)
	1741	0·11	Griffiths (1954)
	500	0·40	Griffiths (1954)
	76	0	Budtz-Olsen and Burgers (1955)
	12	0	Budtz-Olsen and Burgers (1955)

TABLE 6

Distribution of haemoglobin C in sub-equatorial African populations

Population	n	% With haemoglobin C trait	Reference
CONGO (LÉOPOLDVILLE) (formerly Belgian Congo)			
BANTU			
Shi	301	o	Neel *et al.* (1956)
Miscellaneous	400	o	Vandepitte (unpublished)
TANZANIA (formerly Tanganyika and Zanzibar)			
BANTU			
At Dar-es-Salaam	100	o	Roberts and Lehmann (1955)
	104	o	Lehmann and Mackey (1955)
RWANDA and BURUNDI (formerly Ruanda-Urundi)			
BANTU			
Imbo	328	o	Neel *et al.* (1956)
Tutsi	306	o	Neel *et al.* (1956)
ZAMBIA (formerly Northern Rhodesia)			
BANTU			
Tonga (Valley)	85	1·2	Jenkins and Anderson (1963, unpublished)
ANGOLA			
BANTU			
Chokwe (Quioco)	600	o	David *et al.* (1962)
Lunda	600	o	David *et al.* (1962)
Mbangala	600	o	David *et al.* (1962)
Nungo (Minungo)	485	o	David *et al.* (1962)
Shinji (Xinje)	600	o	David *et al.* (1962)
Songo	600	o	David *et al.* (1962)

TABLE 6 (*cont.*)

Population	*n*	% With haemoglobin C trait	Reference
		BECHUANALAND	
NON-BANTU			
BUSHMAN			
Southern and Central	110	0	Jenkins (1964, unpublished)
BANTU			
Kgalakadi	60	0	Jenkins (1964, unpublished)
		REPUBLIC OF SOUTH AFRICA	
NON-BANTU			
Cape Coloured	219	0·9	Brain (1955)
	74	0	Jenkins (1965, unpublished)
BANTU			
Pedi	40	0	Jenkins (1965, unpublished)

TABLE 7

Distribution of haemoglobin K in sub-equatorial African populations

Population	*n*	% With haemoglobin K	Reference
		ANGOLA	
BANTU			
Chokwe (Quioco)	600	0·16	David *et al.* (1962)
Lunda	600	0·16	David *et al.* (1962)
Mbangala	600	0	David *et al.* (1962)
Nungo (Minungo)	485	0·21†	David *et al.* (1962)
Shinji (Xinje)	600	0	David *et al.* (1962)
Songo	600	0	David *et al.* (1962)

† Quoted by David *et al.* (1962) as 0·16 per cent: one case in 485 should, however, be 0·21 per cent.

TABLE 8

Distribution of haptoglobins in sub-equatorial African populations

Population	n	% Frequency					Gene frequency			Reference
		1–1	2–1	2–1M	2–2	Neg	Hp^1	Hp^2	Hp^0	
NON-BANTU			CONGO (LÉOPOLDVILLE)							
PYGMOID										
Congo pygmy	125	—	—	—	—	—	0·4	0·6	0·3	Motulsky and Giblett (1960)
BANTU										
'Metropolitan'	186	—	—	—	—	—	0·6	0·4	0·05	Motulsky and Giblett (1960)
'Non-Metropolitan'	468	—	—	—	—	—	0·6	0·4	0·21	Motulsky and Giblett (1960)
Congolese Bantu	99	38·4	44·5	2·0	13·1	2·0	0·61	—	—	Van Ros et al. (1963)
Congolese Bantu (at Léopoldville)	150	59·0	37·5	0	3·5	0	0·77	—	—	Sonnet and Michaux (1960)
			RWANDA and BURUNDI							
			(formerly Ruanda-Urundi)							
BANTU										
Tutsi (of Burundi)	86	27·9	47·7	0	22·1	2·3	0·52	—	—	Van Ros et al. (1963)
Hutu (of Burundi)	96	28·2	47·9	0	19·8	4·1	0·52	—	—	Van Ros et al. (1963)

TABLE 8 (cont.)

Population	n	% Frequency					Gene frequency			Reference
		1–1	2–1	2–1M	2–2	Neg	Hp^1	Hp^2	Hp^0	
BECHUANALAND										
NON-BANTU										
BUSHMAN										
Central	113	10·6	35·4	0	52·2	1·8	0·29	0·71	0·02	After Barnicot et al. (1959)
Central and Southern	125	9·8	39·3	1·6	49·2	2·5	0·30	0·70	—	Jenkins (1965, unpublished)
BANTU										
Kgalakadi	52	32·7	32·7	5·8	25·0	3·8	0·54	0·46	—	Jenkins (1965, unpublished)
REPUBLIC OF SOUTH AFRICA										
NON-BANTU										
HOTTENTOT										
Richtersveld	59	30·5	42·4	0	27·1	0	0·51	0·49	—	After Barnicot et al. (1959)
CAPE COLOURED	88	19·3	55·7	0	25·0	0	0·47	0·53	—	After Barnicot et al. (1959)
	100	16·0	46·0	0	38·0	0	0·39	0·61	—	After Gordon et al. (1964)
	75	33·3	12·0	0	52·0	2·7	0·28	0·72	—	Jenkins (1965, unpublished)
BANTU										
Xhosa and Sotho	315	—	—	—	—	—	0·55	0·45	0·05	Giblett and Zoutendyk (1960)
Pedi	78	41·0	24·4	3·8	12·8	17·9	0·55	0·45	—	Jenkins (1964, unpublished)
Zulu	113	31·9	39·8	2·6	25·7	2·6	0·53	0·47	0·03	After Barnicot et al. (1959)
Miscellaneous	100	34·0	43·0	0	22·0	1·0	0·56	0·44	—	Gordon et al. (1964)

TABLE 9

Distribution of transferrins in sub-equatorial African populations

Population	n	Incidence C	CD_1	D_1	B_2C	Gene TfD_1	Reference
		UGANDA					
BANTU							
Ganda	165	160	5	o		1·5	Barnicot (1961)
		CONGO LÉOPOLDVILLE (formerly Belgian Congo)					
BANTU							
Baka	97	96	1	o		0·5	Barnicot (1961)
		BECHUANALAND					
NON-BANTU							
BUSHMAN							
Ghanzi district	113	99	13	1		6·6	Barnicot (1961)
		REPUBLIC OF SOUTH AFRICA					
NON-BANTU							
CAPE COLOURED	100	97	3		o		Gordon et al. (1964)
BANTU							
Shangaan	172	162	10	o		2·9	Barnicot (1961)
Tswana	152	137	15	o		4·9	Barnicot (1961)
Xhosa	69	67	2	o		1·5	Barnicot (1961)
Zulu	116	113	3	o		1·3	Barnicot (1961)
Miscellaneous	100	94	6		o		Gordon et al. (1964)

TABLE 10

Distribution of serum cholinesterase in sub-equatorial African populations

Population	n	Usual	Unusual	Reference
	REPUBLIC OF SOUTH AFRICA			
NON-BANTU				
CAPE COLOURED	100	98	2	Gordon et al. (1964)
BANTU				
Miscellaneous	100	99	1	Gordon et al. (1964)

TABLE 11

Distribution of glucose-6-phosphate dehydrogenase deficiency in sub-equatorial African populations

Population	n	% Enzyme deficient	Reference
		KENYA	
BANTU			
Digo	26♂	23·1	After Allison (1960)
	33♀	18·2	After Allison (1960)
Giryama	101♂	16·8	After Allison (1960)
	65♀	15·4	After Allison (1960)
Kikuyu	70♂	2·9	After Allison (1960)
	73♀	2·7	After Allison (1960)
		UGANDA	
BANTU			
Ganda	40♂	15·0	After Allison (1960)
	46♀	10·9	After Allison (1960)
		CONGO LÉOPOLDVILLE	
NON-BANTU PYGMOID			
Ituri	?	4	Motulsky et al. (unpublished)
BANTU			
Hutu	?	7	Motulsky (unpublished)
Shi	?	14	Motulsky (unpublished)
Bwaka	?	6	Motulsky (unpublished)
Yaka	?	15–28	Motulsky and Vandepitte (unpublished)
Léopoldville area	?	18–23	Vandepitte and Motulsky (unpublished)
	522	21·5	Sonnet and Michaux (1960)
Stanleyville area	?	14–15	Motulsky et al. (unpublished)
		TANZANIA (formerly Tanganyika and Zanzibar)	
BANTU			
Bondei	121♂	27·3	After Allison (1960)
	124♀	19·3	After Allison (1960)
Sambaa	29♂	20·7	After Allison (1960)
	33♀	15·1	After Allison (1960)

TABLE 11 (cont.)

Population	n	% Enzyme deficient	Reference
	TANZANIA (cont.)		
BANTU (cont.)			
Zigua	26♂	23·1	After Allison (1960)
	29♀	13·8	After Allison (1960)
	RWANDA and BURUNDI (formerly Ruanda-Urundi)		
BANTU			
Tutsi	?	1–2	Motulsky (unpublished)
	BECHUANALAND		
NON-BANTU			
BUSHMAN	?	1–2	Bothwell (unpublished)
Pooled (Northern and Central)	29♂	3·4	After Charlton and Bothwell (1961)
	41♀	2·4	After Charlton and Bothwell (1961)
	REPUBLIC OF SOUTH AFRICA		
NON-BANTU			
CAPE COLOURED	159	1·9	After Bernstein (1963)
CAPE MALAY	51	2·0	After Bernstein (1963)
BANTU			
Bacha	30	0	Bernstein (1963)
Hlubi	17	5·9	Bernstein (1963)
Pedi	45	6·7	Bernstein (1963)
Pondo	44	0	Bernstein (1963)
Shangaan	81	9·9	Bernstein (1963)
Sotho	74	2·7	After Charlton and Bothwell (1961)
	85	4·7	Bernstein (1963)
Tswana	25	8·0	After Charlton and Bothwell (1961)
	85	7·0	Bernstein (1963)
Xhosa	43	2·3	After Charlton and Bothwell (1961)
	184	3·8	Bernstein (1963)
Zulu	73	1·4	After Charlton and Bothwell (1961)
	116	4·3	Bernstein (1963)
Miscellaneous	38	0	After Charlton and Bothwell (1961)
	310	0	After Charlton and Bothwell (1961)
Miscellaneous (at Johannesburg)	204	2	After Charlton and Bothwell (1959)

TABLE 12

Distribution of serum component Gc in sub-equatorial
African populations

Population	n	Frequency of Gc^2	Reference
		KENYA	
BANTU			
Bondei	57	0·10	Hirschfeld (1962)
		UGANDA	
BANTU			
Ganda	81	0·09	Hirschfeld (1962)
		CONGO (LÉOPOLDVILLE)	
BANTU			
Tribe unspecified	100	0·09	Hirschfeld and Sonnet (1961)

TABLE 13

Incidence of colour-blindness in sub-equatorial African populations

Population	n	% Colour-blind	Reference
		UGANDA	
BANTU			
Ganda	537♂	1·9	Simon (1951)
	31♀	0	Simon (1951)
		RWANDA and BURUNDI (formerly Ruanda-Urundi)	
BANTU			
Hutu	1000♂	2·7	Hiernaux and Van Der Borght (1953)
Tutsi	1000♂	2·5	Hiernaux and Van Der Borght (1953)
'Negroes'	929	1·7	Appelmans et al. (1953)

TABLE 13 (*cont.*)

Population	n	% Colour-blind	Reference
		ZAMBIA (formerly Northern Rhodesia)	
BANTU			
Tonga (Valley, adults)	250♂	2·8	Tobias (1959, unpublished)
Tonga (Valley, schoolboys)	285♂	4·6	Tobias (1959, unpublished)
Tonga (Plateau)	80♂	3·7	Tobias (1959, unpublished)
		BECHUANALAND	
NON-BANTU			
BUSHMAN			
Northern	12♂	16·7	Tobias (1958–9, unpublished)
	11♀	0	Tobias (1958–9, unpublished)
Central	41♂	0	Tobias (1958–9, unpublished)
	42♀	4·7	Tobias (1958–9, unpublished)
Southern	22♂	0	Tobias (1958–9, unpublished)
	30♀	0	Tobias (1958–9, unpublished)
BANTU			
Tswana	407♂	3·0	Squires (1942)
	574♀	0·4	Squires (1942)

TABLE 14

Incidence of taste-sensitivity to phenyl thiocarbamide (PTC) in sub-equatorial African populations

Population	n	% Non-tasters	Reference
		KENYA	
BANTU			
Giryama	208	3·8	Allison (1951)[†]
		RWANDA and BURUNDI (formerly Ruanda-Urundi)	
BANTU			
Hutu	20	5	Hiernaux (1954)[‡]
Tutsi	55	0	Hiernaux (1954)[‡]
		ZAMBIA (formerly Northern Rhodesia)	
BANTU			
Lenje	159	6·9	Jenkins (1965, unpublished)[†]
Lunda	83	13·3	Jenkins (1965, unpublished)[§]

TABLE 14 *(cont.)*

Population	n	% Non-tasters	Reference
		BECHUANALAND	
NON-BANTU			
BUSHMAN			
Pooled Central and Southern	85	7·1	Jenkins (1965, pending)‖
BANTU			
Kgalakadi	38	5·2	Jenkins (1965, pending)¶
		REPUBLIC OF SOUTH AFRICA	
NON-BANTU			
CAPE COLOURED	103	10·7	Jenkins (1965, unpublished)¶
BANTU			
Miscellaneous	86	2·3	Jenkins (1965, pending)‖

† Dividing threshold between 325 mg/l. and 81·3 mg/l.
‡ Only 1 solution used: 2·5/1000.
§ Dividing threshold at 81·3 mg/l.
‖ Dividing threshold at 325 mg/l.
¶ Dividing threshold at 162·5 mg/l.

TABLE 15

Distribution of dermatoglyphic patterns in sub-equatorial
African populations

Population	n	% Frequency			Reference
		Whorls	Loops	Arches	
		CONGO (LÉOPOLDVILLE)			
NON-BANTU					
PYGMY and PYGMOID					
Eastern groups					
Efé	153♂	19·6	64·4	15·9	Dankmeijer (1947)
	54♀	19·6	62·7	17·6	
	80♂	16·2	74·3	9·5	Valsik (1938)
	62♀	16·4	57·9	25·6	
Ituri pygmies	405 ♂	17·3	70·0	12·7	Geipel (1948)
(Basúa, Aka, and	♀	18·1	68·9	13·0	
Twa)					
Western groups					
Kola	130♂	36·4	57·6	6·1	Dankmeijer (1947)
	103♀	34·0	57·7	8·3	
Yaka	203♂	41·5	52·6	5·9	Dankmeijer (1947)
	100♀	44·1	52·0	3·9	
Negro-Pygmy	16♂	20·9	69·7	9·3	Valsik (1938)
crosses	9♀	15·5	70·2	14·1	

TABLE 15 (cont.)

Population	n	% Frequency Whorls	Loops	Arches	Reference
		CONGO (LÉOPOLDVILLE) (cont.)			
NON-BANTU (cont.)					
Negro-Basúa	12♂	25·2	63·4	11·3	Valsik (1938)
crosses	12♀	30·0	64·4	5·5	
Congo (incl.	87	39·8	52·9	7·3	Mutrux-Bornoz (1937)
Negrillos and	(♂+♀)				
Pygmies)					
Congo pygmies	886	16·2	69·2	14·6	Abel (1940) (quoted by
	(♂+♀)				Gessain, 1957)
BANTU					
Sanga	115♂	31·5	60·1	8·4	Dankmeijer (1947)
	119♀	29·0	61·4	9·6	
Shi	88♂	27·2	68·5	4·3	Hiernaux (1964)
Central Africa	17♂	38·2	57·4	4·3	Valsik (1938)
and Congo	9♀	35·2	52·2	12·5	
Congo	357	22·6	71·0	6·4	Abel (1940) (quoted by
	(♂+♀)				Gessain, 1957)
BANTU		CONGO BRAZZAVILLE			
Bamba	50♂	29·4	62·2	8·4	Gessain (1957)
	50♀	33·0	57·1	9·8	
Lali	50♂	31·2	65·0	3·8	Gessain (1957)
	50♀	31·5	60·0	8·4	
BANTU		RWANDA and BURUNDI (formerly Ruanda-Urundi)			
Tutsi	113♂	39·8	55·8	4·3	Hiernaux (1964)
BANTU		MOZAMBIQUE			
Chaca	63♂	21·3	73·2	5·5	Dos Santos, Jr. (1950)
Cherima	42♂	26·9	67·6	5·5	Dos Santos, Jr. (1950)
Cuabo	59♀	18·3	72·4	9·3	Dos Santos, Jr. (1950)
Coti	24♂	31·3	65·0	3·7	Dos Santos, Jr. (1950)
Erati	80♂	28·5	67·0	4·5	Dos Santos, Jr. (1950)
Makua	209♂	28·9	67·5	3·5	Dos Santos, Jr. (1950)
	61♀	26·2	65·7	8·0	
Maindo	51♂	34·3	61·4	4·3	Dos Santos, Jr. (1950)
Marrovoni	80♂	32·8	61·5	5·7	Dos Santos, Jr. (1950)
Matatani	50♂	29·4	67·0	3·6	Dos Santos, Jr. (1950)
	29♀	28·6	56·6	14·8	
Moniga	34♂	30·6	62·9	6·5	Dos Santos, Jr. (1950)
Nyaringa	58♂	27·9	67·4	4·7	Dos Santos, Jr. (1950)
Nyungwe	57	16·8	77·4	5·8	Dos Santos, Jr. (1950)
Sena	54♂	25·2	69·3	5·5	Dos Santos, Jr. (1950)
	17♀	28·2	62·4	9·4	
Shangaan	132	20·5	75·8	3·7	Dos Santos, Jr. (1950)
Tswa	65♂	25·5	67·1	7·4	Dos Santos, Jr. (1950)
Miscellaneous	59♂	20·7	76·6	2·7	Dos Santos, Jr. (1950)
	51♀	22·7	66·3	11·0†	

TABLE 15 (*cont.*)

Population	n	% Frequency			Reference
		Whorls	Loops	Arches	
		ZAMBIA			
NON-BANTU	(formerly Northern Rhodesia)				
PYGMOID					
Twa	26	20·8	70·0	9·2	Tobias (unpublished)
BANTU					
Tonga (Valley)	441♂	24·3	65·3	10·5	Tobias (1961, and un-
	343♀	22·2	66·0	11·8	published)
		ANGOLA			
BANTU					
Chokwe (Quióco)	107	21·1	73·3	5·5	Sarmento (1939)
	100	25·7	67·5	6·7	Sarmento (1940)
Nyemba	113	26·7	70·1	3·2	Sarmento (1939)
NON-BANTU	BECHUANALAND				
BUSHMAN					
Northern Bushman					
Auen	32♂	19·6	62·6	17·8	Tobias (1961)
Kun	164♂	15·1	71·9	13·0	Cummins (1955)
	181♀	17·1	63·6	19·4	
Heikum	17♂	30·6	67·0	2·4	Cummins (1955)
	20♀	24·5	65·0	10·5	
Central Bushman					
Barakwengo	44♂	30·7	64·1	5·2	Cummins (1955)
	61♀	25·9	64·6	9·6	
Kanikwe	23♂	38·7	54·3	7·0	Cummins (1955)
	34♀	32·1	61·7	6·2	
Miscellaneous	101	30·2	59·7	10·1	Tobias (1961)
Southern Bushman					
(Magon)	40	39·2	47·8	13·0	Tobias (1961)
Miscellaneous	32	15·1	68·5	16·4	Weninger (1936)
(♂ + ♀)					
	SOUTH-WEST AFRICA				
NON-BANTU					
HOTTENTOT					
(42♂ + 8♀)	50	18·6	76·3	5·1	Fleischhacker (1934)
	REPUBLIC OF SOUTH AFRICA				
NON-BANTU					
CAPE COLOURED	21	37·9	59·2	2·9	Rife (1956)
	14	27·1	65·0	7·9	Rife (1956)
	55	30·8	66·4	2·8	Rife (1956)
	45	29·4	62·8	7·8	Rife (1956)

† Erroneously given as 1·09 in Dos Santos Jr. (1950).
‡ Erroneously given as 441 Tonga (♂+♀) in Tobias (1961).

TABLE 16

Mean Cummins Index in sub-equatorial African populations
(Whorls × 2) + Loops

Population	n	Cummins Index	Reference
CONGO (LÉOPOLDVILLE)			
NON-BANTU			
PYGMY and PYGMOID			
Eastern groups			
Efé	153♂	10·36	Dankmeijer (1947)
	54♀	10·20	
Efé	80♂	10·67	Valsik (1938)
	62♀	9·1	
Ituri pygmies	347♂	9·90	Geipel (1948)
(Efé, Basúa,	369♀	9·30	
Aka, and Twa)			
'Congo pygmy'	101♂	8·60	Abel (quoted by Rife, 1953)
Western groups			
Kola	130♂	13·04	After Dankmeijer (1947)
	103♀	12·57	
Yaka	203♂	13·46	After Dankmeijer (1947)
	100♀	14·02	
Congo, including	87	13·25	After Mutrux-Bornoz (1937)
Negrillos and	(♂+♀)		
Pygmies			
BANTU			
Sanga	115♂	12·31	After Dankmeijer (1947)
Shi	88♂	12·29	After Hiernaux (1964)
Central Africa	25	13·00	After Valsik (1938)
and Congo	(♂+♀)		
Congo	357	11·62	After Abel (1940) (quoted by
	(♂+♀)		Gessain, 1957)
ZAMBIA			
(formerly Northern Rhodesia)			
BANTU			
Tonga (Valley)	441♂	11·38	Tobias (1961)
	343♀	11·03	Tobias (unpublished)
ANGOLA			
BANTU			
Chokwe	107	11·5	After Sarmento (1939)
(Quióco)	100	11·89	After Sarmento (1940)
Nyemba	113	12·3	Sarmento (1939)
(Nhemba)			

TABLE 16 (*cont.*)

Population	n	Cummins Index	Reference

BECHUANALAND

NON-BANTU
BUSHMAN
Northern Bushman

Population	n	Cummins Index	Reference
Auen	32♂	9·72	Tobias (1961)
	21♀	7·45	Tobias (1961)
Kun	164♂	10·21	Cummins (1955)
	181♀	9·78	Cummins (1955)
Heikum	17♂	12·82	Cummins (1955)
	20♀	11·40	Cummins (1955)
Central Bushman			
Barakwengo	44♂	12·55	Cummins (1955)
	61♀	11·64	Cummins (1955)
Kanikwe	23♂	13·17	Cummins (1955)
	34♀	12·59	Cummins (1955)
Miscellaneous	101♂	12·19	Tobias (1961)
	79♀	10·52	Tobias (1961)
Southern Bushman			
Magon	40♂	12·47	Tobias (1961)
	41♀	11·28	Tobias (1961)

SOUTH-WEST AFRICA

NON-BANTU
HOTTENTOT

Population	n	Cummins Index	Reference
(42♂ + 8♀)	50	11·35	Fleischhacker (1934)

REPUBLIC OF SOUTH AFRICA

NON-BANTU
CAPE COLOURED

Population	n	Cummins Index	Reference
(♂ + ♀)	76	12·93	Rife (1956)
	59	12·10	Rife (1956)

TABLE 17

Percentile occurrence of palmar patterns in sub-equatorial African populations

Population	n	I/II	II/III	III/IV	IV/V	H	Reference

ZAMBIA

NON-BANTU
PYGMOID

Population	n	I/II	II/III	III/IV	IV/V	H	Reference
Twa	26	15·4	5·8	38·5	78·9	50·0	Tobias (unpublished)

TABLE 17 (cont.)

Population	n	I/II	II/III	III/IV	IV/V	H	Reference
			ZAMBIA (cont.)				
BANTU							
Tonga							
Valley:							
Sinazongwe	283♂	6·5	5·3	34·6	66·4	23·1	Tobias (1957–8
	259♀	8·9	4·8	23·9	77·8	24·5	unpublished)
Simamba	144♂	13·2	5·5	36·1	71·9	25·3	Tobias (1957–8
	114♀	13·2	5·7	30·3	78·1	27·6	(unpublished)
Sinadambwe	146♂	11·3	14·0	40·4	72·3	22·3	Tobias (1957–8
	117♀	13·3	6·4	27·8	79·9	17·5	(unpublished
Plateau:							
Simwatacela	160♂	11·6	13·7	31·9	77·8	21·3	Tobias (1957–8
	148♀	8·1	7·1	25·7	75·3	24·0	unpublished)
			BECHUANALAND				
NON-BANTU							
BUSHMAN							
Northern Bushman							
Auen	14	32·1	28·5	33·3	71·4	46·4	Tobias (1961)
Heikum	39 (♂+♀)	15·9	17·1	48·2	85·9	31·8	Cummins (1955
Kun	411 (♂+♀)	37·2	33·4	53·3	84·4	29·0	Cummins (1955
Central Bushman							
Barakwengo	143 (♂+♀)	12·8	21·2	45·8	71·8	23·5	Cummins (1955
Kanikwe	63 (♂+♀)	29·8	21·8	37·1	89·2	31·6	Cummins (1955
Miscella-neous	52	37·2	28·2	48·5	73·8	25·4	Tobias (1961)
Southern Bushman							
Magon	81	15·4	8·0	44·4	48·8	0·6	Tobias (unpublished)
			SOUTH-WEST AFRICA				
NON-BANTU							
HOTTENTOT (42♂+8♀)	50	21·0	0	54	45	15	Fleischhacker (1934)
			REPUBLIC OF SOUTH AFRICA				
NON-BANTU							
CAPE	76	26·3	23·7				Rife (1956)
COLOURED (♂+♀)	59	11·9	8·5				Rife (1956)

TABLE 18

Summary of anthropometric surveys on sub-equatorial African populations

Population	n	No. of measurements recorded		No. of indices recorded		Reference
		Head	Body	Head	Body	
		UGANDA				
NON-BANTU						
Luo	64–76♂	16	15	17	23	Oschinsky (1954)
BANTU						
Ganda	300–424♂	16	15	17	23	Oschinsky (1954)
	34–38♀	18	16	18	25	
Hiru	44–50♂	16	15	17	23	Oschinsky (1954)
Swahili	104–114♂	16	15	17	23	Oschinsky (1954)
Toro	56–71♂	16	15	17	23	Oschinsky (1954)
		CONGO (LÉOPOLDVILLE)				
NON-BANTU						
PYGMY and PYGMOID						
Ituri Pygmy						
Aka	115♂ 110♀	38	28	13	14	Gusinde (1948)
Beyru	13♂ 9♀	38	28	13	14	Gusinde (1948)
Efé and Basua	386♂ 263♀	38	28	13	14	Gusinde (1948)
Twa	113♂	18	18	3	9	Hiernaux (1954)†
BANTU						
Bali	22♂ 26♀	28	38	14	13	Gusinde (1948)
	12 ?	6	3	7	2	Czekanowski (1922)
Beyru	35♂ 18♀	38	28	13	14	Gusinde (1948)
	35 ?	6	3	7	2	Czekanowski (1922)
Bira	342 ?	6	3	7	2	Czekanowski (1922)
Budu	62 ?	6	3	7	2	Czekanowski (1922)
Fulero	100♂	16	16	3	3	Hiernaux (1956)
Havu	100♂	16	16	3	3	Hiernaux (1956)
Humu	100♂	14	13	3	3	Hiernaux (1956)
Hunde	100♂	16	16	3	3	Hiernaux (1956)
Lese	36♂ 39♀	38	28	13	14	Gusinde (1948)
	7 ?	6	3	7	2	Czekanowski (1922)

TABLE 18 (cont.)

		No. of measurements recorded		No. of indices recorded		
Population	n	Head	Body	Head	Body	Reference

CONGO (LÉOPOLDVILLE) (cont.)

BANTU (cont.)

Population	n	Head	Body	Head	Body	Reference
Lika	56 ?	6	3	7	2	Czekanowski (1922)
Mbisa	37	6	3	7	2	Czekanowski (1922)
Mbuba	44 ?	6	3	7	2	Czekanowski (1922)
	100♂	16	16	3	3	Hiernaux (1956)
Medjé	24 ?	6	3	7	2	Czekanowski (1922)
Momvu	246 ?	6	3	7	2	Czekanowski (1922)
Ndaka	6 ?	6	3	7	2	Czekanowski (1922)
	54♂ 16♀	28	38	14	13	Gusinde (1948)
Nyanga	100♂	16	16	3	3	Hiernaux (1956)
Rega	100♂	16	16	3	3	Hiernaux (1956)
Rumbi	6 ?	6	3	7	2	Czekanowski (1922)
Shi	108♂	16	16	3	3	Hiernaux (1956)
Shu	100♂	16	16	3	3	Hiernaux (1956)
Swaga	100♂	16	16	3	3	Hiernaux (1956)
Tembo	100♂	16	16	3	3	Hiernaux (1956)

TANZANIA
(formerly Tanganyika and Zanzibar)

NON-BANTU

Population	n	Head	Body	Head	Body	Reference
Sandawe	100♂	7	3	3	2	Trevor (1947)
for 94 of these:		7	4	3	3	
for 56 of these:		9	3	4	2	

BANTU

Population	n	Head	Body	Head	Body	Reference
Nyaturu	50♂	7	3	3	2	Trevor (1947)
for 47 of these:		7	4	3	3	
for 35 of these:		9	3	4	2	
Miscellaneous	226♂	17	34	16	26	Tobias (1959–60,
(measured in Johannesburg)						unpublished)†

RWANDA and BURUNDI
(formerly Ruanda-Urundi)

NON-BANTU
PYGMY and PYGMOID

Population	n	Head	Body	Head	Body	Reference
Mbuti	514♂ 382♀	9	28	3	14	Gusinde (1949)
Twa	64♂ 10♀	7	3	4	2	Czekanowski (1922)
	101♂ 84♀	28	34	14	13	Gusinde (1949)

TABLE 18 (*cont.*)

Population	n	No. of measurements recorded		No. of indices recorded		Reference
		Head	Body	Head	Body	
		RWANDA and BURUNDI (*cont.*)				
BANTU						
Hutu	112♂	7	3	4	2	Czekanowski (1922)
	98–106♂	16	15	17	23	Oschinsky (1954)
	43–45♀	18	16	18	25	Oschinsky (1954)
(Rwanda)	254♂	18	18	3	9	Hiernaux (1954)†
(Burundi)	216♂	18	18	3	9	Hiernaux (1954)†
Tutsi	89♂	7	3	4	2	Czekanowski (1922)
	94–110♂	16	15	17	23	Oschinsky (1954)
	78–82♀	18	16	18	25	Oschinsky (1954)
(Rwanda)	177♂	18	18	3	9	Hiernaux (1954)†
(Burundi)	119♂	18	18	3	9	Hiernaux (1954)†
		MOZAMBIQUE				
BANTU						
Chopi	67♂ + 105♀	—	—	2	—	Barreto (1953)§
Ronga	24♂ + 69♀	—	—	2	—	Barreto (1953)§
Shangaan	99♂ + 197♀	—	—	2	—	Barreto (1953)§
Miscellaneous (measured in Johannesburg)	40♂	17	34	16	26	Tobias (1959–60, unpublished)†‡
		MALAWI (formerly Nyasaland)				
BANTU						
Miscellaneous (measured in Johannesburg)	129♂	17	34	16	26	Tobias (1959–60, unpublished)†‡
		ZAMBIA (formerly Northern Rhodesia)				
NON-BANTU PYGMOID						
Twa	36–39♂	14	—	15	—	Tobias (1958, unpublished)†
BANTU *Tonga (Valley)*						
Sinazongwe	133–144♂	18	34	17	28	Tobias (1957–8, unpublished)†
Simamba	41–44♂	18	34	17	28	Tobias (1957–8, unpublished)†
Sinadambwe	29–34♂	18	34	17	28	Tobias (1957–8, unpublished)†

TABLE 18 (*cont.*)

Population	n	No. of measurements recorded		No. of indices recorded		Reference
		Head	Body	Head	Body	
ZAMBIA (*cont.*)						
BANTU (*cont.*)						
Mwemba	63–73♂	18	34	17	28	Tobias (1957–8, unpublished)†
Mamba	19–21♂	18	34	17	28	Tobias (1957–8, unpublished)†
Tonga (Plateau)						
Simwatacela	42–56♂	18	34	17	28	Tobias (1957–8, unpublished)†
Siachitema	31–38♂	18	34	17	28	Tobias (1957–8 unpublished)†
Miscellaneous (measured in Johannesburg)	40♂	17	34	16	26	Tobias (1959–60, unpublished)†‡
ANGOLA						
NON-BANTU						
BUSHMAN						
Casama	48♀	—	10	—	—	Almeida (1957)
Bushman (Bosquimanas)	192♀	—	10	—	—	Almeida (1957)
BANTU						
Kwangare	109♂	—	1	1	—	Almeida (1957)‖
	25♀	—	10	—	—	Almeida (1957)‖
Mucusso	100♂	—	1	1	—	Almeida (1957)‖
	25♀	—	10	—	—	Almeida (1957)‖
Miscellaneous (measured at Johannesburg)	40♂	17	34	16	26	Tobias (1959–60, unpublished)†‡
BECHUANALAND						
NON-BANTU						
BUSHMAN						
Northern Bushman						
Kun	58♂ 77♀	17	1	13	—	Lebzelter (1931)†
	43♂	7	1	3	—	Wells (1952)
Makoko	29♂ 18♀	17	34	16	26	Tobias (1958–9, unpublished)†
Auen	12♂ 8♀	15	4	16	5	Tobias (1955–6)†

TABLE 18 (*cont.*)

Population	n	No. of measurements recorded		No. of indices recorded		Reference
		Head	Body	Head	Body	

BECHUANALAND (*cont.*)

NON-BANTU (*cont.*)
Central Bushman

| Naron | 10♂ 7♀ | 15 | 4 | 16 | 5 | Tobias (1955–6)† |
| Miscellaneous | 65♂ 57♀ | 17 | 34 | 16 | 26 | Tobias (1958–9, unpublished)† |

Southern Bushman

/ ?Auni- ≠ Khomani	20♂ 21♀	20	11	22	14	Dart (1937)†
Magon	31♂ 15♀	17	34	16	26	Tobias (1958–9, unpublished)†
Sarwa	24♂ 26♀	17	34	16	26	Tobias (1958–9, unpublished)†
Pooled Central and Southern	48 (♂ + ♀)	13	9	14	7	Jenkins (1965, (unpublished)

BANTU

| Ovambo | 50♂ 20♀ | — | 1 | 20 | 14 | Galloway (1937)† |

REPUBLIC OF SOUTH AFRICA

NON-BANTU
  BUSHMAN

| At Lake Chrissie | 10♂ 8♀ | 15 | 14 | 11 | 7 | Toerien (1958)† |

  HOTTENTOT

Korana	57♂	25	45	14	19	Grobbelaar (1956)
	30♀	23	19	13	9	Grobbelaar (1956)
Links clan	?♂	—	—	20	13	Galloway (1937)†
	?♀	—	—	20	5	Galloway (1937)†
Taaibosch clan	5♂ 2♀	15	3	5	—	Tobias (1955)†
Nama	71–72♂	13	3	11	2	Schultze (1928)
	30–31♀	2	1	3	—	Wells (1952)

BANTU

| South African Bantu | 98♀ | 4 | 4 | 2 | 12 | Orford and Wells (1937)† |

† Non-metrical features in addition.
‡ In some of these groups, not all the measurements and indices were done
on each individual.
  § Cephalic and nasal indices.
  ‖ Stature and cephalic index.

TABLE 19

Summary of data on dental characteristics of living sub-equatorial African populations

Population	n	Characteristics recorded	Reference
TANZANIA (formerly Tanganyika)			
BANTU Miscellaneous	226♂	Prodontism, eruption, bite, ablation or filing, size, Carabelli cusp, shovel-shaped incisors, diastemata, crowding	Tobias *et al.* (1959–60, unpublished)
MOZAMBIQUE			
BANTU Miscellaneous	40♂	As for Tanzania	Tobias *et al.* (1959–60, unpublished)
MALAWI (formerly Nyasaland)			
BANTU Miscellaneous	129♂	As for Tanzania	Tobias *et al.* (1959–60, unpublished)
ZAMBIA (formerly Northern Rhodesia)			
BANTU Tonga (4 clans)	183♂ 300–420♂	As for Tanzania	Tobias *et al.* (1957–8, unpublished)
Miscellaneous	40♂	As for Tanzania	Tobias *et al.* (1959–60, unpublished)
ANGOLA			
BANTU Miscellaneous	40♂	As for Tanzania	Tobias *et al.* (1959–60, unpublished)

TABLE 19 (*cont.*)

Population	*n*	Characteristics recorded	Reference
BECHUANALAND			
NON-BANTU			
BUSHMAN			
Northern	29♂ ⎱ 20♀ ⎰	⎧ Dental eruption, re- tained deciduous teeth, supernumeraries, tooth size, attrition,	Tobias *et al.* (1959, un- published)
Central	58♂ ⎱ 50♀ ⎰	bite, tooth spacing, diastemata, prodont- ism, caries, Carabelli	
Southern	40♂ ⎱ 40♀ ⎰	cusp, shovel-shaped incisors, and dental ⎩ mutilation	
Mixed Central and Southern	215♂ ⎱ 191♀ ⎰	Dental eruption, tooth size, attrition, bite, spacing, diastemata, caries, Carabelli cusp, arch form, relation of dental arch to basal bone, arcadal index, height of palate, free- way space, hypocalcifi- cation, tooth mutila- tion, inverse Monson's curve	Van Reenen (1964)
Mostly Southern	52 (♂ + ♀)	Curve of occlusion, mandibular condyle movements	Van Reenen (1964, un- published)
SOUTH-WEST AFRICA			
NON-BANTU			
BUSHMAN			
?/Auni-‡Khomani	14♂ ⎱ 9♀ ⎰	Arcadal index, palatal depth, tooth crowding	Sperber (1958)
REPUBLIC OF SOUTH AFRICA			
NON-BANTU			
BUSHMAN			
At Lake Chrissie	4–9♂ ⎱ 5–7♀ ⎰	Arcadal index, tooth crowding, palatal depth	Sperber (1958)

TABLE 20
Serum proteins of Bushmen

Group	Total Protein (g%)	Albumin (g%)	Globulin (g%)					A/G Ratio	Reference
			Total	α1	α2	β	γ		
Ghanziveld Bushmen (Mainly Central) Nomadic (n = 27)	8·0 ±0·61	2·80 ±0·48	5·22	0·47 ±0·11	0·97 ±0·19	1·19 ±0·24	2·59 ±0·74	0·54	Bersohn and Tobias (unpublished)
Ghanziveld Bushmen (Mainly Central) Farm (n=63)	7·9 ±0·64	3·19 ±0·51	4·72	0·45 ±0·33	0·94 ±0·21	1·17 ±0·23	2·16 ±0·53	0·68	Bersohn and Tobias (unpublished)
S.W.A. Bushmen (Kun-Northern) (n = 94)	8·24 ±0·68	3·46 ±0·31	4·78	0·39 ±0·10	0·75 ±0·16	0·96 ±0·14	2·68 ±0·58	0·72	Bronte-Stewart et al. (1960)

TABLE 21

Percentages of serum protein fractions in Bushmen and Bantu

Group	Albumin	Globulin				Reference
		α1	α2	β	γ	
Ghanziveld Bushmen (mainly Central) Nomadic (n = 27)	34·9	6·0	12·0	15·0	32·0	Bersohn and Tobias (unpublished)
Ghanziveld Bushmen (mainly Central) Farm (n = 63)	40·4	5·5	11·8	15·0	27·1	Bersohn and Tobias (unpublished)
Okavango (S.W.A.) Riverine Bushmen (n = 20)	41·1	4·2	7·5	10·4	36·9	Computed from Bronte-Stewart's 1960 figures
S.W.A. Bushmen 20 miles from Okavango River (n = 30)	42·3	4·8	8·8	11·5	32·4	Computed from Bronte-Stewart's 1960 figures
S.W.A. Bushmen 50 miles from Okavango River (n = 44)	42·1	5·1	9·6	12·3	30·5	Computed from Bronte-Stewart's 1960 figures
Bantu (Cape Town) (n = 71)	49·1	5·6	10·4	12·1	22·9	Computed from Bronte-Stewart's 1960 figures

TABLE 22

Cholesterols in Bushmen†

	Ghanzi Farm Bushmen	Ghanzi Nomadic Bushmen
Total cholesterol (mg%)	$145 \cdot 0 \pm 36 \cdot 0$ $(n = 66)$	$121 \cdot 0 \pm 26 \cdot 10$ $(n = 22)$
β-cholesterol A (%)	$30 \cdot 4 \pm 5 \cdot 5$	$30 \cdot 2 \pm 5 \cdot 6$
β-cholesterol B (%)	$69 \cdot 4 \pm 5 \cdot 5$	$69 \cdot 7 \pm 5 \cdot 6$
Lipoprotein A (%)	$35 \cdot 5 \pm 4 \cdot 5$ $(n = 5)$	$43 \cdot 0 \pm 2 \cdot 4$ $(n = 3)$
Lipoprotein B (%)	$64 \cdot 5 \pm 4 \cdot 5$ $(n = 5)$	$57 \cdot 0 \pm 2 \cdot 4$ $(n = 3)$

† Bersohn and Tobias, 1961: unpublished data.

REFERENCES

ALBERTO, M. S., 1953. 'Contribution to the study of the relation between the blood groups and the physical characters among Mozambique negroes (Shangana-Tonga tribe)'. Presented to the 51st Annual Congress of the South African Association for the Advancement of Science, Bulawayo, 1953.
—— 1961. 'Elementos para o readjustamento da carta hematológica dos povos negros da Africa a sul do equador', Bol. Soc. Estud. Mocam. 30, 128.
—— and BARRETO, A. D., 1955. Bol. Soc. Estud. Mocam. 81. Summary: Anthropologie 59, 143 (quoted by MOURANT et al., 1958).
ALLARD, 1955. Annls. Soc. belge Méd. trop. 35, 649 (quoted by VANDEPITTE, 1959).
ALLISON, A. C., 1951. 'A note on taste-blindness in Kenya Africans and Arabs', Man 205.
—— 1954. 'The distribution of the sickle-cell trait in East Africa and elsewhere, and its apparent relationship to the incidence of sub-tertian malaria', Trans. R. Soc. trop. Med. Hyg. 48, 312.
—— 1960. 'Glucose-6-phosphate dehydrogenase deficiency in red blood cells of East Africans', Nature, Lond. 186, 531.
—— IKIN, E. W., MOURANT, A. E., and RAPER, A. B., 1952. 'Blood groups in some East African tribes. I. Blood groups in some Kenya tribes', J. R. anthrop. Inst. 82, 55–59.
—————— 1954. 'Blood groups in some East African tribes', J. R. anthrop. Inst. 84, 158–162.

ALMEIDA, A. DE, 1954. 'Contribuicao para o estudo da antropologia serologica dos nativos de Angola (Nota preliminar)', *Est. col.* 1-3, 220-232.

—— 1965. *Bushmen and other non-Bantu peoples of Angola*, eds. P. V. TOBIAS and J. BLACKING. Institute for the Study of Man in Africa, Johannesburg.

—— and BASTO, M. E., 1957. 'Contribuicao para o estudo da sero-antropologia dos Bòsquimanos de Angola (Mucuancalas)', *Ass. port. Prog. Ciencias*, 23, 5-11.

ALMEIDA, M. E. C., DE, 1952. 'Contribuicao para o estudo da sero-antropologia dos Bantos', *Garcia de Orta* 3, 272-283.

—— 1957. 'Canones de mulheres indigenas de Angola', *Ass. port. Prog. Ciencias*, 23, 6-16.

ALTMANN, A., 1945. 'The sickle-cell trait in the South African Bantu', *S. Afr. med. J.* 19, 457.

APPELMANS, M., WEYTS, J., and VANKAM, J., 1953. *Bull. Soc. belge Opthal.* 103, 226 (quoted by POST, 1962).

BADENHORST, L. T., 1951. 'Population distribution and growth in Africa', *Popul. Stud.* 5, 23-34.

BARKER, E. M., IKIN, E. W., and MOURANT, A. E., 1953. *Heredity* 7, 131-133 (quoted by MOURANT *et al.*, 1958).

BARNICOT, N. A., 1961. 'Haptoglobins and transferrins', *Genetical Variation in Human Populations* (ed. G. A. HARRISON). Pergamon Press, Oxford.

—— GARLICK, J. P., SINGER, R., and WEINER, J. S., 1959. 'Haptoglobin and transferrin variants in Bushmen and some other South African peoples', *Nature, Lond.* 184, 2042.

BARRETO, A. D., 1953. 'Contribution to the study of the cephalic and nasal indices of the Mozambique natives.' Communication to the 51st Annual Meeting of the South African Association for the Advancement of Science, Bulawayo.

—— and ALBERTO, M. S., 1952. 'Contribution for the study of blood groups as an ethnological character of human races.' MS. only.

BEET, E. A., 1946. 'Sickle-cell disease in the Balovale district of Northern Rhodesia', *E. Afr. med. J.* 23, 75.

—— 1947. 'Sickle-cell disease in Northern Rhodesia', *E. Afr. med. J.* 24, 212.

—— 1949. 'The genetics of the sickle-cell trait in a Bantu tribe', *Ann. Eugen.* 14, 279.

BERNSTEIN, R. E., 1963. 'Occurrence and clinical implications of red cell glucose-6-phosphate dehydrogenase deficiency in South African racial groups', *S. Afr. med. J.* 37, 447.

BERSOHN, I., 1959. 'Prison research project on the long-term effects of diet on lipid metabolism: urinary oestrogen excretion', *Ann. Rep., S. Afr. Inst. med. Res.* 1959, p. 46.

—— and OELOFSE, P. J., 1957. 'A comparison of urinary oestrogen levels in normal male South African Bantu and European subjects', *S. Afr. med. J.* 31, 1172-1174.

—— —— 1958. 'Urinary oestrogen levels in myocardial infarction', *S. Afr. med. J.* 32, 979-983.

BOTHWELL, T. H., Unpublished data. Quoted as a personal communication to MOTULSKY and CAMPBELL-KRAUT, 1961.

BRAIN, P., 1952. 'The sickle-cell trait—its clinical significance', *S. Afr. med. J.* **26**, 925.

—— 1953. 'The sickle-cell trait.' Thesis submitted for the degree of M.D., University of Cape Town, unpublished.

—— 1955. 'Incidence of Haemoglobin C in the "Coloured" population of Cape Town', *Nature, Lond.* **175**, 262.

BRONTE-STEWART, B., BUDTZ-OLSEN, O. E., HICKLEY, J. M., and BROCK, J. F., 1960. 'The health and nutritional status of the Kung Bushmen of South West Africa', *S. Afr. J. Lab. clin. Med.* **6**, 188–216.

BRUYNOGHE, R. and WALRAVENS, P., 1926. *C. r. Séanc. Soc. Biol.* **95**, 739–740 (quoted by MOURANT *et al.*, 1958).

BUCKWALTER, J. A., KARK, A. E., and KNOWLER, L. A., 1961. 'A study in human genetics: the ABO blood groups and diseases in South Africa', *Archs. intern. Med.* **107**, 558–567.

BUDTZ-OLSEN, O. E. and BURGERS, A. C. T., 1955. 'The sickle-cell trait in South African Bantu', *S. Afr. med. J.* **29**, 109.

BUETTNER-JANUSCH, J., GERSHOWITZ, H., POSPISIL, L. J., and WILSON, P., 1960. 'Blood groups of selected aboriginal and indigenous populations', *Nature, Lond.* **188**, 153.

BURKE, J., DE BOCK, G., and DEWULF, O., 1958. 'La drépanocytémie simple et l'anémie drépanocytaire au Kwango (Congo belge)', *Mém. Acad. r. Sci. colon. Cl. Sc. nat. méd.* 8°, **7**, 1–128.

CAPPIERI, M., 1950. 'Population trends among primitive and isolated racial groups and the Bantu', *Proc. XIV Int. Congr. Sociol.* **4**, 1–18.

CECCALDI, J., TRINQUIER, G., and VARGUES, R., 1946. *Bull. Soc. Path. exot.* **39**, 424–428.

CHARLTON, R. W. and BOTHWELL, T. H., 1959. 'The incidence of glutathione instability of the red blood cells in South African Bantu', *S. Afr. J. med. Sci.* **24**, 88–89.

—— —— 1961. 'Primaquine-sensitivity of red cells in various races in Southern Africa', *Br. med. J.* **1**, 941.

CHARNOCK, J. S., CASELY-SMITH, J., and SCHARTZ, C. J., 1959. 'Serum magnesium-cholesterol relationships in the Central Australian Aborigine and in Europeans with and without ischaemic heart disease', *Aust. J. exp. Biol. med. Sci.* **37**, 509–516.

CLEVE, H. and BEARN, A. G., 1962. 'The group specific component of serum: genetic and chemical considerations', *Progress in Medical Genetics* (ed. A. G. STEINBERG), Vol. II, Ch. III. Grune and Stratton, New York.

COLE, D. T., 1963. 'Bushman languages', *Encyclopaedia Britannica*. London and Chicago, William Benton.

CUMMINS, H., 1955. 'Dermatoglyphs of Bushmen (South Africa)', *Am. J. phys. Anthrop.* **13**, 699–710.

CZEKANOWSKI, J., 1922. 'Wissenschaftliche Ergebnisse der deutschen Zentral-Afrika-Expedition 1907–1908', Bd. I. *Ethnographie-Anthropologie, IV Anthropologische Beobachtungen*. Leipzig.

DANKMEIJER, J., 1934. 'De beteekenis van vingerafdrukken voor het anthropologisch onderzoek.' Dissertation, University of Utrecht. Bosch & Zoon, Utrecht (quoted by DANKMEIJER, 1947).

—— 1947. 'Fingerprints of African pygmies and negroes', *Am. J. phys. Anthrop.* **5**, 453.

DART, R. A., 1937. 'The physical characters of the /?Auni- ≠ Khomani Bushmen', *Bantu Studies*, Sept. 1937, 176–295.

DAVID, J. SANTOS, 1949. *Companhia de Diamantes de Angola, Publicaçoes Culturais*, No. 3, 55–71 (quoted by MOURANT *et al.*, 1958).

—— 1960. *Subsidios para o estudo da Antropologia na Lunda: A drepanocitémia e a Antropologia.* Companhia de Diamantes de Angola, Lisbon.

—— PIRES, F. M., and TRINCAO, C., 1962. 'Abnormal haemoglobins in the district of Lunda and the neighbouring district of Songo, Angola', *Man* 48, 37.

DAVIES, J. N. P., 1949. 'Sex hormone upset in Africans', *Br. med. J.* 2, 676–679.

DELBROUCK, J., 1958. 'Contribution à la génétique de la sicklémie: maintien de la fréquence élevée de la sicklémie, au Congo belge', *Annls Soc. belge Méd. trop.* 38, 103–134.

DE MEILLON, B., 1951. *Bull. Wld Hlth Org.* 4, 419 (quoted by BRONTE-STEWART *et al.*, 1960).

DOS SANTOS, JR., J. N., 1949. 'Impressões dermopapillares de indigenas de Moçambique—I—Sobre os desenhos das cristas das polpas dos dedos das mãos', *Trabhs Soc. port. Antrop. Etnol.* fasc. 3–4, 12, 209–256.

—— 1950. 'Impressões dermopapillares de indigenas de Moçambique—II—Novos elementos para o estudo dos desenhos das cristas digitais das mãos', *Junta Invest. colon., Lisb.* 5, 1–97.

DOS SANTOS, J. R., 1934. First Congr. Antrop. colon, Porto. Abstract in *Bull. clin. statist.*,s. ii, 7 (3 suppl.), 111.

—— 1937. *Trabhs Soc. port. Antrop. Etnol.* 8, 213 (quoted by MOURANT *et al.*, 1958).

ELSDON-DEW, R., 1936. 'The bloodgroups of the Bantu of South Africa', *Publs S. Afr. Inst. med. Res.* 7, 221–300.

—— 1939. 'Bloodgroups in Africa', *Publs S. Afr. Inst. med. Res.* 9, 29–94.

ENGLISH, R. B., 1945. 'Sicklaemia occurring in Africans in Northern Rhodesia', *S. Afr. med. J.* 19, 431.

ESRACHOWITZ, S. R., FRIEDLANDER, S., RAGLOFF, G., and SAUNDERS, S., 1952. 'The sickle-cell trait in Cape Coloured persons', *S. Afr. med. J.* 26, 239.

FLEISCHHACKER, H., 1934. 'Untersuchungen über das Hautleistensystem der Hottentotten-Palma', *Anthrop. Anz.* 11, 111.

FOY, H., KONDI, A., REBELLO, A., and MARTINS, F., 1952. 'The distribution of sickle-cell trait and the incidence of sickle-cell anaemia in the negro tribes of Portuguese East Africa', *E. Afr. med. J.* 29, 247.

—— —— TIMMS, G. L., BRASS, W., and BUSHRA, F., 1954. 'The variability of sickle-cell rates in the tribes of Kenya and the Southern Sudan', *Br. med. J.* 1, 294.

—— BRASS, W., MOORE, R. A., TIMMS, G. L., KONDI, A., and OLUOCH, T., 1955. 'Two surveys to investigate the relation of sickle-cell trait and malaria', *Br. med. J.* 2, 1116.

GALLOWAY, A., 1937. 'A contribution to the physical anthropology of the Ovambo', *S. Afr. J. Sci.* 34, 351–364.

GEIPEL, G., 1948. 'Die palmaren Hautleisten: Hinweise auf die Rassen-einordnung der afrikanischer Bambutiden', *see* GUSINDE, 1948, p. 399.

GELFAND, M., 1946. Personal communication to BEET, 1946.
GESSAIN, M., 1957. 'Les dermatoglyphes digitaux des noirs d'Afrique', *L'anthropologie, Paris* **61**, 239–267.
GIBLETT, E. R. and CHASE, J., 1959. 'Js^a, a "new" red cell antigen found in Negroes: evidence for an eleventh blood group system', *Br. J. Haemat.* **5**, 319–326.
—— and ZOUTENDYK, A., 1960. 'Haptoglobin and transferrin types of the Xhosa and Msutu tribes of South Africa' (quoted by SUTTON *et al.*, 1960, as in press).
GILLMAN, J. and GILLMAN, T., 1951. *Perspectives in Human Malnutrition.* Grune and Stratton, New York.
GORDON, H., ROBERTSON, M., BLAIR, J. M., and VOOIJS, M., 1964. 'Genetic markers in liver disease', *S. Afr. med. J.* **38**, 734.
GRIFFITHS, S. B., 1952. 'Sickle-cell trait in Africans', *Br. med. J.* **2**, 441.
—— 1953. 'Absence of the sickle-cell trait in the Bushmen of South-West Africa', *Nature, Lond.* **171**, 577.
—— 1954. 'The distribution of the sickle-cell trait in Africa', *S. Afr. J. med. Sci.* **19**, 56.
GROBBELAAR, C. S., 1955. 'The distribution of the blood groups of the Koranas', *S. Afr. J. Sci.* **51**, 323.
—— 1956. 'The physical characteristics of the Korana', *S. Afr. J. Sci.*, Spec. Publ. No. 1, **53**(4), 99–143.
GUSINDE, M., 1936. 'Erforschung der Bambuti-Pygmäen und ihrer Blutgruppen', *Z. Rassenphysiol.* **8**, 12–20.
—— 1948. *Urwaldmenschen am Ituri.* Springer-Verlag, Vienna.
—— 1949. *Die Twa-Pygmäen in Ruanda.* Missionsdruckerei St. Gabriel, Wien-Mödling.
HEINZ, H. J., 1961a. 'Factors governing the survival of Bushman worm parasites in the Kalahari', *S. Afr. J. Sci.* **57**, 207–213.
—— 1961b. 'The parasitology of the Bushmen, as seen in a restricted area of the Kalahari'. Unpublished.
HENNINGSEN, K., 1950. 'Étude d'ensemble du facteur sanguin P', *Révue Hémat.* **5**, 276–285.
HEUSE, G. A., 1957. 'La drepanocytose: état actuel de la recherche anthropologique et observations sur la biologie des noirs sicklémiques', *Bull. Soc. Anthrop.* **8**, 17.
HIERNAUX, J., 1953. 'Les caractères physiques des Bashi', *Mém. Inst. r. colon. belge Sect. Sci. nat. méd.* 4°, **23**, 5–47.
—— 1954. 'Les caractères physiques des populations du Ruanda et de l'Urundi', *Mém. Inst. r. Sci. nat. Belge.* 2ème serie, **52**, 3–111.
—— 1955a. 'L'intérêt anthropologique du taux de sicklémie.' Communication to the 5th Int. Congr. on Blood Transfusion, Paris 1954.
—— 1955b. 'Physical anthropology and the frequency of genes with a selective value: the sickle-cell gene', *Am. J. phys. Anthrop.* **13**, 455–472.
—— 1956. 'Analyse de la variation des caractères physiques humains en une région de l'Afrique centrale: Ruanda-Urundi et Kivu', *Annls Mus. r. Congo belge, Sér.* 8°, Sciences de l'homme **3**, 7–131.
—— 1962. 'Données génétiques sur six populations de la République du Congo (groupes sanguins ABO et Rh, et taux de sicklémie)', *Annls Soc. belge Méd. trop.* **2**, 145–174.
—— 1963. 'Sur la relation entre la sicklémie et les groupes sanguins Rh au Congo', *Annls Soc. belge Méd. trop.* **6**, 879–882.

HIERNAUX, J., 1964. 'Les dermatoglyphes digitaux des Tutsi du Rwanda et des Shi du Congo', *Bull. Soc. Anthrop., Paris* **6**, XIᵉ serie, 369–385.

—— and VAN DER BORGHT, H., 1953. 'La fréquence du Daltonisme chez les Batutsi et Bahutu du Ruanda-Urundi', *Annls Soc. belge Méd. trop.* **33**, 43–46.

HIRSCHFELD, J., 1962. 'The Gc system', *Progr. Allerg.* **6**. Karger, Basel.

—— and SONNET, J., 1961. 'Distribution of group-specific components (Gc) in the sera of native Africans', *Nature, Lond.* **192**, 766.

HIRZFELD, L. and HIRZFELD, H., 1919. *Lancet* **2**, 675–679.

HUBINONT, P. O., HIERNAUX, J., and MASSART-GUIOT, Th., 1953. 'Fréquence des gènes conditionnant l'apparition des groupes sanguins ABO, MN et CDE-cde (Rh) parmi les indigènes Batutsi du Ruanda-Urundi', *C. r. Séanc. Soc. Biol.* **146**, 334.

—— —— —— 1953. 'Blood groups of the ABO, MN and CDE-cde systems in the native populations of Ruanda-Urundi territories', *Ann. Eugen.* **18**, 13–21.

JACOB, G. F., 1957. 'A study of the survival rate of cases of sickle-cell anaemia', *Br. med. J.* **1**, 738.

JADIN, J., 1935. 'Les groupes sanguins des Pygmées', *Mém. Inst.-colon. belge Sci. nat. méd.* 8°, **4**, 1–26, in reprint.

—— 1940. 'Les groupes sanguins des Pygmoïdes et des Nègres de la Province Equatoriale (Congo Belge)', *Mém. Inst. r. colon. belge Sci. nat. méd.* 8°, **10**, 1–42, in reprint.

—— 1963. 'Les groupes sanguins et la répartition de la sicklémie dans les populations congolaises', *Annls Soc. belge Méd. trop.* **4**, 437–484.

—— and BRUYNOGHE, G., 1952. *Bull. Inst. r. colon. belge* **23**, 1116–1124 (quoted by MOURANT *et al.*, 1958).

JENKINS, T., 1963. 'Sickle-cell anaemia in Wankie, Southern Rhodesia', *C. Afr. J. Med.* **9**, 307.

—— 1965. 'The ability to taste phenyl thiocarbamide among Kalahari Bushmen and Southern Bantu'. To be published.

JULIEN, P., 1935. 'Bloedgroepenonderzoek der Efe-Pygmeën en de omwonende Negerstammen.' *Mém. Inst. r. colon. belge Sci. nat. méd.* 8°, **4**, 1–33, in reprint.

KAMINER, B., and LUTZ, W. P. W., 1960. 'Blood pressure in Bushmen of the Kalahari desert', *Circulation*, **22**, 289–295.

LAING, J., 1955. 'The arcadal index', *J. dent. Ass. S. Afr.* **10**, 376–378.

LAMBILLON, J. and DENISOFF, N., 1940. 'Etude de l'organisation d'un service de transfusions sanguines dans un centre hospitalier d'Afrique', *Annls Soc. belge Méd. trop.* **20**, 279.

LAMBOTTE-LEGRAND, J. and LAMBOTTE-LEGRAND, C., 1950. 'Repartition des groupes sanguins des types A, B, O et Rh chez les indigènes du Bas-Congo', *Annls Soc. belge Méd. trop.* **30**, 547–552.

—— —— 1951. 'L'anémie à hématies falciformes chez l'enfant indigène du Bas-Congo', *Mém. Inst. r. colon. belge Sci. nat. méd.* 8°, **19**, 1–93 (quoted by HIERNAUX, 1962).

LEBZELTER, V., 1931. 'Zur Anthropologie der Kung-Buschleute', *Anz. Akad. Wiss. Wien*, M-N, Kl. **68**, 24–26.

LEHMANN, H., 1954. 'Distribution of the sickle-cell gene. A new light on the origin of the East Africans', *Eugen. Rev.* **46**, 1–23.

—— and MACKEY, J., 1955. *Man* **55**, 186.

—— and RAPER, A. B., 1949. 'Distribution of the sickle-cell trait in Uganda, and its ethnological significance', *Nature, Lond.* **164**, 494.

LEHMANN H. and RAPER, A. B., 1956. 'Maintenance of high sickling rate in an African community', *Br. med. J.* **1**, 333.

LEJEUNE, 1952. 'Premiers résultats d'une enquête sur la fréquence du "sickle-cell trait", chez les nourrissons des consultations du Cercle de Feshi', *Rapport FOREAMI*, 102–106 (quoted by HIERNAUX, 1962).

LESCHI, J., 1950. 'Empreintes digitales et races: essai de synthèse', *L'anthropologie, Paris* **54**, 35–66.

LESSA, A., 1953. *Prim. Colóquio hemat. Afric.*, Lisboa, 43–54 (quoted by MOURANT *et al.*, 1958).

LIODT, V. and POJARSKI, N., 1929. *C. r. Séanc. Soc. Biol.* **101**, 889–890 (quoted by MOURANT *et al.*, 1958).

MACKEY, J., 1949. Correspondence, *E. Afr. med. J.* **26**, 172.

MARRET, J. R. de la H., 1936. *Race, Sex and Environment*. Hutchinson, London.

MAYOR, L., 1954. *Bull. Clin. statist.* s. ii, **7** (3 suppl), 126–127 (quoted by MOURANT *et al.*, 1958).

MILETTO, 1951. 'Notes sue les ethnies de la région du Haut-Ogooué', *Bull. Inst. Etud. cent. afr.* N.S., No. 2, 19–48 (quoted by JADIN, 1963).

MOORE, R. A., BRASS, W., and FOY, H., 1954. 'Sickling and malaria', *Br. med. J.* **2**, 630.

MOTULSKY, A. G., 1960. 'Metabolic polymorphisms and the role of infectious diseases in human evolution', *Hum. Biol.* **32**, 28.

—— Unpublished data. Quoted by MOTULSKY and CAMPBELL-KRAUT, 1961.

—— and CAMPBELL-KRAUT, J. M., 1961. 'Population genetics of glucose-6-phosphate dehydrogenase deficiency of the red cell', *Genetic Polymorphisms and Geographic Variations in Disease* (ed. B. BLUMBERG). Grune and Stratton, New York.

—— DHERTE, and NINANE. Unpublished data. Quoted by MOTULSKY and CAMPBELL-KRAUT, 1961.

—— and GIBLETT, E. R., 1960. 'Some genetically-determined characteristics of Belgian Congo natives' (quoted by SUTTON *et al.*, 1960).

—— and VANDEPITTE, J. Unpublished data. Quoted by MOTULSKY and CAMPBELL-KRAUT, 1961.

VANDEPITTE, J. and MOTULSKY, A. G. Unpublished data. Quoted by MOTULSKY AND CAMPBELL-KRAUT, 1961.

MOURANT, A. E., 1954. *The Distribution of Human Blood Groups*. Blackwells, Oxford.

—— 1961. 'Evolution, Genetics and Anthropology'. The Huxley Memorial Lecture. *J. R. anth. Inst.* **91** (2), 151–165.

—— 1962. 'The use in anthropology of blood groups and other genetical characters', *J. Afr. Hist.* **3** (2), 291–296.

—— KOPEC, A. C., and DOMANIEWSKA-SOBCZACK, K., 1958. *The ABO Blood Groups—Comprehensive Tables and Maps of World Distribution*. Blackwells, Oxford.

MUTRUX-BORNOZ, H., 1937. *Les Troublantes Révélations de l'Empreinte digitale et Palmaire*. Roth et Cie., Lausanne. (Quoted by DANKMEIJER, 1947.)

NEEL, J. V., 1956. 'The genetics of human haemoglobin differences: problems and perspectives', *Ann. hum. Genet.* **21**, 1–30.

—— HIERNAUX, J., LINHARD, J., ROBINSON, A., ZUELZER, W. W., and LIVINGSTONE, F., 1956. 'Data on the occurrence of haemoglobin C and other abnormal haemoglobins in some African populations', *Am. J. hum. Genet.* **8**, 138.

ORFORD, M. and WELLS, L. H., 1937. 'An anthropometric study of a series of South African Bantu females', *S. Afr. J. Sci.* **33**, 1010–1036.

OSCHINSKY, L., 1954. *The Racial Affinities of the Baganda and other Bantu Tribes of British East Africa.* Heffer, Cambridge.

PIJPER, J., 1930. 'The blood groups of the Bantu', *Trans. r. Soc. S. Afr.* **18**, 310–315.

—— 1932. 'Blood groups of Bushmen', *S. Afr. med. J.* **6**, 35–37.

—— 1935. 'Blood groups in Hottentots', *S. Afr. med. J.* **9**, 192–194.

PIRIE, J. H., 1921. *Med. J. S. Afr.* **16**, 109–112 (quoted by MOURANT et al., 1958).

POST, R. H., 1962. 'Population differences in red and green color vision deficiency: a review, and a query on selection relaxation', *Eugen. Q.* **9**, 131–146.

REBELLO, A., 1955. Quoted by A. LESSA in *A individualidade biológica do sangue.* Porto, Dr. thesis (quoted by MOURANT et al., 1958).

RESSELER, J. J. C., 1962. *Considérations sur les groupes sanguins et l'immunisation groupale au Congo.* Thèse d'agréation. Université Catholique de Louvain. Ed. Arscia., Bruxelles (quoted by JADIN, 1963).

—— and LEGROS, A., 1957. 'Groupes sanguins Rhésus dans la population noire de Bukavu', *Annls Soc. belge. Méd. trop.* **37**, 285.

RIFE, D. C., 1953. 'Fingerprints as criteria of ethnic relationship', *Am. J. hum. Genet.* **5**, 389–399.

—— 1956a. 'Associations between weight discrimination and hand prints', *Eugen. Q.* **3**, 213–218.

—— 1956b. Personal communication to MOURANT et al., 1958.

ROBERTS, D. F., 1956. 'The distribution of some human serological characters in Africa', *Adv. Sci.* **51**, 194–196.

—— and LEHMANN, H., 1955. 'A search for abnormal haemoglobins in some southern Sudanese people', *Br. med. J.* **1**, 519–521.

RONSE, C. S., 1952. 'Anémies malariennes des enfants et transfusions sanguines avec observations sur les groupes sanguins des Bakongo', *Mèm. r. colon. belge Sci. nat. méd.* 8°, **20**, 63 (quoted by JADIN, 1963).

SARMENTO, A., 1939. 'As figuras papilares digitais nos aborigines de Angola', *Trabhs Soc. port. Anthrop. Etnol* **9**, 113–117.

—— 1940. 'Impressões digitais nos indígenas de Angola', *Africa méd.* **3**, 6 (quoted by GESSAIN, 1957).

—— 1953. *Bull. clin. statist.* **6** (6). Abstract in *Bull. clin. statist.* 1954, s. ii, **7** (3 suppl.), 111 (quoted by MOURANT et al., 1958).

SCHAPERA, I., 1930. *The Khoisan peoples of South Africa.* Routledge and Kegan Paul, London.

SCHULTZE, L., 1928. 'Zur Kenntnis des Körpers der Hottentotten und Bushmänner', *Denkschr. med.-naturw. Ges. Jena* **17**, 145.

SEINER, F., 1912. 'Beobachtungen und Messungen an Buschleuten', *Z. Ethnol.* **44**, 275.

SELIGMAN, C. G., 1957. *Races of Africa*, 2nd ed. Butterworth, London.

SEYMOUR, A. and GELFAND, M., 1960. *C. Afr. J. Med.* **6**, 401.

SHAPIRO, M., 1951a. 'The ABO, MN, P and Rh blood group systems in the South African Bantu: a genetic study', *S. Afr. med. J.* **25**, 165–170.

—— 1951b. 'Further evidence of homogeneity of blood group distribution in the South African Bantu', *S. Afr. med. J.* **25**, 406–411.

SHAPIRO, M., 1952. 'Observations on the Kell-Cellano (K-k) blood group system', S. Afr. med. J. 26, 951–955.
—— 1953. 'Blood groups and skin colour', J. forens. Med. 1, 2–10.
—— 1956. 'Inheritance of the Henshaw (He) blood factor', J. forens. Med. 3, 152–160.
—— and VANDEPITTE, J., 1954. Quoted by VANDEPITTE, 1959.
SILBERBAUER, G. B., 1965. Bushman Survey Report. Bechuanaland Press, Gaberones.
SIMON, K., 1951. 'Colour vision of Buganda Africans', E. Afr. med. J. 28, 75–80.
SINGER, R., 1953. 'The sickle-cell trait in Africa', Am. Anthrop. 55, 634–648.
—— 1961. 'Serum haptoglobins in Africa', S. Afr. med. J. 35, 520–523.
—— and WEINER, J. S., 1963. 'Biological aspects of some indigenous African populations', SWest. J. Anthrop. 19, 168–176.
—— —— and ZOUTENDYK, A., 1961. 'The blood groups of the Hottentots', Proc. 2nd Int. Congr. hum. Genet., Rome.
SNOECK, J. and HUBINONT, P. O., 1949. 'Les groupes sanguins des systèmes ABO, MN et Rh-Hr (CDE-cde) chez les Pygmoïdes de l'Equateur (Congo belge)', Bull. Acad. r. Méd. Belg. 14, 456–465.
SONNET, J. and MICHAUX, J. L., 1960. 'Glucose-6-phosphate dehydrogenase, haptoglobin groups, blood groups and sickle-cell trait in the Bantus of West Belgian Congo', Nature, Lond. 188, 504.
SPERBER, G. H., 1958. 'The palate and dental arcade of the Transvaal Bushmen, the /?Auni-≠Khomani Bushmen and Bantu-speaking Negroes of the Zulu tribe', S. Afr. J. med. Sci. 23, 147–154.
SQUIRES, B. T., 1942. 'Colour vision and colour discrimination amongst the Bechuana', Trans. r. Soc. S. Afr. 29, 29–34.
—— 1953. 'Human salivary amylase secretion in relation to diet', J. Physiol. 119, 153–156.
STIJNS, and DELVILLE, 1952. Annls Soc. belge Méd. trop. 32, 479 (quoted by VANDEPITTE, 1959).
TEIXEIRA, W. G., 1944. 'Hematias falciformes nos indígenas de Angola', An. Inst. Med. trop. 1, 365.
—— 1946. In MAYOR, L. and TEIXEIRA, W. F., 1953. Prim. Coloquio hemat. Afric., Lisboa. p. 55 (quoted by MOURANT et al., 1958).
TOBIAS, P. V., 1955. 'The Taaibosch Koranas of Ottosdal: a contribution to the study of the Old Yellow South Africans', S. Afr. J. Sci. 51, 263–269.
—— 1955–56. 'Les Bochimans Auen et Naron de Ghanzi. Contribution à l'étude des "Anciens jaunes" Sud-Africains', L'anthropologie, Paris 59, 235–252; 59, 429–461; 60, 268–289; 60, 22–52.
—— 1956. 'On the survival of the Bushmen, with an estimate of the problem facing anthropologists', Africa 26, 174–186.
—— 1957. 'Bushmen of the Kalahari', Man 36, 33–40.
—— 1959. 'The Nuffield-Witwatersrand University Expeditions to Kalahari Bushmen, 1958–59', Nature, Lond. 183, 1011–1013.
—— 1961a. 'Studies of Bushmen in the Kalahari', S. Afr. J. Sci. 57, 205–206.
—— 1961b. 'Fingerprints and palmar prints of Kalahari Bushmen', S. Afr. J. Sci. 57, 333–345.
—— 1961c. 'Physique of a desert folk', Nat. Hist. 70, 16–25.

TOBIAS, P. V., 1962. 'On the increasing stature of the Bushmen', *Anthropos* **57**, 801–810.
—— 1964. 'Bushman hunter–gatherers: a study in human ecology', *Ecological studies in Southern Africa* (ed. D. H. S. DAVIS), pp. 67–86. Junk, The Hague.
TOERIEN, M. J., 1958. 'The physical characters of the Lake Chrissie Bushmen', *S. Afr. J. med. Sci.* **23**, 121–124.
TREVOR, J. C., 1947. 'The physical characters of the Sandawe', *J. R. Anthrop. Inst.* **77**, 61–77.
—— 1955. 'Race', *Encyclopaedia Hebraica*.
TROWELL, H. C., RAPER, A. B., and WELLBOURN, A. F., 1957. 'The natural history of homozygous sickle-cell anaemia in Central Africa', *Q. J. Med.* **26**, 401.
VALSIK, J. A., 1938. 'The fingerprints of Central African pygmies, Negroes and their crossbreeds', *Anthropologie, Prague* **16**, 84.
VAN DEN BERGHE, L. and JANSSEN, P., 1950. 'Maladie à sickle cells en Afrique noire', *Annls Soc. belge Méd. trop.* **30**, 1553–1566.
VANDEPITTE, J., 1954. 'Aspects quantitatifs et génétiques de la sicklanémie à Léopoldville', *Annls Soc. belge Méd. trop.* **39**, 501–516.
—— 1959. 'The incidence of haemoglobinoses in the Belgian Congo', *The Abnormal Haemoglobins* (eds. JONXIS and DELAFRESNAYE). Blackwells, Oxford.
VAN REENEN, J. F., 1964. 'Dentition, jaws and palate of Kalahari Bushmen', *J. dent. Ass. S. Afr.* **19**; part 1: 1–15; part 2: 38–44; part 3: 67–80.
VAN ROS, G. and JOURDAIN, R., 1956. *Annls Soc. belge Méd. trop.* **36**, 307–334 (quoted by MOURANT *et al.*, 1958).
—— VAN SANDE, M., and DRUET, R., 1963. 'Groupes d'haptoglobine et de transferrine dans des populations africaines et européennes', *Annls Soc. belge Méd. trop.* **4**, 511–534.
WEINER, J. S. and ZOUTENDYK, A., 1959. 'Blood group investigations on Central Kalahari Bushmen', *Nature, Lond.* **183**, 843.
WELLS, L. H., 1952. 'Physical measurements of Northern Bushmen', *Man* **52**, 53–56.
WENINGER, M., 1936. 'Untersuchungen über das Hautleistensystem der Buschmänner; ein Beitrag zur Stellung der Buschmanrasse', *Mitt. anthrop. Ges. Wien* **66**, 30–46.
—— 1937. 'Fingerabdrücke von zentralafricanischen Batwa-Pygmoïden des Kivu-Gebietes', *Mitt. anthrop. Ges. Wien* **67**, 162–168.
WESTPHAL, E., 1962. 'A re-classification of Southern African Non-Bantu languages', *J. Afr. Languages* **1**, 1–8.
WOHLGEMUTH, 1932. Quoted by STEFFAN and WELLISCH in: *Handbuch der Blutgruppenkunde* (ed. P. STEFFAN), pp. 396–433. München, 1932.
ZAIL, S. S., CHARLTON, R. W., and BOTHWELL, T. H., 1962. 'The haemolytic effect of certain drugs in Bantu subjects with a deficiency of glucose-6-phosphate dehydrogenase', *S. Afr. J. med. Sci.* **27**, 95–99.
ZOUTENDYK, A., 1947. 'Rhesus factor blood types in South African Bantu', *S. Afr. J. med. Sci.* **12**, 167.
—— 1955a. Personal communication to MOURANT (quoted by MOURANT *et al.*, 1958).

ZOUTENDYK, A., 1955*b*. 'The blood groups of South African Natives with particular reference to a recent investigation of the Hottentots'. Paper presented at the Vème Congrès Int. de Transfusion sanguine, Paris 1954, pp. 247–249.
—— KOPEC, A. C., and MOURANT, A. E., 1953. 'Blood groups of Bushmen', *Am. J. phys. Anthrop.* **11**, 361.
—— —— —— 1955. 'Blood groups of Hottentots', *Am. J. phys. Anthrop.* **13**, 391.

7

SOUTHERN AFRICAN ETHNIC ADAPTATION TO TEMPERATURE AND EXERCISE

C. H. WYNDHAM

Director, Human Sciences Laboratory, Transvaal and Orange Free State Chamber of Mines, Johannesburg, South Africa

Introduction

LITTLE is known of the possible differences between various ethnic groups in their physiological reactions to the stresses of heat, cold, and exercise. Caucasians, Bantu, and Bushmen in southern Africa differ greatly in their morphological characteristics. These differences may be expected to influence their reactions to these stresses. On the other hand, the differences in the climates they live in, the differences in their patterns of activity and in their nutrition, and in the use they make of clothing, shelter, and fire, may exert the greater influence and overshadow the differences in their anthropometry. Also genetic factors, other than those which are manifest in morphological differences, may be responsible for the observed differences in physiological reactions. Samples of young male Caucasians, Bantu, and Bushmen in southern Africa were studied in an endeavour to evaluate some of these various influences on their physiological reactions to heat, cold, and exercise. Comparisons are also made with Caucasians and Arabs in the Sahara Desert and Caucasians and Aborigines in the hot, humid tropics of Australia.

Anthropometry

In Table 1 are given the mean heights, weights, and surface areas (calculated with the Du Bois equation) of the various ethnic groups studied, together with the standard deviations of the means. Also given are the calculated ratios of surface area to weight and the mean skinfold thicknesses (averages of seven measurements).

Certain striking differences in the morphology of these peoples can be observed in this table. Caucasians are tall and heavy with relatively large skinfold thicknesses. At the other extreme are the desert Bushmen, who are short, light, and slender with very small skinfold thicknesses. The Bantu are intermediate between the Caucasians and the Bushmen in these characteristics. The differences in weight of these three ethnic groups are proportionately greater than the height differences and in consequence there are also great differences between these groups in the surface area to weight ratios. In considering these ratios it should be borne in mind that a low ratio favours heat conservation, whereas a high ratio is the design used by heating engineers to promote heat transfer from a body to the atmosphere by convection and evaporation. The Caucasians have a low ratio, the Bushmen a high ratio, and the Bantu an intermediate ratio. Certain of the other ethnic groups studied differ greatly in these particular morphological characteristics from those of these ethnic groups. The 'river' Bushmen are relatively tall for their weights, being as tall as the Caucasians, and they have high ratios and very small skinfold thicknesses. The Australian Aborigines show these characteristics to an even greater extent, being as tall as the Caucasians but weighing much less. They have, therefore, a very high surface area to weight ratio. The Chaamba, an Arab tribe at Hassi-Messoaud in the Sahara Desert, are also light and slender, but are not as tall; they also have a high surface area to weight ratio. The skinfold thicknesses of both the Chaamba and the Aborigines are greater than those of the Bushmen and the Bantu in South Africa.

Environments

In Fig. 1 is plotted the mean daily maximum air temperature in southern Africa for the midsummer month of January. This is between 30 and 32·5°C in the Kalahari Desert and between 27·5 and 30°C in Johannesburg. The mean daily minimum air temperatures for January in these two areas are 18·0 and 14·5°C respectively (Fig. 2). For comparison the mean maximum temperature for the midsummer month of July in the Sahara Desert is 35–37·5°C and the mean minimum temperature is 26°C. It is not only in the air temperature that heat stress exists. In the Sahara Desert the direct and reflected solar radiation from the

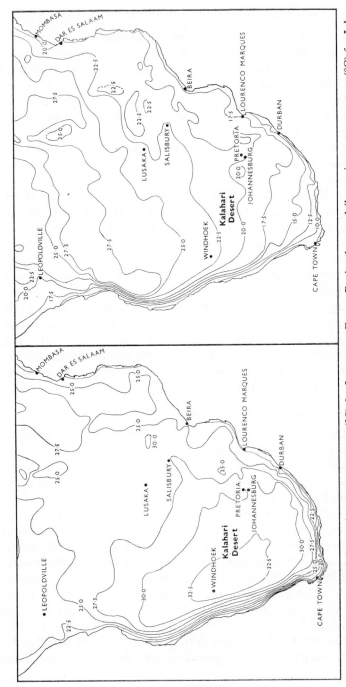

FIG. 1. Regional mean daily maximum temperature (°C) for January.　　FIG. 2. Regional mean daily maximum temperature (°C) for July.

bare sand is great; in the Kalahari Desert, the soil is covered by grass and other vegetation and this ameliorates considerably the effect of long range radiation. For example, a 6-inch blackened globe in direct sunlight rises to a temperature of 60°C in the Sahara Desert; in the Kalahari Desert it records just over 50°C. In these areas the relative humidity is not high and does not add to the heat stress.

In winter the Sahara Desert is much cooler than the other two regions. The mean maximum and minimum air temperatures for January in the Sahara Desert are 10–12·5°C and 4°C respectively. In the Kalahari Desert (Fig. 2) comparable figures are 20–22·5°C and 3·0–3·5°C respectively and in Johannesburg they are 20° and 4·0°C respectively. The mean annual rainfall is less than 100 mm in the Sahara Desert; between 400 and 600 mm in the Kalahari Desert and 600 mm in Johannesburg. These climatic data were obtained from the *Climatological Atlas of Africa* (Jackson, 1961).

The degree of heat stress experienced by Bushmen in the Kalahari Desert in summer is therefore nowhere nearly as great as that which the Arabs are exposed to. The cold in winter is sharp and water freezes at night on some nights, but the winters are relatively short. The Caucasian and Bantu samples in Johannesburg live in a climate that is relatively temperate.

Patterns of activity and nutrition

The three ethnic groups are very different in their levels of activity and in their nutrition. The Bushmen are still nomadic hunters and live a life which is probably close to that of our Stone Age ancestors. Both the male and the female lead active physical lives. The male tracks the game which he shoots with a bow and poisoned arrows. The female spends her days collecting berries, roots, and water. Trudging through the sands of the desert is energy consuming, even for these light-weight, little people. The staple diet consists of roots, bulbs, and berries. Occasionally there is a kill, and in consequence there is a surfeit of protein in the camp for a few days. Fat is almost non-existent in the Bushmen diet. Salt, too, is a prized luxury. The ravages of infant malnutrition are not seen in the Bushmen. The mothers suckle their infants for three years, during which time they are taboo for their menfolk. This wise provision sees the infant through the

'Kwasiorkor' period of its life. Quantitative studies of Bushmen diets have not been carried out as far as I am aware.

The Bantu studied were all recruits to the gold mines. They do not work hard in their homelands as they lead an essentially pastoral life; the soil, which is cultivated, is tilled by the women with primitive hoes. The Bantu men walk long distances when herding their cattle, to visit their neighbours (they are a convivial people) and to make their purchases at the trading stores. The exercise they take is intermittent. The staple diet of the Bantu in southern Africa is the mealie, and consequently the animal protein and fat content of the diet is low. In the mines the metabolic and nutritional patterns of these men change radically. They work a regular 8-hour shift for 6 days a week and, being the manual workers, they expend energy at a moderate rate. They are presented with a more than adequate diet, which comprises 4000 cal/day/man; this diet contains 120 g of protein, of which 60 g are from animal or fish sources. The actual intake of calories of the 'average' mine labourer has been assessed and is about 3200 cal/day (Fleming, 1961). As a result of the change in diet and in work on the mine the Bantu, on an average, gains about 7·7 lb in weight over a 4-month period. The major proportion of this gain is in the first month and is associated with an increase in the measured maximum oxygen intakes from 2·7 to 3·0 l./min (Wyndham et al., 1963).

Three groups of Caucasians were studied. The group exposed to heat was male medical students in the second year of study and they were mainly of British and Jewish origin. The cold tolerance studies were made on learner officials at a mine training school. They were recent matriculants, between 17 and 19 years old, and were of Afrikaans and British origin. The group subjected to exercise studies were young recruits to the Air Force Gymnasium and were similar in age and origin to the last group. Most of the men in these three groups stated that they took some form of sport, but it was only the recruits from the Air Force Gymnasium who were subjected to a regular, daily routine of physical exercise. It is unlikely that these men were as physically active as the Bushmen, but their physical efforts probably compare with those of the Bantu. The diets of the Caucasians are typical of the more affluent sections of Western countries, being high in protein and fat. This was reflected in their skinfold thicknesses, which were significantly greater than those of both the Bushmen and the Bantu.

Shelter

These three ethnic groups—Bushmen, Bantu, and Caucasians—differed greatly in the cultural adaptations they have made to protect themselves against heat and cold. This is seen in the manner in which they use clothing, shelter, and fire, and also in the way in which they modify their physical activities.

The Bushman in the Kalahari Desert kills game with a slow poison, and when he is on the hunt he has to follow the game which he has shot, even when the sun is at its fiercest. I had the personal experience of trying to keep up with Bushmen while they were tracking down an antelope at midday in midsummer. I had to give up from thirst and exhaustion with my clothes wet with sweat. The Bushmen, being lighter, had a greater advantage in that their energy expenditure, while trudging through sand, was much less than mine. They are also unencumbered with clothing, as they wear only a narrow genital covering of skin, and therefore heat losses by convection and evaporation are not interfered with as they are in the Caucasian. The Bushman's sweat losses are probably high, because, as will be demonstrated later, he sweats at a relatively high rate under the standard heat stress condition and he may in a long hunt on a hot day approach dangerous levels of dehydration. Under similar climatic conditions sweat losses of 4 to 5 litres were recorded on young Caucasians on a 18-mile route march (Strydom and Wyndham, 1964). The Bushman's family, on the other hand, are commonly seen at rest in the shade of trees in the midday heat.

The Bantu in his home territory makes two obvious concessions to the heat of summer. He rises early and gets most of his physical work done before the heat of the day. Unlike the Bushmen the Bantu adjusts his activities to the air temperature. The sight of a Bantu sprawled asleep, 'lazing in the noonday sun', is very common and leads the more dynamic Caucasian to draw unfavourable conclusions about the Bantu's work habits, little realizing that a decrease in activity is a normal and favourable reaction to heat. The other adjustment the Bantu makes to heat in his homeland is to wear a minimum of clothing, usually only a leather genital cover. As the Bantu becomes absorbed into Western culture, however, so he adopts 'European' clothing, often to his discomfort in hot weather. The Caucasian is generally affluent enough to protect himself against the worst of the heat by the design and construction of his buildings and the air-conditioning of them.

During the winter in the Kalahari Desert, the minimum temperatures during the night are only a few degrees above freezing point and water often freezes at night. Cold south winds add to the chill of the night. The Bushman has made a much better cultural adaptation to cold than the Australian aboriginal. In the early part of the evenings the Bushman sits around the fire huddled in his skin cloak. An interesting sociological division occurs in the tribe when they retire to sleep. The suckling mothers and their small children all retire around one fire. The mothers lie around the fire with their feet towards it and the children creep up under the skin cloaks to cuddle next to their mothers' warm bodies. The young unmarried men and the husbands (whose wives are taboo) sit around other fires, away from the suckling mothers and the family groups. When they retire they also lie with their feet to the fire and have their skin cloaks tucked in around their bodies and over their heads. Families in which the mother is not suckling form small independent groups away from the others and all the members seem to huddle together, sharing the cloaks and the warmth of their bodies. The Bushmen appear to use their feet as primitive thermostats. When the fires die down on the colder nights they wake up and stoke the fires. The innumerable hunting dogs sleep indiscriminately wherever they can lodge themselves between the Bushmen. They make efforts to creep under the cloaks and the nights are punctuated with yelps as the Bushmen angrily dislodge them. By the skilful use of fire and a skin cloak the Bushman creates a micro-climate around his body which is close to the thermoneutral temperature of about 25°C (Wyndham and Morrison, 1958). The Bushmen do not use their impermanent huts of grass and boughs to sleep in. The huts appear to act mainly as a windbreak or they build a 2- to 3-foot high windbreak of grass and boughs in the form of a half circle for this purpose. The pre-dawn winds herald the coldest period of the night and the windbreaks temper the icy blasts and make them bearable.

The Bantu protects himself much more adequately against the cold with clothing, shelter, and fire. He has permanent shelters and, generally, burns a fire throughout the night in the colder period. Most Bantu adults have some form of winter clothing for their protection during the day, but it is still common to see nearly naked children frolicking about in the warming rays of the sun even in midwinter. The degree of cold that the Bantu is exposed to is probably less than that of the Bushmen, but is certainly greater than that of the Caucasian. The Caucasians in Johannesburg are exposed to air temperatures which are as cold as those in the Kalahari desert and the chill of the south winds is greater. The Caucasian, however, has warm clothing, adequate shelter and can generally afford to warm the air within his shelter. His exposure to cold is short and intermittent and occurs in journeying from one heated building to another.

Reactions to exercise

In recent years a reliable method has been developed for assessing an individual's capacity for physical effort of an endurance nature. This consists of measuring the individual's maximum rate of oxygen consumption, or as the Astrands refer to it, the maximum aerobic capacity (Astrand, 1952; Taylor *et al.*, 1955; Wyndham *et al.*, 1959). The maximum oxygen intakes of samples of young males of Caucasian, Bantu, and Bushmen origin were determined by means of a simple, quick, and reliable test introduced by the Human Sciences Laboratory (Maritz *et al.*, 1961). It consists of making measurements of heart rates and oxygen consumptions of the subjects at four different rates of stepping on and off a stool, one foot high. The heart rates are plotted against oxygen consumption for each individual and a straight line is fitted to the plotted points. The straight line is extrapolated to the maximum heart rate predetermined for each ethnic group. This is 180 beats/min for the Bantu and Bushmen and 185 beats/min for the Caucasians (Wyndham *et al.*, 1959 and Maritz *et al.*, 1961). The oxygen consumption corresponding to the maximum heart rate is read off the graph and is taken to be the individual's maximum oxygen intake. Recent comparisons in this laboratory of the assessments of maximum oxygen intakes of relatively large samples of 20 to 40 men have demonstrated that assessment by means of the step-test procedure is reliable, compared with the measurements on a treadmill and on a bicycle ergometer (Wyndham *et al.*, 1964).

A measure of the gross mechanical efficiency of the individual is obtained from the straight line fitted to measurements of oxygen consumption plotted against the four work rates. Regression lines, based on the lines fitted to each individual's data, can be drawn for each of the different populations, and suitable confidence limits can be fitted for comparison of the gross mechanical efficiencies of different ethnic groups.

In Table 2 are given the mean maximum oxygen intakes, the mean body weights, the mean maximum oxygen intakes per kilogram of body weight, and the standard deviations about the means (Wyndham et al., 1963). In the table are also given the available data on other ethnic groups in various parts of the world. Where the information is given in the original papers, 95 per cent confidence limits have been calculated so that it can be seen at a glance whether the means of the different samples are significantly different. For the convenience of making comparisons of the different ethnic groups, the data have been sorted into those pertaining to very fit young men, to young men who are physically active, and to those who take only intermittent exercise.

The first point to make from this table is that in spite of the very great differences in the morphological characteristics of the Caucasians, Bantu, and Bushmen, the mean maximum oxygen intakes per kilogram of body weight are very closely similar, i.e. about 48 ml/kg/min. This conclusion applies to men who were physically active at the time of the study. These findings compare well with those reported by Robinson et al. in 1941 on Negro and Caucasian share-croppers in the southern states of the U.S.A.; with the data of Taylor et al. in 1955 on young U.S. Army recruits; and with Lange Andersen's results on Arctic Indians.

The maximum oxygen intake figures for young active adults are considerably lower than those reported on international class athletes, which is 68 ml/min/kg (Lange Andersen, 1960) and those of very fit young Swedish gymnasts, which is 58 ml/min/kg (Astrand, 1952). They are, however, higher than the values on sedentary and less active men. Our own values are between 39 and 44 ml/min/kg and compare well with Lange Andersen's values of 44 ml/min/kg. From these results it would appear that the difference between sedentary and very fit men in maximum oxygen intake per kilogram is about 40 per cent and between moderately active and very fit men it is about 20 per cent.

It is a great surprise to us that the values for the Bushmen were no better than those for moderately active men of other ethnic groups although it must be conceded that the sample was small. Legend has it that they can perform prodigious feats of endurance, such as running while tracking the game they have shot with poisoned arrows, and they are said to be able to run a horse to a stand-still. On these results we do not find them to be better endowed physiologically for endurance exercise than the average man of other ethnic groups. Their legendary abilities in this regard may stem, therefore, from the fact that they are well trained for endurance running by the nomadic hunting existence they lead, rather than that they are physiologically superior. Their state of physical fitness for endurance effort is undoubtedly affected by the amount of hunting they do.

A second study was made on twelve Bushmen at the Motokwe water hole in 1962 during a period of prolonged drought. The Bushmen at Motokwe were part of a group that had been forced by a lack of water to temporarily abandon their traditional ways of living and take service with Bantu of the Bakaladhi tribe at the

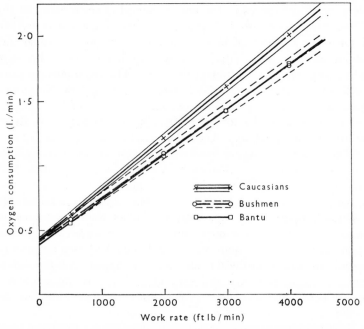

FIG. 3. Oxygen consumption versus work rate, with 83 per cent confidence limits (Caucasians and Bushmen) and with the Bantu means superimposed.

water-hole in return for food and water. They appeared to one of the experienced observers from this laboratory, who had been on previous expeditions to the Kalahari Desert, to be in poor physical shape. This was borne out in the determinations of their maximum oxygen intakes, which gave an average of 42·8 ml/min/kg.

The mechanical efficiency of the three ethnic groups in the task of stepping on and off a 1 ft-high stool has been compared at various rates. Straight lines were fitted to the oxygen consumptions plotted against work rates and 83 per cent confidence limits were fitted (Fig. 3). Where the limits do not overlap, it can be stated with confidence at the 5 per cent level that they are significantly different. It is clear that both Bantu and Bushmen are more mechanically efficient than the Caucasians, i.e they require less oxygen per unit rate of work. The mechanical efficiencies of the Bantu and Bushmen are almost identical. One must point out, however, that, although the Caucasian is less mechanically efficient than the Bantu and the Bushmen, the differences are in fact quite small.

Reactions to heat

There are a few studies in the literature on the physiological reactions to heat of men of Caucasian and African origin in different parts of the world. Unfortunately no two research teams used the same conditions of heat and work in their studies. The result is that, while there are qualitative similarities in certain of the reactions of these two different ethnic groups to heat stress, it is quite impossible to say whether the quantitative differences observed in the different studies are due to variations in the states of acclimatization of the various samples, or whether they are due to the differences in the degree of heat stress imposed.

It is most important to place any studies of the heat reactions of different ethnic groups in various parts of the world upon an exact quantitative basis. With this object in view the Human Sciences Laboratory decided to use *one* standard condition of heat and work stress for all its comparisons of the heat reactions of different ethnic groups. Furthermore, in order to express quantitatively the degree of acclimatization of the particular ethnic group under study it is important that their reactions should be compared with those of both unacclimatized and highly acclimatized men. The reactions of the last two groups to a 'standard' heat stress could be used as a frame of reference against which the state of acclimatization, or heat tolerance, of the ethnic group under study, could be judged. Appropriate techniques of variance analysis were used to test statistically whether the reactions of the sample studied were significantly different from those of either the unacclimatized or the highly acclimatized 'control' groups.

The degree of heat and work stress selected was a combination which unacclimatized men would find difficult, but which acclimatized men would endure with ease. The rate of work chosen was 1560 ft lb/min. This was obtained by having the men step on and off a stool at 12 steps/min. The height of the stool was adjusted to the body weights of the men to give the required rate of work. The oxygen consumption for this rate of work is just under 1·0 l./min. This is moderate work, with a heat production of approximately 300 cal/h. The air condition used was 93°F dry-bulb (D.B.) temperature and 90°F wet-bulb (W.B.) temperature and an air movement of 80 ft/min. The acclimatization procedure was at the same rate of work but at an air condition of 96°F D.B., 93°F W.B. and 80 ft/min air movement. This lasted for two weeks with a break on the Sunday—a total of twelve days.

The Human Sciences Laboratory considers it most important that studies of heat tolerances of different ethnic groups should be made as close to the subjects' homes as possible. To do this a mobile climatic tent was designed and constructed at low cost which could be transported on a 1½-ton truck to outlying areas, such as the Kalahari Desert (Minich, 1960). This requirement placed a restriction upon the air conditions which could be used for these tests. It is much easier, with cheap and simple equipment, to obtain accurate and stable control of temperature and humidity in a room when the air is nearly saturated with water vapour than it is to control the air conditions within the same close limits when the air is only partially saturated. The reason for making the studies as near as possible to the subjects' homes was to ensure that there would not have been any alterations in their daily patterns of activity and sleep, in their diets, and in the air conditions they were accustomed to before the studies. These are all factors which, if altered, are known to change the state of acclimatization to heat of the subjects (Machle and Hatch, 1947). It is most surprising therefore that recently studies have been reported on the heat reactions of men soon after they have been transported halfway around the world in jet aircraft. Diurnal rhythms, sleep, activity, and diet are all altered in such situations and it is not known with any certainty how soon men return to the physiological normal. Yet the findings are said to refer to the 'natural' states of acclimatization to the climates the men have just left.

In embarking upon this programme of research the first object then was to establish the reactions of the unacclimatized and highly acclimatized 'control' groups. For this purpose samples of young male Caucasians and Bantu were studied in the standard heat stress condition in the winter of Johannesburg's temperate climate, i.e. when it was considered that these men would be in their most unacclimatized states; samples of these two ethnic groups were then acclimatized at the same rate of work in severe heat and subsequently they were tested in the standard heat stress condition. The Caucasians were male medical students in their second year of study; the Bantu were a 'mixed' group of Xhosa, Tswana, Shangaan, and Zulu men from within the borders of South Africa.

Having established this frame of reference within which to judge the 'natural' states of acclimatization of other ethnic groups and of Bantu of different tribes, the following samples of young male adults were studied.

(a) Men of the following nine Bantu tribes in southern Africa :
    Xhosa, Zulu, Basutu, Tswana, Mpedi, Shangaan, Barotsi, Angolans, and Nyasas.

(b) Bushmen living in the desert at Takatschwane in the Kalahari and 'river' Bushmen living near Tschakawe, where the Okavanga river enters the Bechuanaland Protectorate and breaks up into the Okavanga swamps.

(c) Arabs of the Chaamba tribe living near Hassi-Messaoud in the Sahara Desert and Australian Aborigines living at Weipa and Aurukun on the west coast of the Cape York Peninsula in northern Australia.

(d) French and Australian Caucasians living respectively at Hassi-Messaoud in the Sahara Desert and at Weipa in the hot, humid tropics of the Cape York Peninsula of northern Queensland in Australia.

The data on the ethnic groups living in the desert and in the hot, humid tropics are included in these comparisons so that the reactions of the Caucasians, Bantu, and Bushmen in southern Africa can be compared with those of men in their 'natural' states of acclimatization to these two extreme climates.

Comparison of Bantu and Caucasians in unacclimatized and highly acclimatized states

In the unacclimatized state the performances of a group of 'mixed' Bantu, i.e. men of various tribes in South Africa, were superior to those of the Caucasians. Not one of the 22 Bantu subjects failed to complete the 4-hour period of the tests, while 50 per cent of the 20 Caucasians were withdrawn either because of hyperpyrexia (104°F rectal temperature) or because of exhaustion or collapse. The rectal temperatures and heart rates of the Caucasians rose to significantly higher levels during work than those of the Bantu (Fig. 4 and Table 3). Sweat rates of the Bantu, however, were significantly lower even when their smaller body sizes were taken into account by expressing the sweat rates per m²/h.

After samples of these ethnic groups had been acclimatized to severe heat (96°F dry-bulb and 93°F wet-bulb temperatures) they all completed the 'test' conditions with ease and their rectal temperatures and heart rates were closely similar (Fig. 4 and Table 3). The Bantu still sweated significantly less than the Caucasians.

From these data we can conclude that the Bantu in their 'natural' state of acclimatization are better adapted to work in heat than the Caucasians are, but that after acclimatization to severe heat, the level of acclimatization reached by both ethnic groups is closely similar, judged by their rectal temperatures and heart rates (Wyndham et al., 1964).

States of acclimatization of different Bantu tribes in Southern Africa

Samples of about twenty men of the Xhosa (Transkei), Basutu (Basutuland), Zulu (Zululand), Mpedi (northern Transvaal), Shangaan (Mozambique), Tswana (Bechuanaland), Angolas (Angola), Barotsi (Barotseland) and Nyasas (Tanzania) were studied in summer in contrast to those of the first group of 'mixed' Bantu, which were made in the late winter. The physical characteristics of the various tribes are given in Table 1 and their tribal territories in Fig. 5.

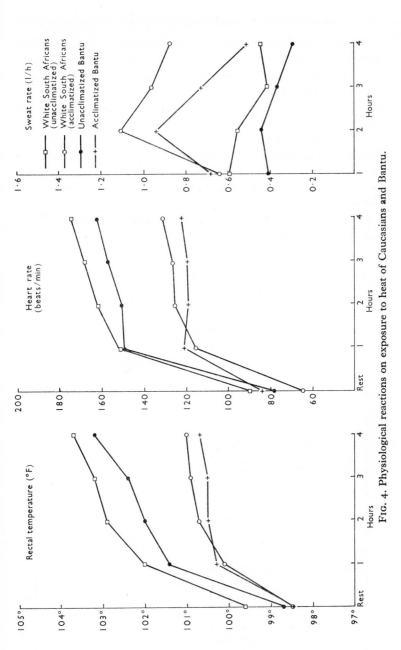

Fig. 4. Physiological reactions on exposure to heat of Caucasians and Bantu.

The mean rectal temperatures, mean heart rates, and mean sweat rates, with their standard deviations, are given in Table 3 for each hour of exposure to the standard test conditions. Use of the Scheffé method of multiple comparison showed that the summer data of rectal temperatures, pooled from the various tribes, were significantly lower than the 'winter' data of the 'mixed' Bantu and that there were no significant differences between the various tribes. Similar results were found for heart rates. There were no significant differences between pooled 'summer' sweat rates and the 'winter' data, but the sweat rates of the Pedi, Shangaans, and Tswana were significantly higher than those of the other tribes.

From the rectal temperatures and heart rates one can conclude that there is a significant, but small, increase in the state of

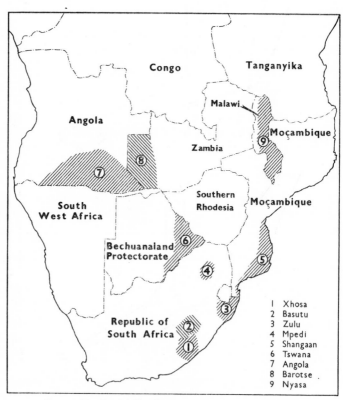

FIG. 5. Territorial distribution of Bantu tribes studied.

acclimatization of these men in the summer compared with the winter. There are, however, no significant differences between the various tribes in their states of acclimatization (Wyndham *et al.*, 1964). It might well be that the range of heat stress, which the various tribes experience in the different tribal territories, is too small to lead to differences in their states of acclimatization. This question was examined by taking the mean daily maximum temperatures and the 1500 h relative humidity figures of the meteorological stations in these various regions and calculating the basic Effective Temperatures, assuming a wind-velocity of zero. These calculations are given in Table 4, together with those for Johannesburg, for Hassi-Messaoud in the Sahara Desert and Darwin in the tropics of Australia. The last two are given in order to compare the climates of a hot desert and a hot, humid region with those of the tribal territories in which these Bantu live.

State of acclimatization of Bushmen in the Kalahari Desert and of 'river' Bushmen in the Okavango swamps

The physiological reactions of the desert and river Bushmen were measured in summer and are compared with those of the 'winter' unacclimatized and highly acclimatized Bantu in Table 3. Using the Scheffé method of multiple comparison, the rectal temperatures of desert and river Bushmen are not different from each other or from those of the 'winter' unacclimatized Bantu. The heart rates of the river Bushmen are not significantly different from those of the unacclimatized Bantu, but those of the desert Bushmen are significantly lower than both river Bushmen and unacclimatized Bantu. The sweat rates of both groups of Bushmen are significantly higher than those of the unacclimatized Bantu and significantly lower than those of the acclimatized Bantu (Wyndham *et al.*, 1964).

On these data it is not possible to make an unequivocal statement about the state of acclimatization, or heat tolerance, of the Bushmen. Their sweat rates are higher than those of the unacclimatized Bantu and this would suggest that they are more highly acclimatized, but in the case of the river Bushmen this is not associated with lower rectal temperatures and heart rates. The heart rates and rectal temperatures of the desert Bushmen are paradoxical: the heart rates are lower, which is support for a higher degree of acclimatization, but the rectal temperatures are the same as those of the unacclimatized Bantu.

Comparison between Bushmen in the Kalahari Desert and Arabs in the Sahara Desert

In Table 3 are given the physiological reactions of desert Bushmen and Chaamba, an Arab tribe in the Sahara Desert, in conjunction with the data on unacclimatized and highly acclimatized Bantu.

There are no significant differences in rectal temperature between the two groups of desert dwellers. Nor are their rectal temperatures different from those of the unacclimatized Bantu. The heart rates of the desert Bushmen are lower than those of Chaamba and the unacclimatized Bantu. Sweat rates of both groups of desert dwellers are similar and are significantly higher than those of the unacclimatized Bantu.

These results present the paradox of both groups of desert dwellers having very significantly higher sweat rates than unacclimatized Bantu, which would indicate a greater degree of acclimatization to heat, but rectal temperatures which are the same as those of the unacclimatized Bantu. The low heart rates of the desert Bushmen are in line with their higher sweat rates, but the high heart rates of the Chaamba are not.

States of acclimatization of Caucasians in South Africa, in the Sahara Desert and in the hot, humid tropics of Cape York Peninsula

In Table 3 and Fig. 6 are given the physiological reactions of the 'winter' unacclimatized and highly acclimatized Caucasians in Johannesburg and also the data obtained on young Frenchmen who had been at least three months at Hassi-Messaoud in the Sahara Desert and Australians living at Weipa, a mission station on the west coast of Cape York peninsula in northern Queensland, Australia (Wyndham et al., 1964).

From these data it is clear that men resident in these hot climates are partially acclimatized, judged by their lower rectal temperatures and heart rates and higher sweat rates, when compared with the 'winter' unacclimatized Caucasians in Johannesburg. They are, however, significantly less well acclimatized than the Caucasians acclimatized in the laboratory to work at a moderate rate in severe heat.

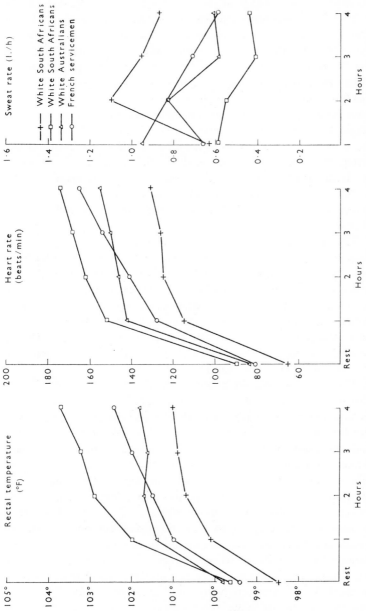

FIG. 6. Physiological reactions on exposure to heat of Caucasians in South Africa, in Australia, and of French servicemen.

Discussion on heat reactions

The first conclusion that can be drawn from these studies is that in their 'natural' states of acclimatization to winter in Johannesburg, the Bantu are significantly better adapted to heat than Caucasians, judged by their lower rectal temperatures and heart rates, but their sweat rate is lower, even when a correction has been made for the differences in surface areas. Similar results have been reported upon previously in studies on men of African origin and Caucasians in various parts of the world, such as the comparison by Robinson *et al.* of Caucausian and Negro share-croppers in a tropical region of the U.S.A. (1941), Baker's report on U.S. army recruits of Caucasian and Negro origin (1958), Ladell's study of Nigerians and Caucasians (1950), and the first comparison of Bantu and Caucasian reactions by Wyndham *et al.* (1952).

The lower rectal temperatures and heart rates of the men of African origin would appear to be a result of differences in activity patterns and, possibly, in the degree of heat exposure, because when samples of Bantu and Caucasian origin were exposed to the same severe acclimatization procedure, the differences in rectal temperatures and heart rates disappeared. Although, however, the sweat rates of both groups increase greatly during acclimatization, the sweat rates of the Bantu in the acclimatized state are still much less than those of the Caucasians.

The second conclusion relates to the effects of living in different climates on men of the same ethnic group. The Bantu tribes lived as far afield as the Shangaans on the tropical coast of Mozambique, the Tswana in the semi-desert region of the eastern Bechuanaland, and the Pedi in the temperate highland area of the northern Transvaal. Expressed in terms of the basic Effective Temperatures of the mean daily maximum temperatures and 1500 hours relative humidity figures for January, a midsummer month, the range of Effective Temperatures in these regions is 8°F, varying from 71°F in the Pedi territory to 79°F in the Shangaan homelands. No significant differences were observed in the heat reactions of the various tribes of Bantu living in these different climates. There were, however, significant differences in the physiological reactions of these Bantu between winter and summer observations. The variations in climate between summer and winter are much greater, there being a 14–18°F difference between summer (January) and winter (July) in the mean daily maximum temperatures in the home territories of these men.

The Caucasians were studied in the 'winter' unacclimatized and highly acclimatized states in Johannesburg and also in the hot, dry Sahara Desert. The range of these climates is 30°F. Expressed in Effective Temperatures, the temperatures vary from 56°F in Johannesburg's winter and 69°F in Johannesburg's summer to 87°F at Hassi-Messaoud in the Sahara Desert and 85°F at Weipa in Cape York peninsula. The Caucasians in the hot, dry and the hot, humid regions were significantly better adapted to heat than the unacclimatized men in Johannesburg in winter and significantly less well acclimatized than the men who were acclimatized in the laboratory to work in severe heat, i.e. approximately 92°F Effective Temperature.

From these studies it can be concluded that the range of climates in southern Africa in summer and the levels of heat stress are not sufficiently severe to produce significant differences in the 'natural' states of acclimatization of different Bantu tribes. The differences in the climates between summer and winter are much greater, varying from 14 to 18°F, and this apparently is sufficient to produce significant differences in the states of acclimatization. Differences between the climates of Johannesburg and of the hot, humid tropics and the hot, dry deserts are also relatively large, being over 30°F Effective Temperature and the heat stress in these regions is sufficiently severe to produce a state of partial acclimatization in peoples living in these extreme climates.

The third conclusion is that living in the semi-desert climate of the Kalahari, or the desert of the Sahara, results in a significant increase in sweat rates of the Bushmen and Arabs respectively when compared with the 'winter' unacclimatized Bantu. There is, however, no consistent association between the changes in sweat rates and in the rectal temperatures and heart rates. The rectal temperatures of desert and river Bushmen and the Chaamba are all similar and are not significantly different from those of the 'winter' unacclimatized Bantu. They are, however, significantly lower than those of 'winter' unacclimatized Caucasians. The heart rates of the desert Bushmen are significantly lower, but those of the river Bushmen and the Chaamba are not. The lack of consistency between sweat rates, rectal temperatures, and heart rates might be due to differences in the activity patterns of these three groups of men. The desert Bushmen were the most physically active of the three groups. In laboratory studies a decrease in rectal temperature and heart rate and an increase in sweat rate are generally regarded as the necessary criteria for acclimatization. This is well shown in the results in 'winter' unacclimatized and highly acclimatized Bantu and Caucasians. Changes in rectal temperature and heart rate during acclimatization are probably more dependent upon physical activity than they are upon heat exposure, whereas the increase in sweat rate appears to be more dependent upon the degree of heat stress of the environment (Strydom, Wyndham, *et al.*, 1965). Accordingly, the increased sweat rates of these desert dwellers might be regarded primarily as a measure of their adaptation to the thermal stresses of their climates and the changes in rectal temperatures and heart rates as a measure mainly of their physical activities in these climates.

The fourth conclusion relates to the relationship between morphology and the reactions to heat. Bergman (1847) postulated a relationship between body size and climate: 'Within a polytypic warm-blooded species the body size of the subspecies usually increases with decreasing temperature of its habitat'. Roberts (1953) put forward evidence that this rule applies to man also and showed that the size (weight) of men living in tropical climates is less than that of men living in temperate climates. Baker (1958) considered that the main influence of Bergman's law would be manifested in differences between individuals in the ratio of surface area to mass. The more the ratio approximates to one, the better are the heat transfer characteristics of the individual.

In these samples of different ethnic groups the surface area to mass ratios, in cm²/kg, vary greatly (Table 1). If this morphological feature is an important determinant of heat transfer, then the rank order of the various ethnic groups in temperature regulation, in terms of the levels of rectal temperature, should correspond with the rank order of their ratios. The results suggest that there is little or no association between the heat reactions of these various ethnic groups and their morphologies. The Bantu, Bushmen, and Arabs all differ in this ratio, but their temperature regulation, judged by the levels of rectal temperature, is not significantly different. The Caucasian, in the 'natural' state of acclimatization, has an expected, significantly higher rectal temperature and this accords with his smaller ratio. But when he is fully acclimatized there is no significant difference between his temperature regulation and that of the Bantu, in spite of a large difference between them in this particular ratio. The Frenchmen and the Arabs in the Sahara Desert represent the extremes in this ratio, i.e. 2·60 and 2·91 respectively, and yet the Frenchmen, if anything, appear in the standard heat stress condition to be better acclimatized. This is not to deny that within an ethnic group the thin slender men will not be more heat-tolerant than the big, fat ones. The point of this study is that if there are differences in the natural states of acclimatization (or heat tolerances) which are due to morphological differences, then they are small and are greatly overshadowed by the relatively large differences in the states of acclimatization due to the variety of climates and the physical activities which the different ethnic groups experience.

A greater surface area to mass ratio, however, may confer an advantage in another way. The total heat losses from the surface might remain constant, i.e. the temperature regulation would be unaffected, but the proportion of heat lost by radiation and convection may increase with a resultant decrease in evaporative losses. This would reduce the rate of sweating and lead to water conservation. At first sight this hypothesis appears to apply. The Caucasian has a low ratio and is a prolific, wasteful, sweater in hot, humid conditions. The Bantu has a higher ratio and regulates his body temperature on a smaller sweat loss. The hypothesis breaks down when one considers the desert dwellers. The Bushmen and the Arabs both have high ratios and need to conserve water, but they regulate their body temperatures with much greater rates of sweating per square metre of body surface at the same level as the Bantu. The greater ratios of the Bushmen therefore lead neither to a lower body temperature, nor to conservation of water by lower sweat rates.

In the study of the reactions to a standard heat stress condition of men with different morphological characteristics there is no support for the application of Bergman's rule to man.

Reactions to cold

There are a large number of studies in the literature on the reactions to cold of men of different ethnic groups. Unfortunately, as with the studies on heat tolerance, no two research teams have used the same air conditions, amounts of clothing, body postures, or lengths of exposure. One team even prefers to study men when they are asleep. Certain qualitative similarities appear to characterize the reactions of various ethnic groups to cold but it is impossible to say whether the quantitative differences observed are due to differences in experimental methods (such as one team measuring the metabolic rates of sleeping subjects and another measuring them in subjects when awake), or whether the quantitative differences represent differences in the states of acclimatization to cold.

Moreover, the classic studies of Gagge *et al.* (1936) and Du Bois and Hardy (1940) demonstrated that the body calls upon a variety of different physiological mechanisms to regulate its temperature as the air temperature falls below the thermoneutral zone. It therefore seemed more logical to the Human Sciences Laboratory to study metabolic rates and body temperatures over a range of air temperatures rather than to select one air temperature only. The air temperatures chosen were 27°C, the thermoneutral temperature, 20°, 15°, 10°, and 5°C. Metabolic rates, skin temperatures, and rectal temperatures were measured repeatedly over a 2-hour period of exposure while men were lying naked at each of these air temperatures, and at an air movement of 80 ft/min. A standard posture was adopted. The men lay on a stretcher with their legs spread apart and their arms away from the body. The stretcher gave support only to the heels, the buttocks, the shoulders, and the occiput. The men were in the post-absorptive state (12 hours) and their activities for the 24 hours prior to the study were restricted to light tasks. All studies were made in the mornings. The men were naked or wore only brief shorts.

Comparisons of cold reactions of Caucasians and Bantu

A fresh sample of eleven subjects of Caucasian and Bantu origin were studied at each of the above air conditions. This was done to avoid any trend due to cold acclimatization which might have developed if men had been repeatedly exposed to cold.

Curves with 78 per cent confidence limits were fitted to the mean values of the various physiological reactions measured at each of the air conditions for both groups of subjects. Where the confidence limits do not overlap, the populations are significantly different at the 5 per cent level of confidence. Judged on

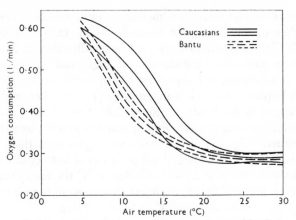

FIG. 7. Oxygen consumption versus air temperature, with 78 per cent confidence limits (Caucasians and Bantu).

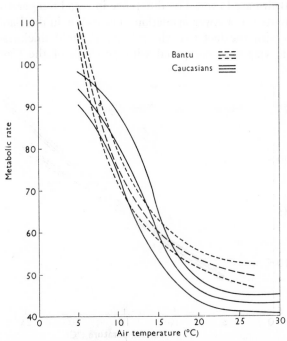

FIG. 8. Metabolic rate in cal/m²/h versus air temperature; with 78 per cent confidence limits (Caucasians and Bantu).

these statistical criteria, the metabolic rates of the Caucasians are higher than those of the Bantu in the air temperature range 14–8°C (Fig. 7). When, however, the metabolic rates are expressed per square metre then the situation changes and the Bantu have higher metabolisms at temperatures above 17°C and below 6°C, but not between these air temperatures (Fig. 8). Toe and finger temperatures of the Bantu are lower than those of the Caucasians above temperatures of 17°C (Figs. 9 and 10), and the average skin temperatures (Fig. 11) of the Bantu are higher than those of the Caucasians below 10°C. Rectal temperatures of both ethnic groups are exactly the same at 27°C but below 17°C the rectal temperatures of the Bantu (Fig. 12) are lower than those of the Caucasians, and at 5°C the difference, 0·8°C, is relatively large.

From these data it can be concluded that the percentage increases in metabolism per square metre are similar in Bantu and Caucasians. In spite of the similarities in the increase in heat production, due to the cold air temperature, the rectal temperatures of the Bantu are lower. The difference in rectal temperature must be attributed to a lower insulation to heat-flow in the Bantu. This accords with the fact that the average skinfold thickness of the Bantu is 5·25 mm, compared with 7·71 mm of the Caucasians.

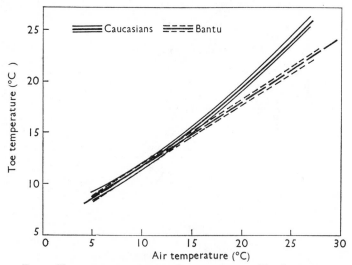

FIG. 9. Toe temperature versus air temperature, with 78 per cent confidence limits (Caucasians and Bantu).

The Bantu appear to have a high vasomotor tone in toes and fingers at air temperatures above 17°C judged by their lower finger and toe temperatures.

One can thus conclude that the metabolic reactions to cold of the Bantu are quantitatively similar to those of the Caucasians. Because, however, of the smaller insulation to heat flow, the increase in metabolic rate of the Bantu does not prevent a fall in rectal temperature. In the Caucasian the rectal temperature is maintained (Wyndham *et al.*, 1964).

Comparisons of reactions to cold of Bushmen, Bantu, and Caucasians

Experiments on Bushmen in the Kalahari Desert had to be modified from the design in the climatic room as not enough Bushmen were available to permit a fresh group to be exposed at each of the air temperatures studied in the previous experiment. In one expedition in 1958, eight Bushmen were exposed on three separate occasions during the winter nights while the air temperature fell from about 20°C, at the time of the first metabolic measurement, to as low as 3°C, at the time of the pre-dawn readings. In a second expedition in 1962, a sample of fifteen

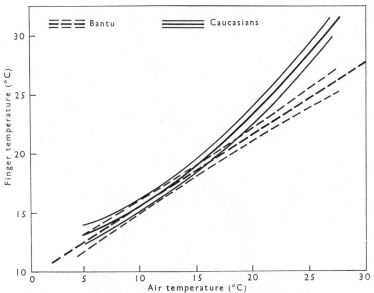

FIG. 10. Finger temperatures versus air temperature, with 78 per cent confidence limits (Caucasians and Bantu).

Bushmen were exposed at only two air conditions, namely 27°C and 5°C, which made the handling of the statistical data easier. The men were all in the post-absorptive state and rested before the studies. They were screened from the low sky radiation by stretching a piece of canvas above them.

The main findings are that the Bushmen reacted metabolically to cold in exactly the same manner as the Bantu (Fig. 13). Metabolic rates per square metre of both Bushmen and Bantu are significantly higher than those of the Caucasians at 27° and 5°C, but the percentage increases over this range of temperature are similar in the three groups. Finger and toe temperatures of Bushmen (Figs. 14 and 15) were higher than those of the Bantu

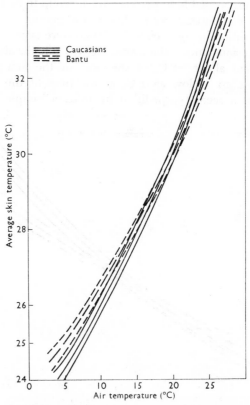

FIG. 11. Average skin temperature versus air temperature with 78 per cent confidence limits (Caucasians and Bantu).

but average skin temperatures were closely similar (Fig. 16). Rectal temperatures of both Bantu and Bushmen were closely similar (Fig. 17) and therefore at 5°C, the rectal temperatures of Bushmen were significantly lower than those of the Caucasians (Wyndham *et al.*, 1964).

Discussion on cold reactions

The first conclusion that emerges from this investigation is that the metabolic and average skin temperature reactions to cold of Caucasians, Bantu, and Bushmen are quantitatively similar, but that in cold air conditions the rectal temperatures of both Bantu and Bushmen are lower than those of Caucasians.

These two findings indicate that the insulation against heat flow in the Bantu peoples is less than that in the Caucasians. This accords with the differences in skinfold thicknesses, the average values of which for Bushmen, Bantu, and Caucasians are 4·75, 5·25, and 7·71 mm respectively. These findings suggest that the lower rectal temperature of the Bushmen and Bantu is not a reaction to cold, but is due to the differences in nutrition and activities of the Bantu and Bushmen, which lead to small skinfold thicknesses and to a lower insulation against cold.

This conclusion conflicts with that of Hammel (1962) who claims that the Bushmen show 'insulative-hypothermic' acclimation while Caucasians have a 'metabolic' acclimation. Hammel also claims that the Bushmen's reaction is similar to that of the Australian aboriginal. Hammel's data contradict his own conclusion, because on exposure to cold in a sleeping bag the Aborigines have a *fall* in rectal temperature with *no rise* in

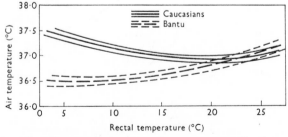

Fig. 12. Rectal temperatures versus air temperature with 78 per cent confidence limits (Caucasians and Bantu).

metabolism, whereas Bushmen under these conditions have a *fall* in rectal temperature and a *rise* in metabolism. The reaction of the Bushmen is therefore qualitatively similar to that of the Caucasian but is qualitatively different from that of the Australian aboriginal.

The second important conclusion is that, judged on the lower toe and finger temperatures, the Bantu and Bushmen have a higher vasomotor tone of the blood-vessels of the hands and feet in the range of air conditions where the regulation of body temperature is dependent upon alterations in vasomotor tone, i.e.

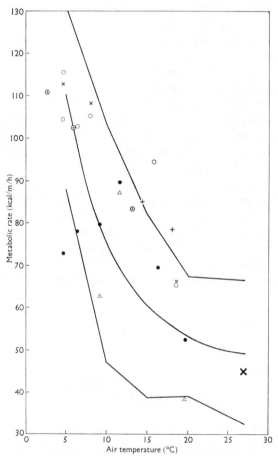

FIG. 13. Curve of Bantu metabolic rate versus air temperature, with 95 per cent significance intervals and with the data on the Bushmen superimposed.

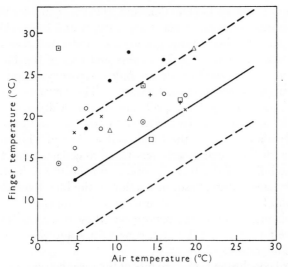

FIG. 14. Curve of Bantu finger temperatures versus air temperature, with 95 per cent significance intervals and with the data on the Bushmen superimposed.

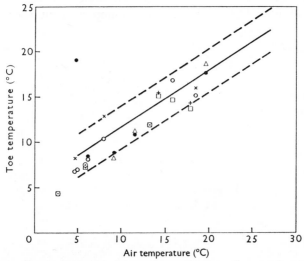

FIG. 15. Curve of Bantu toe temperatures versus air temperature, with 95 per cent significance intervals and with the data on the Bushmen superimposed.

between 27 and 17°C (Du Bois and Hardy, 1936). In these air temperatures the mean rectal temperatures and mean skin temperatures of the three ethnic groups are similar and therefore the greater vasomotor tone of the fingers and toes of the Bantu and Bushmen is not attributable to reflex vasoconstriction due to lower temperatures in these two areas. The lower temperatures of the hands and feet are probably due to a difference in the threshold of reflex vasoconstriction to cold of the blood-vessels of the hands and feet of the Bantu and Bushmen. This would be in line with the much greater resistance to collapse, due to vasomotor stability, of the Bantu peoples on exposure to heat. Below 17°C air temperature, vasoconstriction of the blood-vessels of the hands and feet is probably maximal and air temperature plays the prodominant role in the temperatures of these two areas. There are therefore no significant differences between Caucasians and Bantu in air temperatures below 17°C.

A third conclusion is that in spite of the great cultural differences in these two peoples there are no significant differences between Bushmen and Bantu in metabolic reactions, rectal temperatures, and average skin temperatures. They come from the same ethnic stock (Weiner and Zoutendyk, 1959), but culturally they are separated by many centuries. This is reflected in their different ways of life. The Bushman has an impermanent shelter and

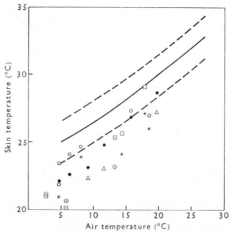

FIG. 16. Curve of Bantu average skin temperatures versus air temperature, with 95 per cent significance intervals and with the data on the Bushmen superimposed.

meagre clothing and, at first sight, would appear to be less well protected against the winter cold than the Bantu. However, as it was shown in a publication from this laboratory (Wyndham and Morrison, 1958) the Bushman makes excellent use of his skin cloak and fire so that even on very cold nights the microclimate around his body is not far from the thermoneutral temperature. With this simple, but effective, cultural method of adaptation to cold the Bushman is not subjected to a much greater degree of cold than the Bantu; nor is there any evidence that his physiological reactions to cold in the range 27–5°C differ from those of the Bantu.

The fourth conclusion relates to the possible influence on the reactions to cold of differences in morphology of the three ethnic groups. Baker (1958) suggested that it is in the surface area to weight ratio that man's morphological adaptation to climate is manifested. The Caucasian with a ratio of 2·60 cm²/kg should be a much better conserver of heat than the Bantu with a ratio of 2·80 cm²/kg or the Bushman with a ratio of 3·11 cm²/kg. In fact, the Caucasian increases his metabolic rate as much as the Bantu and is maintaining his rectal temperature. In addition to having an advantage in this ratio for conserving heat, the Caucasian also has much larger skinfold thicknesses. It is difficult to distinguish

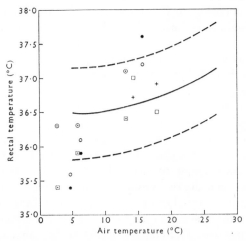

Fig. 17. Curve of Bantu rectal temperatures versus air temperatures, with 95 per cent significance intervals and with the data on the Bushmen superimposed.

between these two factors in the lower metabolic rates at 5°C of the Caucasian as compared to the Bushmen and Bantu. In the Bushmen and Bantu this complication does not exist. Their average skinfold thicknesses are very similar but there is quite a large difference in the surface area to mass ratio. The Bantu on these grounds should have an advantage in heat conservation. In fact, the metabolic and body temperature reactions of these two ethnic groups are not significantly different. There is therefore again no support in these results on cold tolerance for the application of Bergman's rule to man.

Finally, these results can be compared with the studies of Adams and Covino (1958) and Iampietro *et al.* (1959) on Caucasians and Negroes in the U.S.A. The former team exposed men sitting in trunks for 2 hours at 10°C and a high wind velocity. The latter team used an air temperature of 17°C, with a low air movement for 115 minutes. Iampietro *et al.* found no differences between the two groups in metabolic rates, or in rectal temperatures, or in hand and foot temperatures; Adams and Covino found lower metabolic rates in the Negroes, but no other differences. The failure of these two research teams to find the same clear-cut differences in physiological reactions as we demonstrated, i.e. the lower rectal temperatures below 17°C and the lower hand and foot temperatures above this air temperature, is difficult to explain. In choosing 10°C Iampietro *et al.*, in using a high wind velocity, should have been able to demonstrate changes in rectal temperature and in metabolic rates if they existed. Adams and Covino's choice of air temperature, 17°C, is on our results the one least likely to bring out differences in metabolism and rectal temperature.

The failure to demonstrate unequivocal evidence of differences in physiological reactions may, however, be due to another cause. The American Negro is culturally much closer to the Caucasian than the Bantu is to the Caucasian in South Africa. The American Negro has adopted western dietary habits and there is now a close similarity between the two groups in anthropometry, whereas the Bantu is significantly shorter and significantly (and very much) lighter than the Caucasian in South Africa. Furthermore, the Negro lives in a manner, as far as clothing, shelter, air-conditioning, &c., are concerned, which is closely similar to that of his Caucasian neighbour. This can be expected to have brought his 'comfort' zone and physiological reactions to cold close to that of the North American Caucasian. The Bantu in the tribal temperatures in South Africa, by contrast, live in much the same manner as their ancestors did over many centuries. Their clothing and dwellings, compared with that of the Caucasians, provide them with much less protection against the cold of the winter. In these characteristics the Bantu is closer to the Bushman in the Kalahari desert than to the Caucasian.

General conclusions

On exposure in their natural states to the standard heat stress used by this laboratory, the Caucasians were less well acclimatized to heat than the Bantu and the Bushmen, when judged by their higher rectal temperatures and heart rates. At first sight this might be attributed to the less favourable surface area to weight ratio of the Caucasians. This argument falls away, however, because in the highly acclimatized state the temperatures and circulatory reactions of the Caucasians and Bantu were identical. The differences in heat reactions between the Caucasians and the Bantu in their natural states are probably attributable to differences in their states of activity, which is well-known to effect the level of acclimatization.

Some measure of the differences in climate, which are necessary in order to produce measurable differences in the state of acclimatization, is contained in these results. Thus small, but significant, differences were found between summer and winter observations in the Bantu. The difference between summer (January) and winter (July) in mean daily maximum temperature is about 14–18°F. However, in summer no significant differences were found in the physiological reactions of different tribes of Bantu living in climates as far apart as Inhambane on the Mozambique coast and the mountain highlands of Basutuland. The difference in the climates is about 8°F Effective Temperature (based on the January mean daily maximum temperatures and 1500 hours relative humidities). Parallel studies of Caucasians in summer and winter and living in various climates in southern Africa are also needed to establish whether the same pattern in differences is also true for the Caucasians.

When the differences in climates are even greater, significant and relatively large effects are observed on the state of acclimatization.

There is a 30°F Effective Temperature difference between Johannesburg in the winter and the climate in the Sahara Desert or the hot, humid tropics of Australia. Caucasians living in these last two areas are significantly better acclimatized to heat than Caucasians in winter in Johannesburg.

The general conclusion is that peoples of different ethnic origins, morphology, activities, nutritional states, and degrees of exposure to the local climate show only small differences in their reactions to a standard heat stress. By contrast, men of the same ethnic group who live in climates as different as those of Johannesburg in winter, or the Sahara Desert, or the hot, humid tropics of Australia, show significant and relatively large differences in their states of acclimatization. It appears that the climate in which men live and their levels of activity play a greater part in their states of acclimatization to heat than do differences in morphology.

On exposure to cold the reactions of the Bantu and Bushmen are almost identical, in spite of their differences in morphology, in the use they make of shelter to protect themselves against cold, in their nutritional states and in their physical activities. Their reactions differ from those of the Caucasians in that the rectal temperatures of both the Bantu and Bushmen fall, whereas the rectal temperatures of the Caucasians are maintained. This happens in spite of the fact that the increases in heat production of the Bantu and Bushmen are slightly greater than those of the Caucasians at 5°C. It can therefore be concluded that the Bantu and Bushmen have less insulation against heat flow than the Caucasian and this proposal is in accord with the differences found on skinfold thicknesses. The skinfold thicknesses are 4·75, 5·25, and 7·71 mm respectively for the Bushmen, Bantu, and Caucasians. The differences which we observe in the reactions to cold are therefore, in our view, due to the differences in the nutritional states and the physical activities of the peoples and are *not* an 'acclimatization' process to cold. The two Bantu peoples are also different from the Caucasians in that they have lower temperatures in body extremities in mild cold. This we attribute to a greater vasomotor tone of the blood-vessels in hands and feet.

Exercise studies bring out the fact that the maximum oxygen intakes of physically active Caucasians, Bantu, and Bushmen are closely similar when expressed per kilogram of gross body weight, in spite of the differences in morphology, nutritional states, and patterns of activity. The Bantu and Bushmen are mechanically more efficient than the Caucasians at a step-climbing procedure. This difference is probably attributable to the fact that the Bushmen and Bantu are more accustomed to walking and running than the Caucasians in the Republic of South Africa. The lower mechanical efficiency of the Caucasians may also be attributed in part to the fact that they have a greater skinfold thickness than the two Bantu groups, because significant differences in oxygen consumption have been found between fat and thin people doing the same rate of external work (Henschel and Strydom, 1963).

The Bushmen, Bantu, and Caucasians differ greatly in anthropometrical characteristics, in their physical activities, in their nutritional states and in the use they make of shelter for protection against climatic extremes. There are also significant differences in certain details of their physiological responses, to the stresses of heat, cold, and exercise, although the differences are small. In spite of these differences, however, the predominant impression one gathers from the results of these studies is the remarkable similarity in their physiological reactions.

TABLE 1

Anthropometric characteristics of various ethnic groups

Subjects	No.	Height (cm)	Weight (kg)	Surface area (m²)	Ratio surface area/wt. (cm²/kg)	Skin-folds (mm)
Caucasians						
S. African						
1. Hot study						
(i) Unacclimatized	20	175·9	70·24	1·86	2·65	8·09
		(7·71)	(7·016)	(0·130)	(0·119)	(2·994)
(ii) Acclimatized	10	174·6	69·34	1·84	2·65	8·27
		(6·54)	(6·972)	(0·122)	(0·251)	(2·621)
2. Cold study	44	172·6	70·91	1·84	2·60	7·72
		(7·30)	(9·331)	(0·155)	(0·182)	(1·732)
3. Exercise	68	174·6	66·9	1·85	2·75	7·52
		(6·45)	(7·86)	(0·142)	(0·214)	(2·013)
Frenchmen	15	170·1	69·96	1·81	2·60	9·82
		(5·00)	(9·311)	(0·131)	(0·144)	(2·914)
Australian	7	175·3	77·00	1·93	2·50	—
		(6·81)	(6·921)	(0·185)	(0·241)	—

TABLE 1 (cont.)

Subjects	No.	Height (cm)	Weight (kg)	Surface area (m^2)	Ratio surface area/wt. (cm^2/kg)	Skin-folds (mm)
Bantu						
'Mixed' tribes						
1. Hot studies						
(i) Unacclimatized	22	165·9	59·09	1·66	2·82	5·45
		(6·03)	(6·079)	(0·109)	(0·420)	(1·049)
(ii) Acclimatized	20	166·8	60·48	1·68	2·78	5·95
		(5·87)	(5·919)	(0·097)	(0·135)	(1·637)
2. Cold study	56	166·6	55·72	1·62	2·91	5·25
		(4·77)	(4·815)	(0·100)	(0·262)	(0·735)
3. Exercise	26	166·5	55·16	1·61	2·91	5·32
		(5·72)	(5·837)	(0·112)	(0·145)	(1·002)
Individual tribes						
Nyasas	20	163·8	56·86	1·62	2·85	—
		(6·15)	(3·862)	(0·256)	—	—
Zulu	20	168·3	60·44	1·68	2·78	—
		(6·83)	(4·885)	(0·248)	—	—
Mpedi	17	166·4	56·69	1·63	2·88	—
		(5·33)	(5·831)	(0·272)	—	—
Shangaan	20	166·4	57·89	1·65	2·85	—
		(6·17)	(6·148)	(0·114)	—	—
Tswana	15	165·1	53·80	1·58	2·94	—
		(5·77)	(4·825)	(0·270)	—	—
Barotse	20	168·1	56·81	1·63	2·87	—
		(8·38)	(2·022)	(0·240)	—	—
Basutu	20	167·6	56·81	1·64	2·89	—
		(5·34)	(4·752)	—	—	—
Xhosa	20	167·4	58·96	1·68	2·88	—
		(4·42)	(6·654)	—	—	—
Angola	20	167·6	60·38	1·69	2·80	—
		(5·36)	(5·802)	—	—	—
Bushmen						
1. Maxqonbi						
(i) At Takat-schwane	8	160·5	47·56	1·47	3·11	4·75
		(6·08)	(5·178)	(0·105)	(0·027)	(1·985)
(ii) At Motokwe	15	157·8	47·74	1·48	3·05	4·47
		(6·35)	(6·061)	(0·364)	(0·122)	(0·725)
2. Makanchwe Okavango swamps	10	171·3	61·22	1·74	2·85	4·73
		(6·73)	(4·894)	(0·092)	(0·143)	(0·035)
Arabs						
Chaamba at Hassi-Messaoud	15	165·4	55·18	1·60	2·91	6·15
		(5·51)	(5·474)	(0·087)	(0·158)	(3·350)
Aborigines						
At Weipa, N. Queensland	31	172·0	56·48	1·67	2·97	6·63
		(5·25)	(6·466)	(0·104)	(0·156)	(2·120)

TABLE 2

Comparison of ethnic groups on mean maximum oxygen intake per kilogram of gross body weight, O/K (with 95 per cent confidence limits)

Ethnic group	n	Mean max O_2	Mean weight (kg)	O/K	S.D. O/K	Upper limit	Lower limit
		Very fit men					
Caucasians							
Astrand's Swedish gymnasts	42	4·11	70	58·5	0·66	59·8	57·2
Astrand's athletes	14	4·66	—	66·8	0·29	67·3	66·1
(Lundy—4 min-miler)	1	5·04	66	76·6	—	—	—
Andersen's athletes	7	4·60	69	68·0	—	—	—
		Men engaged in physical effort					
Caucasians							
H.S.L.'s S.A. Army recruits (ergometer test)	35	3·47	72	48·3	0·75	49·9	46·8
H.S.L.'s S.A. Army recruits (step test)	35	3·28	72	45·6	1·11	47·9	43·4
Taylor *et al.*'s Army recruits	69	3·60	74	48·3	0·94	50·2†	46·4
Robinson *et al.*'s White share-croppers	8	3·25	65	49·6	0·52	50·6†	48·6
Men of African origin							
Robinson *et al.*'s Negro share-croppers	14	3·20	64	49·9	0·51	50·9†	48·9
H.S.L.'s Series II S.A. Bantu	23	2·85	59	48·0	1·96	52·0	43·9
H.S.L.'s Series III S.A. Bantu	23	2·75	58	47·7	1·66	51·1	44·2
H.S.L.'s Bantu accustomed to hard work	7	3·18	67	47·7	0·55	48·7	46·2
H.S.L.'s Bushmen in Kalahari Desert	3	2·39	51	47·1	6·98	59·8	25·3
		Sedentary or inactive men					
Caucasians							
H.S.L. Staff	7	3·11	79	39·1	1·78	43·5	34·7
Andersen's subjects	12	3·20	73	44·1	1·07	46·5†	41·7
Bantu							
H.S.L. Series I	26	2·27	55	41·3	2·00	45·3	37·2
H.S.L.	338	2·63	59	44·6	6·45	45·5	43·7
Bushmen	12	2·07	48	42·8	1·33	45·5	39·7

† Confidence limits are only approximate 95 per cent limits, as adequate data are not given in papers for their determination.

TAB

Heat reactio

			Rectal temperature (°F)				
Ethnic group	Statis-tics	N	Rest	1st h	2nd h	3rd h	4t
Winter unacclimatized	Mean	22	98·70	101·39	102·03	102·38	103
Bantu S.A.	S.D.		0·888	0·483	0·744	0·736	0
Winter unacclimatized	Mean	20	99·58	102·00	102·87	103·17	103
Caucasians S.A.	S.D.		0·585	0·628	0·787	0·632	1
Highly acclimatized	Mean	18	98·51	100·27	100·51	100·48	100
Bantu S.A.	S.D.		0·380	0·397	0·512	0·484	0
Highly acclimatized	Mean	10	98·48	100·14	100·72	100·89	101
Caucasians S.A.	S.D.		0·329	0·268	0·301	0·354	0
Bantu tribes (S.A.)							
Barotsi	Mean	20	98·90	100·97	101·63	102·00	102
	S.D.		0·670	0·598	0·793	0·999	1
Mpedi	Mean	17	98·74	100·88	101·44	101·96	102
	S.D.		0·659	0·463	0·732	0·869	0
Nyasa	Mean	20	98·96	101·04	101·86	102·42	102
	S.D.		0·879	0·596	0·546	0·762	0
Shangaan	Mean	20	98·80	100·96	101·73	102·13	102
	S.D.		0·690	0·352	0·587	0·677	0
Tswana	Mean	15	98·89	101·00	101·50	101·89	102
	S.D.		0·561	0·534	0·675	0·797	0
Zulu	Mean	20	98·85	100·73	101·43	101·86	102
	S.D.		0·494	0·559	0·483	0·658	0
Basutu	Mean	20	98·75	101·02	101·64	102·17	102
	S.D.		0·934	0·519	4·785	0·806	0
Angola	Mean	20	98·61	100·83	101·62	102·10	102
	S.D.		0·972	0·913	0·935	1·008	1
Xhosa	Mean	21	98·81	100·89	101·61	102·06	102
	S.D.		0·446	0·626	0·590	0·742	0
Kalahari and Okavango (summer)							
Desert Bushmen	Mean	11	98·67	101·55	102·14	102·10	102
	S.D.		0·721	0·615	0·812	0·585	0
River Bushmen	Mean	8	98·78	101·45	101·94	102·22	102
	S.D.		0·609	0·676	0·648	0·655	0
Australia (hot, humid)							
Aborigines	Mean	31	99·62	101·35	101·67	102·03	102
	S.D.		0·355	0·471	0·608	0·698	0
Caucasians	Mean	7	99·77	101·44	101·67	101·64	101
	S.D.		0·330	0·162	0·309	0·378	0
Sahara Desert (hot, dry)							
Chaamba Arabs	Mean	15	98·42	101·27	101·97	102·39	102
	S.D.		0·298	0·530	0·560	0·676	0
Caucasians	Mean	15	99·39	101·01	101·52	101·97	102
	S.D.		0·289	0·504	0·384	0·566	0

rent ethnic groups

st	Heart rate (beats/min)				Sweat rate (ml/h)				
	1st h	2nd h	3rd h	4th h	1st h	2nd h	3rd h	4th h	ml/m²/h
18	149·27	150·00	157·36	161·91	405·3	438·5	361·4	289·0	224
63	11·00	14·63	15·42	14·62	160·6	106·2	117·3	131·5	79·2
00	152·40	162·21	168·00	173·60	592·7	547·1	417·8	446·1	276
80	22·59	17·50	13·64	16·59	221·6	195·6	188·5	201·4	112·0
60	121·00	118·67	118·89	122·33	674·8	937·6	720·2	508·4	428
03	11·48	13·41	11·13	13·94	164·6	71·7	116·1	81·6	68·7
00	115·00	124·60	126·00	131·40	634·0	1101·6	958·4	867·5	478
28	15·27	13·83	14·70	16·65	157·4	159·7	227·3	231·8	107·6
1	137·0	143·1	149·1	154·5	319·0	445·1	353·2	307·0	232
46	15·47	16·64	15·94	15·53	94·69	131·04	93·87	60·00	61·00
9	136·1	146·1	154·2	161·9	405·5	578·6	427·9	367·6	273
69	9·99	14·17	15·92	10·99	104·04	177·07	153·16	120·32	82·2
1	137·9	148·8	157·2	162·6	272·2	375·0	369·0	289·0	202
16	18·30	18·28	18·28	15·82	109·84	139·60	104·10	91·37	69·5
4	141·5	152·9	158·0	165·1	401·2	612·3	462·4	389·6	294
89	15·12	18·10	16·53	16·70	130·28	205·51	130·53	82·24	84·7
6	140·3	149·7	155·7	166·0	407·5	583·9	445·4	379·9	297
97	17·74	17·61	18·28	13·03	159·06	179·83	104·15	54·85	79·9
3	130·0	138·7	145·8	154·9	361·4	512·5	411·2	360·0	246
44	17·94	18·45	18·17	16·43	112·99	152·03	108·28	80·04	67·4
6	134·2	141·40	149·8	155·7	361·4	495·9	410·2	347·5	246
62	18·14	20·26	17·56	16·08	148·13	192·44	136·92	84·27	82·4
8	136·7	147·5	153·6	154·6	348·4	530·9	412·4	361·8	245
15	20·22	19·17	19·87	17·78	159·24	132·21	125·96	79·80	73·2
2	135·4	145·3	154·0	162·00	303·9	428·6	383·5	306·6	211
19	13·59	15·30	17·32	20·34	120·20	125·49	99·53	71·19	62·4
55	125·82	132·36	134·00	142·91	592·7	643·4	591·9	481·0	392
77	12·73	16·37	15·10	14·15	139·7	181·8	128·8	90·5	90·8
50	147·75	150·25	154·50	159·50	484·9	772·6	650·0	505·5	347
46	18·56	19·23	18·29	14·88	137·9	258·3	136·2	143·2	96·5
58	147·39	153·58	160·00	167·39	444·3	468·0	390·8	322·6	237
02	16·45	12·19	11·92	13·52	168·8	139·7	100·6	74·8	69·2
14	142·00	145·71	150·29	154·57	951·4	823·6	585·0	607·9	384
11	8·88	17·79	17·22	18·54	131·3	111·6	183·8	125·5	76·8
47	143·88	156·33	162·61	167·36	576·8	740·7	571·2	486·7	371
13	17·61	20·34	18·62	18·24	185·2	235·9	212·3	147·7	122
73	128·13	140·53	153·71	164·61	653·9	826·8	704·6	594·2	384
42	11·32	17·72	18·34	14·10	144·4	230·8	246·9	247·1	121·7

TABLE 4

Climatic conditions in tribal territory in January

Tribe	Met. station	Mean daily max. (°F)(Jan.)	Rel. hum. and wet bulb (°F)		Effec. temp. (°F) (basic) zero wind
Tswana	Mahelopye	83·2	44	67	74
Pedi	Pietersburg	78·0	50	65	71
	Koppiesonder	82·6	41	66	73
Zulu	Melmoth	77·8	60	68	72·5
Barotse	Mongu	78·3	65	69·5	73
	Sesheke	81·7	61	71·5	75·5
Nyasa	Zomba	77·0	70	70	72
	Blantyre	79·3	68	71·5	74·5
	Lilingwe	77·0	67	69	72·5
	Port Herald	88·3	63	77·5	81
	Fort Johnson	83·8	63	74	77·5
Shangaan	Inhambane	85·5	62	75	78·5
	Conecado	87·5	54	74·5	79
Temperate					
	Johannesburg	75·6	50	63·5	69
Desert					
	Hassi-Messaoud (Sahara)	107·6	30	80·0	87
Hot, humid					
	Lagos (Nigeria)	89	67	80	82·8
	Weipa (N. Queensland)	92	60	81	84·2
	Darwin (N. Territory) Australia	90	71	82	84·3
Sub-tropics					
	Durban	81		79·0	76·5
	Brisbane (Queensland)	86	60	76·0	79·3

REFERENCES

ADAMS, T. and COVINO, B. G., 1958. 'Racial variations to a standardized cold stress', *J. appl. Physiol.* 12, 9–12.

ANDERSON, K. LANGE, BOLSTED, A., LYNING, V., and IRVING, L., 1960. 'Physical fitness of Arctic Indians', *J. appl. Physiol.* 15, 645–648.

ASTRAND, P. O., 1952. *Experimental Studies of Physical Working Capacity in Relation to Work and Age.* Munksgaard, Copenhagen.

BAKER, P., 1958. 'Racial differences in heat tolerance', *Am. J. phys. Anthrop.* 16, 287–305.

BERGMANN, C., 1847. 'Ueber die Verähltnisse der Wärmeökonomie der Tiere zu ihrer Grösse', *Gottinger Studien* **3**, 595–708.

DU BOIS, E. F. and HARDY, J. D., 1940. 'Differences between men and women in their response to heat and cold', *Proc. natn. Acad. Sci. U.S.A.* **26**, 389–398.

FLEMING, P. W., ADDERLEY, P., BETTENCOURT, J. J., HEWSON, G. R., NEL, J. G., COLF, S. W. V. D., VERNER, P. W., and VILJOEN, J. A., 1961. Interim report on the direct measurement of food issued to 'Bantu labourers housed in compounds'. *Report of Human Sciences Laboratory, A.P.L.* 7/61.

GAGGE, A. P., WINSLOW, C. A. A., and HERRINGTON, L. P., 1938. 'The influence of clothing on the physiological reactions of the human body to varying environmental temperatures', *Am. J. Physiol.* **124**, 30–50.

HAMMEL, J. D., 1962. Communication to Temperature Regulation Symposium at 22nd Int. Physiol. Congr., Leiden.

HENSCHEL, A. and STRYDOM, N. B., 1963. 'The relationship of oxygen consumption to body weight during work on a bicycle ergometer', International Congress on Occupational Health, Madrid, September 1963.

IAMPIETRO, P. F., GOLDMAN, R. F., BUSKIRK, E. R., and BASS, D. E., 1959. 'Responses of Negro and white males to cold', *J. appl. Physiol.* **14**, 798–800.

JACKSON, S. P., 1961. *Climatological Atlas of Africa.* C.C.T.A./C.S.A. Lagos–Nairobi, 1961. Printed by the Government Printers, Pretoria.

LADELL, W. S. S., 1950. 'Inherent acclimatization of indigenous west Africans', *Proc. physiol. Soc.* **112**, 24.

MACHLE, W. and HATCH, T. F., 1947. 'Heat: man's exchanges and physiological responses', *Physiol. Rev.* **27**(2), 200–227.

MARITZ, J. S., MORRISON, J. F., PETER, J., STRYDOM, N. B., and WYNDHAM, C. H., 1961. 'A practical method of estimating an individual's maximum oxygen intake', *Ergonomics* **4**, 97–122.

MINICH, G. S., 1960. 'An inexpensive portable hot room', *J. appl. Physiol.* **15**, 1154–1155.

ROBERTS, D. F., 1953. 'Body weight, race and climate', *Am. J. phys. Anthrop.* **11**, 533–558.

ROBINSON, S., DILL, D. B., HARMON, P. M., HALL, F. G., and WILSON, J. W., 1941. 'Adaptations to exercise of Negro and white sharecroppers in comparison with northern whites'. *Hum. Biol.* **13**, 139–158.

STRYDOM, N. B., WYNDHAM, C. H., HOLDSWORTH, L. D., MORRISON, J. F., and VAN GRAAN, C. H., 1964. 'The influence of water restriction on the performance of men on a route march', *Report by Human Sciences Laboratory C.O.M. Research Report* 25/64.

—— —— WILLIAMS, C. G., MORRISON, J. F., BREDELL, G. A. G., BENADE, A. J. S., and VON RAHDEN, M., 1965. 'Acclimatization to humid heat and the role of physical conditioning'. Submitted to *J. appl. Physiol.* 1965.

TAYLOR, H. S., BUSKIRK, E. R., and HENSCHEL, A., 1955. 'Maximal oxygen intake as an objective measure of cardiorespiratory performance', *J. appl. Physiol.* **8**, 73–80.

WEINER, J. S. and ZOUTENDYK, A., 1959. 'Blood group investigation on Central Kalahari Bushmen', *Nature, Lond.* **183**, 843–844.

WYNDHAM, C. H., BOUWER, M. V. D., PATERSON, H. F., and DEVINE, M. G., 1952. 'Physiological responses', *J. appl. Physiol.* **5**, 290–301.

—— and MORRISON, J. F., 1958. 'Adjustment to cold of Bushmen in the Kalahari Desert', *J. appl. Physiol.* **13**(2), 219–225.

—— STRYDOM, N. B., MARITZ, J. S., MORRISON, J. F., PETER, J., and POTGIETER, Z. U., 1959. 'Maximum oxygen intake and maximum heart rate during strenuous work', *J. appl. Physiol.* **14**, 927–936.

—— —— MORRISON, J. F., PETER, J., MARITZ, J. S., and WARDEN, J. S., 1963. 'The influence of a stable diet and regular work on body weight and capacity for exercise of African mine recruits', *Ergonomics* **5**, 435–444.

—— —— —— —— WILLIAMS, C. G., BREDELL, G. A. G., and JOFFE, A., 1963. 'Differences between Ethnic groups in physical working capacity', *J. appl. Physiol.* **18**(2), 361–366.

—— —— LEARY, W. P., DU RAAN, A. J. N., VAN RENSBURG, A. J., VILJOEN, J. H., FRANKEN, J. J., and KLÖHN, B. H., 1964. 'A comparison of measurements of maximum oxygen intakes after: (a) a continuous treadmill test, (b) an intermittent treadmill test and (c) a step test, using 4 submaximal levels of work'. *Report of Human Sciences Laboratory C.O.M. Research Report* 24/64.

—— —— MORRISON, J. F., WILLIAMS, C. G., BREDELL, G. A. G., VON RAHDEN, M. J. E., HOLDSWORTH, L. D., VAN GRAAN, C. H., VAN RENSBURG, A. J., and MUNRO, A., 1964. 'Heat reactions of Caucasians and Bantu in South Africa', *J. appl. Physiol.* **19**(4), 598–606.

—— —— MUNRO, A., MACPHERSON, R. K., SCHAFF, G., and SCHIEBER, J., 1964. 'Heat reactions of Caucasians in temperate, in hot, dry and in hot, humid climates', *J. appl. Physiol.* **19**, 607–612.

—— —— WARD, J. S., MORRISON, J. F., WILLIAMS, C. G., BREDELL, G. A. G., VON RAHDEN, M. J. E., HOLDSWORTH, L. D., VAN GRAAN, C. H., VAN RENSBURG, A. J., and MUNRO, A., 1964. 'Physiological reactions to heat of Bushmen and of unacclimatized and acclimatized Bantu', *J. appl. Physiol.* **19**(5), 885–888.

—— —— WILLIAMS, C. G., MORRISON, J. F., BREDELL, G. A. G., PETER, J., VAN GRAAN, C. H., HOLDSWORTH, L. D., VAN RENSBURG, A. J., and MUNRO, A., 1964. 'Heat reactions of some Bantu tribesmen in southern Africa', *J. appl. Physiol.* **19**(5), 881–884.

—— WARD, J. S., STRYDOM, N. B., MORRISON, J. F., WILLIAMS, C. G., BREDELL, G. A. G., PETER, J., VON RAHDEN, M. J. E., HOLDSWORTH, L. D., VAN GRAAN, C. H., VAN RENSBURG, A. J., and MUNRO, A., 1964. 'Physiological reactions of Caucasian and Bantu males in acute exposure to cold', *J. appl. Physiol.* **19**(4), 583–592.

8

A PROSPECTUS FOR GENETIC STUDIES ON THE AMERICAN INDIANS†

J. V. NEEL and F. M. SALZANO

Department of Human Genetics, University of Michigan Medical School, Ann Arbor, U.S.A.
and
Departamento de Genética, Instituto de Ciências Naturais, Universidade do Rio Grande do Sul, Pôrto Alegre, Brazil

Introduction

THE American Indian today presents a series of unusual—and in some respects unique—biological, medical, and humanitarian challenges. It will be the purpose of this presentation to attempt to delineate the nature of some of these challenges, and especially those of a genetic nature. Meeting these challenges will not only provide data of considerable scientific importance, but also data of real value to the Indian as in the Americas he progresses towards those greater opportunities which must be his.

We realize there is an element of presumption in relative new-comers to the field such as ourselves entitling this presentation a 'prospectus'. Many people, some of whom in due course we will acknowledge, have thought long and hard about the problems we will be discussing. However, to the best of our knowledge, to date no one has essayed a comprehensive look at the series of related genetic and para-genetic questions posed by the American Indian. It seems particularly timely to do so now, when there is pending an International Biological Programme, one of whose foci of interest will be the surviving groups of primitive people.

Man reached the American continent at a relatively late stage

† Paper presented by F. M. Salzano at the Wenner-Gren Foundation Symposium on the 'Biology of Populations of Anthropological Importance', held in 1964. A very similar paper with the same title was read by J. V. Neel at the Twenty-ninth Cold Spring Harbour Symposium on Quantitative Biology held in the same year. The authors' researches in this subject were supported in part by the U.S. Public Health Service, World Health Organization, U.S. Atomic Energy Commission, Rockefeller Foundation, and National Research Council of Brazil.

in his evolution. That the Bering Strait constituted his major and perhaps sole route of access, and that he may first have trod this route some 30,000 to 20,000 years ago, seem relatively clear. Much less clear are such details as the period of time over which this immigration was spread; whether it was a more or less continuous process or occurred in waves, perhaps separated by minor periods of glacial advance and retreat; and the numbers of people involved. For no other large area of the earth can we date and place the arrival of its first inhabitants with such accuracy, inhabitants who then fanned out over vast areas in small bands, to occupy almost all the types of ecological habitats now recognized.

The genetic problems posed by the descendants of these immigrants would appear in the main to fall into three overlapping categories, as follows.

(1) What is the degree of genetic divergence which has arisen between these groups since their arrival? This is in many respects a taxonomic problem, involving not only a determination of the frequencies of genes responsible for specific traits, but also the continuing study of certain physical characteristics whose precise genetic basis is now unclear but will surely be better understood in the future. Because, as noted above, we can time the arrival of the Indian on the American continent, here is an unusual opportunity to determine the tempo of human evolution.

(2) For such of these groups as still persist in an essentially pre-Columbian state, to what extent can we identify the significant biological parameters, parameters which we may presume to have obtained over the majority of human evolution? In connection with this question, let us quickly recognize that there is no Indian group completely untouched by the discovery of America and subsequent contacts, direct or indirect, with the Western World. But the fact remains that there are still a number of Indian groups whose economy is essentially that of hunting-and-gathering, supplemented by incipient agriculture. What are the significant biological determinants in these groups? More specifically, to what extent do these groups provide an opportunity to study the nature of the natural selection to which man was subjected during most of his evolution?

(3) What new disease patterns will emerge as these primitive groups make the transition from a near-Stone Age to an Atomic Age existence, and to what extent is there provided an opportunity

to study in an intensified and telescoped form the genetic adjustments which presumably occurred as other groups, including our own ancestors, made this transition?

Before we proceed to a somewhat detailed consideration of the possibilities and limits inherent in each of these questions, let us pause to recognize some of the present deficiencies in knowledge, which will mean that for the time being—and perhaps forever—the answers to these questions cannot be clear and unequivocal, but will consist of establishing a range of possibilities within which the correct answer is to be found.

The first deficiency in information concerns the ancestry of the American Indian. Although this is undoubtedly predominantly mongoloid, at one time or another a variety of other contributory elements have been suggested (reviews in Imbelloni, 1950; Birdsell, 1951; Rivet, 1958; Stewart, 1960; Greenman, 1963; Salzano, 1963 and 1964). Even with respect to the nature of the mongoloid contribution, there is room for a wide divergence of opinion. In this connection, we would emphasize the potential value of extensive gene frequency studies in Eastern Siberia and adjacent areas, although at the same time recognizing that human migration, resulting from a changing ecology, such as advancing glaciation, or displacement of one human group by another, will undoubtedly have produced a complex situation.

The second deficiency in information concerns the numbers of immigrants who reached the American continent. Since we may presume Eastern Siberia itself to have been rather thinly populated by hunters-and-gatherers at the time of the immigrations, it seems unlikely that the first nomadic bands who moved into North America were either large or numerous. It is an interesting thought that even if man arrived on this continent as recently as 15,000 years ago (see below), so that, with an average generation time of 20 years, some 750 generations have now elapsed since this arrival, an initial group of 400 could have increased to 10,000,000 with only a 1·4 per cent increase per generation. However, even if the original groups were small and for many generations their descendants few in number and well dispersed in the vastness of America, contiguous populations—or even those some distance apart—may rarely have been truly isolated from one another. The picture which emerges whenever these small bands of hunters-and-gatherers is studied is one of genetic exchange. There are frequent marriages between partners living in different groups of the same tribe, and the custom of raiding enemy groups for wives may have provided sufficient genetic exchange even among some ostensibly hostile groups that they should be considered as a single breeding unit. Therefore, contrary to the implication of Stewart (1960), it does not follow from the fact that the groups which first populated the Americas may have been small and scattered that there should be a homogeneity of type within the group.

Thirdly, we do not know the exact time or times of arrival of these bands. However, a number of archaeological findings support the argument that man may have reached western North America some 30,000 to 20,000 years ago (Agogino, 1963). Entry during the earlier portion of this time span would imply immigration during the interstadial between the early and late Wisconsin glaciation, or even in pre-Wisconsin times. Since there may well have been post-Wisconsin immigration, the possibility of discontinuity in the peopling of the North American continent, and of important differences between the various founding stocks is strong. In this connection, we are specifically excluding the Eskimos and Aleuts from these considerations (cf. Laughlin, 1963).

Fourthly, the time scale for the dispersion of the Indian throughout the Americas is poorly known. Since spatial barriers between genetic exchange are an important factor in evolution, this lack of knowledge impedes a number of genetic formulations and inferences. Incidentally, the very fact that man did spread throughout the length and breadth of the American continent in some 30,000 years is in our opinion a striking testimony to human mobility and a strong argument against any hypothesis which visualizes man as having come into existence at multiple, independent foci (Coon, 1962).

Finally, as already alluded to, we have no way of knowing with certainty to what extent the surviving groups of primitive Indians have had their way of life seriously disrupted by the events of the past 450 years, a fact which must be borne in mind wherever we attempt to extrapolate from these groups to Stone Age and pre-Stone Age man. In this same vein, to what extent are these groups the victims of a cultural regression in consequence of which they are not typical of any stage in human evolution?

These uncertainties seriously interfere with the interpretation of much of the existing genetic data on the American Indian, as well as the data to be collected in the near future. However, if the developments of the past century are any guide, the future will bring clarification of many of these points. To hold back on research on the three questions stated earlier until this clarification is achieved would, in view of the current rate of disruption of Indian communities, result in the loss of opportunities which can never be recaptured.

Microevolution in the Indian

We proceed now to a discussion of the first of the three questions posed at the outset, namely, the light the Indian can throw on the tempo and direction of human evolution. The primary contribution of the geneticist here consists of intensive and extensive studies of the frequency of the genes responsible for specific traits. From such studies will emerge a kind of genetic taxonomy. It is important that this approach be combined with the techniques of the physical anthropologist, since many of the traits with which he is concerned also have a genetic basis, unclear though this may be at the moment. It is equally important that when the time comes to attempt to relate these data to a general taxonomic schema and a time scale, due consideration be given to cultural and linguistic evidence.

TABLE 1

Some distinctive genetic features of the American Indian

ABO system:	high frequency of I^0.
MN system:	high frequency of L^M.
Rh system:	the frequency of R^2 is higher than anywhere else in the world; r and R^0 low or absent.
Kell system:	K may have been absent in pre-Columbian Indians.
Duffy system:	high frequency of Fy^a.
Diego system:	high frequency of Di^a.
Lewis system:	almost all populations show Le $(a-)$ only.
Lutheran system:	almost all populations show Lu $(a-)$ only.
Haemoglobin types:	abnormal types very rare or absent.
Colour blindness:	low frequency of defectives.

The genetic characteristics of all the American Indian groups thus far studied have been sufficiently similar to one another but different from those of other groups that they have been recognized as a distinct sub-group of the human species (Boyd, 1963 and earlier papers). Some of these characteristics are listed in Table 1.

TAB

Genetic studies in S[...]

	No. studied	No. of surveys	Gene			
ABO system	24,515	109				
			I^0	0·751–0·800 — 1	0·801–0·850 — 0	0·851–c[...] — 2
			I^A	0 — 60	0·001–0·050 — 40	0·051–0[...] — 8
			I^B	0 — 62	0·001–0·010 — 26	0·011–0[...] — 5
MN system	5747	108	L^M	0·300–0·399 — 1	0·400–0·499 — 1	0·500–c[...] — 8
MNSs system	2718	24	L^{MS}	0·001–0·100 — 3	0·101–0·200 — 6	0·201–0[...] — 5
			L^{Ms}	— — —	1	2
			L^{Ns}	2	7	9
			L^{NS}	0–0·040 — 9	0·041–0·080 — 7	0·081–0[...] — 4
P system	3074	29	P_1	0·100–0·199 — 2	0·200–0·299 — 7	0·300–0[...] — 10
Rh system (5 sera)	2909	30	R^1	0·200–0·299 — 1	0·300–0·399 — 4	0·400–c[...] — 4
			R^2	0–0·099 — 2	0·100–0·199 — 8	0·200–0[...] — 7
			R^Z	0 — 5	0·001–0·040 — 14	0·041–0[...] — 3
			R^0	0 — 7	0·001–0·050 — 11	0·051–c[...] — 6
			r	25	—	1
Kell system	3284	30	k	0·970–0·999 — 7	1·000 — 23	
Duffy system	3446	35	Fy^a	0·100–0·199 — 1	0·200–0·299 — 1	0·300–0[...] — 3
Diego system	4161	47	Di^a	0 — 4	0·001–0·100 — 19	0·101–0[...] — 14
Kidd system	1993	21	Jk^a	0·300–0·399 — 2	0·400–0·499 — 7	0·500–0[...] — 5
Lewis system	2313	19	Le(a+)	0 — 14	0·1–5·0(%) — 5	
Lutheran system	1148	9	Lu^a	0 — 7	0·001–0·010 — 2	
Js system	825	8	Js^a	0 — 4	0·001–0·020 — 4	
Haptoglobin types	2769	26	Hp^1	0·200–0·299 — 1	0·300–0·399 — 2	0·400–0[...] — 5
Haemoglobin types	2652	28	Hb^A	0·995–0·999 — 1	1·000 — 27	
Colour blindness	586 (males)	13	cv^+	0·940–0·999 — 2	1·000 — 11	

† Studies in the following systems are not presented because the data available is yet too scarce to provide any generalization: Wright blood group, G-6-PD deficiency and esterases in the red blood cells; transferrins, Gm, Gc, and Ag serum groups; secretion of ABH and Le^a in saliva; PTC.

merican Indians†

Gene frequencies

0·901–0·950	0·951–0·999	1·000	
16	34	56	
0·101–0·150	0·151–0·200	0·201–0·250	
0	0	1	
0·021–0·030	0·031–0·040	0·041–0·050	
7	8	1	
0·600–0·699	0·700–0·799	0·800–0·899	0·900–1·000
20	13	4	1
0·301–0·400	0·401–0·500	0·501–0·600	0·601–0·699
8	1	1	—
6	6	6	3
6	—	—	—
0·121–0·160	0·161–0·200		
2	2		
0·400–0·499	0·500–0·599	0·600–0·699	
7	1	2	
0·500–0·599	0·600–0·699	0·700–0·799	0·800–0·899
6	7	7	1
0·300–0·399	0·400–0·499	0·500–0·599	0·600–0·699
7	4	1	1
0·081–0·120	0·121–0·160	0·161–0·200	
6	1	1	
0·101–0·150	0·151–0·200	0·201–0·250	
2	2	2	
3	—	—	

0·400–0·499	0·500–0·599	0·600–0·699	0·700–0·799	0·800–0·899	0·900–0·999	1·000
4	7	9	6	3	0	1
0·201–0·300	0·301–0·400	0·401–0·500				
6	3	1				
0·600–0·699	0·700–0·799					
4	3					

0·500–0·599	0·600–0·699	0·700–0·799	0·800–0·899
3	4	10	1

However, the extent of the intertribal differences so far found is not commonly realized. Table 2 illustrates some of these differences as they were encountered in South American Indians alone. In the preparation of this table we have encountered all the difficulties which arise wherever one attempts a *critical* tabulation. What findings should be excluded on the grounds that the investigator was the victim of poor anti-sera, an inadequate sample of the population, or unrecognized racial admixture ? The temptation is strong to question or even exclude from such a tabulation results falling outside the usual range, but this may lead one to discard some of the most important material. We have recently reported a frequency of non-secretors of 43·6 per cent among Xavante Indians (Neel, Salzano, Junqueira, Keiter and Maybury-Lewis, 1964). This is so out of line with other findings that a tabulator would be tempted to regard it as due to laboratory error, but we have now confirmed this in a second group of Xavantes and also in a second laboratory. However, although unusual findings may be valid, a certain amount of selection must go into a compilation of this sort; findings completely out of line and not confirmed by subsequent work have been omitted. The reader is referred to the original references presented in the appendix for an evaluation of the degree of selection used in the manipulation of these data.

The data presented in Table 2 present two aspects which are worth discussing. Firstly, although nine of the genetic characteristics exhibit a narrow range of variation (genes I^0, I^A, r, k, Lu^a, Js^a, Hb^A, and cv^+, as well as the frequencies of Le(a) positives), this is not true for the remaining 15 genes. The most extreme example of a wide range is presented by the R^2 gene. Its lowest frequency (0·064) was observed among 141 Waica of Venezuela (Layrisse, Layrisse and Wilbert, 1962), its highest (0·630) found among 100 Tunebo from Colombia (Layrisse, Layrisse and Wilbert, 1963a). The latter is 9·8 times higher than the first! Another gene which shows frequencies highly variable is Fy^a. Its lowest frequency was observed among 143 Kariri from Brazil (0·131—Pedreira, Peixoto and Castro, 1961), its highest (1·000) among 22 Indians from Southern Surinam (Nijenhuis, 1961). The highest value is 7·6 times larger than the lowest. In this case the divergence may be explained by postulating an effect of White and Negro admixture (which certainly has occurred) among the Kariri and an accident of sampling among the Surinam Indians.

But even then the next lowest frequency is the 0·237 which was found among 55 Brazilian Carajás by Junqueira and Wishart (1956) and the next highest 0·833, observed among 72 Warrau and 108 Taurepan, both from Venezuela (Layrisse, Arends and Wilbert, 1958; Layrisse, Layrisse, Garcia and Wilbert, 1962). The difference is halved; the highest value is only 3·5 times larger than the lowest; but this is still a very broad range. Approximately the same amount of variability can be demonstrated for all the other 13 genes listed. They provide strong evidence against any tendency to simplified statements about the gene pool of the American Indian (see, for instance, Stewart, 1960). On the other hand attempts at establishing a racial classification on the basis of genetic data in the future should avoid relying too heavily on 'typical populations'. This typological approach so criticized by the proponents of the 'new physical anthropology' when used to define morphological types, is now being utilized by geneticists to define ethnic groups on the basis of gene frequencies. As was emphasized by Newman (1963) unless the data now available are re-examined in detail to verify how much the several genetically controlled traits are geographically associated, these attempts will not bring anything new to the field. A proper taxonomic schema must simultaneously take into consideration a great variety of points. The problem of doing this in a properly weighted and unbiased fashion has plagued many investigators. Hanna's (1962) and Cavalli-Sforza and Edwards' (1964) efforts in this direction may prove helpful as additional information accumulates.

Secondly, there are hints of bimodality in the distribution of three genes: I^B, R^Z, and Hp^1. Concerning the I^B gene there is no doubt that in many cases its presence may be explained by White or Negro admixture, but the fact that 47 (43·1 per cent) of the 109 samples tested showed the presence of I^B indicates that the assumption that the I^B gene was not present in pre-Columbian Indians may have to be revised, at least in relation to the Andean Indians (Salzano, 1957, 1964b). It is recognized that the detection of bimodality, where the samples on which the tabulation is based are small, is difficult. Bimodality may appear to be present when one interval is used for tabulation and absent with a different interval. Chance alone may lead to the appearance of bimodality in a normal or skewed frequency distribution. On the other hand, one must not be overly cautious in recognizing a possible bimodality, since the resulting suggestion of subpopulations can be followed up by recourse to other genetic systems. For instance, the Macushi of British Guiana (Layrisse, Layrisse, and Wilbert, 1963b; Arends and Gallango, 1962b) occupy 'secondary peaks' in the distribution of both R^Z and Hp^1. The Irapas showed differences from other Yupa tribes not only in relation to their Di^a distribution but in relation to genes of the MNSs and Rh system as well (Layrisse, Layrisse, and Wilbert, 1960a).

The whole problem of the possible existence of discontinuity in the distribution of genes among South American Indians can be discussed in the light of the distribution of the Diego antigen. Layrisse and Wilbert (1961) have advanced the hypothesis that there may be a discontinuity in the distribution of Diego positives. (This discontinuity is not apparent on our tabulation but can be brought out if different intervals are used.) According to them the absence of the gene in Waica, Bari, and one Warrau population and its low frequency in another Warrau group and among the Yaruro contrast with its higher frequency in other groups with a higher culture. This has led them to raise the question of the possibility that the low-Diego tribes are representatives of an early wave of human migration into this area ('Marginal American Indians'), who were followed by a later wave with a 'higher' culture and higher Diego frequency.

This is a stimulating hypothesis but difficult to prove. Several exceptions to this rule were already found. For instance, the low frequency of this trait among the Tunebo, Irapa, Colla, Oma-guaca, and Mapuche required additional hypotheses; its high frequency among the Xavante remains unexplained. On the other hand, Layrisse and Wilbert's (1961) definition of a Marginal Indian tribe is open to criticism due to their attempts to correlate a given physical type with specific cultural and sociological traits; moreover, the recognized scarcity of good morphological data on South American Indian groups indicates the need for caution in any generalization like this one.

Attempts to explain the diversity of American Indians in terms of migrations are not new. Once this 'wave' hypothesis is introduced it seems logical to postulate a third 'wave' which would have brought the high-A frequencies of the Indians of north-western North America. But alternative hypotheses cannot be excluded at present. For instance, the average frequency of the

Di^a gene is sufficiently low in many groups that the possibility of random gene extinction at the time a splinter group breaks off or through genetic drift must be considered, a process which in time leads to an accumulation of groups in which the gene is lacking.

In any attempt to use gene frequency data for taxonomic purposes, one is of course aware of the possibility that local variations in selective forces have significantly altered 'original' gene frequencies. However, with the possible exceptions of the genes responsible for haemoglobins S and C and the glucose-6-phosphate dehydrogenase deficiency, precise data on the extent to which local selective factors may obscure genetic relationships is unclear. Furthermore, in the case of the three genetic traits just mentioned, the fact that they respond to local selective factors impairs but by no means invalidates their usefulness as indicators of genetic relationship.

The dynamics of Stone Age populations

With the antiquity of man currently estimated at 1,000,000 to 2,000,000 years, it follows that the major extent of man's evolution occurred under conditions far more comparable to those to be observed in the surviving primitive groups of the world than in today's major culture-complexes. Such groups—and the American Indian is pre-eminent among them—present an unusual and fast-disappearing opportunity to study the selective forces which shaped modern man. It is towards this opportunity that our own recent studies of the Indian have been especially directed.

To say that a meaningful study of natural selection is going to be difficult is a classic in understatement. The methodology of such studies is still in its infancy, both in theory and in practice. It is clear that only a rather comprehensive approach to these populations will yield meaningful results, but the term 'comprehensive' is so open-ended and the logistics of these studies so troublesome, that obviously a number of difficult decisions must be reached concerning the precise nature of the field work to be undertaken.

The kinds of data to be collected can to a first approximation be considered under six headings: (1) data, both morphological and genetic, which are descriptive of the group. A list illustrative of the possibilities will be found in the *World Health Organization*

Technical Report No. 279 which contains the collective views of a Scientific Group on Research in the Population Genetics of Primitive Groups convened by the World Health Organization in 1962. These data, the raw material of the taxonomic approach discussed in the preceding section, serve in the present context a much wider objective, as will be apparent shortly; (2) data on those aspects of the cultural pattern with biological implications. Since without detailed knowledge it is impossible to dismiss any aspect of culture as without biological relevance, the implication is that these genetic studies must be paralleled by equally complete cultural studies; (3) data on population structure, the term including birth and death rates, mean completed family size, polygamy, age distribution, inbreeding, migration between villages of the same tribe, and between tribes of the same region, &c.; (4) data on biological pressures, the term including exposure to agents of disease and the manner of acquisition of immunity as well as an evaluation of elements in the diet which when deficient or in excess are disease producing; (5) data on psychological pressures, with particular reference to the relation they bear to survival and reproduction; and (6) the utilization of all these data on genotype, biological pressures, and population structure in an effort to relate the probability of reproduction to genotype.

In passing, it might be noted that certain of the Central and South American tribes (Aztecs, Incas, Mayas, and their predecessors) have demonstrated the capacity to evolve a high-order civilization. Some of the primitive groups who never evolved beyond the Stone Age are sufficiently closely related to these that it is difficult to conceive of significant intellectual differences. What are the psychological factors that promote innovation in one group and inhibit it in another?

Table 3 represents an attempt at a listing of those American Indian groups persisting in a relatively 'unspoiled' form whose economy was based on hunting, gathering, and incipient agriculture. In the preparation of this list we have drawn heavily on the Bulletins of the International Committee on Urgent Anthropological and Ethnological Research, of the International Union of Anthropological and Ethnological Sciences; on the *Handbook of South American Indians* (ed. J. H. Stewart), on Gama Malcher's (1964) compilation of Brazilian Indians, and on the report of the WHO Scientific Group referred to earlier, as well as our own field experience. Any such listing is outdated before it is prepared, both because of the rapidity with which cultural change is occurring and the discovery of new groups, but the very fact that we can list some forty groups is some indication of the opportunities which exist. Figure 1 shows the location of these populations.

TABLE 3

Some surviving primitive groups in the Americas

Location	Group
Nicaragua	1. Sumu
	2. Ulva
Panamá—Colombia border	3. Choco
Venezuela	4. Bari (Motilones Bravos)
	5. Panare
	6. Piaroa
	7. Warao
Venezuela—Brazil border	8. Yanoama (Waica, Shiriana, &c.)
Brazil—British Guiana border	9. Parikotó
	10. Wai-wai
Brazil—Surinam border	11. Tirió
Brazil	12. Araras
	13. Asurini
	14. Boca Negra
	15. Canoeiros
	16. Gaviões
	17. Guajá
	18. Ipewi
	19. Kabixi
	20. Maku
	21. Mandawáka
	22. Maopityan
	23. Mayongong (Iekuana)
	24. Northern Cayapo
	25. Parakanan
	26. Sheta
	27. Suya
	28. Tapayúna
	29. Waimirí
	30. Xavante
Brazil—Bolivia border	31. Pakaánovas
Peru	32. Amahuaca
	33. Jivaro
	34. Mashco
	35. Yaminahua
Bolivia	36. Siriono
Paraguay	37. Guayaki
Argentina	38. Morotoko

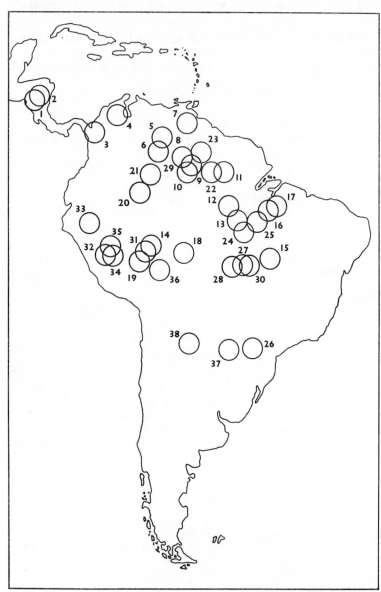

FIG. 1. Location of some surviving primitive groups in Central and
South America (numbers correspond to those used in Table 3).

Our own experience with such groups is confined to a single tribe, the Xavante Indians of the Brazilian Mato Grosso. We have visited them on three different occasions. The results of the first study, performed in the summer of 1962 among the Xavantes of São Domingos, located near the Rio das Mortes, have already been reported (Neel, Salzano, Junqueira, Keiter and Maybury-Lewis, 1964). During the summer of 1963 one of us (FMS) obtained demographic, genealogic, and genetic information concerning the Xavante population of São Marcos, who live in close proximity to a Catholic Mission near the river Boqueirão. In 1964 the authors in collaboration with Dr. J. D. Niswander and Dr. E. D. Weinstein carried out additional field work among the Xavantes living close to the Post Simões Lopes, near the Paranatinga River, and the Xavantes of São Marcos were again visited, this time by Dr. J. D. Niswander and ourselves, to complete some of the studies begun in 1963 and to obtain new information. All these populations are located in the Brazilian State of Mato Grosso.

It is obviously impossible to try to summarize here all the results obtained; besides, the laboratory work on the material collected in 1963 and 1964 is still going on. We shall restrict ourselves, therefore, to a discussion of some aspects of the São Domingos study indicating, where needed, in what way the new information now available changed or confirmed our first impression concerning this group.

The Xavantes are a Ge-speaking tribe numbering between 1,500 and 2,000 individuals living in a number of autonomous or semi-autonomous communities along the Rio das Mortes, from the Ilha do Bananal in the east to the region of the headwaters of the Rio Telles Pires in the west. In 1958 there were at least nine autonomous Xavante communities. One of these had had no friendly contacts with the outside world and its exact location was unknown. By 1962 the number of localities had been reduced to eight, and it was rumoured that the group which had not previously accepted outsiders had established peaceful contact with the Neo-Brazilians. At the present time the number of autonomous groups has been further reduced by migration and fusion of one of these groups with two others previously existent.

We have found in São Domingos (Neel et al., 1964) a striking degree of village endogamy: 93 per cent of the fifty-four marriages from which it was possible to obtain information were contracted within the community. The evidence obtained from the two other Xavante populations, however, show that the São Domingos group may be exceptional in this respect, perhaps due to the relatively prolonged and dominant nature of Apewe's chiefship, as was already suggested in the 1962 paper. The picture which is now emerging is the following: the several Xavante groups are nomadic and generally until recently did not stay too long in a single place. They undergo what may be called a periodic cycle of split-fusions. A certain band headed by a dominant person may stay for some years in a village, then split from it and join another group; afterwards the new group formed may split again and so on. An extreme example of this is Sebastião's group, now in São Marcos, which roamed the length of Xavante land before coming to its present place. Another is the group which left São Domingos and established itself nearby, as mentioned by Neel et al. (1964). They had a semi-independent life until 1963; afterwards about one-third of them went to São Marcos; the destination of the remaining two-thirds is unknown but they probably went to Areões, a place near Xavantina where there is a SPI Post, and some may have returned to the São Domingos village. The situation in Simões Lopes is somewhat similar to the two-village system found in São Domingos in 1962. The Simões Lopes group is an offshoot of a once larger group living along the Culuene river. From that region they went to where now the SPI Post Marechal Rondon is located at the margins of the Batovi river; afterwards the group under discussion separated from those who stayed there, living for some time near the Bakairi and then establishing themselves at their present location, 12 km from the Simões Lopes Post. They enjoy an almost complete autonomy but in important matters, like when and where they should go on treks and who should go, they still obey orders from the Batovi group chief, Seremessê. There is also a constant flux of families between the two places.

Other demographic points of interest can be summarized as follows, in relation to the São Domingos group: polygamy is common and sterility is rare; fertility differentials (achieved mainly through polygamy) have far more significance there than is true for civilized man today; the population appears to be at the replacement level, achieving this by moderately high birth-rates accompanied by moderate death-rates prior to reproduction.

Morphologic studies can be of invaluable help in estimating population variability. The Xavantes of São Domingos were compared in this regard with a cosmopolitan town (Hamburg) and while they appear to be less variable in the various morphological traits under consideration, the differences are not large. This point will be further studied since it can contribute to a basic question: are the populations living in small bands at the hunting-and-gathering stage of culture genetically less variable than those of the large cities of today? On an intuitive basis they should be, but the point to be studied is how less variable they are. The pattern of split-fusions above described for the Xavante groups may be a significant factor in increasing this variability. The main handicap facing us in the interpretation of such findings is our relative lack of knowledge of both the genetic and environmental components of most human quantitative traits.

Physical examination of the São Domingos group revealed a population which is superficially healthy. The only agent of disease directly identified was the malaria parasite, in three persons. Since our studies were conducted at the height of the dry season, these findings provide a very minimum estimate of the impact of malaria. By inference from the eosinophilia, intestinal parasitism is common. So, by inference from the antibody studies, are viral infections. The latter studies raise some very fundamental questions concerning the epidemiological characteristics of such groups. Specifically, how has a group which appears so healthy acquired antibodies to so many pathogens?

In São Domingos there is a high proportion of individuals with antibodies to poliomyelitis. It is not clear to what extent this is due to a natural oral immunization beginning while the infant still has a passive partial immunization acquired from the mother, to the death of the more severely affected, or to the characteristics of the disease in very young children. Similar uncertainties exist concerning the manner of acquisition of certain other of the antibodies encountered in these studies. Consider for instance the salmonelloses. The deposits of human faeces about the village, the swirling clouds of dust, the low levels of hygiene, the obvious stickiness of the ever-flowing Indian breast—all lead to a very early exposure to the *Salmonella* group of bacteria, with the possibility either of severe clinical disease and death or of sub-clinical or mild disease due to active immunization beginning while passive protection is still present. The literature on the transfer of antibodies by milk after the neonatal period is extensive and controversial. None of the observations to date deals with hyperimmunized populations such as the Xavante. Are these hyperimmunized mothers able to transmit significant amounts of maternal antibody to the child during the prolonged period of breast feeding, with partial neutralization or attenuation of a variety of agents of disease either in the intestinal tract or following absorption of small amounts of unchanged maternal antibody from the intestinal tract? We have no data on the prevalence and aetiology of diarrhoeal diseases among infants at this level of culture that would enable us to reach sound judgements concerning the manner of acquisition of these antibodies.

Selective forces must be concerned in the maintenance of the many genetic polymorphisms studied. Difficult though the problem of amassing significant numbers might be, the future undoubtedly will bring a number of studies seeking evidence for such forces. It will be important that such studies are accompanied by adequate data on the mortality and morbidity structure of the populations concerned, since a given level of mortality may be reached in many ways, some possibly involving a given genetic system, others not. In this connection we want to mention that the Simões Lopes study was much more complete than the one performed in São Domingos. The collection of faeces and urine and the performance of some special tests with the bloods shall enable us to obtain a much better picture of the disease pressures in this community. In addition, data concerning births and deaths have been carefully collected by the Indian Post agent since the group arrived there in 1957. Therefore it was possible to obtain precious information documenting some of the events which occurred in this group just after their first contacts of a more permanent nature with the neo-Brazilian culture.

An example of the unexpected in these studies concerns some recent observations regarding plasma uric acid values. When we persuaded Dr. William Mikkelsen to undertake plasma uric acid determinations on a batch of specimens obtained in the 1963 field work at São Marcos, it was with every expectation that the values to be obtained would be as low as any on record. Instead, the mean value for 19 males aged 20–39 was $6 \cdot 0 \pm 0 \cdot 2$ mg per cent, and for 29 females of the same age, $5 \cdot 3 \pm 0 \cdot 1$ mg per cent. We are now in the midst of extending this observation to a second group of Xavantes. Whether these high values are genetic or acquired is as yet unknown. However, it is an interesting and possibly highly relevant coincidence that the three other populations thus far known to have similar high values are the Maoris of New Zealand, Filipinos, and the Chamorros of Guam. Japanese do not show high values. Here may be additional genetic evidence concerning a possible genetic relationship between Polynesians (and their relatives) and some American Indian groups, to be considered in conjunction with the blood-group data reviewed by Mourant (1954), Simmons, Graydon, Semple and Fry (1955), and Simmons (1962). Data on uric acid values in other Indian groups are greatly to be desired. In exhuming this frequently buried theory, we assure you we are not thinking in terms of a contribution of one to the other so much as some degree of common ancestry. Of course, the obvious alternative possibility of the occurrence of the same local selective mechanism in these different populations should also be considered.

The emergence of new disease patterns

The deleterious effects upon the health of the Indian of coming into contact with Western man and Western culture are well known. But surprisingly little exists in the way of accurate documentation or analysis. Since it is reasonable to assume that these contacts may demand genetic adjustments which for Western man were spread over a much longer period of time, here may be an important opportunity to gain insight into the selective forces of recent centuries.

This question may be considered under two headings, namely, response to infectious disease, both acute and chronic, and appearance or increase in frequency of so-called constitutional diseases. As regards acute infectious disease, the impact on primitive populations of such a disease as measles is well known. Why this should be so is in our opinion still a complete mystery. To the best of our knowledge, really detailed medical observations have never been made on the course of a measles epidemic in a primitive group, Indian or otherwise. The high gamma globulin values observed in a number of primitive groups would seem to indicate no lack of ability to react to an agent of disease (references in Neel *et al.*, 1964). Why, then, the high death rate ? In our opinion, the answer may rest as much with a general breakdown in community life in time of epidemic and in attitude toward disease as in temperature curves and antibody responses.

As regards chronic infectious disease, we are equally in the dark as to why such a disease as tuberculosis runs so devastating a course in the Indian. There has been much loose speculation about a genetically determined susceptibility. However, our own studies of the past several months revealed that 42·7 per cent of the 82 persons tested in one Xavante village reacted positively to histoplasmin, an extract from a fungus responsible for another form of acute and/or chronic lung disease—but physical signs of chronic lung diseases were observed in only one old woman, and she reacted negatively to both histoplasmin and tuberculin. While there are many differences in the clinical course of tuberculosis and histoplasmosis, the evidence, as far as it goes, fails to suggest an especial susceptibility of the Indian to chronic lung disease. The answer to the devastating course of tuberculosis in the Indian is again as apt to be found in the deterioration in his nutrition and hygiene which follows contact with the Western World as in any innate susceptibility.

If our dental colleagues will be a little indulgent, we would like to consider dental caries in this section devoted to chronic infectious disease. In the first Xavante village we studied, the caries rate was very low (Neel *et al.*, 1964), but in a second village just studied, Dr. J. Niswander observed caries to be much more common (although still a relatively low rate). An important difference between the dietary habits of the two villages was that although the first group had been in permanent contact with an SPI Post for a considerably longer period of time, it had no access to sugar cane, whereas the second village had been introduced to sugar cane when it established permanent contacts only six years ago, and chewing sections of sugar cane was extremely popular. We would suspect, although we cannot document the hypothesis adequately, that the higher caries rate of the second village is not due to the introduction of a cariogenic strain of lactobacilli but to the creation, in the absence of oral hygiene, of conditions unusually favourable for the activity of lactobacilli. In the absence of a documented comparable experience for a Caucasian group, this cannot be taken as evidence that the Indian is more susceptible to caries than his white brother.

As regards the constitutional diseases, a number of reports raise the possibility that the 'civilized' Indian may have an unusually high frequency of such diseases as diabetes mellitus and cholecystitis with cholelithiasis (references in Sievers and Marquis, 1962; Mayberry and Lindeman, 1963). Unfortunately, while these reports serve to identify possible differences, because of dissimilar dietary patterns between the Indian and Caucasian groups compared, problems in drawing comparable samples of subjects, and mean age differences between groups, precise statements are impossible.

Not only is it impossible at present to state to what degree, under comparable circumstances, Indians and Caucasians will differ in the frequency of certain constitutional diseases, but also we know so little about the frequency of these diseases in the primitive state what it will be difficult for some time to come to know whether a given figure for civilized Indians represents an increase or decrease over the primitive state. Because of the low mean age in most primitive groups and the relatively low proportion of persons of 40 or over (6·1 per cent of 133 persons in the Xavantes of São Domingos), these are data it is going to be very difficult to collect.

In summary, we know very little indeed about the Indians' biological response to 'new' diseases and unfamiliar cultural patterns. Here is an almost virgin field of investigation.

Humanitarian considerations

The history of the relations of the West with the Indian constitute one of the more sordid chapters in a book which would be titled 'Might Makes Right'. The chapter is not yet finished— there are even today countries in South America where, contrary, of course, to all official policy, the Indian is still being hunted down like a wild animal. In Brazil, fifty-five years ago, large regions of the territory could not be reached because of the hostile activities of the Indians. The situation was so anomalous that in 1907 a well-known scientist, Hermann von Ihering, wrote an article advocating the complete extermination of the Indians. 'Since they constitute a serious handicap for the colonization of the regions where they live it seems that there is no other measure we can take but their extermination', he said (Ihering, 1907). Fortunately, this article was answered by a violent wave of protests and in 1910 the Indian Protective Service (SPI) was created. The new institution received for some years all the aid necessary for its development especially because of the pressure of the public opinion and because of Marshall Candido M. da Silva Rondon's influence. However, since then the appropriations in money for the SPI decreased relatively as compared to the rise in the cost of living. As a matter of fact, Ribeiro (1962) was able to show, based on calculations performed by T. P. A. Borges, that the SPI was receiving in 1960 only 10 per cent of the money furnished in 1910, if due consideration is given to the inflation which has gone on in Brazil since that time. The situation in the frontier zones of colonization and even in other areas, however, is by no means settled. Some months ago the director of the SPI denounced through the press the action of some persons in the Brazilian Northeast who have been paying others to kill Indians.

The United States, on the other hand, must acknowledge room for great improvement in its own present efforts to solve the Indian problem. Now, during a time of awakened social conscience in that country, we suggest an extension of the thinking beyond the descendents of those who were brought there in involuntary slavery, to the descendents of those who were the original inhabitants of the country, but whose socioeconomic and medical status is below that of the Negro.

The past can never be fully undone. However, it is not too late to adopt more enlightened policies towards the approximately 16,000,000 Indians still to be found in the New World. The programme here outlined will inevitably yield data of value in the transition of the Indian to full citizenship. It is for governments to utilize these data.

A matter of urgency

In closing, we would like to direct your attention to the urgency of certain aspects of this programme. Were a twenty-year moratorium called on the majority of biomedical investigations, the opportunities would still be there when the moratorium was lifted. This would not be so with respect to certain aspects of this programme, and especially those aimed at studying the dynamics of primitive groups. Populations suitable for such studies are being disrupted at an ever accelerating rate; in twenty years there will be very few left. So rapidly is the way of life of the

Xavantes of Simões Lopes and São Marcos being altered that it seems safe to say that although their permanent contacts with the non-Indian would go back only six years, in another six years they will be unsuitable for studies on the dynamics of hunting-gathering early agriculture groups. The acculturation of these groups is inevitable and imminent. We as scientists can do nothing to retard this process, but we as scientists might through proper studies do much to facilitate it and at the same time contribute to one of the great unknowns in our knowledge of human genetics—the nature of natural selection.

REFERENCES

Only the papers cited in the text which do not contain specific new genetic information about the South American Indians are listed here. All others are listed in the appendix.

AGOGINO, G. A., 1963. Comment on Greenman's article, *Curr. Anthrop.* **4**, 66.

BIRDSELL, J. B., 1951. 'The problem of the early peopling of the Americas as viewed from Asia', *Physical Anthropology of the American Indian* (ed. W. S. LAUGHLIN), pp. 1–68. Edwards, Ann Arbor, Michigan.

BOYD, W. C., 1963. 'Genetics and the human race', *Science* **140**, 1057–1064.

CAVALLI-SFORZA, L. L. and EDWARDS, A. W. F., 1964. 'Analysis of human evolution', *Proc. XI Int. Conf. Genet.* **3**, pp. 923–932.

COON, C. S., 1962. *The Origin of Races.* Knopf, New York.

GAMA MALCHER, J. M., *Indios. Grau de Integração na Comunidade Nacional, Grupo Linguístico, Localização.* Conselho Nac. de Proteção aos Índios, Rio de Janeiro.

GREENMAN, E. F., 1963. 'The upper palaeolithic and the New World', *Curr. Anthrop.* **4**, 41–91.

HANNA, B. L., 1962. 'The biological relationships among Indian groups of the Southwest', *Am. J. phys. Anthrop.* **20**, 499–508.

IHERING, H. VON., 1907. 'A anthropologia do estado de São Paulo', *Revta. Mus. paul.* **7**, 202–257.

IMBELLONI, J., 1950. 'La tabla clasificatoria de los indios a los trece años de su publicación', *Runa* **3**, 200–210.

LAUGHLIN, W. S., 1963. 'Eskimos and Aleuts: their origins and evolution', *Science* **142**, 633–645.

MAYBERRY, R. H. and LINDEMAN, R. D., 1963. 'A survey of chronic disease and diet in Seminole Indians in Oklahoma', *Am. J. clin. Nutr.* **13**, 127–134.

MOURANT, A. E., 1954. *The Distribution of the Human Blood Groups.* Thomas, Springfield.

NEWMAN, M. T., 1963. 'Geographic and microgeographic races', *Curr. Anthrop.* **4**, 189–207.

RIBEIRO, D., 1962. *A Política Indigenista Brasileira.* Ministério da Agricultura, Rio de Janeiro.

RIVET, P., 1958. *As Origens do Homen Americano.* Anhambi, São Paulo.

SALZANO, F. M., 1957. 'The blood groups of South American Indians', *Am. J. phys. Anthrop.* **15**, 555–579.

—— 1963. 'Some genetic aspects of the demography of American Indians', *Proc. Entretiens de Monaco en Sciences Humaines* **1**, 23–39.

—— 1964. 'A origem do homem americano', *Revta. Antrop.*, *S. Paulo* **11**, 1–8.

SIEVERS, M. L. and MARQUIS, J. R., 1962. 'The southwestern American Indian's burden: biliary disease', *J. Maine med. Ass.* **182**, 172–174.

SIMMONS, R. T., 1962. 'Blood group genes in polynesians and comparisons with other Pacific peoples', *Oceania* **32**, 198–210.

—— GRAYDON, J. J., SEMPLE, N. M., and FRY, E. I., 1955. 'A blood group genetical survey in Cook islanders, Polynesia, and comparisons with American Indians', *Am. J. phys. Anthrop.* **13**, 667–690.

STEWARD, J. H. (ed.), 1948–1950. 'Handbook of South American Indians', *Bull. Bur. Am. Ethnol.* **143**, Washington, D.C. (6 volumes).

STEWART, T. D., 1960. 'A physical anthropologist's view of the peopling of the New World', *SWest. J. Anthrop.* **16**, 259–273.

WRIGHT, S., 1949. 'Adaptation and selection', *Genetics, Paleontology and Evolution* (eds. G. L. JEPSON *et al.*), pp. 365–389. Princeton University Press, Princeton, New Jersey.

APPENDIX

A LIST OF THE PAPERS PUBLISHED ABOUT THE GENETICS OF THE SOUTH AMERICAN INDIANS

ALLEN, JR., F. H., 1958. 'Inheritance of the Diego (*Di^a*) blood group factor', *Am. J. hum. Genet.* **10**, 64–67.

—— 1959. 'Summary of blood group phenotypes in some aboriginal Americans', *Am. J. phys. Amthrop.* **17**, 86.

ALVAREZ, A. G., 1939. 'Comprobaciones biológicas en aborígenes argentinos—Consideraciones sobre los grupos sanguíneos de los Matacos', *Comisión Hon. de Reduciones de Indios (Buenos Aires) Publ.* **6**, 25–34.

ARCE LARRETA, J., 1930. 'Doscientas determinaciones de grupos sanguíneos en los indios del norte del Peru', *An. hosp.*, *Lima* **3**, 74–77.

ARCILA VELEZ, G., 1943. 'Grupos sanguíneos entre los indios Paez', *Revta. Inst. etnol. nac., Bogotá* **1**, 7–14.

—— 1946. 'Los Caramanta', *Univ. Antioquia* **20**, 445–452.

—— 1953. 'Grupos sanguíneos de los indios Katios de Antioquia', *Bolm. Inst. Antrop. (Medellin, Colombia)* **1**, 65–79.

ARENDS, T., 1960. 'Estudio electroforético de la hemoglobina de los índios Paraujanos', *Sangre* **5**, 261–270.

—— 1961a. 'Absence of abnormal haemoglobins in Colombian Tunebo Indians', *Nature, Lond.* **190**, 93–94.

—— 1961b. 'Frecuencia de las hemoglobinas anormales en Venezuela', *Archos. Hosp. Vargas* **3**, 225–236.

—— 1961c. 'El problema de las hemoglobinopatías en Venezuela', *Revta. venez. Sanid. Asist. soc.* **26**, 61–68.

—— 1962. 'Thalassemia and its variants in Venezuela', *Proc. VIII Int. Congr. Haemat.* pp. 1214–1217.

—— 1963a. 'Estado actual del estudio de las hemoglobinas anormales en Venezuela', *Sangre* **8**, 1–14.

—— 1963b. 'Frecuencia de hemoglobinas anormales en poblaciones humanas suramericanas', *Acta cient. venez. Supl.* **1**, 46–57.

GENETIC STUDIES ON AMERICAN INDIANS 269

ARENDS, T. and GALLANGO, M. L., 1960. 'Haptoglobin types in a Paraujano Indian population', *Vox Sang.* **5**, 452–461.
—— —— 1962a. 'Haptoglobin and transferrin groups in Venezuela', *Proc. VIII Congr. Int. Soc. Blood Transf.*, pp. 379–382.
—— —— 1962b. 'Frecuencia de haptoglobinas en varias poblaciones suramericanas', *Acta cient. venez.* **13**, 116–119.
—— —— 1964. 'Transferrins in Venezuelan Indians: high frequency of a slow-moving variant', *Science* **143**, 367–368.
—— and LAYRISSE, M., 1956. 'Investigación de las hemoglobinas anormales en Venezuela. Primeros casos de hemoglobina C', *Mems. VI Congr. venez. Cienc. Med.* **2**, 777–786.
BEST, W. R., 1959. 'Absence of erythrocyte glucose-6-phosphate dehydrogenase deficiency in certain Peruvian Indians', *J. Lab. clin. Med.* **54**, 791.
—— LAYRISSE, M., and BERMEJO, R., 1962. 'Blood group antigens in Aymara and Quechua speaking tribes from near Puno, Peru', *Am. J. phys. Amthrop.* **20**, 321–329.
BIOCCA, E. and OTTENSOOSER, F., 1944. 'Estudos etno-biológicos sôbre os índios da região do Alto Rio Negro-Amazonas. I. Grupos sanguíneos comuns e fatores M e N', *Archos. Biol., S. Paulo* **28**, 1–8.
BLUMBERG, B. S. and RIDDELL, N. M., 1963. 'Inherited antigenic differences in human serum beta lipoproteins. A second antiserum', *J. clin. Invest.* **42**, 867–875.
CARBONELL, L. M. and ALEMÁN, C. A., 1951. 'Investigación de la drepanocitemia entre los índios de la Sierra de Perijá', *Gac. méd. Caracas* **59**, 2–8.
COLLIER, W. A., 1955. 'The MN blood groups in the Arawaks of Matta, Surinam', *Documenta Med. geogr. trop.* **7**, 359–360.
—— FROS, J., and SCHIPPER, J. F. A., 1952. 'Blood groups of some American Indian settlements', *Documenta Med. geogr. trop.* **4**, 225–226.
DA SILVA, E. M., 1948a. 'Grupos sanguíneos comuns e fatores M e N em índios Canella (Ramkokamekra) do Maranhão', *Revta. Mus. paul.* **2**, 271–274.
—— 1948b. 'Absence of sickling phenomenon of the red blood corpuscle among Brazilian Indians', *Science* **107**, 221–222.
—— 1948c. 'Verificações sôbre a incidência de siclemia em índios brasileiros. I. Índios Pariukur, Galiby, Caripuna, Canella e Carnijó', *Mems. Inst. Oswaldo Cruz* **46**, 125–134.
—— 1949. 'Blood groups of Indians, Whites and White-Indian mixtures in Southern Mato Grosso, Brazil'. *Am. J. phys. Anthrop.* **7**, 575–585.
DÍAZ UNGRÍA, A. G., 1961. 'Percepción del sabor de la phenylthiourea en los Guajiro', *Folia Antrop.* **2**, 1–7.
—— 1962. 'Los grupos sanguineos del sistema MN en poblaciones indígenas de Venezuela', *Folia Antrop.* **3**, 1–26.
—— 1963. *El Poblamiento Indígena de Venezuela a Través de la Genética*. Fac. de Economia, Univ. Central, Caracas.
DROOGLEVER FORTUYN, A. B., 1946. 'Some data on the physical anthropology of Oajana Indians', *Konink. Veren. Indisch Inst., Medeleeling* **69**, *Afd. Volkenkunde* **22**, 1–24.

DUQUE GOMEZ, L., 1944. 'Grupos sanguíneos entre los indígenas del Departamento de Caldas', *Revta Inst. etnol. nac.*, *Bogotá* **1**, 623–653.

ELLIS, F. R., CAWLEY, L. P., and LASKER, G. W., 1963. 'Blood groups, hemoglobin types and secretion of group-specific substance at Hacienda Cayalti, North Peru', *Hum. Biol.* **35**, 26–52.

FERNANDES, J. L., 1939. 'Notas hemato–antropológicas sôbre os Caingangues de Palmas', *Revta méd. Paraná* **8**, 1–8.

—— JUNQUEIRA, P. C., KALMUS, H., OTTENSOOSER, F., PASQUALIN, R., and WISHART, P., 1957. 'P.T.C. thresholds, colour vision and blood factors of Brazilian Indians. I. Kaingangs', *Ann. hum. Genet.* **22**, 16–21.

FIGUEROA, E. R., 1948. 'Resultado de algunas investigaciones del Rh (1945)', *Archos. venez. Puericult. Pediat.* **11**, 42.

FRIMM, C. E., 1947. A Drepanocitose. Doctorate thesis, School of Medicine, Univ. Rio Grande do Sul, Pôrto Alegre, Brazil.

GALLANGO, M. L. and ARENDS, T., 1959. 'Distribution of haptoglobins in native Venezuelans', *Nature, Lond.* **183**, 1465–1466.

—— 1963. 'Incidence of *Gmᵃ* and *Gmˣ* genes among Venezuelan Indians and Mestizos', *Hum. Biol.* **35**, 361–365.

GIBLETT, E. R. and BEST, W. R., 1961. 'Haptoglobin and transferrin types in Peruvian Indians', *Nature, Lond.* **192**, 1300–1301.

GOLDEN, G., 1930. 'Distribution of blood groups in South American Indians', *Lancet* **2**, 278–279.

HENCKEL, K. O., CASTELLI, A., and DAL BORGO, J., 1941. 'Algunas observaciones acerca de la proporción de los grupos sanguíneos M y N de los indios Mapuches', *Boln. Soc. Biol.*, *Concepción* **15**, 37–41.

HERNÁNDEZ PIERETTI, O., 1954. 'Estudio hematológico de sangre periférica, las proteinas plasmáticas, serologia y grupos sanguíneos en 100 indígenas del Território Federal Delta Amacuro. Hallazgo de microfilarias en frotis estudiados'. *Banco de Sangre del Distrito Federal (Caracas)* (mimeographed).

HOFFSTETTER, R. and MARTELLY, J., 1949. 'Características serológicas (sistema ABO) de los índios del Ecuador (Estudio crítico de los resultados experimentales de A. Santiana)', *Ciencia* **9**, 101–118.

JUNQUEIRA, P. C., KALMUS, H., and WISHART, P., 1957. 'P.T.C. thresholds, colour vision and blood factors of Brazilian Indians. II. Carajás', *Ann. hum. Genet.* **22**, 22–25.

—— and WISHART, P. J., 1956. 'Blood groups of Brazilian Indians (Carajás)', *Nature, Lond.* **177**, 40.

—— —— OTTENSOOSER, F., PASQUALIN, R., FERNANDES, P. L., and KALMUS, H., 1956. 'The Diego blood factor in Brazilian Indians', *Nature, Lond.* **177**, 41.

KAHN, M., 1936. 'Blood grouping of 336 Upper Aucaner Bush Negroes and 70 Alkuyana Indians in Dutch Guiana', *J. Immun.* **31**, 377–385.

KELSO, A. J., 1961. 'Variation in the ABO blood groups among American Indians: a possible association with dietary differences', *Am. J. phys. Anthrop.* **19**, 98.

LAYRISSE, M., 1958. 'Anthropological considerations of the Diego (*Diᵃ*) antigen', *Am. J. phys. Anthrop.* **16**, 173–186.

—— and ARENDS, T., 1956a. 'High incidence blood group found in Venezuelan Indians', *Science* **123**, 633.

LAYRISSE, M., 1957. 'The Diego system—steps in the investigation of a new blood group system. Further studies', *Blood* 12, 115–122.
—— ARENDS, T., and SISCO, R. D., 1955. 'Nuevo grupo sanguíneo encontrado en descendientes de índios', *Acta Med. venez.* 3, 132–138.
—— —— and WILBERT, J., 1958. 'Peculiar distribution of the Diego factor among the Warrau', *Nature, Lond.* 181, 118–119.
—— and LAYRISSE, Z., 1959. 'Frequency of the new blood group antigen Js^a among South American Indians', *Nature, Lond.* 184, 640.
—— —— GARCÍA, E., and WILBERT, J., 1961. 'Blood group antigen tests of the Yaruro Indians', *SWest. J. Anthrop.* 17, 198–204.
—— —— —— —— 1962. 'Blood group antigens of the Pemon Indians of Venezuela', *Am. J. phys. Anthrop.* 20, 411–420.
—— —— —— —— and PARRA, R. J., 1961. 'New Rh phenotype, *Dcce^ie^if*, found in a Chibcha Indian tribe', *Nature, Lond.* 191, 503–504.
—— —— and WILBERT, J., 1960a. 'Blood group antigen tests of the Yupa Indians of Venezuela', *Am. Anthrop.* 62, 418–436.
—— —— —— 1960b. 'Blood group antigens among the Paraujano', *Am. J. phys. Anthrop.* 18, 131–139.
—— —— —— 1961. 'The blood group antigens in Goajiro Indians', *Am. J. phys. Anthrop.* 19, 255–262.
—— —— —— 1962. 'Blood group antigen tests of the Waica Indians of Venezuela', *SWest. J. Anthrop.* 18, 78–93.
—— —— —— 1963a. 'Blood group antigen studies of four Chibchan tribes', *Am. Anthrop.* 65, 36–55.
—— —— —— 1963b. 'The blood groups of northern continental Caribs', *Hum. Biol.* 35, 140–166.
—— —— —— 1964. 'Blood group antigen tests of the Barí Indians of Venezuela', *Hum. Biol.* 36, 235–245.
—— and WILBERT, J., 1960. *El antígeno del sistema sanguíneo Diego.* Editorial Sucre, Caracas.
—— 1961. 'Absence of the Diego antigen, a genetic characteristic of early immigrants to South America', *Science* 134, 1077–1078.
—— WILBERT, J., and ARENDS, T., 1958. 'Frequency of blood group antigens in the descendents of Guayqueri Indians', *Am. J. phys. Anthrop.* 16, 307–318.
LEHMANN, H., ARAUJO, A. C., and CHAVES, M., 1946. 'Grupos sanguíneos entre los indios Kwaiker', *Bol. Arqueol., Bogotá* 2, 227–230.
—— DUQUE, L., and FORNAGUERA, M., 1943. 'Grupos sanguíneos entre los indios Guambiano—Kokonuko', *Revta Inst. etnol. nac., Bogotá* 1, 197–208.
LEITE, G. M., VILLELA, M. O., and VEGAS, V. S., 1958. 'A distribuição de alguns fatores de grupos sanguíneos em índios brasileiros do Alto Xingu', *Revta paul. Med.* 53, 370–372.
LIMA, P. E., 1950. 'Grupos sanguíneos dos índios do Xingu', *Bolm. Mus. nac., Rio de J.* 11, 1–4.
LIPSCHUTZ, A., MOSTNY, G., and ROBIN, L., 1946. 'The bearing of ethnic and genetic conditions on the blood groups of three Fuegian tribes', *Am. J. phys. Anthrop.* 4, 301–322.
MARROQUIN, J., 1946. 'Particularidades antropológicas del indígena puneño', *Revta Mus. nac., Lima* 15, 13–32.

MARTINS, A. V. and BASTOS, T., 1935. 'Sôbre a distribuição dos grupos sanguíneos entre os índios Botocudos do Rio Doce', *Bras.-méd.* **49**, 108–109.

MATTOS, R. B., 1958. 'Acuidade visual para longe e freqüência de discromatopsia em índios brasileiros', *Archos. bras. Oftal.* **21**, 105–253.

MAZZA, S., 1939. 'Los fatores M y N en sangre de indígenas del Chaco argentino comparados con los de nativos de Buenos Aires', *Soc. Arg. patol. Reg.*, 9a *Reunión, Mendoza* **3**, 1916–1918.

—— and FRANKE, I., 1927. 'Grupos sanguíneos de indios y de autóctonos del norte argentino', *Prensa méd. argent.* **14**, 408–409.

—— SCHURMANN, K., and GUTDEUTSCH, H., 1933. Cited by STEFFAN, P. and WELLISCH, S., 1936. 'Die geographische Verteilung der Blutgruppen', *Z. Rassenphysiol.* **8**, 38–47.

MEZA ARRAU, C., STAEDING, J., and NIJAMKIN, A., 1958. 'Investigación del "Sistema Diego" en la población chilena en general y especialmente en los indios Mapuches', *Sangre* **3**, 360–365.

MONTENEGRO, L., 1958. 'Siclemia em índios Maués', *Revta clín., S. Paulo 'Sanguis'* **34**, 85–86.

NAGEL, R. and ETCHEVERRY, R., 1963. 'Types of haptoglobins in Araucanian Indians of Chile', *Nature, Lond.* **197**, 187–188.

NEEL, J. V., SALZANO, F. M., JUNQUEIRA, P. C., KEITER, F., and MAYBURY-LEWIS, D., 1964. 'Studies on the Xavante Indians of the Brazilian Mato Grosso', *Am. J. hum. Genet.* **16**, 52–140.

NEWMAN, M. T., 1960. 'Blood group systems in Latin American Indians', *Am. J. phys. Anthrop.* **18**, 334–335.

NIJENHUIS, L. E., 1961. 'Blood group frequencies in the Netherlands, Curaçao, Surinam and New Guinea. A study in population genetics'. Doctorate thesis, University of Amsterdam.

NUÑEZ MONTIEL, A. E. and NUÑEZ MONTIEL, J. T., 1958. 'Investigación del factor Diego y otros fatores hemáticos (ABO, Rh-Hr, MN, Duffy y Kell) en los indios Macoitas de la Sierra de Perijá', *Sangre* **3**, 38–43.

NUÑEZ MONTIEL, A., OSÓRIO, A., and WEIR, J. E., 1960. 'Estudio del sistema Rh-Hr en donantes de sangre con comparaciones hechas en indios', *Acta cient. venez.* **11**, 91–96.

NUÑEZ MONTIEL, J. T. and NUÑEZ MONTIEL, A., 1957. 'El factor Diego y otros sistemas Rh-Hr, ABO, MN en los indios Rionegrinos', *Acta cient. venez.* **8**, 134–136.

—— PEREZ, R. A., and NUÑEZ MONTIEL, A. E., 1957. 'Estudios hematológicos en grupos indígenas del Estado Zulia. Sistemas ABO, MN, Rh, Duffy, Kell y Diego', *Acta cient. venez.* **8**, 10–13.

ONETTO, A. E. and CASTILLO, F. J., 1930. 'Sobre grupos sanguíneos en los araucanos', *Revta Inst. bact., Chile* **1**, 17–24.

OTTENSOOSER, F. and PASQUALIN, R., 1949. 'Blood types of Brazilian Indians (Mato Grosso)', *Am. J. hum. Genet.* **1**, 141–155.

PAEZ PEREZ, C. and FREUDENTHAL, K., 1944. 'Grupos sanguíneos entre los indios Sibundoy, Santiagueños, Kwaiker, e indios e mestizos de los arredores de Pasto', *Revta Inst. Etnol. nac., Bogotá* **1**, 411–415.

PANTIN, A. M. and JUNQUEIRA, P. C., 1952. 'Blood groups of Brazilian Indians', *Am. J. phys. Anthrop.* **10**, 395–405.

PARKER, W. C. and BEARN, A. G., 1961. 'Haptoglobin and transferrin gene frequencies in a Navajo population: a new transferrin variant', *Science* **134**, 106–108.

PAULOTTI, O. L. and ALEGRIA, L. G., 1943. 'Grupos sanguíneos de los nativos de la Puna Jujeña', *An. Mus. argent. Cienc. nat.* **41**, 21–28.

PEDREIRA, C. M., PEIXOTO, L. I. S., and CASTRO, R. L. R., 1961. 'Grupos sanguíneos de remanescentes da tribo Kariri de Mirandela, Bahia', *Actas*, 1° *Simp. Sul-Amer. Genet.*, pp. 315–316.

—— PEIXOTO, L. I. S., and ROCHA, L. M. G. I., 1959. 'Determinação de grupos sanguíneos em índios Pataxós do vale do rio Colônia, Bahia', *Anais*, 1ª *Reunião Bras. Genet. Hum.*, pp. 84–88.

RAHM, G., 1931. 'Los grupos sanguíneos de los Araucanos (Mapuches) y de los Fueguinos', *Investnes. Progr.*, *Madrid* **5**, 160.

RAMOS DE ANDRADE, R., LASCANO, C., and ZÁRATE, M., 1959. 'Grupos sanguíneos (sistema ABO) de los índios y mestizos de los alrededores de Quito', *Humanitas* **1**, 19–21.

REICHEL-DOLMATOFF, A. and REICHEL-DOLMATOFF, G., 1944. 'Grupos sanguíneos entre los indios Pijao del Tolima', *Revta Inst. Etnol. nac.*, *Bogotà* **1**, 507–520.

REYNAFARJE, C., 1957. 'El factor Rh y otros grupos sanguíneos en los índios peruanos', *An. Fac. Med., Univ. S. Marcos* **40**, 573–584.

RIBEIRO, L., BERARDINELLI, W., and ROITER, E. M., 1935. 'Grupo sanguíneo dos índios Guaranys', *Archos. Med. leg. Ident.*, *Rio de J.* **5**, 59–65.

SACCHETTI, A., 1953. 'Studi ematologici nella zona del Lago Titicaca, Bolivia', *Riv. Antrop.* **40**, 189–231.

SALZANO, F. M., 1961a. 'Studies on the Caingang Indians. I. Demography', *Hum. Biol.* **33**, 110–130.

—— 1961b. 'Studies on the Caingang Indians. III. Blood groups', *Am. J. phys. Anthrop.* **19**, 391–404.

—— 1961c. 'Rare genetic conditions among the Caingang Indians', *Ann. hum. Genet.* **25**, 123–130.

—— 1963. 'Selection intensity in Brazilian Caingang Indians', *Nature, Lond.* **199**, 514.

—— 1964a. 'Demographic studies on Indians from Santa Catarina, Brazil', *Acta Genet. med. Gemell.* **13**, 278–294.

—— 1964b. 'Salivary secretions of Indians from Santa Catarina, Brazil', *Am. J. hum. Genet.* **16**, 301–310.

—— 1964c. 'Blood groups of Indians from Santa Catarina, Brazil', *Am. J. phys. Anthrop.* **22**, 91–106.

—— 1964d. 'Color blindness among Indians from Santa Catarina, Brazil', *Acta genet. Statist. med.* **14**, 212–219.

—— MARÇALLO, F. A., FREIRE-MAIA, N., and KRIEGER, H., 1962. 'Genetic load in Brazilian Indians', *Acta genet. Statist. med.* **12**, 212–218.

—— and STEINBERG, A. G., 1965. 'The Gm and Inv groups of Indians from Santa Catarina, Brazil', *Am. J. hum. Genet.* **17**, 273–279.

—— and SUTTON, H. E., 1963. 'Haptoglobin and transferrin types in Southern Brazilian Indians', *Acta genet. Statist. med.* **13**, 1–8.

—— —— 1965. 'Haptoglobin and transferrin types of Indians from Santa Catarina, Brazil', *Am. J. hum. Genet.* **17**, 280–289.

SANDOVAL, L. and HENCKEL, C., 1954. 'The ABO, MNS and Rh–Hr blood groups of the Mapuche Indians of Cautin Province, Chile', *Hum. Biol.* **26**, 324–329.

SANDOVAL, L., HENCKEL, C. O., and GIVOVICH, L., 1946. 'Grupos, subgrupos y factores Rh sanguíneos en los indios Mapuches de la Provincia de Cautin', Notas Mus. La Plata 11, Antropologia 35, 283–299.

SAN MARTIN, M., 1951. 'Equipos sanguíneos y factor Rh en un grupo de nativos del Departamento de Junin', An. Fac. Med. Univ. S. Marcos 34, 276–279.

SANTIANA, A., 1944. 'Los grupos sanguíneos de los indios del Ecuador. Comunicación preliminar', Notas Mus. La Plata 9, Antropologia 30, 431–438.

—— 1947. Los grupos sanguíneos de los indios del Ecuador. Comunicación definitiva. Impr. de la Univers., Quito.

—— 1952. 'Los indios del Ecuador y sus características serológicas', Terapia 10, 13–18.

SCARO, J. L., 1957. 'Distribución racial de los sistemas ABO, Rh y MN en la población de la Provincia de Jujuy', Revta Soc. argent. Biol. 33, 117–120.

—— 1958. 'Investigación del factor Diego en aborígenes de la Quebrada de Humahuaca', Revta Soc. argent. Biol. 34, 71–74.

SILVER, R. T., HABER, J. M., and KELLNER, A., 1960. 'Evidence for a new allele in the Kidd blood group system in Indians of northern Mato Grosso, Brazil', Nature, Lond. 186, 481.

—— 1962. 'Blood group studies of jungle Indians of the Mato Grosso', Transfusion 2, 110–114.

SORIANO-LLERAS, A. and MARTINEZ-SILVA, R., 1960. 'Estudios inmuno-hematológicos entre los indios Lloroes', Revta Fac. Med. Univ. nac. Colomb. 28, 101–106.

TONDO, C. V. and SALZANO, F. M., 1960. 'Hemoglobin types of the Caingang Indians of Brazil', Science 132, 1893–1894.

TORREALBA, J. F., RAMOS, I., MARROQUIN, F. R., GONZÁLEZ, D., VÁSQUEZ, A. D., OSÍO, G. P., ACOSTA, J. A., and RODRIGUEZ, I. R., 1956. 'Algunas consideraciones sobre la enfermedad de hematíes falciformes o enfermedad de Herrick en Venezuela (Addendum)', Gac. méd. Caracas 63, 53–73.

URIZAR, R., 1942. 'Grupos sanguíneos de autóctonos del Chaco Paraguayo', Am. indíg. 2, 49–50.

WEISS, P., 1948. 'Estudio sobre los lamistas; su grupo sanguíneo; algunas pruebas psico-técnicas', Revta Mus. nac., Lima 18, 19–41.

9

ECOLOGICAL AND PHYSIOLOGICAL ADAPTATION IN INDIGENOUS SOUTH AMERICANS

WITH SPECIAL REFERENCE TO THE PHYSICAL ENVIRONMENT

PAUL T. BAKER

*Department of Sociology and Anthropology,
The Pennsylvania State University*

FOR reasons still poorly understood, the South American land mass was not involved in the evolution of higher primates until quite recently. Despite the presence in reasonable variety of the lower primates, neither the apes nor their close relative, man, evolved in the Western Hemisphere. Man first entered South America in his *sapiens* form, bringing with him a knowledge of fire, clothing, and chipped tools. With the exception of Antarctica, South America appears to have been nearly the last major land mass to be occupied by man. Exact dates are not yet established, but he first arrived in South America more than 10,000 but probably less than 20,000 years ago (Steward and Faron, 1959). Although he brought only the technology of a hunter-and-gatherer, man spread rapidly. By the time of European contact all of the continent was inhabited. Man had adapted sufficiently to allow his survival from the wet cold of Tierra del Fuego to the wet heat of the Amazon Basin and from the driest desert in the world to one of the highest occupied mountain regions of the world.

Cultural invention was clearly of significance in the adaptive process, but since there is evidence that man occupied all of these areas before the development of agriculture and its collateral technological complexity, it appears that even with simple tools man rapidly developed the ability to survive in all the basic parameters of the South American physical environment.

Physical environmental stress in South America

The physical environment of South America contains a more limited variety of climatic stress than its counterpart to the north. In terms of land area it is predominated by hot wet conditions. Parts of Brazil seasonally resemble hot desert conditions, but there are no extensive hot dry areas such as are found in Asia, Africa, and North America.

There are also no extensive areas of extreme cold. The southern part of the continent has a seasonal climatic change on the eastern side of the mountains which produces distinctly cold winters. This was an area of very sparse population at the time of European contact and we have virtually no information about the native groups (Cooper, 1946). On the western side there is a cold wet maritime climate which, judged by the standards of modern technology, would be called mild but must have constituted significant cold stress to the technologically simple hunters-and-gatherers who occupied it in pre-contact times.

A rather unique type of cold stress is found in the occupied part of the Andes. The high radiation and relative dryness of this area make midday temperatures rise to a non-stressful level, but for the same reasons the night-time temperatures, even in the lower elevations, reach a level of significant cold stress for an unprotected man (Drewes and Drewes, 1957).

Of course, the temperature stress of the high Andes is secondary to the hypoxia resulting from the extreme altitudes of this region. With the exception of the Himalayas, this is the only extensive area of the world which is high enough to produce significant altitude stress for man. The Andean plateau is of special interest because in spite of its relatively small area it contained approximately one-third of the population of the Western Hemisphere when the Europeans arrived (Steward and Faron, 1959), and despite steady contact since the first European arrivals some 450 years ago, there is good population evidence to suggest that the adaptation achieved has not been significantly enhanced by European culture. The Andean population is also biologically unique in the history of the Western Hemisphere. Of all the major Indian populations living in areas amenable to the agricultural practices of Europeans, only the highland Quechua and Aymara have not been either displaced or mixed to a major extent with intrusive peoples (Kubler, 1952). The strong continuity of the culture and biology of this human group suggests that they had attained an adaptation to their environment which incoming populations have so far not been able to match.

Other stress in the South American environment

In the succeeding parts of this paper I will review what evidence is available on man's adaptation to the stresses of the physical environment in South America. However, it should first be pointed out that there existed, and in many cases continue to exist, a number of other stresses to which man must have adapted in the past. Many of these must have produced adaptations which affected adaptation to the physical environment. Therefore it is clear that eventually any attempt to understand adaptation to the physical environment will lead us into a broad ecological approach with attention to the full scope of the environmental stresses.

At least three such types of stress immediately suggest themselves: nutrition, disease, and subsistence activity. The nutrition of a group is governed by an interaction between the nutritional resources of an area and the cultural determination of its utilization. For hunters-and-gatherers adequately balanced diets are the rule unless the group lives in a specialized area such as the Arctic. Human groups almost never use every food resource in an area, but for most hunters-and-gatherers the omissions are more symbolic than nutritionally significant. The diversity of natural foods in most regions thus guarantees a balanced, if occasionally scant, diet.

Agricultural societies also exploit most available food resources, but the denser population which can be supported by agriculture provides the possibilities for man virtually to ignore or to over-exploit the natural foods. Whether or not he does so may be determined in part by the nutritional adequacy of his domesticated plants and animals. South America had three basic agricultural areas. Corn formed the basic crop of the 'Circum-Caribbean' culture area shown in Fig. 1 and was also probably the staple on the coast of Peru. Potatoes were the major source of calories in the Andes, while manioc was the major crop in the Tropical Forest (Sauer, 1950). None of these staples has high protein content but manioc is outstandingly low in protein. The staples were supplemented by high protein crops such as beans in the

FIG. 1. Map of South America showing the different cultural areas.

corn area and *Chenopodium* spp. plus domestic animals in the highlands. The Tropical Forest peoples seem to have been dependent on the sparse game and more prevalent fish for protein. If the latter suggestion is verified by close study, it may help explain the very low population densities and waterway locations of the Tropical Forest groups.

Such a brief comment only hints at the important problems of how man must have adapted to his nutritional environment. In particular, we must learn the extent and spacing of caloric intakes as well as the nutrient stresses to which the populations adapted before we can assess with exactness adaptations to climatic and altitude stress.

Infectious diseases represent radical selective stresses to which a group must be adapted for survival. South America provided the broad spectrum of infectious agents common to a tropical zone and today these remain the major cause of death. In some manner man made his accommodation as host to these predators, but so far no detailed study of how non-westernized groups in South America adapted to the presence of a chronically high death rate has been made. In present-day South American groups disease often leads to death in over 50 per cent of the individuals between birth and two years of age.

Modern societies have a variety of occupations which are most efficiently filled by people of differing sizes, shapes, and capabilities. In the technologically simpler societies, including a peasant society such as the Inca Empire, there were very few occupations.

Thus the basic type of physical activity required of most individuals in the native society was dictated by the economy of the group. The Alacaluf male was a sea hunter and his capability in running and walking mattered little, while his paddling ability was a measure of ability to obtain food.

The plainsman of the Argentine stalked and chased his food, while the Quechua Indian dug the ground, cultivated, and harvested with a dawn-to-dusk tenacity. In each instance, a different combination of skills and physical characteristics would be favoured, suggesting that the subsistence activity may act as a selective force.

The obvious importance of only these three parameters in the non-physical environment suggests why adaptation to a single environmental component such as climate can best be understood only in the context of the total environment. For example, if differences in body size and shape have significance in the adaptation of a group to the climatic environment as has been often indicated, then these same characteristics probably also have significance in adaptation to nutrition, disease, and subsistence activity. A small body size may be adaptive to low caloric or protein intakes; a low amount of body fat may increase the severity of tuberculosis; and the squat, muscular body build has advantages for the canoe paddler, but is poorly suited for pursuing game over an open plain.

Adaptation to climate and altitude

Wet cold. As the European travellers of the previous centuries were passing through the Straits of Magellan, they often marvelled at the native in an open boat with virtually no clothing, while a cold rain or snow blustered through the area. Perhaps even more impressive is the fact that most of this population's food was obtained by wading or diving in water that rarely rises above 9°C.

A cursory examination of this group might suggest that the culture provides a minimum of protection from the cold, but in many subtle ways the culture provides significant protection without which it is doubtful that the group could have survived. Indeed, Hammel (1961) suggests that they were never exposed to extreme cold for more than brief intervals.

The native technology of the group provided them with shelters made of bent saplings covered with skin, fire, and skin capes for clothing (Bird, 1946). The effectiveness of this technology in protecting the individual from cold exposure is impossible to determine. However, based on the similar technology of the modern Alacaluf, a few measurements by Hammel suggest that, as judged by modern Western standards, the group must have been exposed to at least a modest chronic cold exposure with extreme cooling when they were in the water. He found that while their present-day shelters provided protection against wind and precipitation, they did not remain warmer than outside except for short periods when a fire was maintained. From his observation and skin temperature measurements on children, it appears that they were comfortable only when active during the day and were thus often chronically chilled. The clothing of adult and child alike offered no significant insulation during rain or snow. When it is remembered that almost all of the food supply came from the sea, it becomes clear that the amount of food which could be obtained was closely related to the amount of total body cooling which could be tolerated.

Hammel and his colleagues tested the cold tolerance of a small group of Alacaluf by two methods. As their major test of response to total body cooling they measured metabolic rate, rectal temperature, and skin temperature during all-night sleep in a light sleeping bag in air temperatures between 0 and 3°C. The results of these studies on nine male subjects is shown in Fig. 2. Evaluation of these results is somewhat difficult because control data were not obtained. Hammel (1964) and Elsner (1963) suggested that, compared to Europeans, the Alacaluf had a higher metabolism and lower average skin temperatures during the latter part of the night. They also suggest that the population demonstrates metabolic acclimatization, i.e. a higher metabolic response to cold than unacclimatized Europeans. These suggestions may be valid but, as Hammel (1964) pointed out, the exposure conditions between the Alacalufs and the European data used for comparison are not comparable if for no other reason than that differences in the clo values of the sleeping bags would be produced by differences in atmospheric humidity during testing.

As a second measure of cold tolerance, the heat loss from the hands and feet of the Alacaluf were compared to European investigators by immersing the feet in 10°C water and the hand in 5°C water. Temperature rise in the water was measured over a 30-minute period. I have been unable to find a detailed report on the results of this study, but in Hammel's original report (1961) Elsner stated that while there was no apparent group difference in heat output of the hand, the foot heat-output showed high individual variability which overlapped the measurements on 'white' men.

The possible role of body size, shape, and composition in adapting the Alacaluf population has not been evaluated, but a few observations may be made from the published data. The small sample of males used in the physiological sample were relatively heavy by world standards, averaging 66 kilograms, yet they were relatively short, averaging only 162 cm. Coon (in Hammel, 1961) reported that the group approached world records in having large

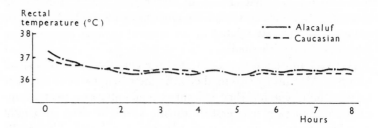

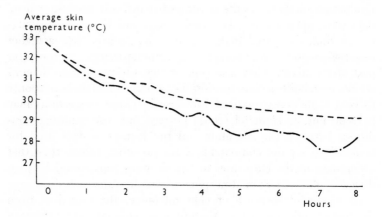

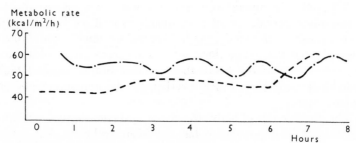

FIG. 2. Body temperature and metabolic rate of Alacaluf and Caucasians during all-night sleeping exposure to cold (modified from Elsner, 1963).

trunks, long arms, and short legs. While not fat by European and U.S. standards, they were fatter than most non-Caucasians who have been measured (Elsner, 1963). If heat production per unit of muscle mass were constant, then the size, &c., of this group should give them a low loss of heat per unit of production. That this may indeed be the case is shown by the fact that of the groups which have been tested, using the sleeping-bag technique, the Alacaluf maintained the highest rectal temperature, one of the lowest average skin temperatures, and a metabolic rate near the average of the non-European groups. These findings are summarized in the measure of body conductance, which is lower in the Alacaluf than any group measured, with the exception of the Australian Aborigine (Hammel, 1964, and Elsner, 1963).

In summary, thanks to Hammel and his collaborators we know something about how the natives of South America's stormy and chilly south-west coast adapted to their climate. However, the data are by no means complete. Only a skeleton of cultural adaptation is known, and while physiological tolerance to cold has been partially explored, responses to the extreme total body cooling, required for obtaining food, needs to be studied with adequate controls. Our data will also not permit any thoroughly adequate partitioning of the biological adaptation into genetic and environmental components even though it is clear that the body structure uniqueness must be mostly attributed to genetic origins.

Altitude cold. Two studies have so far been directed towards investigating the cold adaptation of the high Andean native. The first was a study by Elsner and Bolstad (1963) of a group of pastoral Quechua-speakers living in the Southern Highland of Peru at an altitude around 4500 metres (LaRaya). The second was a study by the present author of a Quechua agricultural group near Cuzco (Chinchero) at an altitude averaging about 3800 metres (Baker, 1963a). The difference in altitude between these two groups introduces a significant difference in the physical environment and this is reflected in a significant difference in culture.

In the Southern Peruvian Highland 4000 metres of altitude marks a significant line in subsistence activity, since above this altitude agriculture is seriously hampered by temperatures below freezing every month of the year. Despite these frosts some crops such as the native grains and some varieties of potatoes will grow.

Thus the area above 4000 metres is predominantly pastoral with some agriculture, while below it is agricultural with some pastoralism. From recent nutritional surveys, it appears that the people of the higher region have a better balanced diet and a greater caloric intake (Mazess and Baker, 1964).

The cool days and even colder nights of the Sierra provide the possibility that the indigenous population would be subject to significant cold exposure. However, a number of cultural elements help to moderate and determine the nature of this cold exposure. Behaviour patterns, clothing, shelter, and heating are some of these cultural elements. Behaviour of the people in Chinchero is closely allied to the sun cycle. The hour of sleep is at sunset and the hour of awakening is shortly after sunrise. During the cold night, shelter is taken in the adobe houses. The use of adobe for house construction and the judicious use of fire for cooking provides significant protection from outside cold. In Chinchero early evening temperatures within eight native houses which were studied were more than 10°C above outside temperatures, and during the night these houses reached an average minimum temperature of 7°C, while outside temperature reached an average minimum of 0°C. The micro-climate of the individual is further modified by the use of blankets. Little discomfort due to night cold is apparent.

Most of the waking hours are spent in agricultural or pastoral activities and these activities are outdoor ones. These normal daily activity patterns substantially raise heat production over basal rates and, combined with the insulation provided by the heavy clothing worn, act to prevent chronic total cold stress during the day. The face, hands, and feet are apparently the body areas most directly exposed to cold because these areas are not covered by garments.

The actual degree of possible micro-cold stress cannot be determined accurately without core and skin temperatures of the natives during their normal activity. On the basis of the data collected, it is suggested that the total body cold experienced by the individuals in this community is not of very long duration nor of very intense nature. Such exposure as does occur will probably primarily affect the hands, face, and feet, with only a secondary overall cold stress. Of course, the data collected concern the normal cultural situation and it may be anticipated that all individuals living in this culture are at some times during their lives exposed to a considerably greater micro-cold stress than is apparent from these observations.

At the same altitude level the seasonal temperature changes become more pronounced farther south. Thus, a winter study in the Lake Titicaca area (village of Camicachi) showed that, primarily because of the greater precipitation and the greater annual variation in the temperature, the external environmental cold stress is somewhat greater than it is in the Chinchero district. However, the people of this area are somewhat wealthier and seem to provide themselves with a greater amount of cultural protection against cold. This is shown by the tighter construction of the houses, with resulting higher temperatures within, and by greater amount of clothing worn by the men as well as the frequent use of shoes by the men. This does not mean that they may not occasionally be exposed to cold stresses greater than that encountered in Chinchero, but on the basis of this short observational study it would appear that the people of this area use the same cultural mechanisms for adapting to and protecting themselves from the cold environment but use the methods more efficiently and more intensively. The greater cultural protection may either be because of greater wealth or the greater amount of cold stress encountered.

Although the nature of cultural adaptation to cold thus appears rather constant in the lower agricultural zone of the Andes, it would be unsafe to extrapolate to the higher ecological zone since the different subsistence activity modifies several aspects of the culture. For example, the need to move with the flocks of sheep, alpaca, and llama now raised in this area makes the permanent adobe house often impractical, and while some of the population build adobe houses, many live in small shelters of piled rocks capped with movable straw roofs. The area is also too cold to support the eucalyptus tree which is used for cooking in lower zones, and the animal-dung fires commonly used for cooking provide little heat.

No detailed studies of cultural adaptation to cold in the zone have been attempted, but a superficial examination of the technology suggests that the population may be exposed to a much greater micro-cold stress than the peoples of the lower zone.

Elsner and Bolstad (1963) studied the cold tolerance of eight

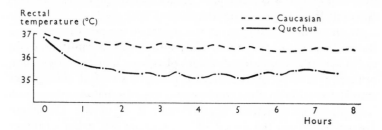

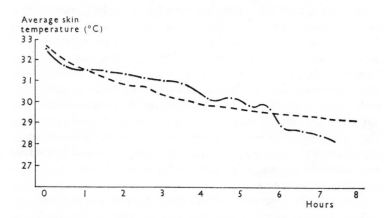

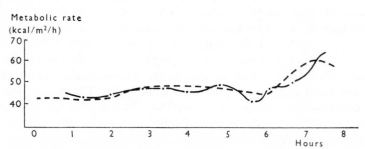

FIG. 3. Body temperature and metabolic rate of Quechua and Caucasians during all-night sleeping exposure to cold (modified from Elsner, 1963).

males from La Raya, using the all-night sleeping-bag technique. They measured metabolic rate, rectal temperature, and skin temperature. Their results are summarized in Fig. 3. These results show responses in some ways unique for populations tested by this method. Average skin temperature and metabolic rates are similar to Caucasians who have been tested under similar conditions. However, rectal temperatures fell to a lower level than any other group. The source of extra heat loss seems to be the hand and foot temperatures which stayed higher than any other group. Hammel terms these findings 'hypothermic acclimatization' (1964), but he does not elaborate on the significance of the findings.

In the study of Chinchero natives, nude exposures to 14°C for two hours were used to test response to total body cooling, while immersions of the fingers in 0°C water for one hour was used to test peripheral responses to extreme cooling (Baker, 1963a, b). During total body cooling, rectal and eleven points of skin temperature were measured. Metabolism was not measured. In the finger immersion test, temperatures on the palmar surface of the middle finger were recorded.

In an attempt to distinguish genetic from acclimatization factors in the responses, four groups were measured under identical cold exposure conditions. In the total body cooling study, the four groups were 5 U.S. Whites, 12 University of Cuzco' students of European ancestry, 12 University of Cuzco, students of Quechua ancestry, and 24 Chinchero natives. For the finger-cooling study, 26 White students, 23 Indian students, and 33 Chinchero natives were studied.

The basic results of the total body cooling studies are shown in Fig. 4. In some ways these findings seem to parallel those of Elsner and Bolstad. The hand and foot temperatures of the natives were significantly higher than those of any other group and the toe temperature of the U.S. Whites was essentially ambient temperature during the study. Rectal temperatures of the natives were significantly higher than the students, but the apparent difference in rectal temperature between the natives and U.S. Whites is probably a sampling artifact. There were only five U.S. Whites and the rectal temperatures were not significantly different from the natives as measured statistically.

In mean weighted skin temperature the Chinchero natives were significantly higher throughout the test period than all of the

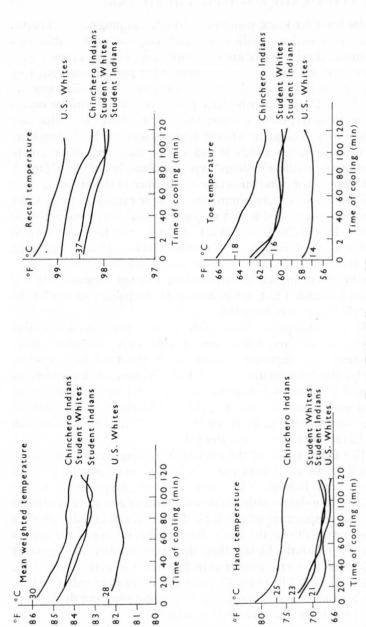

FIG. 4. Body cooling at 14°C.

other groups. Toe temperature was not included in this estimate of overall skin temperature, but analysis of the other points suggested that the major difference was in the arms and legs, while trunk and head temperatures were similar to the other groups. While metabolism was not measured on these groups, the higher rectal and skin temperature of the Chinchero natives compared to the students suggested an elevated metabolic response to the cold. The U.S. Whites appear to have had less heat loss from the core to surface. No detailed observations on shivering were made but it appeared to the investigators that they shivered the most and the Chinchero natives the least.

Perhaps the most interesting finding was that when Highland Indians had less lifelong cold exposure (i.e. the students), their temperature responses to overall moderate cooling were the same as the individuals of European ancestry. Whether the Caucasians would react the same as the Chinchero natives with a comparable history of cold exposure is unknown, but clearly the 'native response' required a previous exposure to their environment for an unknown length of time.

The results of the finger cooling tests are shown in Table 1. The comparison of the four groups is probably not completely valid because testing conditions were not exactly comparable. The two University groups were measured in matched pair design which ensured comparability. However, the Chinchero group was measured wearing native clothing in a slightly cooler room. How much these conditions may have affected results is not clear. All three of the Peruvian groups analyzed in the hand cooling study show a high percentage of individuals with significant rewarming in the finger. Over the one-hour period during which the test was conducted, only one test subject failed to show significant rewarming. The complex nature of the temperature cycling which occurs during this kind of study makes analysis somewhat difficult. Of the seven different measures used to analyse temperature cycling characteristics, only the rewarming cycle presented in Table 1 demonstrated statistically significant differences between groups. The Chinchero group showed the shortest time before finger rewarming. The Highland student group of Indians had the highest finger temperature at the end of the initial drop and they also had the highest amplitude of rewarming. While the other group differences are significantly different at the 0·05 level by *t* test, it seems worthwhile to note that the Highland students showed the highest mean finger temperature throughout the test, they had the highest maximum finger temperature, and on the average their finger temperature did not drop as low as did the other two groups. In subsequent order of rank, the Chinchero group is second and the student Whites last. Furthermore, the differences between the Indian groups and the White group appear to be greater than the differences between the Indian groups. This, of course, follows the same pattern shown in the initial cycle measurements but does not reach the same level of statistical significance.

TABLE 1

Fingers immersed 60 minutes in 0°C water

Derived measurement	Highland White students (N=26)		Highland Indian students (N=23)		Chinchero Indians (N=33)	
	Mean	SD	Mean	SD	Mean	SD
Time before 1st rewarming cycle (min)	9·94	4·07	9·91	3·33	7·78	2·70
Temperature before 1st rewarming	1·47°C	1·00°C	2·18°C	1·77°C	2·13°C	1·70°C
Amplitude of rewarming cycle	6·07°C	2·21°C	6·58°C	2·24°C	6·02°C	2·46°C
Mean temp. 1st 30 min	4·17	1·76	4·97	1·59	4·69	1·50
Mean temp. 2nd 30 min	4·32	2·00	4·98	1·57	4·77	1·66
Minimum finger temp.	1·29	0·93	1·74	1·50	1·71	1·05
Maximum finger temp.	7·36	2·54	8·29	2·17	7·69	2·42

The use of the *t* test may be questioned in its application to these results, since some of the measurements used are significantly skewed. Differences therefore may be more or less significant than the t test shows. Other forms of statistical testing of differences are being explored and these results will be in the final report of the study. However, the results as presently analysed indicate the possibility of a genetic difference between the Indian and White population which is significant to finger temperatures under extreme cold exposure.

The fact that the Chinchero group was tested under different conditions than the student groups makes it possible that a difference between them and the students exists, although it was not found in the study. On the other hand, the student groups were not only tested under identical conditions but also had cultural and physical environmental backgrounds which were quite similar. The preponderance of evidence, therefore, suggests that the difference between Indian and White genetic inheritance was of more significance than environmental exposure.

On the four groups used in the Chinchero study, an analysis was made relating body size, shape, composition, skin colour, and age to the temperature responses of the individual during the two-hour cooling exposure (Baker, 1963b). The results of this analysis showed some interesting differences from the relationship previously found on U.S. Whites (Baker and Daniels, 1956) and Koreans (Hong, 1963). In these previous studies subcutaneous fat and body mass were the prime factors in individual differences in response to cold. The same was found to be the case in the small sample of U.S. Whites studied in Chinchero. However, in the other three groups there was very little variation in body fat, and while body size remained a significant factor, age was the most significant factor found in the rectal and skin temperatures of the Chinchero natives.

Of course, these four groups were not matched for body composition and age. Therefore, correlation analysis may give a misleading picture. However, previous attempts to relate age to the thermal responses in cold of U.S. Whites have not shown precisely the same relationships (Horvath et al., 1955).

From these results, it appears that the Highland native may have an increasingly maladaptive response to cold with ageing and he does not appear to have a body structure particularly adapted to total body cold stress. In the group of 33 Chinchero males which was measured, body weight averaged only 56 kilograms, stature averaged 156 cm, and body fat, using the estimation formulas developed by Pascale *et al.* (1956), averaged only 7·8 per cent.

The combined results of all the studies on adaptation to high altitude cold in the Andes obviously suggest more problems than they solve. They certainly show that cultural adaptations to cold are a prominent feature of Quechua culture. They also show that whether a group is chosen from the lower or higher ecological zone they demonstrate different thermal regulatory responses to cold than unacclimatized Caucasians. Just how they are different and what the differences are between the zones remains to be more fully explored. However, the most striking results are the consistently higher hand and foot temperatures of the native. It may not be too speculative to suggest that this is associated with altitude adaptation, and we will not understand it until altitude and cold adaptation are simultaneously explored.

Hot wet. In terms of area, the major portion of South America might be classified as a hot, wet environment. Along the north coastal parts of the hot wet area there was, at the time of European contact, a cultural form which Steward calls 'Circum-Caribbean' (Steward, 1948*b*). This culture supported a moderate-sized population and today the Circum-Caribbean area continues to support a much denser population than the vast Amazon Basin. The basin (Steward, 1948*a*) is almost all well within the geographer's definition of hot wet. It was apparently always occupied by a very sparse population, most of whom had a simple technology based on manioc cultivation, fishing, and hunting.

Although contact with the natives in the jungle interior has occurred rapidly in the last fifteen years, it remains one of two areas of the world containing groups which have no contacts with the technology of modern civilization. It also remains as an enormous block of native tropical peoples whose adaptation to hot wet conditions remains largely unexplored. A significant quantity of ethnological literature exists for these groups, but these reports have not yet been directed towards the study of climatic adaptation. Compared to the relative wealth of information on Africa (Ladell, 1964), the complete lack of information on South America is striking.

The only direct attempt to study adaptation to jungle heat in South America of which I am aware was a brief study by the present author during 1962. For this study a group of Peruvian jungle Indians called Shibipo were investigated. This language-defined group lives along the middle reaches of the Ucayali River and has had some contact with Europeans over several centuries (Girard). While this contact has undoubtedly had effects on living patterns, it appeared that the basic material culture and behaviour patterns in relation to heat have not been significantly altered.

The majority of the study was performed in a village now named San Francisco located only some 20 kilometres from the present-day Peruvian town of Pucallpa. What might be called the almost world-wide types of cultural adaptations to hot wet conditions were found. The village was located on a rise of ground a short distance from a lake. The houses were unsided and the forest in the immediate area was cut so that any wind movement was noticeable in the houses.

Acculturative influences have resulted in the use of clothing but it still is at a minimum, and despite considerable pressures from missionaries and others, the women often wear no more than a cotton wraparound skirt.

Behavioural adjustments to the heat showed striking sex differences. The women performed practically no hard work and spent much of their time in the shade of the open house. Even when cooking, measures were taken to ensure that the work was done in the shade. In this area, where normal daytime maximums are only about 33°C, it is doubtful whether the women are ever exposed to more than very sporadic heat stress.

Although males also make efforts to reduce heat stress by doing heavy work in the early morning and late evening, many of their activities produce significant exposure to heat and radiation during occasions when they have high metabolic heat outputs. Children up to the age of 7 or 8 are probably no more exposed to the climate than the women. However, past this age, the boys begin to participate in the male role behaviour. Of course, these descriptions apply only to normal activity patterns, and since the tropical forest area was indigenously one of chronic marauding, maximum physical performance in the heat may have once been a significant factor in genetic selection.

Biological measures of heat adaptation were made by testing responses to two levels of metabolic activity over a 12-day period. Twenty Indian males and twenty *Mestizo* males from Pucallpa walked in bathing trunks one to two hours per day and on alternate days sweat loss, rectal temperature, and pulse rate were recorded at the end of one hour. Experimental design and conditions are illustrated in Table 2.

TABLE 2
Exposures and conditions of heat response in jungle heat test

| | | | Walk speed all groups (km/h) | Walk time in hours Shibipo | | Pucallpa | |
Day	Av. dry bulb	Av. wet bulb		Gp. 1 (N=9)	Gp. 2 (N=9)	Gp. 1 (N=10)	Gp. 2 (N=10)
1	31·5	26·2	5	1†	2	1†	2
2	26·4	22·1	5	2	1†	2	1†
3	28·5	23·3	5	1†	2	1†	2
4	28·4	23·0	5	2	1†	2	1†
5	31·7	25·0	5	1†	2	1†	2
6	31·1	24·8	5	2	1†	2	1†
7	32·7	25·2	8·3	1†	2	1†	2
8	32·2	24·8	8·3	2	1†	2	1†
9	28·7	24·3	8·3	1†	2	1†	2
10	30·6	25·1	8·3	2	1†	2	1†
11	30·6	24·6	8·3	1†	2	1†	2
12	32·2	25·5	8·3	2	1†	2	1†

† Measurement of rectal temperature, sweat loss, and pulse rate made on these exposures.

This design was used in order to study performance and acclimatization on as large a comparative group as technical personnel and equipment would allow. Shibipo and Pucallpa *Mestizo* groups were matched as closely as possible for age, body size, and body composition. In these measures there were no statistically significant differences in the groups except for a slightly greater fatness in the Pucallpa group. The Indians had significantly darker skin colour as measured by a photovolt reflectometer.

In comparing the two groups, there was at no time a significant difference in final rectal temperature. The final pulse rate was significantly lower in the Indians during the initial phase of the test when the groups were walking at only 5 km/h, but when the rate was increased in the second part, this difference disappeared.

Sweat losses were significantly greater in the Indians in both parts of the tests, and this does not appear to be the results of greater body size, since the Indian group was actually 0·5 kg lighter than the *Mestizos*, on the average.

TABLE 3

Physiological responses of Shibipo Indians and Peruvian Mestizos to heat exposure

Group	Final rectal temp. (°C)	Pulse rate (per min)	Sweat loss (g/h)
Shibipos 5 km/h	37·78	93·55	673
Mestizos at 5 km/h	37·83	102·73	618
Shibipos at 5 km/h	37·78	93·55	673
Mestizos at 5 km/h	37·83	102·73	618
Shibipos at 8·3 km/h	38·24	133·33	970
Mestizos at 8·3 km/h	38·24	129·92	913

From this data, it does not appear that either of these groups is seriously stressed by the heat and radiation loads they receive during moderate exercise. From the pulse-rate data it appears that the Indians had a better state of natural acclimatization than the *Mestizos*. However, observation argued against this, since before serving as test subjects the *Mestizos* had been day labourers who generally work harder in the heat than the Indians. The reasons for the greater sweat loss of the Indians are not known.

Unfortunately, these tests tell us little about the maximal heat tolerance of the native Indians, and because the controls were of mixed racial ancestry, we cannot seriously speculate on how Shibipo performance in the heat compares to other racial groups. It seems that we must await studies with better environmental controls and with better control populations before we can determine the physiological adaptation of the South American tropical forest dweller to his hot wet environment.

Hot jungle populations are noted for their small size and it has often been suggested that this is adaptive to a hot wet climate (Roberts, 1953; Newman, 1960). The analysis of the relationship between body structure and physiological response in the Shibipo-*Mestizo* study supports this hypothesis. Space in this paper forbids a presentation of complete results, but analysis by multiple correlation with parsimony indicated that smaller size and younger age were associated with lower final temperature, lower final pulse rates and lower sweat losses. It also suggested that even within the limited skin colour variation for these groups, radiant head loads are affected by skin colour.

The native hot wet area populations of South America are small peoples. They are never, as a group, as small as the pygmies found scattered in the Old World jungles. Some do, indeed, approach pygmy size (Gusinde, 1952), but from the limited information available, it seems most are somewhat larger. Various other male Tropical Forest groups have been reported to average from 154 to 159 cm in stature and from 55 to 58 kg in weight (Newman, 1960). In our sample of 38 Shibipo males, stature averaged 159 cm and weight averaged 59 kg. It therefore appears that if pygmy size is the product of climatic selection at the genetic level, it must be a low order selective pressure which requires a great many generations, or the South American native has otherwise avoided being selected to an extreme extent by this stress.

Altitude stress. The physiological stress of living at the higher altitude of the Andes is so obvious to an intrusive lowland population that even the invading Spanish of the fifteen hundreds commented on the 'thinness' of the air (Acosta, 1608). It also became obvious to the invading Spanish that the native population had an ability to work and reproduce at this altitude which exceeded themselves or any lowland population they tried to introduce. Monge reported that the Spanish encountered great difficulty in reproducing at elevations of 4000 metres and above, and despite the widespread use of Negro slaves in other parts of their colonial empire, attempts to use Negroes in the Andean mines were quickly abandoned because of the Negroes' inability to survive the environmental stresses (Monge, 1948).

The exact effect of altitude on the fecundity and fertility of European and Negro populations is yet to be determined, but the almost complete lack of Caucasians and Negroes in the High-lands and the known effect of altitude on the fertility of other animals make this a problem of considerable interest.

While cultural adaptations to the climatic environment are multiple and often obvious, the possibilities of cultural adaptation to the lowered oxygen pressure of altitude are not obvious. There have so far been no serious attempts to study cultural adaptations, although Monge has written a carefully documented account of how the Incas, and later the Spanish colonists, attempted to manipulate their populations in such a way as to utilize or minimize the stress of movement from one altitude zone to another (Monge, 1948). If maximal work capacity, fertility, and post-natal death rates are affected by the lowered oxygen tension of the Andean plateau, then several types of cultural adaptation might be anticipated. The culture should be adjusted to lowered individual work capacity and should have methods of maximizing reproduction.

That at least post-natal death rates may be affected, even in native populations, is indicated by the recent finding (Mazess, 1965) that in modern Peru neo-natal death rates rise with altitude. On the other hand, Hurtado has presented impressive evidence to indicate that the work capacity of Highland natives at 4500 metres is in no way below that of coastal peoples working near sea level (Hurtado, 1964). From the testing so far accomplished, it is not clear whether the performance of the high altitude Indian matches lowland capabilities in all regards. Maximal oxygen consumptions may be affected and the ability to work at moderate levels over months at a time has not been investigated, but at rather severe levels of treadmill walking, the Indians working at 4500 metres show a most impressive capacity. The results of one of these tests as reported by Hurtado (1964) is shown in Table 4.

Despite intensive investigation over the last thirty years, the mechanisms which allow the high performance of the Andean native are only partially known. Monge spoke of these people as a distinct race, thereby implying a large genetic difference from other peoples. Anatomically, the most obvious uniqueness in the highlander is his chest. The lungs and chests of the Highland Indians are substantially larger than those of the surrounding low altitude natives. This difference seems to occur even when the individual develops at a low altitude. The greater lung capacity of the native certainly enhances his altitude adaptation, but as presently understood, it is a minor aspect of the total adaptive mechanism.

TABLE 4

Performance of Lima natives near sea level and Highland natives at 4500 m

(Treadmill walking—11 per cent grade—132·4 m/min)

	Lima group 34·2 min of exercise	Highland group 59·4 min of exercise
Vent., l./min/m² STPO	37·5	42·2
O_2 consump. l./min/m²	1·33	1·17
CO_2 prod. l./min/m²	2·7	2·4
Res. rate/min	37	36
Pulse rate/min	183	160
Blood Hb g/100 m	16·3	20·1
Lactic acid m Eq/l.	6·4	3·2

Abbreviated from Hurtado, 1964.

In trying to differentiate between acclimatizational and genetic adaptations to altitude, the basic question is whether, with equivalent acclimatization, a lowland population would be as fertile and have the same performance capacity as the Highland native. As pointed out earlier, the evidence on fertility is so far quite indirect but suggests that at higher altitudes lowland populations do not achieve the same level of fertility.

Hurtado (1960) attributes to Balke and Velasquez the findings that in one study temporarily acclimatized new-comers at 4500 metres had nearly the same work capacity as natives, even though the work economy of the natives was higher as measured by a greater extraction of oxygen from inspired air. I have been unable to find the published results of the study from which these conclusions were derived and therefore am unsure of the extent to which they may be generalized. Van Liere and Stickney in their exhaustive review of the literature (1963) conclude that adult sea-level individuals probably cannot as adults achieve the same level of acclimatization.

The chain of functional differences which allow the Highland native a high performance capacity in the presence of low oxygen pressure has been recently proposed by Hurtado (1964). The mechanisms by which Hurtado proposes to explain the reduced total pO_2 gradient in the Highland native are outlined in Fig. 5.

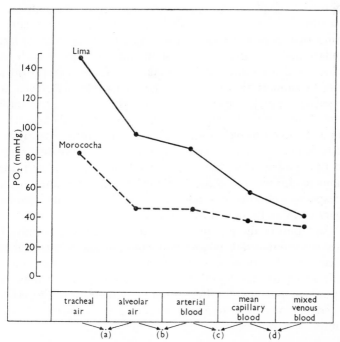

FIG. 5. Structural and functional adaptations to low O_2 pressure (highland and lowland populations compared). (a) Lower drop in highlander because of hyperventilation made possible in part by an increased sensitivity of the respiration centre to CO_2. (b) Less pressure loss, presumably related to increased amount of air contained in the dilated alveoli at the levels of greater residual volumes and functional residual capacities found in the Highland natives. (c) At 4500 m red blood cell counts in millions per mm are 25 per cent greater. Haematocrit in per cent red cells is 33 per cent greater. (d) Highland natives show right displacement of the oxygen dissociation curve with correspondingly greater passage of gas from blood to tissue.

While the dramatic reduction in the pO_2 gradient from tracheal air to mixed venous blood is widely accepted, the mechanisms suggested by Hurtado are still the subject of some controversy.

For example, in a recent article by Kreuzer and others (1964) it was claimed that the alveolar-arterial oxygen gradient was not reduced in Highland natives. Even with the better-adapted total gradient, the capillary blood is oxygenated at below the level of men at low altitudes. Therefore, other mechanisms must be proposed to explain the high work capacity of the natives. At least three such mechanisms have been suggested to explain the greater than expected muscle work capacity. These are (1) larger capillary beds, (2) greater myoglobin content in the muscle, and (3) increased anaerobic cellular metabolism. Considerable evidence exists to support the first two suggestions (Hurtado, 1964, and Reynafarje, 1962), but the suggestion that increased anaerobic metabolism occurs (Barbashova, 1964) is the least documented in man and should prove an interesting area of future investigation.

I have not covered the collateral changes in the body structure and functioning which are required to support the direct adaptations to altitude, but changes in cardio-vascular, endocrine, and perhaps even the nervous system are either known or have been suggested (Van Liere and Stickney, 1963).

Adaptation to the low oxygen pressure of the high Andes has obviously produced a major uniqueness in the adult Highland Indian. At this time it seems premature to speculate on the partition of its development, acclimatization, and genetic and cultural components, but it does not seem too rash to suggest that the adaptations have occurred in all of these facets of man's adaptive system.

Summary and prospects

As a location for the study of human adaptations, South America is an area with the disadvantages of a relatively short human occupation history, and a lack of some of the climatic and disease diversity of the rest of the world. By the same token, the recency of its occupation is one of its advantages. To a greater extent than any other continent, we are assured that a *Homo sapiens* form of man entered this continent and that the cultural and biological methods by which man adapted to its environmental diversity were *sapiens* inventions. It also contains one of the most accessible permanent high-altitude populations of the world. This is not to suggest that other high altitude populations should not be studied. Indeed, the fact that the high altitude groups of the Old World have probably had a longer time in which to adapt suggests the value of comparison.

When the evidence of adaptation to the physical environments of South America are reviewed, the dearth of our knowledge on the subject is apparent. Outside of the extensive studies on physiological acclimatization to high altitude, the topic is covered by a few studies and a variety of anthropological observations not made directly to determine adaptation to the physical environment.

In the face of such a lack of information, it would be presumptive to say exactly which groups should be studied or exactly what kinds of studies should be undertaken. However, many of the native cultures are disappearing and often with them the people who bore these cultures. If studies of these groups are not soon undertaken, the detailed knowledge of their adaptive systems will be lost. Second, the biological and cultural persistence of the Andean Highland native presents a unique challenge to our anthropological understanding of cultural contacts. If the persistence is indeed based on the biological adaptation of this population, its great significance to our mobile modern civilization is obvious.

The types of studies of adaptation which will be undertaken will obviously be dependent on the financial resources and skills of the individuals who direct this work. Nevertheless, it should be remembered that each human community is exposed to a unique set of stresses and in response has developed a unique set of biochemical adaptations. Some types of cultural adaptations have been re-invented many times and some forms of genetic adaptation (i.e. body size) have independently recurred, but any study of a single parameter of adaptation will run the risk of missing the major method by which the group has made a successful accommodation to its environment.

REFERENCES

ACOSTA, JOSEPH DE, 1608. *Historia Natural y Moral de las Indias.* Madrid.

BAKER, P. T., 1963a. 'Adaptation to high altitude cold in the Andes', *Annual Progress Report,* 1 July. Contract No. Da-49-193-MD-2260. Office of the Surgeon General.

—— 1963b. 'The influence of body characteristics on human temperature responses to high altitude cold', *Progress Report,* 1 November. Contract No. Da-49-193-MD-2260. Office of the Surgeon General.

—— and DANIELS, F., JR., 1956. 'Relationship between skinfold thickness and body cooling for two hours at 15°C', *J. appl. Physiol.* **8,** 408–416.

BARBASHOVA, Z., 1964. 'Cellular level of adaptation', *Handbook of Physiology* (eds. D. B. DILL, E. F. ADOLF, and C. B. WILBER), section 4, pp. 625–659. American Physiological Society.

BIRD, J., 1946. 'The Alacaluf', *Handbook of South American Indians* (ed. JULIAN H. STEWARD), Vol. 1, pp. 55–79. Smithsonian Institute, Bureau of American Ethnology, Bulletin 143.

COOPER, J. M., 1946. 'The Patagonian and Pampean hunters', *Handbook of South American Indians* (ed. JULIAN H. STEWARD), Vol. 1, pp. 127–168. Smithsonian Institute, Bureau of American Ethnology, Bulletin 143.

DREWES, W. U. and DREWES, A. T., 1947. *Climate and Related Phenomena of the Eastern Andean Slopes.* Syracuse University Research Institute, Syracuse, N.Y.

ELSNER, R. W., 1963. 'Skinfold thickness in primitive peoples native to cold climates', *Ann. N.Y. Acad. Sci.* **110**, 503–514.

—— and BOLSTAD, A., 1963. 'Thermal and metabolic responses to cold exposure of Andean Indians native to high altitudes', *Arctic Aero-Medical Laboratory Technical Report.*

GIRARD, R., 1958. *Indios Selvaticos de la Armazonia Peruana* (eds. LIBRO MEX.). Mexico.

GUSINDE, M., 1955. 'Are the Yupa-Indians genuine pygmies?' *Am. J. phys. Anthrop.* **13**, 381–382.

HAMMEL, H. T., 1960. 'Thermal and metabolic responses of the Alacaluf Indians to moderate cold exposure', *Aerospace Medical Division, WADD Technical Report,* pp. 60–633.

—— 1964. 'Terrestrial animals in cold; recent studies of primitive man', *Handbook of Physiology* (eds. D. B. HILL, E. F. ADOLF, and C. G. WILBER), Section 4, pp. 413–434. American Physiological Society.

HONG, S. K., 1963. 'Comparison of diving and non-diving women of Korea', *Fed. Proc.* **22**, 831–833.

HORVATH, S. M., RADCLIFFE, C. E., HUTT, B. K., and SPURR, G. B., 1955. 'Metabolic responses of older people to a cold environment', *J. appl. Physiol.* **8**, 145–148.

HURTADO, A., 1960. 'Parameters of human adaptation to altitude', *Physics and Medicine of the Atmosphere and Space* (eds. OTIS O. BENSON, JR. and HUBERTUS STRUGHOLD), pp. 352–369. Wiley, New York.

—— 1964. 'Animals in high altitudes: resident man', *Handbook of Physiology* (eds. D. B. DILL, E. F. ADOLF, and C. G. WILBER), Section 4, pp. 843–860. American Physiological Society.

KREUZER, F., TENNEY, S. M., MITHOEFER, J. C., and REMMERS, J., 1964. 'Alveolar-arterial oxygen gradient in Andean natives at high altitude', *J. appl. Physiol.* **19**, 13–16.

KUBLER, G. *The Indian Caste of Peru,* 1795–1940. Smithsonian Institute, Institute of Social Anthropology, No. 14.

LADELL, W. S. S., 1964. 'Terrestrial animals in humid heat: man', *Handbook of Physiology* (eds. D. B. DILL, E. F. ADOLF, and C. G. WILBER), Section 4, pp. 625–659. American Physiological Society.

MAZESS, R. B., 1965. 'Variation in neo-natal mortality and altitude in Peru', *Am. J. phys. Anthrop.* **23**, 209–214.

—— and BAKER, P. T., 1964. 'Diet of Quechua Indians at high altitude: Nunoa, Peru', *Am. J. clin. Nutr.* **15**, 341–351.

MONGE, C., 1948. *Acclimatization in the Andes.* Johns Hopkins Press, Baltimore.

MONGE, C., 1953. 'Biological basis of human behavior', *Anthropology To-day* (ed. ALFRED L. KROEBER). University of Chicago Press, Chicago.
NEWMAN, M. T., 1960. 'Adaptations in the physique of American Aborigines to nutritional factors', *Hum. Biol.* **32**, 288–313.
PASCALE, L. R., GROSSMAN, M. I., SLOANE, H. S., and FRANKEL, T., 1956. 'Correlations between skinfolds and body density in 88 soldiers', *Hum. Biol.* **28**, 165–176.
REYNAFARJE, B., 1962. 'Myoglobin content and enzymatic activity of muscle and altitude adaptation', *J. appl. Physiol.* **17**, 301–305.
ROBERTS, D. F., 1953. 'Body weight, races and climate', *Am. J. phys. Anthrop.* **11**, 533–558.
SAUER, C. O., 1950. 'Cultivated plants of South and Central America', *Handbook of South American Indians* (ed. JULIAN H. STEWARD), Vol. 6, pp. 487–543. Smithsonian Institution, Bureau of American Ethnology, Bulletin 143.
STEWARD, JULIAN H. (ed.), 1948a. *Handbook of South American Indians,* Vol. 3, *The Tropical Forest Tribes.* Smithsonian Institution, Bureau of American Ethnology, Bulletin 143.
—— (ed.), 1948b. *Handbook of South American Indians,* Vol. 4, *The Circum-Caribbean Tribes.* Smithsonian Institute, Bureau of American Ethnology, Bulletin 143.
—— and FARON, L. C., 1959. *Native Peoples of South America.* McGraw-Hill, New York.
VAN LIERE, E. J. and STICKNEY, J. C., 1963. *Hypoxia.* University of Chicago Press, Chicago and London.

10

GENETIC ADAPTATION IN MAN

L. D. SANGHVI

Indian Cancer Research Centre, Parel, Bombay-12, India

HUMAN adaptability is that quality of man which makes him tolerant of a great variety of circumstances and environments. Problems in this field can be divided into two broad classes. One class is concerned with explorations of the physiological, social, psychological, and other adjustments of individuals and populations to a set of environmental conditions, genetic composition remaining unchanged. The second class deals with the question as to how this quality of adaptability has been acquired and is being transmitted. Its central theme is genetic adaptation in man. It investigates the genetic composition of individuals and populations and explores the causes of its variation in time and space. The two classes of problems are closely interrelated.

With an increasing number of genetic traits now available for population studies, our knowledge about the genetic composition of man is enlarging at a very rapid rate. What is intrinsically more difficult to explore is the process by which it is brought about. Theoretical models and experimental work in organisms other than man have supplied the general framework for an understanding of this process; it is, however, of limited value for answering questions specific for man.

There are a number of useful studies about mutation in man. Evidence for the occurrence of dominant mutation is direct and convincing; but as I have argued elsewhere (Sanghvi, 1963) the evidence for recessive and sex-linked mutation is indirect and not equally convincing. We are in need of fresh approaches and I have indicated subsequently in this paper one such approach along which evidence can be looked for in South India.

There has been a good deal of advance during the last decade on the subject of genetic selection in man. No one now talks about the so-called neutral genes (see Sanghvi, 1953). Several blood groups, haemoglobin variants, and a number of other commonly distributed genetic traits have been found to have an association with various infectious and metabolic diseases; the protection afforded by sickle-cell haemoglobin against *Plasmodium falciparum* in infancy is a classical example in this field. In this respect we are at a beginning of our knowledge as to how man has adapted himself in his fight against infectious diseases during the last 300–500 generations of his agricultural and pastoral economy.

Our understanding of genetic adaptation to climatic factors is exceedingly meagre. In contrast to his adaptation to infectious diseases, man's adaptation to this seems to be a very slow process, spread over thousands of generations, concomitant with changes in climatic conditions. Major adaptations are all multifactorial in inheritance and seem to have been established largely during his hunting and food gathering stages.

The bulk of the populations of the world is currently passing through the industrial age. Genetic problems that we are likely to face in this new age appear at present to be largely of a negative nature, resulting mainly from control by man of the effects of climatic factors, agents of infection, and so on. The genetic balance which man had achieved by natural selection in the past is being upset in this new age and may possibly bring an increasing amount of genetic load in the immediate future. What positive adaptation is being achieved by man in this new age still remains to be formulated.

People of India

India is unique in several respects as far as its human populations are concerned. It has almost all the major racial groups (see the paper of M. S. Malhotra in the present volume) under a social situation that is favourable for genetic studies. Some of these groups have undergone a high degree of environmental and occupational specialization over tens and hundreds of generations, and provide abundant material for studying whether such specialization has resulted in any genetic adaptation. Some of the groups have practised inbreeding at a very high level over two or more millennia and raise interesting theoretical questions, as well as practical problems, for the populations under consideration. My purpose here is to outline briefly the extent of the variability that exists in these populations and to indicate some of the possibilities that exist for genetic studies.

The composition of the present-day Indian population can be understood in a preliminary way by three different types of groupings. On a religious basis, 75 per cent of the people belong to the Hindu community, 13 per cent to the Muslim community, 8 per cent comprise various tribal groups, and the remaining 4 per cent are divided among the Christians, Sikhs, Jains, Buddhists, Parsees, and Jews. Excepting the Parsees, who migrated to India from Iran about 1300 years ago and have largely married among themselves, most of the other religious groups have their origin in the local populations of the country. Some of the religious influences that have come from outside were brought by a comparatively few individuals, whose impact on the existing gene pool may be considered to be limited.

There are fourteen principal languages in India of which ten belong to the Indo-European group and four, in the south, to the Dravidian group. After the end of the British political rule, the country was reorganized on a linguistic basis and all the states are now homogeneous with respect to the language they use; remains of the earlier languages in use even by the tribal populations are fast disappearing. The third and the most important grouping is by the division of populations into endogamous castes and tribes. Some of the larger of these groups are spread over more than one linguistic region, although a large majority of them are confined to individual states.

Inbreeding in India

There is a widespread misconception that the division of the population of India into a large number of castes and tribes has led to a great deal of inbreeding. In a genetic sense, this is not necessarily true. The numerical strength of these castes and tribes runs into thousands, or even millions, and is sufficiently large not to lead to inbreeding unless there are marriages of close blood relations. Thus, in India, endogamy is to be clearly distinguished from inbreeding.

No feature of the Indian caste society is more resistant to change than its institution of marriage. In recent years, many other aspects such as untouchability, hereditary occupation, and food pollution have weakened. The regulations governing marriage, however, have been little affected in their essential biological aspects, although the ceremonials of marriage are undergoing gradual changes. There are three important regulations which largely explain the pattern of marriages in the country. The first one is the regulation of endogamy (marrying within the group of birth) which is the most important attribute of caste (*jāti*). The second one is the regulation of exogamy (marrying out) which applies to sections in which a caste is divided; it prohibits marriages between individuals who belong to the same section. These exogamous sections are usually small in number (15–25 for Brahmans), are known by a variety of names (*gotra, kul,* &c.) and are transmitted in the male line. One of the important consequences of this regulation as far as inbreeding is concerned is to prohibit marriages between children of two brothers, although there would be no bar to marriages between children of two sisters or of a brother and a sister. The third one is the regulation of consanguineous (*sāpinda*) marriages. It prohibits marriages between two individuals related through a common male ancestor up to the seventh generation on the father's side and the fifth generation on the mother's side.

The Brahmans of North India, in whom this institution has evolved luxuriantly over the last three millennia, have in turn influenced greatly the marriage pattern of other populations in the country. The influence is strongest on the Hindu, but Muslims, Christians, and other communities have not escaped it. Among the Brahmans, there exists a basic difference between the north and the south. The consanguineous (*sāpinda*) regulation has been enforced with great rigidity in the north. In the south, it had to be relaxed to conform to the prevailing custom of great preference for consanguineous marriages at the time of the entry of the Brahman influence in the first millennium B.C. Baudhayana, one of the earliest law-givers, mentioned in his Dharmasutra that this is one of the important customs in which the south differed from the north (Sastri, 1955).

Maharashtra is an interesting region of this culture contact between the north and the south. Its language is Indo-Aryan and thus conforms to the north, but for the consanguineous marriages the population in general follows, and encourages, the customs of the south. Brahmans are caught there in a difficult dilemma.

FIG. 1. The languages and the patterns of consanguineous
marriages in India.

Chitpavans and Madhyandins follow the custom of the north and prohibit consanguineous marriages; Desasth (Rigvedi), Karhada, and Sarswat Brahmans follow the custom of the south and encourage them (see Fig. 1).

Bombay. We studied earlier the extent of inbreeding in twelve endogamous groups in Bombay based on a sample of 6597 marriages (Sanghvi *et al.*, 1956). Seven of these groups were Marathi-speaking Hindu castes, viz. Desasth and Sarswat Brahmans, Kayasth and Pathare Prabhus, Marathas, Agris, and Mahars. Rates of consanguineous marriages were low among the Brahmans and the Prabhus with a coefficient of inbreeding varying from 0·001 to 0·003. In the other three castes, it varied from 0·005 to 0·007. Among these seven castes, the consanguineous marriage type that contributed mainly to inbreeding was the matrilateral cross-cousin. In addition, there were three Muslim groups, viz. Meman, Bohra, and Khoja; a group of Parsees and a Christian group. The coefficient of inbreeding among the Muslims and the Parsees was high, varying from 0·006 to 0·013. The Christians, who were Roman Catholics, gave a value of 0·001. In all these non-Hindu communities, the first-cousin marriages were of all the four possible types. There was evidence of decline in inbreeding among the Parsees, but none in any other group.

Andhra Pradesh. Our study of inbreeding in rural areas of Andhra Pradesh was based on a sample of 6945 marriages. The main feature of the data was a high proportion of uncle-niece and matrilateral cross-cousin types which accounted for two out of every five marriages. The coefficient of inbreeding was 0·032 for autosomal genes and 0·051 for sex-linked genes. The excess for the sex-linked genes being contributed by the matrilateral cross-cousin marriages. These levels of inbreeding, which are exceedingly high for any large human population, may be compared with some theoretical values. If, for instance, a population was perpetuated entirely by first-cousin marriages, the coefficient of inbreeding would be 0·062. If it was continued by marriages only of first-cousin once removed, the coefficient would be 0·0313. The figures for Andhra Pradesh lie between these theoretical values.

Data analysed according to districts (Figs. 2 and 3) showed that the highest concentration of inbreeding was in the coastal areas of Vizhagapatnam and East Godvari and that the concentration

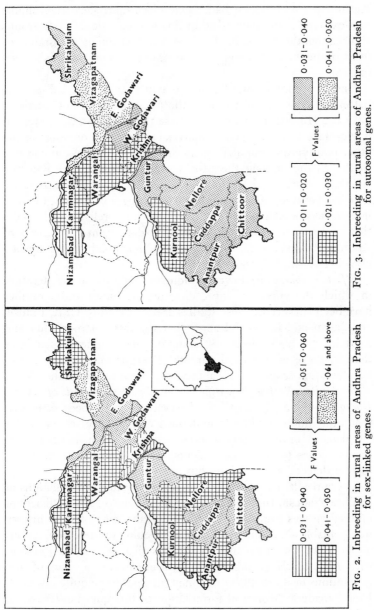

FIG. 3. Inbreeding in rural areas of Andhra Pradesh for autosomal genes.

FIG. 2. Inbreeding in rural areas of Andhra Pradesh for sex-linked genes.

gradually diminished in the interior districts. In the districts of Karimnagar and Nizamabad, uncle-niece marriages were almost non-existent. Data analysed according to occupational-caste groups showed that the inbreeding levels were lowest among the Brahmans (0·019) and highest among the shepherds (0·038) and fishermen (0·047).

One of the interesting features that the study revealed was the pattern of consanguinity among the Muslims and the Christians. Like the Hindus in this region, these two communities practised uncle-niece and cross-cousin marriages; but did not resort to the other two types of parallel cousin marriages. This was in contrast to the custom among the Muslims and Christians of Bombay, where they practised all the four types of first-cousin marriages. The local custom of consanguineous marriages in Andhra Pradesh had deeper roots than could be modified by the religious influences that came there at a later stage. The data from rural areas of Andhra Pradesh, with detailed discussion, are being published elsewhere (Sanghvi, 1965).

Effects of inbreeding. Several studies are reported in the literature in which the effects of inbreeding on morbidity and mortality have been surveyed. These studies are restricted to USA, France, and Japan and in general show that the rates of morbidity and mortality are higher in the offspring of consanguineous marriages than in those of unrelated parents. These studies, which are of very unequal scope and reliability, are summarized in the *Report of the United Nations Scientific Committee on the Effects of Atomic Radiation* (1962). From these observations it has been estimated that individuals in these populations carry, on an average, 2–4 lethal genes (or their equivalents) which cause death, and 2–4 detrimental genes (or their equivalents) which cause malformations, mental defects, and other serious anomalies.

These results cannot be extended directly to the populations of Andhra Pradesh. In the studies mentioned above, the coefficient of inbreeding was comparatively low (less than 0·01) and no history was available about the practice of inbreeding in these populations in the past. For a population such as that of Andhra Pradesh, with high levels of inbreeding continued over a span of 100 generations or more, the effects may turn out to be quite different. I have made a theoretical formulation of this question (Sanghvi, 1965) and it becomes evident that the frequency of deleterious genes would have considerably declined in this population. Moreover, the rate and extent of decline turns out to be quite different for the genes which are maintained by mutation compared to the genes which are maintained by heterozygote advantage. An observational study would thus furnish direct evidence as to whether a gene under consideration is maintained by mutation or by selection.

Nature of genetic variation

The distribution of common traits with a simple mode of inheritance supplies us with a wealth of information for understanding the biology of human populations. Such data are, however, available only for a few population groups in India. In order to illustrate the nature of genetic variation as evident from these studies, I have selected the State of Gujarat and summarized the available data in the appended paper (see Appendix). The study covers six castes, six hill-tribes, and one semi-tribe. The genetic data include A_1A_2BO, MN, Rh, P, and Duffy blood groups, secretion of ABH substances in saliva, ability to taste phenyl-thio-carbamide, and red-green vision defect.

I have outlined in this paper the reasons that strongly support the view that all the six hill-tribes under study have a common origin from an ancestral stock of the large tribe of Bhils. If this view is correct, the observed genetic variation among these tribes, which is quite considerable in several instances, may be largely a result of their adaptation to their local environments over a span of several generations since their separation. The extent of this variation can be seen in Tables 2–5 and Figs. 1 and 3 in the Appendix. It is interesting to note that the alleles for haemoglobin-S as well as blood groups Rh(d) and B are far more variable in these environments than the alleles for blood groups A_2, O, and R_0.

Genetic variation among the castes is influenced by their racial history in addition to their adaptation to local environments, occupational specialization, &c. The two trading castes under study seem to be of different origin and are grouped only artificially under the caste of traders. The two Brahman castes also appear to be of different origin. This has been found to be true in general of Brahman castes in other regions also. Genetically, they seem to be a mixed bag, with a considerable contribution, in some cases, from the indigenous people of the region. The traditional division of Hindu India into four main castes is only a superficial one, into which developing castes were made to fit as they came along. Several of these castes have, in the past, occupied variable positions in the fourfold hierarchy according to their relations with the ruling kings.

The most notable difference between the tribes and the castes exists in the presence of haemoglobin-S in the former and its absence in the latter. This may reflect a difference in their malarial experience. Interesting in this respect are the higher values of blood group R_1 and lower values of colour vision defects among the tribes than among the castes (Fig. 3 in the Appendix) which may reflect a similar difference of genetic adaptation.

This brief summary is intended to indicate the scope that exists in India for further and more extensive observations, for careful analysis and for reflection. One area which is not touched upon above is a comparative study of occupational or artisan castes. In South India, it is possible to select artisan castes in which one can be reasonably sure of their uniform racial origin. In these castes, genetic variation, if any, would in large measure reflect an occupational adaptation.

REFERENCES

SANGHVI, L. D., 1953. 'Comparison of genetical and morphological methods for a study of biological differences', Am. J. phys. Anthrop. 11, 385–404.

—— VARDE, D. S. and MASTER, H. R., 1956. 'Frequency of consanguineous marriages in twelve endogamous groups in Bombay', Acta genet. Statist. med. 6, 41–49.

—— 1963. 'The concept of genetic load: a critique', Am. J. hum. Genet. 15, 298–309.

—— 1965. 'Inbreeding in rural areas of Andhra Pradesh'. Paper presented at the Mendel Symposium, New Delhi.

SASTRI, K. A. N., 1955. A History of South India. Oxford University Press, Madras.

UNITED NATIONS, 1962. Report of the Scientific Committee on the Effects of Atomic Radiation, Seventeenth Session Suppl. No. 16 (A/5216). United Nations, New York.

APPENDIX

THE NATURE OF THE GENETIC VARIATION IN SOME CASTES AND TRIBES OF GUJARAT

Since the publication of our study on the incidence of blood groups and other genetic traits in six endogamous groups of Bombay (Sanghvi and Khanolkar, 1949), work has been extended to cover several castes and tribes of Gujarat (Vyas *et al.*, 1958; and Vyas *et al.*, 1962). The time is now ripe for taking an overall look at this material and I am planning to discuss in this paper the available genetical data of six castes and seven tribes.

TABLE 1

Numerical strength and geographical distribution of the castes and tribes studied

Caste or tribe	Numerical strength (in thousands) 1901 census	1931 census	Geographical distribution
Brāhmans			
Audich Brāhman (AB)	178	—	All over Gujarāt
Nāgar Brāhman (NB)	22	—	All over Gujarāt
Traders			
Kapol Vāniā (KV)	352	—	Mainly in Saurāshtra, and in Bombay
Cutchi Luvānā (CL)	—	58	Mainly in Cutch, and in Bombay
Farmers			
Pātidār Kanbi (PK)	925	—	All over Gujarāt
Scavengers			
Bhangi Harijan (BH)	81	79	All over Gujarāt
Semi-tribe of the plains			
Koli (Ko)	1714	1635	All over Gujarāt
Hill and forest tribes			
Bhil (Bh)	560	777	Gujarāt excluding Cutch and Saurāshtra
Dublā (Du)	101	83	Bharuch, Surat, and Thānā districts
Nāikā (Na)	59	102	Mainly in Surat district
Dhānkā (Dk)	—	35	Mainly in Bharuch district
Dhodiā (Dd)	94	140	Surat and Thānā districts
Gāmit (Ga)	—	12	Mainly in Surat district

Among the castes that have been studied there are two types of Brahmans, two trading castes, one caste of farmers, and one caste of scavengers (the so-called untouchables). Among the tribes there are six hill and forest tribes and one semi-tribal group of the plains. Table 1 gives the numerical strength and geographical distribution of these castes and tribes. The available census figures for 1901 and 1931 are given in this table as no comparative figures have been published after 1931.

All the castes included in the present study are primarily the castes of Gujarat except Luvanas (traders). They are found in much larger numbers in the Punjab and Sind (Pakistan) and are also said to be present in Afghanistan and Southern Russia. The semi-tribe of Koli, which is present in large numbers all over the plains of Gujarat, is also found in small numbers in Maharashtra. The tribe of Bhil which is the most numerous hill-tribe of Gujarat has a wide geographical distribution beyond Gujarat and is found in considerable numbers in the hilly regions of Rajputana, Central India, and in Maharashtra with an overall strength of more than 2 millions. The census figures cannot be taken as a good guide for the strength of the hill and forest tribes, as a number of small tribes including Dhanka, Dhodia, and Gamits are often mixed with Bhils in enumeration. The five tribes other than Bhils have a more localized distribution, as indicated in the table.

TABLE 2

$A_1 A_2 BO$ gene frequency

	A_1	A_2	B	O
Castes				
Audich	17.96 ± 2.02	4.72 ± 1.19	17.02 ± 1.97	60.30 ± 2.65
Nagar	17.05 ± 1.97	2.16 ± 0.80	15.83 ± 1.91	64.96 ± 2.54
Vania	25.46 ± 2.36	0.67 ± 0.47	11.95 ± 1.68	61.92 ± 2.64
Luvana	14.72 ± 1.84	1.21 ± 0.59	26.19 ± 2.38	57.88 ± 2.69
Kanbi	12.42 ± 1.71	2.06 ± 0.77	25.15 ± 2.35	60.37 ± 2.66
Bhangi	17.38 ± 1.99	4.12 ± 1.10	27.17 ± 2.41	51.33 ± 2.78
Semi-tribe				
Koli	11.41 ± 1.75	1.60 ± 0.71	20.80 ± 2.30	66.19 ± 2.69
Tribes				
Bhil	20.31 ± 2.40	0.79 ± 0.56	25.66 ± 2.65	53.24 ± 3.01
Dubla	15.05 ± 1.81	1.68 ± 0.68	25.40 ± 2.28	57.87 ± 2.62
Naika	18.07 ± 2.19	1.83 ± 0.80	21.06 ± 2.34	59.04 ± 2.88
Dhanka	16.57 ± 1.92	1.80 ± 0.72	23.38 ± 2.24	58.25 ± 2.65
Dhodia	25.25 ± 2.34	1.00 ± 0.58	12.72 ± 1.72	61.03 ± 2.64
Gamit	27.38 ± 2.41	1.00 ± 0.58	14.72 ± 1.83	56.90 ± 2.70

TABLE 3

Rh gene frequency

	R_1	R_2	R_0	R_z	r	r'	r''
Castes							
Audich Nagar	55·53±2·49	8·38±1·42	5·24±1·87	—	30·85±2·77 (34·64±3·36)	—	—
Vania	52·56±2·63	12·79±1·75	5·82±2·04	0·51±0·48	27·39±2·82	0·93±0·89	—
Luvana	65·13±2·39	8·85±1·46	8·05±2·66	0·37±0·37	17·60±2·99	—	—
Kanbi	58·48±2·56	4·84±1·09	6·86±2·13	—	29·00±2·85	0·82±0·82	—
Bhangi	60·26±3·48	14·12±1·80	13·65±3·38	—	7·73±3·20	4·24±2·68	—
Semi-tribe							
Koli	65·19±2·55	6·04±1·31	4·90±2·16	0·43±0·43	23·44±2·92	—	—
Tribe							
Bhil	67·27±2·71	1·32±2·11	12·14±3·62	2·28±1·01	13·26±3·66	—	3·73±2·29
Dubla	67·11±2·90	7·09±1·27	10·08±2·97	—	12·78±3·04	2·94±1·99	—
Naika	75·05±2·35	6·90±1·40	8·83±3·47	0·39±0·39	8·83±3·47	—	—
Dhanka	76·89±2·09	4·96±1·10	9·86±3·30	0·32±0·32	7·97±3·25	—	—
Dhodia	79·33±2·03	6·95±1·30	6·24±3·10	0·32±0·32	7·16±3·13	—	—
Gamit	76·04±3·57	5·91±1·19	10·98±3·26	—	3·55±3·00	3·52±3·02	—

All these endogamous castes and tribes were studied for A_1A_2BO, MN, and Rh blood groups, for secretion of ABH substances in saliva, for ability to taste phenyl-thio-carbamide (PTC), and for red-green colour vision defect. Several castes and tribal groups were examined for P and Duffy blood groups also. Some castes and all the tribes were tested for haemoglobin variants.

TABLE 4

Gene frequency for MN, P, and Duffy blood groups

	M	P_1	Fy^a
Castes			
Audich	$62·56 \pm 2·43$		$45·93 \pm 3·01$
Nagar	$70·50 \pm 2·28$	$44·34 \pm 4·93$	
Vania	$60·50 \pm 2·45$		$43·97 \pm 3·16$
Luvana	$62·50 \pm 2·42$		$53·87 \pm 3·24$
Kanbi	$59·50 \pm 2·45$		$42·86 \pm 5·86$
Bhangi	$54·75 \pm 2·49$		$40·36 \pm 2·88$
Semi-tribe			
Koli	$63·64 \pm 2·56$	$58·68 \pm 5·02$	$40·09 \pm 4·53$
Tribes			
Bhil	$58·54 \pm 2·77$		
Dubla	$60·38 \pm 2·38$		$40·97 \pm 2·87$
Naika	$49·42 \pm 2·70$	$55·28 \pm 6·67$	$42·62 \pm 4·52$
Dhanka	$55·15 \pm 2·46$	$27·28 \pm 3·37$	
Dhodia	$44·78 \pm 2·48$	$40·66 \pm 4·78$	$40·98 \pm 4·28$
Gamit	$53·69 \pm 2·47$	$48·17 \pm 5·22$	

All the original records have been re-examined. Some errors were found and corrected.[†] Gene frequencies were estimated afresh by maximum likelihood procedures. The frequencies and standard errors for the A_1A_2BO blood groups were obtained by the help of a computer[‡] (Table 2). The Rh frequencies and standard errors were obtained by

[†] The discrepancy pointed out by Dronamraju and Meerakhan about the incidence of colour vision defects in the Nagar Brahmans was typographical (*Ann. Hum. genet. Lond.* **25**, 110, 1961). The individual No. 92 in our paper (*Ann. Eugen.* **15**, 52, 1949) was colour defective (+) and not normal (−) as it appears in Appendix B, p. 61. The value given in Table 2 (p. 56), however, remains as it stood before.

[‡] Thanks are due to Dr. W. J. Schull who provided to the author the facilities of a computer at the University of Michigan, where this program was prepared with the assistance of Mr. A. Soni.

the simplified maximum likelihood method originally derived by Boyd (1954, 1955) and further simplified by Balakrishnan (1962) (Table 3). A note prepared by Balakrishnan comparing the results obtained by this method with that of Mourant (1954) is appended to this paper. Tables 4 and 5 include the gene frequency estimates with standard errors for the other traits under study.

TABLE 5

Gene frequency for secretion of ABH substances in saliva, for ability to taste phenyl-thio-carbamide (PTC), for red-green colour vision defect and for haemoglobin-S

	Secretor	Taster	R-G colour vision defect	Hb-S
Castes				
Audich	57·63 ± 3·24	33·42 ± 3·79	8·08 ± 2·74	0·0
Nagar		48·39 ± 3·04	10·00 ± 3·00	
Vania	60·13 ± 3·28	30·00 ± 3·57	5·00 ± 2·18	
Luvana	52·62 ± 3·15	32·92 ± 3·61	6·00 ± 2·37	
Kanbi	58·14 ± 3·26	34·22 ± 3·69	3·13 ± 2·17	0·0
Bhangi	48·23 ± 3·07	28·18 ± 3·57	1·01 ± 1·00	
Semi-tribe				
Koli	50·79 ± 3·85		8·96 ± 3·49	2·22 ± 0·77
Tribes				
Bhil	63·28 ± 4·93	33·39 ± 3·03	0·70 ± 0·70	8·10 ± 1·34
Dubla	58·97 ± 3·21	27·63 ± 3·37	2·75 ± 1·57	4·86 ± 1·05
Naika	49·08 ± 4·78		2·78 ± 2·74	8·40 ± 1·49
Dhanka	53·12 ± 3·27	20·80 ± 2·91	1·80 ± 1·26	10·82 ± 1·50
Dhodia	52·86 ± 4·43		0·0	9·36 ± 1·41
Gamit	56·17 ± 3·15	25·00 ± 2·76	2·72 ± 1·34	17·18 ± 1·85

Genetic variability in the tribes

In the computation of 'genetic distance' between two population groups (Sanghvi, 1953 and Pollitzer, 1958) equal weights were given to each gene. I had, however, realized that this was not an ideal procedure for racial analysis, as it did not distinguish the genes which were less variable from the ones which were subject to greater adaptation to local environments. Our knowledge about the adaptive nature of certain genes has advanced during the last ten years, but it is not yet enough to help us to attach weights to these genes in racial analysis.

An alternative approach to this question seems to me feasible. Let us assume that there is a large breeding population from which sizable sections have continued to separate over a period of time to form endogamous groups. The genetic differences in such endogamous groups will have been brought about as a result of selection on these genes within the groups, if one could rule out the possibility of gene mixture from external sources and of genetic drift. If the size of the sections at the time of their separation is large and continues to be large, it would largely rule out the effect of genetic drift. Under these circumstances, it might be possible to distinguish genes which are less variable than others for the types of environments in which these endogamous groups live.

These conditions appear to be largely satisfied for the six hill and forest tribes of Gujarat. Bhils belong to an ancient tribal group to which references are found in early Sanskrit literature, beginning at least from the second or third century B.C. As indicated above, it is distributed over a large area, and all over the extent of its geographical distribution there are a number of smaller tribal groups, with many cultural traits in common with the surrounding Bhils. Two of the tribes of the present study, Dhanka and Gamit were considered part of the Bhil tribe in the 1901 census but were recognized as separate tribes in the 1931 census.

Independent support for this contention comes from the anthropometric survey carried out by Dr. Stephen Fuchs, who has spent many years among the Bhils and the neighbouring tribes. His conclusion quoted by P. G. Shah (1963) bears out this point:

'The measurements taken of five Gujarat tribes, the Bhils, the Naikas, the Dublas, the Gamits, and the Dhankas, show that all the five tribes have racially much in common and, as a group, differ from the non-tribal population of Gujarat more than from each other. It is probable that all are merely sub-sections of the great Bhil tribe, going under different names and having separated from the original stock for various reasons, which may be geographical (isolation), social (various degrees of Hinduization) or economic (various transitional stages to plough cultivation).'

The amount of admixture with the Hindu castes and other populations of the plains is likely to be limited by the nature of their geographical distribution. Moreover, endogamy has been a rather rigid feature of the Indian culture, whether it be caste or tribal, and any lapse in this behaviour was punishable by stringent measures so as to prevent its frequent occurrence. The following passage about the customs in Dhodias in the early part of this century (Enthoven, 1920) is of interest.

'If a girl commits sexual indiscretions before marriage with a man of her caste, the fathers of the girl and the man involved are fined five rupees, and if the man belongs to a different *kul*, the girl is married to him. When a girl commits sexual indiscretions with a man of a lower caste, such as a Dubla, a Chodhra or a Naikda, the girl and her father are excommunicated, and are not re-admitted until they offer to the panch of their caste a goat, a feast or some fine. In some places, when the girl is re-admitted into caste she is made to drink a mixture of cowdung and cow's urine. Girls committing sexual indiscretions, before marriage, with impure castes like Bhangias or Dhedas are excommunicated for ever. If a girl cohabits with a Parsi, in some places they purify her by making her drink water in which a Brahman has washed his toe.'

Regarding the size of a tribal group at the time of its formation it may be mentioned that the factors which bring about the formation of such new tribes are themselves dependent upon a growing size and necessity for an independent identity. The instances where some information is available favour the view that the size of such tribes is in thousands rather than in tens at the time of their formation. This would, however, need a further and more critical exploration.

The semi-tribe of Kolis, on the other hand, is primarily a tribe of the plains and is different from the six hill and forest tribes in several cultural characteristics. The genetical analysis that was carried out earlier (Vyas *et al.*, 1962) by the computation of 'genetic distance' also supported this view. For these reasons, Kolis have not been included in the analysis of this section.

Measure of genetic variability. The next step in this analysis was to obtain a satisfactory measure of genetic variability. As an illustration, I will consider the A_1A_2BO gene frequencies of the six tribes (Table 2). In order to be able to apply the procedure of analysis of variance, it is necessary to apply the angular transformation so that the variance will be independent of the values of gene-frequencies. Figure 1 illustrates at a glance the nature of variability of the A_1, A_2, B, and O genes in the six tribes. It becomes evident that the genes A_2 and O are much less variable than A_1 and B.

It is possible to use the variance of the transformed gene frequency as a measure of variability of the gene amongst the six tribes. An approximation to this can be obtained by running a χ^2 test of homogeneity directly on the gene-frequencies without angular transformation. Such a procedure has been adopted for the 12 genes for which data are available for all the six tribes. The gene-complexes r, r', and r'' have been combined together to give one value Rh(d). The values of χ^2 are given in Table 6.

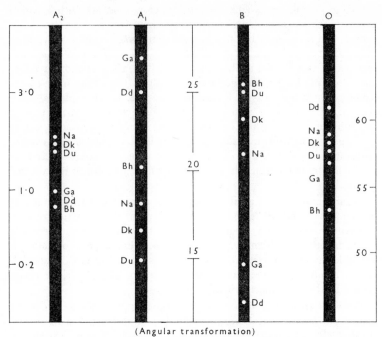

(Angular transformation)

FIG. 1. A_1A_2BO gene frequency of the six tribes.

TABLE 6

Variability of genes in six tribes probably separated from one parental stock

Least variable		Moderately variable		Most variable	
Gene	χ^2	Gene	χ^2	Gene	χ^2
		R-G defect	4·07		
A_2	1·09	R_2	4·70	B	9·40
O	1·38	Se	4·99	$Hb\text{-}S$	9·62
R_0	2·34	MN	6·55	$Rh(d)$	10·68
		R_1	6·90		
		A_1	7·08		

It will be seen that the genes A_2 and O which indicated lower variability on the chart give 1·09 and 1·38 as values for χ_2. In contrast, the A_1 gene gives a value of 7·08 and the B gene gives a value of 9·40.

I have arbitrarily divided the twelve genes into three classes. For the Rh blood groups, it turns out that R_0 is the least variable gene, R_1 and R_2 are moderately variable, and Rh(d) is the most variable gene. Hb-S and Rh(d) in which the effects of selection are well known came out in the most variable categories. Red-green colour vision defect, secretion of ABH substances in saliva, and MN blood-group genes are moderately variable. The present analysis indicates that genes B, Rh(d), and Hb-S are subject to greater selection in the local environments than the other genes in this study. In contrast, the genes A_2, O, and R_0 seem to be least affected in the environments in which these six tribes live. The remaining six genes have an intermediate status.

Genetic variability in the castes

Next, I intend to examine the genetic variability of the castes of Gujarat and discuss its implication in the light of the information available about these castes, particularly in relation to their origin. All six castes have been studied morphologically by D. N. Majundar (1950) and I will take into account his findings in the following discussion.

Brahmans (Audich; Nagar). The Audich and the Nagars, two important Brahman groups of Gujarat do not show a significant difference for A_1A_2BO and Rh blood groups or for the red-green colour vision gene. They do show, however, a significant difference for the MN blood groups and for the ability to taste PTC. The Nagars are particularly remarkable for their high frequencies of the M gene (70·5 per cent) and for the PTC taster gene (48·4 per cent) in Gujarat.

The morphological measurements of the Nagars are not significantly different from the Audich except for head breadth. The Nagars have a breadth of 146·66±0·59 against the breadth of 143·59±0·62 for the Audich. It is known that Nagars are generally fairer than the Audich. There are other traditional differences in these two categories of Brahmans. These differences are worthy of further investigation in the light of the possibility suggested by Kosambi (1956), that the priesthood of the incoming Aryans may not have completely submerged the priesthood of the early Indus valley culture. Unfortunately, our genetic study of the Nagars, undertaken in the year 1947, was limited in scope and would now require to be extended to throw further light on this question.

Traders (Vania; Luvana). Vania and Luvana, the two trading castes of Gujarat, are significantly different for A_1A_2BO, Rh, and Duffy blood groups. For the A_1A_2BO groups, Vanias have a very high A_1 (25·46±2·36), the highest amongst the caste Hindus, whereas Luvanas have a very high B (26·19±2·38). In the Rh blood groups, differences are found in the R_1 and r gene complex. Luvanas have the highest incidence of F_y^a blood groups in the entire series.

Our study of thalassemia and other haemoglobin variants in this caste of Luvanas is of great interest. Out of 18 cases of thalassemia major investigated by us (Sukumaran and Sanghvi, 1964) in Gujarat, 10 were from Luvana, 3 from Khoja, 2 from Vania, and 1 from Audich Brahman. It is known that Khoja is a Muslim group converted very largely from the Luvanas. Thus a large majority of cases belonged to the comparatively smaller caste of Luvana. In addition, our study revealed the presence of three other haemoglobin variants, viz. Hb-D, Hb-J, and Hb-L in Luvanas (Sanghvi et al., 1958; Sukumaran et al., 1959, 1960), thus almost giving them a mark of identification.

In morphology, there is a significant difference in head size, both the length and breadth being longer in the Luvanas (184·17±0·57; 146·33±0·51) than in the Vanias (181·35±0·67; 144·22±0·46). The cephalic index, however, is similar for both. There is also a big difference in the nasal index, 77·77 for Vania and 71·83 for Luvana. In this respect Luvanas are similar to Nagars, although the two are different in many genes.

It seems probable that Luvana is a migrant group, perhaps already with a place in early Indian history (fifth century B.C.–fifth century A.D.) but has remained unidentified. The large array of genetic characteristics specifying Luvana may assist in the search for its historical identity.

No specific observations can be made about the origin of Vanias. The Aryans came to India largely as pastoral tribes and had very little, if any, tradition of trading. In contrast, the earlier Indus culture has given a good deal of evidence of trading and this has been strengthened by recent excavations at Lothal in Gujarat (see Fig. 2). It may be worthwhile to explore whether some trading community had any genetic endowment from the Indus valley people.

Farmers (Kanbi). These are significantly different in one or more genetic traits from all the other caste groups of Gujarat, but there is no characteristic feature that can be related to Kanbi, except the lowest frequency of A_1 and a high B. A majority of Gujarat Kanbi has been tentatively assigned by some early workers (Enthoven, 1920) to the Gujar or Gurjar tribe, a large migrant group of people who came to India around the beginning of the Christian era and who have left their traces in Kashmir and the Punjab in their journey south, and who were so important in Gujarat that the state (Gujarat) and its language (Gujarati) are known after their name. A number of occupational castes such as Darji (tailor), Kumbhar (potter), Teli (oil-presser), Soni (gold-smith), and Sutar (carpenter) have endogamous subdivisions of the name Gujar and it would be interesting to test whether all of them belong to a single tribe of the past.

Scavengers (Bhangi). Bhangis who stood lowest in the Hindu social hierarchy in Gujarat for generations and who were untouchables up to

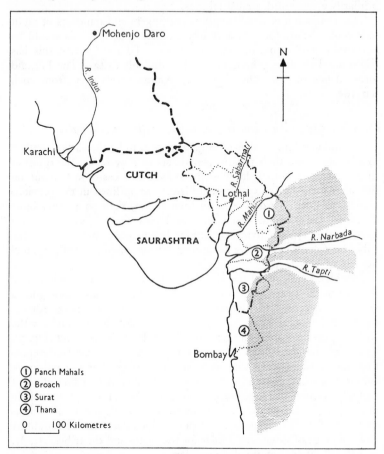

FIG. 2. Excavations at Lothal in Gujarat.

recent time are vastly different from caste Hindus in a number of genetical traits. They have the lowest incidence of r (cde) M and F^a blood-group genes, and the genes for secretion, for ability to taste PTC, and for red-green colour blindness among the caste Hindus. Furthermore, they have the highest incidence of B and R_0 genes and the lowest for the O gene in the entire series. The Bhangis appear to be closer to the tribes than to the castes in their genetic status.

The morphological measurements also reveal a similar relationship of the Bhangi with the tribes, but show them to be distinctly different from the Hindu castes. This would support the view that the Bhangis are very largely recruited from the tribal groups in the area and are not primarily a caste of degraded Hindus.

The occupation of the Bhangis as scavengers and removers of night soil would expose them to a variety of infections, and this would be maximum at the time of major epidemics. To what extent this has contributed to their genetic status it is difficult to say. The hill and forest tribes on the other hand are comparatively free from such hazards.

Comparison of genetic variability among the castes and the tribes

The hill and forest tribes of Gujarat appear to be the earliest settlers in the region and their present genetic status may reflect the result of their adaptation to their local environments. The castes in Gujarat, on the other hand have a very mixed history, as outlined in the previous section. Besides this difference in their origin, there is another basic difference between the castes and the tribes. Castes have enjoyed a more settled type of living conditions in villages and towns but the tribes have continued to live a marginal existence and a life of perpetual hardship.

The high incidence of the Hb-*S* gene in the tribes and their virtual absence in the castes make it evident that the tribes have undergone a very different type of malarial experience from the castes. Almost similar differences between castes and tribes have been found for the R_1 (*CDe*) gene-complex and for red-green colour vision defect (Fig. 3). This might indicate the similar effects of other environmental differences that may exist between the castes and the tribes. For the red-green colour blindness, it remains to be seen whether it is a relaxation of natural selection in the sense conceived by Post (1962) or something more specific. There are other genes such as *A*, *B*, and *O* as well as secretion of ABH substances in saliva for which the extent of variability and the range of values are similar for the castes and the tribes. A_2, *M*, and R_2 fall into an intermediate category.

The semi-tribe of Koli appear to be indigenous by the available accounts and its morphology is more similar to the tribes than to the castes. Its people are neither hunters of the woods nor farmers of the land and their genetical status poses an interesting problem. Their ABO picture is individualistic, characterized by the highest *O* and a low *A*, in the series. They stand intermediate between the castes and the tribes for the R_1 (*CDe*) gene complex and for the Hb-*S* gene. For the Rh(*d*) gene, M-gene, and for red-green colour vision gene, they line up with the high caste Hindus. To what extent this reflects their adaptation to the living condition on the plains of Gujarat and to what extent it reflects their ancestral gene pool would be worthy of exploration.

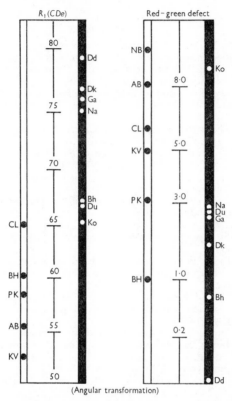

FIG. 3. Variation in R_1 (*CDe*) gene complex and gene for red-green colour vision defect in the castes and tribes of Gujarat.

Summary

(1) Genetical data on six castes and seven tribes of Gujarat published earlier have been re-examined. They include A_1A_2BO, MN, Rh, P, and Duffy blood groups, secretion of ABH substances in saliva, ability to taste PTC, and red-green colour vision defect.

(2) Gene frequencies have been recalculated by maximum likelihood procedures.

(3) Variability of gene frequencies has been classified in the hill and forest tribes which probably separated from one parental stock. It

turns out that A_2, O, and R_0 are less variable than B, Hb-S, and Rh(d) in the environments in which these tribes live.

(4) The genetic variation in the six castes have been used to throw light on their probable origins.

REFERENCES

BALAKRISHNAN, V., 1962. 'Estimation of chromosome frequencies in the rhesus blood group system', *Acta genet. Statist. med.* **12**, 322–351.

BOYD, W. C., 1954. 'Shortened maximum likelihood estimation of Rh gene frequencies', *Am. J. hum. Genet.* **6**, 303–318.

—— 1955. 'Simple maximum likelihood method for calculating Rh gene frequencies in Pacific populations', *Am. J. phys. Anthrop.* **13**, 447–453.

ENTHOVEN, R. E., 1920. *The Tribes and Castes of Bombay*, Vol. I, p. 331; Vol. II, p. 134. Government of Bombay.

KOSAMBI, D. D., 1956. *An Introduction to the Study of Indian History*, pp. 124–127. Popular Book Depot, Bombay.

MAJUMDAR, D. N., 1950. *Race Realities in Cultural Gujarat*. Gujarat Research Society, Bombay.

MOURANT, A. E., 1954. *The Distribution of the Human Blood Groups*, Chap. XIX. Blackwell, Oxford.

POLLITZER, W. S., 1958. 'The negroes of Charleston (S.C.); a study of hemoglobin types, serology and morphology', *Am. J. phys. Anthrop.* **16**, 241–263.

POST, R. M., 1962. 'Population differences in red and green colour vision deficiency: a review, and a query on selection relaxation', *Eugen. Q.* **9**, 131–146.

SANGHVI, L. D. and KHANOLKAR, V. R., 1949. 'Data relating to seven genetical characters in six endogamous groups in Bombay', *Ann. Eugen.* **15**, 52–76.

—— 1953. 'Comparison of genetical and morphological methods for a study of biological difference', *Am. J. phys. Anthrop.* **11**, 385–404.

—— SUKUMARAN, P. K., and LEHMANN, H., 1958. 'Haemoglobin J trait in two Indian women', *Br. med. J.* **2**, 828–830.

SHAH, P. G., 1962. 'Racial survey in Gujarat', *Indian Anthropology* (eds. T. N. MADAN and GOPALA SARANA), pp. 150–162. Asia Publishing House, Bombay.

SUKUMARAN, P. K., SANGHVI, L. D., AGER, J. A. M., and LEHMANN, H., 1959. 'Haemoglobin L in Bombay: findings in three Gujarati speaking Lohana families', *Acta genet. Statist. med.* **9**, 202–206.

—— —— and NAZARETH, F. A., 1960. 'Haemoglobin D-thalassaemia: a report of two families', *Acta haemat.* **23**, 309–319.

—— —— 1964. Unpublished observations.

VYAS, G. N., BHATIA, H. M., BANKER, D. D., and PURANDARE, N. M., 1958. 'Study of blood groups and other genetical characters in six Gujarati endogamous groups in Western India', *Ann. hum. Genet.* **22**, 185–199.

—— SUKUMARAN, P. K., BALAKRISHNAN, V., and SANGHVI, L. D., 1962. 'Study of blood groups, abnormal haemoglobins and other genetical characters in some tribes of Gujarat', *Am. J. phys. Anthrop.* **20**, 255–265.

11

PEOPLE OF INDIA INCLUDING PRIMITIVE TRIBES—A SURVEY ON PHYSIOLOGICAL ADAPTATION, PHYSICAL FITNESS, AND NUTRITION

MANGAL SAIN MALHOTRA

Defence Institute of Physiology and Allied Sciences, Madras 3, India

Physical environment of India

INDIA is a vast country with an area of more than 1·2 million square miles. It lies between 8°N to 37°N latitude and 68° to 97° longitude, and has a land frontier of 8200 miles and a coast line of 2900 miles. According to the configuration of the land, India may be said to consist of a great Himalayan range in the north, the Sutlej, Gangetic, and Brahmaputra plains in the middle, and the triangular Deccan plateau in the south (Fig. 1). The great Himalayan range contains some of the highest peaks of the world and is the source of most of the rivers that flow through the Indo-Gangetic plains. It has been a great barrier to climatic influences and the movements of people. The vast plain lying to the south of this mountain range is watered by the Sutlej, the Jumna, the Ganges, and the Brahmaputra river systems, and is made up of the silt brought down by these rivers. This plain contains the most fertile parts of India and the largest concentration of population. The Deccan plateau lies south of the river Tapti and is bounded by the Western and Eastern Ghats. The plateau which lies between these broken and low-mountain ranges is divided into broad crowded valleys, through which flow the Mahanadi, the Godavari, the Krishna, the Tungabhadra, and the Cauvery rivers, which are sluggish and monsoon-fed.

Climate of India

The climate of India is generally a tropical-monsoon type except in Punjab and Kashmir where there is a subtropical

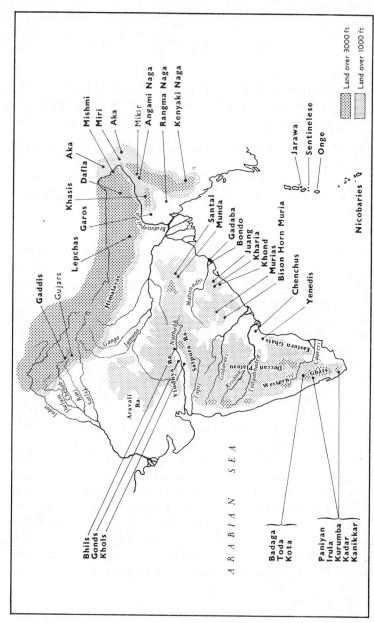

FIG. 1. Map of the Indian subcontinent, showing the location of the 'tribal' groups mentioned in the text.

climate. The seasonal rhythm in India can be broadly classified as follows:

(i) cold season from November to the end of February;
(ii) hot season from the beginning of March to the middle of June; and
(iii) rainy season from the middle of June to the end of October.

In January, a month typical of the cold weather, there is a wide range in temperature from north to south; the days are warm and the nights distinctly cold. The average temperature for January is less than 55°F in the Punjab, about 60°F in the Ganga valley, and about 75°F in Madras. In April and May the sun is vertically over India. These are, as such, the hottest months in most parts of the country. The north of India is hottest with its dry air and cloudless skies. In central India the mean temperature is about 85°F in April and 95°F in May. On an average day in May and June, the dry bulb temperature may exceed 110°F in Punjab and Rajasthan. The temperature over the whole country is remarkably uniform in October, the mean being about 80°F everywhere at sea level. In November it starts getting cooler in the north and the nights in the far north-west are chilly; in December the cold weather season is in full swing.

The climatic regions of India, based on the dominant factor of rainfall, are as follows (Fig. 2):

(i) regions with 20 to 40 inches of rainfall; such as Madras, southern and north-western Deccan, and the upper Ganga plain;
(ii) regions with 40 to 80 inches of rainfall, such as the north-east plateau and the middle Ganga valley;
(iii) regions with more than 80 inches of annual rainfall, such as the West Coast, Bengal, and Assam; and
(iv) the Himalayan regions and Western Ghats with very heavy rainfall over 200 inches per year.

Northern India, in its most easterly and most westerly States in Assam and in Rajasthan presents the greatest possible contrast of dampness and dryness. In Rajasthan, for example, the climate is desert type, which is characterized by high daytime temperatures ranging up to 120°F, low relative humidity, and scanty rainfall. The average annual rainfall in the Rajputana desert is less

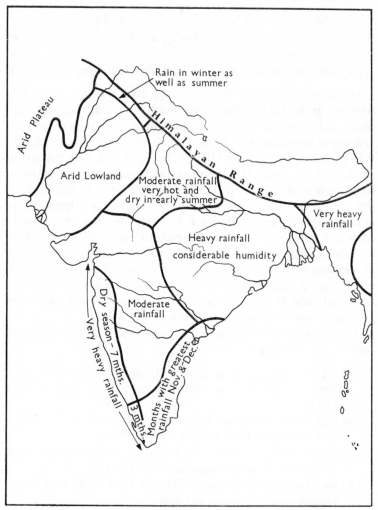

Fig. 2. The climatic regions of India, based on the dominant factor of rainfall.

than 5 inches. In Assam, on the other hand, it is of jungle type, which is characterized by daytime temperatures not above 90–100°F, high relative humidity ranging from 60–90 per cent, and annual rainfall between 100 and 200 inches. At Cherapunji in Assam the yearly rainfall is between 400 and 500 inches.

People of India

India geographically forms a naturally protected region into which man could move only through the difficult gaps in the mountain barriers. The result of this was that the races that had come earlier and were in occupation of the country were not destroyed, but were pushed south and eastwards and to this day they form one of the main components of the Indian population. Similarly, the hills and the forests gave shelter to a large number of primitive tribes, who were left comparatively unmolested and had thus better chances of survival. The Indian population today, which numbers 440 million people according to the 1961 census, contains not only many extremely primitive strains, but also has representative elements from almost all the races of the modern world.

The classification of the Indian people from an anthropometric point of view was first attempted by Sir Herbert Risley and was presented in the Census of India, 1901. Various other anthropologists after him attempted to classify the Indian people in different ways, but none could offer a satisfactory scientific classification. In 1937, Guha revised the earlier account and presented a new classification of the Indian people. He divided them into the following six main racial groups:

(1) the Negrito,
(2) the Proto-Australoid,
(3) the Mongoloid,
(4) the Mediterranean or Indus,
(5) the Western Brachycephals or the Alpo-Dinaric,
(6) the Nordic.

His classification was based on anthropometric and somatoscopic criteria and lacked the support of well-established genetic characters. At that time there was not much emphasis on the blood antigens and antibodies and other genetic entities that are now being commonly studied. Even today no detailed classification of the Indian population based on genetic polymorphism has been attempted; only sporadic reports on gene-frequencies of the heritable characters in different ethnic groups are available. The material contained in these is insufficient for a systematic classification of the Indian population and thus, even now, Guha's classification of Indian people is the only authentic one available.

A limited number of studies have also been done on the ABO blood group distribution in various communities in India. These studies indicate that there is a considerable admixture of various racial and cultural groups in the Indian population. Majumdar (1961), on the basis of such studies, has come to the conclusion that there is a decrease in the frequency of the blood antigen B from East to West and from South to North. This follows the pattern of change in the nasal and cephalic indices.

Tribal population

In the Indian Constitution (Article 342), the aboriginal people are listed as Scheduled Tribes; the social workers, however, call them 'Adivasis' (original inhabitants). To protect their way of life and culture, and to prevent these simple people from being exploited by their more advanced and prosperous neighbours, areas where they live have been demarcated as Scheduled or partially Scheduled areas. The frontiers and border regions in Assam, the Laccadive and Minicoy Islands, and the Lahaul and Spiti areas in Punjab are declared as 'Scheduled areas', and extensive tribal tracts in the States of Madras, Maharashtra, West Bengal, Uttar Pradesh, Bihar, Madhya Pradesh, and Orissa as 'partially Scheduled areas'. These areas are administered by the Governor and not by the elected Government of the State, so that the normal State Legislation is not effective over them. Such areas are also provided with special privileges and aid from the Government. To look after the speedy development of these areas, the Government of India has appointed a Commissioner of Scheduled Tribes and Scheduled Castes with Regional Assistant Commissioners all over the country.

According to the 1961 census, there are 255 different Scheduled Tribes in India with a total population of 30 millions. These form 6·8 per cent of the total population of India. The distribution of tribal population in various States and centrally administered areas of the country and its proportion to the total population of India is given in Table 1. In 1960 the President of India appointed a high-powered commission on Scheduled areas and Scheduled Tribes to study various social, economic, administrative, and other problems of tribal people. The commission has written an exhaustive report on the subject and has listed the tribes in the various States which are in the extremely underdeveloped stage

TABLE 1

Population of India including tribal, statewise—as per census of 1961

Sl. No.	Name of State	Population (millions)	Scheduled tribes (millions)	Percentage of scheduled tribes to the total population
	(A) States			
1	Andhra Pradesh	35·98	1·32	3·68
2	Assam	11·87	2·07	17·42
3	Bihar	46·46	4·20	9·05
4	Gujarat	20·63	2·75	13·36
5	Jammu and Kashmir	3·56	—	—
6	Kerala	16·90	0·21	1·23
7	Madhya Pradesh	32·37	6·68	20·63
8	Madras	33·69	0·25	7·49
9	Maharashtra	39·55	2·40	6·06
10	Mysore	23·59	0·19	0·81
11	Orissa	17·55	4·22	24·07
12	Punjab	20·31	0·01	0·07
13	Rajasthan	20·16	2·31	11·46
14	Uttar Pradesh	73·75	—	—
15	West Bengal	34·93	2·06	5·91
	(B) Centrally administered areas			
1	Andaman	0·06	0·01	22·22
2	Delhi	2·66	—	—
3	Himachal Pradesh	1·35	0·11	8·01
4	Laccadive	0·02	0·02	97·02
5	Manipur	0·78	0·25	31·91
6	Tripura	1·14	0·36	31·52
7	Dadra and Nagar Haveli	0·06	0·05	88·44
8	Goa	0·63	—	—
9	N.E.F.A.	0·34	0·01	1·50
10	Nagaland	0·37	0·34	9·31
11	Pondicherry	0·37	—	—
12	Sikkim	0·37	0·16	23·10
	Total for India	439·45	29·98	6·82

(Table 2). These tribes live either by food gathering, hunting or by practising *jhum* or shifting cultivation using hoes or digging sticks. About 2·6 million people, belonging to 109 different tribal communities, live in this manner.

TABLE 2

List of tribes still at an underdeveloped stage

ANDHRA PRADESH
Lingadhari Koya
Chenchu
Yenadi

ASSAM
Mikir
Abor

BIHAR
Birhor
Asur
Korwa
Kharia
Sauria Paharia

KERALA
Kadar
Irular
Paniyan
Kattunayakan
Vishavan

MADHYA PRADESH
Pahadi Korwa
Baiga in Baigachuk
Abuj Madia (Bastar)
Birhor
Sehariya
Binjhwar

MADRAS
Kadar
Irular
Paniyan
Malayali

MAHARASHTRA
Katkari
Hill Gond (Chanda District)

MYSORE
Kadu-Kuruba
Jenu-Kuruba
Koraga
Irular

ORISSA
Birhor
Bonodo Proraja
Juang
Kotia-Khond
Hill Bhuiya of Bhuiya Pirh
Lanjia Saora
Koya
Paidi Bhuiya of Bonai

RAJASTHAN
Sehria

WEST BENGAL
Asur
Birhor
Sauria Paharia
Toto
Rabba
Lepcha

ANDAMAN AND NICOBAR ISLANDS
Jarawa
Onge
Sentineless
Shom Pen

Broadly speaking, the aboriginal population in India can be divided into three distinct zones, viz. Southern, Central, and North-Eastern zones.

Southern zone. Though the tribes are scattered, their concentration is found chiefly in the southern-most part of the Western Ghats stretching from Wynaad to Cape Comorin. They are the most ancient inhabitants now living in India. South of the Krishna river, in the Nallaimallais Hills, live Chenchus and Yenadis. The Todas, Badagas and Kotas inhabit the Nilgiri Hills. Paniyan, Irula, and Kurumba live in Wynaad, and sheltered in the isolation of forests are found the most primitive of the Indian aborigines, such as the Kadars and Kanikkars, with many of their original traits still preserved.

In the majority of cases, these people are of short to medium stature, the skin colour is dark chocolate brown, approaching black, the nose is flat and broad and, not infrequently the lips are everted. The Kadars have a peculiar habit of chipping the incisor teeth to the shape of a cone. It is said to be a painful procedure but is gone through by every boy and girl with an eye to aesthetics. Blood groups show a preponderance of A.

Excepting the Todas, Badagas, and Kotas of the Nilgiri Hills, the other primitive tribes in this zone subsist mostly on hunting and food gathering. They collect edible roots, tubers and honey, and hunt birds and small animals for their subsistence. Until lately their wearing apparel consisted only of an apron made of grass, or a skirt of leaves.

The Todas of the Nilgiris are a pastoral community and keep large herds of cattle, particularly buffaloes. A Toda is of medium height, well-built, with regular features and perfect teeth. This tribe is fast disappearing; their number in 1931 was 900 and in 1941 it was 630. No children have, in fact been born in this community during the last 30 years. This can partly be attributed to the small number of women in the community, but is mostly due to high prevalence of venereal disease. Only recently, after a lapse of about 30 years, have the first babies been born in this community. Polyandry prevails and is perhaps devised by the tribe for overcoming the shortage of women as well as for preservation of the tribal community.

Central zone. The central mountain barrier, between the rivers Narbada and Godavari, that divides the northern part of India from the Peninsular India has provided refuge for primitive tribes from times immemorial. This contains the largest assembly of Indian aboriginal tribes, numbering several millions. Beginning from the east, the most important tribes are the Gadaba and Bondo of Ganjam district, the Juang, Kharia, and Khond of the Orissa hills, and the Santal and Munda of Chotanagpur. In the western portion of the central mountain belt are Bhils, Kols, and Gonds. In the Bastar State, there are Murias and Bison-horn Murias.

These people have a dark skin and a short to medium stature, with a long head. The nose is sunken at the root and is fleshy and broad. The hair on the face and body is not profuse. Physically, they are strong, muscular, and well-built. The blood group B is in preponderance.

Generally speaking, these tribes are in a higher stage of cultural development. Instead of food gathering and hunting, they practise a shifting cultivation and the life is more settled. The houses are well built, and handicrafts like basketry, wood carving, and the making of different implements are well developed. The communal life is well organized, with village councils under a headman. Among the more advanced of these tribes, like the Santals, there is, in addition to the village councils, a supreme council of the whole tribe, elected on a democratic basis for settling inter-village disputes. The characteristic feature in the social life of these tribes is the existence of bachelors' dormitories, separate or joint for boys and girls. In these institutions is taught strict discipline and service to the village and they are also centres of the folk dancing and music that occupy an important place in tribal life. These tribes have had the most contact with civilized or urban people, which has led to an infiltration of Hindu ideas and religious rites, and has also been responsible for the introduction of diseases to which the tribes were not previously exposed.

North-eastern zone. This zone comprises tracts of Assam, the North-East Frontier Agency (NEFA), Nagaland, Tripura, Manipur, and Sikkim, that is, the sub-Himalayan region. The main tribes in these areas are Lepchas in Sikkim, Darjeeling, and West Assam; Mikirs, Garos, and Khasis in Assam, and Aka, Dafla, Mishmi, and Miri in NEFA. Many sects of the Nagas, like the Angami, Rangma, and Kanyak, are the residents of Nagaland, Manipur, and Tripura.

This area is a mountainous country covered with thick forests.

To avoid dampness, the tribesmen live in pile dwellings, which are raised well above the ground. The difficult nature of the terrain has discouraged visitors to NEFA and Nagaland, with the result that these people have remained almost secluded. The environment has shaped their body, their art, their living, and their architecture. On the countless streams and rivers they have built bridges. To protect themselves against insects and pests, particularly the dim-dam flies, they have learnt to weave clothes. The beauty of the countryside has created in them a love of beauty and a desire to make good things. They spend their entire lives on the slopes of mountains and so have grown very strong with well-developed calf muscles. Most of the tribes living in Nagaland and NEFA have an age-old heritage of war. For security reasons, many villages have been established on top of hills and widely separated from each other, and the heritage of war has given the tribesmen spears, swords, crossbows, and ordinary bows and has made them good marksmen and expert hunters.

These people live by shifting, or *jhum*, cultivation. In this, the forests are burnt down and in the cooled ashes are sown the seeds, with the help of hoes. In certain areas, however, the people have learnt to settle down in agriculture and have adopted terraced cultivation.

The tribes in this zone have typical Mongoloid features, the most distinguishing being the almond-shaped eye, with a rounded inner and pointed outer canthus; as the latter is at a somewhat higher plane, it gives the eye an oblique shape. The face is flat with prominent cheek bones. The head is massive and its dimensions are larger than that of any other race in India. The nose is sunken. They have a medium stature with brown or light brown skin colour. There is a marked preponderance of blood group B.

Like the central tribes, many of these tribes have bachelor dormitories separately for boys and girls and these institutions organize and control the entire youth of the village and help to develop them as fully-trained members of the tribe. Teaching is imparted in defensive and offensive methods in fighting, music, folk dances, and so on.

Apart from these three big zones, there is a small isolated zone, consisting of the Andaman and Nicobar islands in the Bay of Bengal. The main tribes in the Andaman are the Onge, Jarawa, and Sentineless, and in the Nicobar, the Nicobaries. The Onge inhabit the island of Little Andaman, the Jarawa mainly the interior of South Andaman and the Sentineless, the North Sentinel island.

Of these tribes, the Jarawas are very hostile and shoot arrows at anyone going near them. In 1938 some Jarawa children were captured and an attempt was made to train them and later, with their help, to go into the forest and study this tribe. This scheme, however, did not materialize because the tribesmen were also hostile to these men.

The Onge are, however, less risky and can be said to be friendly. An excellent account of their way of life has been given by Buchi (1960).

They are pygmies with a short broad face, flat broad nose, thick everted lips, curly hair, and dark skin. A peculiar feature of the women is the steatopegia, i.e. enormously developed buttocks. They project so much backward as to form a balcony on which children can freely stand. They live almost naked and subsist entirely on the natural products of the sea and the forests. From the sea they catch turtles, fish, and molluscs, and in the forests they hunt for wild pigs, and collect honey and roots. Bows and arrows are used for hunting.

Race element in the Himalayas

The ethnological groups living at the high altitude are distributed mainly in Kashmir, Punjab, Uttar Pradesh, and North-Eastern Frontier Agency (NEFA).

In Kashmir there are no primitive tribes. The highest altitudes are inhabited by the Ladakhis, belonging to Mongoloid race. They live between the altitudes of 10,000 to 15,000 ft and are agriculturists. The environmental temperatures at these heights range between −20° to −40°C during winter. There is practically no rain and the hills are barren. Owing to difficult terrain and the lack of communications, no studies have been done on their physical and physiological adaptation. They offer, however, vast scope for research on the mechanisms of adaptation to the combined effects of extreme cold and high altitude.

In Punjab the main hill tribes are the Gujjars and the Gaddis. These are pastoral tribes and live at altitudes up to 10,000 ft. They come down in winter to graze their cattle and goats. Some anthropological studies have been done on these people (Mehrotra,

1958), but not with a view to the study of their adaptation to their environment. These tribes are not Mongoloid, but have predominantly Alpinoid features.

In Dehradun and Garhwal districts of Uttar Pradesh, there are three important racial strains. The highest altitudes are inhabited by the Tibetans and the other Mongoloid people, the central belt is comprised of a tall, fair race represented by Khas Rajputs and Khas Brahmins, the Kanets, and the Bhats, and a comparatively dark aboriginal type represented by the Doms, who are the artisan class. The lowest rung of the social ladder is occupied by the Kolta, who is the traditional hewer of wood and drawer of water. He lives by working as a domestic servant or an agricultural labourer.

An account of the men inhabiting the North-Eastern Frontier Agency has already been given in detail under 'Tribes of North-Eastern Zone'.

Food intake and nutritional content of the diet of Indians

(a) *Non-tribal population.* A number of studies have been done by the Indian Council of Medical Research (I.C.M.R.) to survey the food intake and nutrient content of the diets of various States in India. Most of these studies have been confined to families in a low income group, consisting of agricultural labourers, small agriculturists, petty tradesmen, and industrial labourers, which form

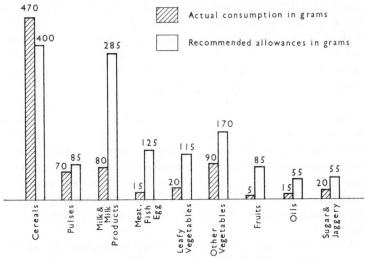

FIG. 3. Average daily consumption of foodstuffs per adult.

the majority of the population of India. The results of the various studies have been compiled by the I.C.M.R. in their special reports Nos. 22, 25, 35, 36, and 37 and by Pandit and Someswara Rao (1960) and Patvardhan and Jagannathan (1962). These surveys have shown that the bulk of the diet of Indians is formed by cereals, which provide 70–90 per cent of the total calories. The consumption of protective foods, like pulses, vegetables, fruits, meat, and milk is very low. This is because they are in short supply and are expensive for ordinary men to buy. Although the food habits differ from region to region, the general food pattern is quite the same. An average daily consumption of various foodstuffs of an Indian adult is shown in Fig. 3. The recommended allowances in this figure are based on the suggestions of the Nutrition Advisory Committee of the Indian Council of Medical Research.

The calorie requirement of an Indian man has been placed at 2400–3900 kcal per adult per day and of a woman, at 2000–2700 kcal per adult per day. The average Indian, however, is not able to get the required number of calories. On the basis of I.C.M.R. reports, Tasker (1956) has calculated the caloric intake and the nutrient content of the diets of various States (Table 3). It will be seen from this table that in Bihar, Madras, Assam, Kerala, and Maharashtra, the calorie content of the food is very low and the people are living in semi-starved condition. The quantity of animal protein in the diet is exceedingly low throughout. In Madras and Kerala the diets are grossly deficient in respect of total proteins also. The best diet seems to be in Punjab and Delhi, where the daily calorie intake is about 3300 kcal and the total protein varies from 91 to 119 g per day.

(b) *Tribal population.* As a rule, the living standard of the tribal people is very low. This is due to the primitive conditions in which they are obliged to earn their living. The diet of the various tribes varies according to the state of their development and the areas they inhabit; some of the very primitive tribes would eat anything they find, like insects, rats, fish, roots, flowers, edible leaves, berries, &c. In general, these tribes are omnivorous. Others at higher level, do cultivate and grow crops of mostly coarse grain, like millet.

An extensive dietary survey has not been done on all the aboriginal tribes, but quite useful work has been done by the

TABLE 3

Mean nutritve value of diets in various States of India

	Calorific value (kcal)	Total protein (g)	Fat (g)	Carbohydrate (g)	Vitamin B_1 (I.U.)	Nicotinic acid (mg)	Riboflavin (mg)	Vitamin C (mg)
Andhra Pradesh	2690	72	32	526	517	12·4	410	24
Assam	2496	72	25	506	585	22·0	746	101
Bihar	2277	74	22	449	490	19·2	601	48
Delhi	3293	119	36	622	596	10·6	64	29
Kashmir	3158	79	37	643	781	29·8	957	68
Kerala	2316	55	43	427	513	19·7	807	74
Madhya Pradesh	2799	95	25	554	712	19·0	396	15
Madras	2068	53	22	416	476	16·5	62	24
Maharashtra	2222	57	57	369	223	6·3	235	48
Mysore	2889	68	18	616	1073	10·1	84	66
Orissa	2617	77	20	547	670	26·5	852	52
Punjab	3330	91	58	607	237	6·0	203	20
Rajasthan	3099	107	52	630	5	0·1	15	5
Uttar Pradesh	2648	77	26	534	425	14·5	438	37
West Bengal	2971	85	37	592	738	26·7	981	140

TABLE 4

Diets of some Indian tribes

Tribes	Cereals	Millets	Roots and tubers	Pulses	Non-leafy vegetables	Leafy vegetables	Milk	Fleshy foods	Oils and fats	Fruits	Sugar and molasses
					Consumption of food groups (oz/day)						
Baiga	5·0	17·5	—	0·86	1·0	2·2	1·8	—	†	—	—
Muria	20·1	3·7	—	2·60	2·2	0·5	—	0·2	†	—	—
Urali	6·1	—	35·1	0·04	1·9	—	0·6	0·5	†	0·6	—
Kanikkar	1·4	—	41·5	0·05	0·8	—	—	0·1	†	†	—
Malapantharam	1·0	—	37·7	—	2·8	—	—	—	†	†	—
Muthuvan	5·0	16·6	6·6	0·50	—	1·9	2·2	—	†	†	—
Ullatan	5·3	—	25·0	0·40	1·5	—	0·5	—	†	†	—
Tripura	23·0	—	1·3	0·20	3·8	0·6	0·6	0·9	0·2	†	—
Riang	28·0	—	4·7	0·10	12·9	0·3	0·3	1·0	0·1	†	—
Miniyong Abor	24·8	—	—	—	0·2	1·1	—	0·1	†	†	—
Padam Abor	26·4	—	0·1	—	1·4	1·8	—	1·3	—	†	—
Gallong Abor	25·0	—	0·7	—	0·2	1·4	—	0·5	†	—	—
Paniyan	16·0	—	0·8	—	6·2	1·5	0·3	0·1	0·1	1·6	—
Mulla Kurumba	23·6	1·7	—	0·2	7·3	†	0·4	†	0·3	†	0·9
Urali Kurumba	19·5	1·4	—	1·3	6·0	0·9	—	0·3	0·2	†	†
Toda	19·5	0·3	—	4·5	9·7	—	23·7	Nil	2·3	†	0·9
Kota	11·6	9·5	10·0	0·3	1·0	—	2·3	—	0·3	†	1·4
Irula	2·7	13·0	—	0·3	0·8	1·7	5·5	0·1	0·2	†	†

† Negligible

TABLE 5

Mean nutritive value of daily diet of some of the aboriginal tribes in India

Tribes	kcal	Total protein (g)	Animal protein (g)	Vitamin B_1 (mg)	Vitamin B_2 (mg)	Niacin (mg)	Vitamin C (mg)
Baiga	2600	75·0	1·7	1·10	—	17·0	59·0
Muria	2760	80·0	1·2	1·60	0·90	21·0	18·0
Urali	2410	28·0	6·2	1·55	0·55	15·0	46·0
Kanikkar	2200	13·0	1·5	0·60	0·54	5·0	5·0
Malapanthram	1850	13·0	0·3	0·55	0·22	6·0	16·0
Muthavan	2640	44·0	2·5	2·30	0·20	11·0	3·0
Ullatan	2450	30·0	0·6	1·00	0·50	12·0	3·0
Tripura	2600	63·0	11·9	2·00	0·30	28·0	12·0
Riang	3150	76·0	9·0	2·70	0·35	37·0	27·0
Padam Abor	2960	80·0	7·0	1·50	0·30	35·0	65·0
Miniyong Abor	2650	68·0	3·0	1·80	0·20	30·0	16·0
Gallong Abor	2950	70·0	3·0	2·40	0·23	38·0	17·0
Paniyan	1975	52·7	3·1	1·52	0·85	21·0	44·0
Mulla Kurumba	2730	56·3	2·2	1·87	0·71	30·0	49·0
Urali Kurumba	2300	61·5	6·3	1·88	0·82	24·0	33·0
Toda	3100	75·1	28·5	1·85	1·14	24·0	35·0
Kota	3060	88·9	2·0	2·75	0·98	25·0	36·0
Irula	1860	50·3	9·0	1·99	0·92	13·0	52·0

Anthropological Department of India on some of the tribes living in the Abor Hills, NEFA (Sengupta, 1952, 1954, and 1955), in southern India (Sengupta and Biswas, 1956a, b), in Tripura and in Madhya Pradesh (Roy and Rao, 1956; Ray, Roy & Biswas, 1957). On the basis of these reports, an analysis of various types of diets taken by different tribes has been compiled (Roy and Rao, 1962) and is given in Table 4. The table shows that most of the tribes do not use any milk, fat or fruit, and that the bulk of their diet is either formed of cereals or of roots and tubers. The intake of fleshy food and milk as a source of animal proteins is also negligible in all the tribes. The only exception to the above are the Todas of the Nilgiri Hills, who take a lot of milk and are lacto-vegetarians. Their economy is based almost entirely on buffalo-rearing. Abors also keep plenty of cows, but these are not milked, in the belief that this unworthy practice may weaken their cows.

The nutrient value of the daily dietary intake of various tribes is given in Table 5 (Roy and Rao, 1962). Although all types of meat are taken by the tribal people, the animal protein content of their food is very low except in the case of the Todas. In fact, in most of the tribes the diet is very deficient in total protein content. This is because the people are too poor to kill their domestic animals, whilst the wild animals are not always available. In the Abor Hills, the tribes depend for their meat supply upon Esso, a semi-domestic animal with the body size of a buffalo and the appearance of a cow. Padam Abors hunt for birds, deer, jungle animals, and lizards for food. Murias have a great liking for the big succulent larvae of certain insects, which they collect from young date palms. They also make pickles of roasted ants and their larvae. The tribes that have extremely deficient diets are scattered in different parts of the Kerala and Nilgiri districts of Madras. The diets of most of the tribes of these two regions are, in fact, much inferior to the grossly deficient diets of the States.

In conclusion, it can be said that the diet of both the tribal and non-tribal population in India is unsatisfactory and is inadequate both from the calorific and nutritional points of view, and a very large population of the country is living in a semi-starved state.

General health of the tribal people

Where the aboriginals still live in the forest or by shifting cultivation, their general level of health is better than that of their civilized neighbours, because malnutrition in them is less pronounced. The abandoning of their original mixed diet in favour of a rice diet has resulted in deficiency diseases. The diseases prevalent in various tribes have been discussed in detail by Shrikant (1960–61), the Commissioner of Scheduled Castes and Scheduled Tribes in India. In tribes of Madras, Kerala, and Andhra Pradesh, malaria, filaria, tuberculosis, yaws, guineaworm, leprosy and venereal disease are common. In Assam also, closer contact with civilization has introduced venereal diseases and tuberculosis into the tribal population. In Maharashtra the general health of the aboriginals is poor; the most common diseases are malaria, guineaworm, and scurvy. Among the Abors in NEFA there is high incidence of goitre, due to deficiency of iodine in water.

Effects of environments on body-build

Not much work has yet been done in India to study human adaptation in response to climatic stress. A number of papers have been written on anthropometric measurements of various tribes, but these have only attempted to distinguish one anthropological group from another, and their main emphasis has been on racial distinctions. A large volume of literature has also been published on the social behaviour and conditions of life in several important tribes in India (Ghurye, 1950, 1953; Memoria, 1957; Elvin, 1960, 1961), but from none of these is it possible to build a coherent picture of adaptive processes that have been at work in shaping different people to their present state of physical and physiological development.

Various limited studies that have been conducted, however, show that the Himalayan people, whether living in the North-Eastern Frontier Agency in the East or in Ladakh in the West possess similar physical features, which have been referred to as Mongoloid characters. These people live thousands of miles apart and have not left these localities for many generations. Whether these men are descended from the same race or whether these characters are adaptive in nature remains to be assessed. It is perhaps as a result of adaptation to the environments that the two great plateaus of the world, the Andes and Tibet are inhabited by Mongoloid people who so greatly resemble each other.

Similarly, the dark pigmentation seen in people of South India and the Andamans (areas which are near the tropics) may also be adaptative in nature; the pigment protecting them against the excessive radiation of the tropical sun. The primitive tribes dwelling in the forests of South India like the Kadars and the Paniyans, and in the Andamans, like the Onge, are dark and short-statured with short, curly hair. These men are separated by a long stretch of sea, the Bay of Bengal; it is quite likely that the short size enables these men to crawl through the narrow meshes of dense forests. Their short, curly hair does not get caught in the bushes whilst they are passing through thick undergrowth. Their body shape, therefore, appears to be that best suited for living in forests and subsisting on what it can supply.

The influence of nutrition on stature

The only adaptive criterion universally studied in India has been that of body weight. The comparison of the heights of the people of different States in India reveals that there is a gradual decline in stature as one proceeds from Punjab to Madras. This difference may be attributed to racial, climatic, or nutritional factors, but the predominant factor in this variation appears to be that of nutrition. The average height of the residents of Punjab/Delhi, according to Majumdar (1961), is 168·4 cm, as compared to 163·74 cm of people from Madras/Kerala (Table 6). The protein

TABLE 6

Effects of nutrition on body height of residents of different States in India

State	General population			I.A.F. personnel			
	Food intake/day		Average ht. (cm) (b)	Food intake/day		Average ht. (cm) (a)	Difference (a−b) (cm)
	kcal	Proteins (g)		kcal	Proteins (g)		
Punjab/Delhi	3330	91	168·4	3960	130	169·98	1·58
Uttar Pradesh	2650	77	166·86	3960	130	168·37	1·51
Bengal/Bihar	2277	74	165·97	3960	130	168·37	2·40
Gujarat/Bombay	2222	57	164·46	3960	130	167·39	2·93
Madras/Kerala	2068	53	163·74	3960	130	167·57	3·83

and calorie intake in Delhi/Punjab is higher, being 91 g and 3330 kcal, as compared to 53 g and 2068 kcal in Madras. The importance of the nutritional factor is further brought out by comparing the heights of the same people after recruitment to the Armed Forces, where they are given an identical diet and are made to live under the same climatic conditions. The recruitment age for the services is between 15 and 17 years, when the men are still in their growth period. The minimum height for the recruitment is 152·40 cm which is lower than the average adult in India. The anthropometric studies conducted on Indian Air Force personnel by Iyer and Bhattacharya (1960) have shown that in all the states the I.A.F. personnel have a greater height than the corresponding civilian population. This effect is most marked in the case of Madras and Gujarat, where the standard of nutrition is very low. This study clearly emphasizes the role of nutrition on body stature.

Another study conducted by Someswara Rao (1956), in which he compared heights and weights of 300 children of Indian parentage (Punjab) born and brought up in Canada, with Punjabi children born in India, also showed the importance of nutrition and environment on body size. He found that Canadian-born Indian children were on the average taller and much heavier at all the age groups than their counterparts born and brought up in India. The differences in height and weight also have been found between Indian and American children, the Indian children being lighter in weight and smaller in size at all age groups. It is quite likely that not only race but nutritional and environmental factors also contribute to this difference.

Acclimatization to heat and cold

No studies have been done on acclimatization of any of the Indian aboriginal tribes to their environmental conditions. Even the studies on general population are very limited. Some aspects of adaptation to heat have been studied on Indians by Malhotra (1958, 1960), Malhotra and Bhattacharya (1959), and Malhatra *et al.* (1959). They have done extensive studies on salt and water balance in Indians during summer, and have found that under very hot environments reaching 110°F dry bulb and 144°F globe thermometer, Indians could maintain their salt balance on a dietary salt intake of 16 g/day. The low salt intake at which balance can be maintained is attributed to a low sodium chloride content in sweat; its average concentration is 0·25 g per cent. This is probably an adaptive phenomenon to conserve salt losses from the body. The average water loss in sweating in the same environments for outdoor workers was found to be 0·75 l./h, the maximum loss being 1 l./h. The salt intake in Indians varies from 14 to 24 g/day, the highest being in South India, where the high figure is most probably due to the perpetual hot climate prevailing there, as it is near the tropics. Some studies on acclimatization to heat in Indians have also been made by Edholm *et al.* (1964) at the Medical Research Council, U.K. They have compared the state of acclimatization of naturally-acclimatized Indian soldiers with that of artificially-acclimatized British troops. The result of their studies are not yet published.

The average basic metabolic rate (B.M.R.) of Indians is lower than that of the western people. Studies conducted by Sen and Banerjee (1958), Malhotra *et al.* (1960), and Shiv Kumar *et al.* (1961) have shown that the B.M.R. of Indians is 7–17 per cent lower than the Mayo Foundation standards. This has been attributed by Banerjee (1962) to the higher surface area of Indians. Banerjee and Sen (1955) have found that the Du-Bois formula as such is not applicable to the Indians for estimation of surface area. According to these authors, if the B.M.R. is expressed as a unit of 'cell mass' or 'cell solids', then there is no difference between Indians and Europeans. Ramaswamy (1953) and Mehra (1958), however, have found that the Du-Bois formula for measuring the surface area is applicable to Indian subjects, and that the error involved is less than 2 per cent. From this, it is obvious that a sound scientific explanation for the low B.M.R. of Indians is not yet known. It may be due to an adaptive phenomenon to a hot environment to reduce the heat production. Extensive studies are necessary to determine the role of different factors like environmental, temperature, nutritional status, racial characteristics, &c., on the BMR.

Physiological responses of Indians to cold have been studied by Davis *et al.* (1963) on two ethnic groups—Tibetans, residents of high altitude and Jats, residents of plains. These men were exposed nude to a mean temperature of 2°C for one hour and, during this period, their oxygen consumption, shivering, skin temperature, and rectal temperature were measured regularly. In both the ethnic groups, the oxygen consumption and shivering increased on exposure to cold, but the rise was significantly less in the Tibetans.

The mean skin-temperature in the Tibetans was maintained at a slightly higher level than the Jats. As regards the rectal temperature, whereas in the Jats it had a tendency to rise, in the Tibetans it was lowered towards the end of the exposure. The responses of Indians to cold could, therefore, be compared to those of urban Europeans and Americans (Hammel, 1961). The Indians increased heat production by shivering whilst the Tibetans did so by non-shivering mechanisms. As regards local adaptation to cold, experiments have been done in the Defence Institute of Physiology and Allied Sciences, Madras, by observing the heat loss from a hand immersed in cold water at 4°C. The subjects, drawn from heterogeneous groups, have shown a considerable variation in their individual response to cold and a significant difference has been found between ethnic groups. The subjects from the South have been found to have lower values as compared to those from the North. The heat output in the same group of subjects at sea level and at an altitude of 11,500 ft was found to be markedly reduced at altitude on all the subjects tested.

Physical work capacity

The low nutritional status of most of the Indians discussed earlier, and the tropical heat prevailing in India in general, seem to be reflected in the physical work capacity of Indians being considerably reduced. For instance, Sengupta *et al.* (1962) have observed a maximum oxygen consumption of 27·6 ml/kg/min in sedentary Indian subjects 18–40 years of age. This is too low a figure as compared to the 39·1–44·6 ml/kg/min reported by Wyndham *et al.* (1963) for sedentary subjects. Considerable data collected on Indian soldiers of good nutritional status and in the age range 18–40 years gave an average of 42·8 ml/kg/min (Malhotra *et al.*, 1964) and it is reasonable to expect that this relatively enhanced value is due partly to better nutritional status and partly to the regimented physical training which they have to undergo. The civil population, however, is not subjected to such regimented physical training. It would be worthwhile to explore the effect of different degrees of nutritional status on the maximal oxygen consumption, and other parameters of physical work capacity, among people in the same climatic zone. Similarly, a study of people of comparable nutritional status, but living in different climatic zones, would throw light on the way that the potential work capacity in these people is influenced by the different natural states of physical activity that depend on these climates.

High altitude

Observations on residents of high altitude show that the mountain tribes are strongly built and are very well adapted to cold and high altitude. In Ladakh and Sikkim, where the temperatures are low and approach freezing point during summer, the local residents do not dress in snow clothing, but wear only a few layers of ordinary woollen clothing. They can carry heavy loads. Pugh (1962) found the Sherpa porters to be superior to the white men in physical performance. The former could climb with a 60-lb load as efficiently as the latter without any load at an altitude of 19,000 ft. A recent study conducted by Malhotra et al. (1964) at an altitude of 11,500 ft on plain dwellers who had been residing at high altitude for one year, and on local residents of that altitude showed that the maximum oxygen consumption of the plain dwellers at high altitude was only 80 per cent of that of the natives. The oxygen extraction of the locals was found to be 4·95 per cent as compared to 4·65 per cent of the plain dwellers. The causes for this high oxygen extraction have not yet been assessed. It may be as a result of genetic adaptation.

Scope for research

From what has been discussed above, it can clearly be seen that in India very limited studies have been done on the lines that the International Biological Programme is planning, except for some nutritional surveys on a few selected tribes. India offers a very vast uncovered field for the various I.B.P. schemes. There is a very big tribal population belonging to different races and all types of climates and terrains are available where the people live in an absolutely primitive state.

In addition to the tribal population, India has a large population, about which very little is known, living almost in isolation at high altitudes in the Himalayas. In the Himalayas, both cold and high altitude combined seem to have a different effect on the human body than when each exists separately. It is quite well-known that the highest altitudes where permanent settlement is found in the Alps, Andes, and Himalayas are different, e.g. in the Alps the limit is 7,000 ft, in the Himalayas 15,000 ft, and in the Andes 17,000 ft.

This may be attributed to various meteorological or other factors and requires investigation. India thus offers most suitable environments for undertaking all the studies being planned under the Human Adaptability Panel of the IBP.

Acknowledgements

The author is very grateful to Shri Hari Bhardwaj for his valuable assistance in the preparation of this manuscript.

REFERENCES

BANERJEE, S. and SEN, R. N., 1955. 'Determination of the surface area of the body of Indians', *J. appl. Physiol.* 7, 585–588.

—— —— 1958. 'Body composition of Indians and its relation to basal metabolic rate', *J. appl. Physiol.* 12, 29–33.

—— 1962. 'Studies in energy metabolism', *Indian Council of Medical Research, Special Report Series No.* 43.

BOOTHBY, W. M., BERKSON, J., and DUNN, H. L., 1936. 'Mayo Clinic Standard', *Am. J. Physiol.* 116, 468.

BUCHI, E. C., 1960. *The Onge of Little Andaman in Adivasis.* Ministry of Information and Broadcasting, Govt. of India Publication—Revised Edition.

CENSUS OF INDIA, 1961. Personal communication, Registrar General of India, Govt. of India.

DAVIS, T. R. A., NAYAR, H. S., SINHA, K. C., NISHITH, S. D., and RAI, R. M., 1963. 'The effect of altitude on the cold responses of low altitude acclimatised Jats, high altitude acclimatised Jats and Tibetans', *Armed Forces Medical Research, Report No. DGAFMS/ HA/6/63.*

EDHOLM, O. G., FOX, R. H., GOLDSMITH, R., HAMPTON, I. F. G. and PILLAI, K. V., 1964. 'A comparison of heat acclimatization in Indians and Europeans'. *J. Physiol.*, 177, 15P.

ELVIN, V., 1960. *The Hill People of North-East India.* Oxford University Press, London.

—— 1961. *Naga Land.* Research Department, Adviser's Secretariat, Govt. of North-East Frontier Agency, Shillong.

GOVERNMENT OF INDIA, 1951. *India—A Reference Annual.* Publications Division, Ministry of Information and Broadcasting, Govt. of India.

GHURYE, G. S., 1950. *The Caste and Class in India.* Popular Book Depot, Bombay.

—— 1953. 'The Aborigines: "So called" and their Future', Gokhale Institute of Politics and Economics, Publication No. 11.

GUHA, B. S., 1937. *An Outline of the Racial Ethnology of India*, pp. 125–139. Indian Science Congress Association.

HAMMELL, H. T., 1961. 'The cold climate man', *Man Living in the Arctic*, pp. 17–34. National Research Council, Washington.

24

INDIAN COUNCIL OF MEDICAL RESEARCH, 1951. 'A review of nutrition studies in India', *Special Report No.* 22.

—— 1953. 'A supplement to the results of diet surveys', *Special Report No.* 25.

—— 1960. 'Dietary allowances for Indians; calories and proteins', *Special Report No.* 35.

—— 1961. 'Review of nutrition surveys carried out in India', *Special Report No.* 36.

—— 1964. 'Diet atlas of India', *Special Report No.* 48, p. 29.

KENDREW, W. G., 1961. 'The Indian Region' (Fig. 68), *The Climates of the Continents*, 5th ed. Chap. 19, p. 185. Clarendon Press, Oxford.

KRISHNA IYER, P. V. and BHATTACHARYA, M. N., 1960. 'Body measurements in relation to cockpit design', *Report No.* 5/60, Defence Science Laboratory, Research and Development Organisation, Ministry of Defence, Government of India.

MAJUMDAR, D. N., 1961. *Races and Cultures of India*, p. 105. Asia Publishing House, Bombay.

MALHOTRA, M. S., 1958. 'Salt requirements in the tropics during summer', *Nature, Lond.* **182**, 1036–37.

—— SHARMA, B. K., and SIVARAMAN, R., 1959. 'Requirements of sodium chloride during summer in the tropics', *J. appl. Physiol.* **14**, 823–828.

—— and BHATTACHARYA, M. N., 1959. 'Physical stress of engine room ratings of Indian Navy', *Bull. natn. Inst. Sci. India* **10**, 86.

—— RAMASWAMY, S. S., and RAY, S. N., 1960. 'Effect of environmental temperature on work and resting metabolism', *J. appl. Physiol.* **15**, 769–770.

—— 1960. 'Salt and water requirements of acclimatised people working outdoors in severe heat', *Indian J. med. Res.* **48**, 212–217.

—— 1964. Unpublished work.

MAMORIA, C. B., 1957. *Tribal Demography in India*. Kitab Mahal, Allahabad.

MEHRA, N. C., 1958. 'Body surface area of Indians', *J. appl. Physiol.* **12**, 29–33.

MEHROTRA, K. C., 1958. 'Ethnology of the Gujars of Chamba with a special reference to the physical characters'. Dissertation submitted to the University of Delhi.

PANDIT, C. G. and SOMESWARA RAO, K., 1960. *Nutrition in India* (1946–58). Indian Council of Medical Research Report.

PATVARDHAN, V. N. and JAGANNATHAN, 1962. 'A review of nutrition studies in India (1955–56)', *Indian Council of Medical Research, Special Report No.* 37.

PUGH, L. G. C. E., 1962. 'Physiological and medical aspects of the Himalayan scientific and mountaineering expedition', *Br. med. J.* **2**, 621–627.

RAMASWAMY, S. S. and MOOKERJEE, G. C., 1953. 'Applicability of Du Bois height weight formula for measurement of body surface area', *Science* **118**, 389–390.

RISLEY, H. H., 1901. 'The People of India', *Census of India*, p. 190. Govt. of India Publication.

Roy, J. K. and Rao, R. K., 1956. 'Diet surveys amongst the tribes of Madhya Pradesh, Part I'. *Bull. Dep. Anthrop., India,* 5, No. 2, 1.
—— and Biswas, S. K., 1957. 'Diet surveys amongst the tribes of Madhya Pradesh, Part II'. *Bull. Dep. Anthrop., India,* 6, No. 1, 21.
—— 1957. 'Investigation on the diet of Murias of Bastar District'. *Bull. Dep. Anthrop. India,* 6, No. 1, 33.
—— and Rao, R. K., 1962. 'Diets of some Indian tribes', *Indian J. med. Res.* 50, 905–915.
Sengupta, A., Lundgren, N. P. V., Saha, P. N., and Rao, M. N., 1962. 'Comparative maximal working capacity of sedentary men at climatic extremes in Calcutta', *Indian J. Physiol. all. Sci.* 16, 79–84.
—— 1952. 'Investigation into the dietary habits of the aboriginal tribes of Abor Hills (North-Eastern Frontier), Part I', *Indian J. med. Res.* 40, 203.
—— 1954. 'Investigations into the dietary habits of the aboriginal tribes of Abor Hills, Part II', *Bull. Dep. Anthrop. India,* 3, No. 2, 155.
—— 1955. 'Investigations into the dietary habits of the aboriginal tribes of Abor Hills (North-Eastern Frontier), Part III', *Bull. Dep. Anthrop. India* 4, No. 2, 69.
—— and Biswas, S. K., 1956a. 'Studies on the diet and nutritional status of Kannikar and Urali tribes of Travancore', *Bull. Dep. Anthrop. India* 5, No. 1, 43.
—— —— 1956b. 'Studies on the diet and nutritional status of Malapantharam, Muthuvan and Ullatan tribes of Travancore', *Bull. Dep. Anthrop. India* 5, No. 2, 9.
Sen, R. N. and Banerjee, S., 1958. 'Determination of basal metabolic rate and blood concentrations of protein bound iodine, cholesterol and glucose in Indians', *Indian J. med. Res.* 46, 759–765.
Shivkumar, N. and Sachar, R. S., 1961. 'Basal metabolic rate in normal Indian adult males', *Br. J. ind. Med.* 12, 239.
Shrikant, L. M., 1960–61. *Tenth Report of the Commissioner for Scheduled Castes and Scheduled Tribes.* Appx. XXXIII, p. 191. Govt. of India.
Someswara Rao, K., Taskar, A. D., and Ramanathan, M. K., 1954. 'Nutritional haemoglobin surveys in children in Nilgiris district', *Indian J. med. Res.* 42, 55.
Taskar, A. D., 1956. 'Regional variation and adequacy of Indian diets—Statistical evaluation of diet surveys', *Indian J. med. Res.* 44, 519–537.
Wyndham, C. H., Strydom, N. B., Morrison, J. F., Peter, J., Williams, C. G., Bradell, G. A. G., and Joffe, A., 1963. 'Differences between ethnic groups in physical working capacity', *J. appl. Physiol.* 18, 361–366.

12

SOUTH-WEST ASIA, WITH SPECIAL REFERENCE TO ISRAEL

O. G. EDHOLM

Area

THE term 'South-West Asia' has several synonyms, including Near East and Middle East. Publications of the World Health Organization and United Nations use South-West Asia to include the following countries: Iran, Turkey, Iraq, Syria, Lebanon, Israel, Jordan, Saudi Arabia, Qatar, Kuwait, Bahrein, Muscat and Oman, Yemen, Aden, and Aden Protectorate. With the exception of Cyprus, which is also included in this term, this list covers all the countries to which reference will be made in this Chapter.

Climate

The climate of this area has been described in detail in a report by the U.S. Army Quartermaster Research and Engineering Command (1959), and is also referred to by Lee (1964). Much of the area is typical desert, but there are many districts with adequate rainfall or water supplied by irrigation. The 'fertile crescent' is a term commonly used to describe the mediterranean coastal zone which today includes principally Lebanon and Israel. The Tigris and Euphrates valleys of Iraq have a high agricultural productivity, and the highlands of the Hejaz and the Yemen provide good farming land. In the central area of Saudi Arabia there are a number of large oases, some of which are very extensive. Turkey and Iran have rather different characteristics; there is very little true desert in Turkey, but Iran has a large central desert and 65 per cent of the country is unsuitable for agriculture. Both countries have great mountain regions, forest areas, and fertile lowland plains.

The whole area has had a turbulent history: armies have marched, wars have disrupted, and there have been frequent mass movements of peoples. In recent years the establishment of the State of Israel has been followed by very large movements of Jewish communities long established in countries such as the Yemen.

The annual pilgrimage to Mecca draws people from many countries. The size of the pilgrimage has increased rapidly over the past few years, and in 1963 there were well over a million pilgrims.

Population

Information concerning populations, mortality, birth rate, &c., can be obtained from the *Population Year Book* of the United Nations. The total population for the whole area is approximately 77 million. There is a low average density of population, and indeed it is the lowest for the whole of Asia, although there are two exceptions, Israel and the Lebanon, with 102 and 158 people per km² respectively. The population, however, is growing very rapidly and has the highest birth rate for the whole of Asia. The quality of the statistical material is extremely variable; it is, for instance, very detailed for Israel, but such figures as are given for the Yemen represent little more than guesses. Although there are a number of large towns, it is estimated that 85 per cent of the population is rural, and agriculture occupies by far the greater part of the people. The standard of health varies considerably. Table 1, taken from Troupin (1955), shows the number of doctors and medical schools in the various countries.

TABLE 1

Medical schools and physicians

Country	Population (millions)	Medical schools	Population/ medical school	No. of doctors	Population/ doctor	Annual graduates
Lebanon	1·35	2	0·677	1,049	1,290	68
Israel	1·69	1	1·69	3,919	431	55
Syria	3·5	1	3·5	670	5,276	56
Iran	20·2	5	4·0	2,302	8,800	320
Turkey	23·0	2	11·5	7,180	3,197	300
Arabia	10·0	—	—	250	40,000	—
Jordan	1·36	—	—	216	6,296	—
Aden	0·8	—	—	43	18,605	—
Bahrein	0·11	—	—	30	3,733	—

Population of Israel. The State of Israel dates from 1948, and at that time the population was 872,678, of whom 716,678 were Jewish and the remaining 156,000 mainly Arab. At the census in 1961 the population was 2,179,491, of whom 1,932,357 were Jewish. In this period of 13 years the population had grown by 2½ times, the Jewish population by 170 per cent and the non-Jewish by 58 per cent. In the latter the increase is due to the difference between births and deaths, but in the Jewish population rather more than two-thirds is due to immigration and only the balance is due to the natural increase.

The immigrants have come from many countries. Before 1948 the bulk were European; since 1948, and up to 1961, 47 per cent have come from Europe and America and the rest from Africa and Asia. The present population of Israel is essentially an immigrant one; in 1948, 35 per cent of the Jewish population were born in Israel but by 1951 this proportion had dropped to 25 per cent. In 1961 it had risen to 38 per cent.

The composition of the Jewish population today can be given, in approximate figures, as 37·8 per cent native born, 13·7 per cent from Asia, 11·2 per cent from Africa, 32·8 per cent from Europe and the remainder from the U.S.A., South America, and South Africa. Immigrants have come from seventy countries, but the main contributors, both before and since 1948, are given in Table 2.

TABLE 2

Immigrants to Israel

| | Immigrants | |
Country	pre-1948	post-1948
Russia and Poland	265,000	322,000
North Africa	1,500	202,000
Germany	88,000	55,000
Iraq and Kurdistan	9,000	124,000
Bulgaria, Yugoslavia, and Italy	18,000	45,000
Yemen	6,000	49,000
Persia, Afghanistan, and Pakistan	3,500	41,000
Cochin, India	—	8,000
America, North and South	7,500	17,000
France	4,000	14,000

The rapid increase of population has been accompanied by a growth of towns, and in 1961 78 per cent of the people were classified as urban dwellers; this figure is in striking contrast with the rest of South-West Asia, where some 85 per cent is rural.

Human biology

Apart from Israel, only a few studies have been made in South-West Asia. In the following account details will be given, where

available, for the whole area. The output of research from Israel is
several times larger than for the whole of the rest of the area put
together, in spite of the fact that Israel represents approximately
2·5 per cent of the total population and approximately o·1 per cent
of the total area.

Clinical studies. There are a number of papers dealing primarily
with clinical aspects, and some of these include material of more
general interest. Kelly and Snedden (1958) examined the incidence
of goitre, which is not endemic, except in the mountains of the
Lebanon in the Taurus mountains of Turkey and in two areas near
to Teheran.

An article by El Ghoroury (1954) on syphilis in Saudi Arabia
includes information on single and multiple marriages. One man
claimed to have been married forty times, and one woman stated
that she had been married ten times. The frequency of multiple
marriages could be a complicating factor in genetic and other
studies. Although syphilis does not appear to be an important
cause of death in the countries of South-West Arabia, El Ghoroury
reports a high rate of infection in the Asir province of Saudi Arabia.
Christiansen (1954) stated that in Turkey 1·2–2·2 per cent of the
population of seventeen provinces was infected.

Farid (1956) discusses the implications of the Mecca Pilgrimage
for a regional malaria eradication programme, and gives details
about pilgrims and their countries of origin. Although malaria is
still widespread throughout Arabia, vigorous eradication programmes have had considerable effect. It has been virtually wiped
out in Israel, although the upper Jordan valley was, until recently,
a serious centre of the disease (Farid, 1954).

Dental health in Iran and Syria has been investigated by Nevitt
(1961). The incidence of dental caries was relatively low.

Bilharziasis has been studied by a number of teams. Azim and
Gisman (1956) state that it is not found in Lebanon or in Turkey,
and is virtually absent from Jordan. There were thousands of
carriers amongst the immigrants to Israel, where some of the
rivers are infected, but an efficient control system has kept down
new cases in recent years to a very small number. There are a
number of cases in the Yemen and Aden. In Saudi Arabia intestinal bilharziasis is as common as renal infection; in Syria it is
limited to an area close to the border with Turkey. The main
centre is in Iraq where it has been studied in detail by Najarian,

Araoz, Klimt, Ani, and Azzani (1961), particularly in the vicinity of Basra. There is often very sharp demarcation between endemic and non-endemic areas; in one district nearly all those examined had evidence of infection, and in an adjoining district scarcely any cases were found.

Although plague has not been observed on a serious scale for some years, there is an important focus in Kurdistan (Baltazard, Bahmanyar, Mostachfi, Eftekhari, and Mofidi, 1960; Baltazard and Seydian, 1960). Trachoma is common in many of the countries of South-West Asia. Winkler (1963) examined the problem in Jordan and found an incidence of 50–65 per cent in the town of Hebron and the surrounding villages. It was, however, relatively mild and developed late in life.

Nutrition. Adolph (1954) reviewed the subject of nutrition in South-West Asia, pointing out that it was only in recent years that there had been any active interest in the subject. He considered that dietary habits are fairly similar for the whole area, apart from the few large towns where the population has sophisticated tastes, and estimated that 85 per cent of the people live in rural areas. The diet is essentially a cereal one, with wheat by far the most important; 30 per cent of agricultural land is used for growing wheat, 12 per cent for barley, and 11 per cent for maize. In the Lebanon the rural diet is estimated to provide 2150 kcal, with 56 g protein, mainly of vegetable origin. There is widespread evidence of inadequate protein intake.

Since 1954 there have been a number of surveys and more detailed nutritional studies. Adolph, Shammas, and Halaby (1955), and Shammas and Adolph (1954), have examined the nutritive value of parboiled wheat or *burghul* which is widely used throughout South-West Asia. The wheat is boiled in water for 2–3 hours, then dried in the sun; it can then be coarsely ground and will keep indefinitely. Although in the process there is considerable loss of riboflavin, the vitamin B and nicotinic acid content of the parboiled wheat is approximately 75 per cent of the original value. Various combinations of the protein available foods used in the Lebanon were evaluated in the feeding trials on rats. Two popular mixtures were tested, the first consisting of equal parts of broad bean, chick pea, and parboiled wheat, and the second two parts parboiled wheat to one of a soured milk resembling yoghourt; both showed excellent results and it was concluded that the rural people, with their limited resources, had developed food mixtures of high nutritive value.

Sabry (1961) estimated that the average calorie intake in Iraq was 2600 kcal daily, with cereals providing 72·5 per cent of the calories and 6·2 per cent coming from fruit and vegetables. Over 80 per cent of the protein intake of 69 g came from cereals, and only 5 per cent from animal sources. Cowan, Sabry, Rinnu, and Campbell (1963) examined some of the sources of protein, including the sweet almond which is widely used to supplement infant food. They found that it was deficient in a number of amino-acids, principally leucine. Corkill (1951) carried out a survey for WHO, covering Iraq, Lebanon, and Syria. Conditions varied very considerably and evidence of malnutrition was equally varied. He gives details of the different dishes prepared in many areas and comments on the seasonal under-nutrition of many of the poorer cultivators.

Demarchi, Hamndi, and Zaki (1961) examined in Baghdad the effect of school meals on the growth of 6- and 7-year-old children. Compared with a control group, the children receiving the school meal which provided 465 kcal and 21 g protein grew significantly more in height and weight. Gounelle et al. (1956) carried out in Iraq a survey of recruits for the Army and the police. On entry they were considered to be underweight for their height, and haemoglobin levels in 60 per cent of them were 80 per cent or less of the standard value of 13·5 g. The diet scales were excellent, the soldiers receiving 3900 kcal with 116 g progein and 88 g fat, and although the police did not get quite as much, their diet amounted to 3500 kcal daily with 105 g protein and 62·5 g fat. Corkill comments on the good nutrition of both police and soldiers.

In Iran there have been extensive nutritional surveys in the Army (Browe, 1961). The intake was high, ranging from 3700–4050 kcal daily, but animal protein was relatively low. On the other hand, surveys by Thomson and Mashayekhi in 1952 in Iran showed considerable evidence of malnutrition in school children. Thomson, Bahadori, and Mashayekhi (1957), in further surveys, stated that it was rare to find a well-nourished child. Bahadori and Claudian (1957) assessed the food intake in an urban and in a rural district of Iran. They divided their subjects into three social groups: landowners, employers and minor officials, and farm labourers. The intake averaged 2660, 2120, and 1850 kcal daily in these three groups, protein amounting to 26·5, 10·7, and 11·5 g/day. Amongst the farm labourers there was a definite seasonal trend, with intakes of 1950 kcal daily in August and 1680 in March.

Halsted, Carroll, Dehgani, Laghmani, and Prasad (1960) investigated the nutrition of villagers in Iran. The diet consisted essentially of wheat bread, with the addition of yoghourt once or twice a week, and meat not more than once a month. In spite of this restricted diet, serum vitamin B_{12} levels were within normal limits.

Nutrition in Turkey. This country is mainly agricultural, and considerable quantities of specialized products—figs, nuts, some fish—are exported. Production, over a large area, is largely dependent on rainfall, of which the variation can be fourfold. There has been a great increase in the area under cultivation, but increased production lags behind the population increase. There are considerable local variations in diet; owing to poor transport, adequate supplies can be available in one district while adjoining areas can be very deficient. A survey of the armed forces (Berry and Schaefer, 1958) showed that daily average intakes in seven different messes ranged from 3200 to 4000 kcal, with an average of 3550 kcal. Protein intake, although mainly vegetable, was high at 113 g/day (range 97–127), and fat was low at 59 g (range 35–87), so 2550 kcal daily were supplied by carbohydrate. The main deficiencies were in vitamin A and vitamin C, and riboflavin intake was inadequate at several messes. The armed forces, undoubtedly, are far better nourished than the civilian population, whose diet resembles those already described for the rest of South-West Asia. From food production and import and export figures, it has been calculated that the average intake is 2660 kcal, with 85·3 g protein and 38·7 g fat. Only 12 g protein are provided by animal sources. In large areas the population would scarcely ever eat meat, and animal protein is mainly obtained from milk and milk products, and eggs. The diet, in general, is better than in most countries of South-West Asia, and frank malnutrition is uncommon. However, marasmus is reported amongst infants (Wray, 1961), and such serious malnutrition as does occur is mainly in children, including infants. Rickets and osteomalacia are regularly observed, and scurvy is a problem in some districts. Gürson, Neyzi, and Gedik (1961) found that malnutrition in infants was relatively common.

Saudi Arabia and Yemen.—There is little information about

nutrition in Saudi Arabia or the Yemen. Fawdry (1955) described a syndrome of splenomegaly, anaemia, and hepatomegaly in patients from the Yemen. Their diet apparently consisted of sorghum with occasional milk. In general, the picture for the whole of South-West Asia, always excepting the towns, conforms with Adolph's description. The rural population, which comprises 85 per cent of the total population, relies mainly on cereals, nearly all wheat, some fruit and vegetables, a little milk or milk products, and only occasional meat. On the other hand, in many areas there are considerable developments both in food production and also in better nutritional standards.

A general account of nutrition in South-West Asia is given by May (1961) with a detailed bibliography.

Nutrition in Israel. Nutrition in Israel is bound up with the history of the State. The mass immigration which followed the establishment of the State in 1948 was accompanied by a cessation of supplies from neighbouring countries. Many of those who came from the countries of South-West Asia were suffering from some degree of malnutrition and also found it difficult to adapt to the new dietary habits imposed by the lack of traditional foods. Rationing was severe for several years, until the increased food production no longer made it necessary. The population increased from 889,000 in 1948 to 2,000,000 in 1958; food production over the same period rose by over 200 per cent. At the present time there is a surplus and a considerable export of foods, principally citrus fruits.

There are two characteristics of Israel which differentiate it from the other countries of South-West Asia. The first is the high density of population. If the population were evenly distributed there would be an average of 102 persons for every km². However, the desert area of the Negev is approximately 70 per cent of the whole country and has about 9 per cent of the population, so in the rest of the country the density is about 320 km². The second characteristic is that the population is urban, not rural, with less than 20 per cent engaged in agriculture.

The Central Bureau of Statistics makes an annual survey of expenditure on food and it was estimated that average intake in 1958 was 2850 kcal/day, with 80 g of fat and 90·9 protein, of which 31·5 g were of animal origin. This is comparable with the nutritional standards of western Europe and is quite different from the rest of South-East Asia.

Nevertheless, there are considerable variations due mainly to poverty and, partly, to ignorance, coupled with the persistence of tradition and prejudice. For example, in many of the countries in this area it is not considered manly to eat eggs, they are only for women. This has meant that in practice a valuable source of protein tended to be reserved for pregnant and lactating women which, with the prevailing shortage of animal protein, was an excellent consequence of tradition. However, in the different conditions experienced in Israel this was no longer so useful a tradition, but it persisted, with a number of others.

Strauss and his colleagues (1954, 1955) surveyed a number of families in successive years. In 1950 the average intake for the whole group of 400 was satisfactory but a quarter of the subjects had an intake below 2400 kcal and less than 25 g animal protein. This was mainly for economic reasons, and in this group there was anaemia and a low serum protein level, while rickets was observed in some of the children in this group. In 1952/53 the position had improved, although the intake of animal protein in the lowest income group was still inadequate. More recently, surveys of food intake have shown a satisfactory level apparently in all groups. There are still differences between those from eastern countries and Europe, the latter having more milk, potatoes and white bread, and the former eating more rice and cereals. The eastern Jews preferred highly spiced food and would buy spices even when there was only a limited income for food. Since children had school meals they adapted more easily to the Israeli diet and, in turn, influenced food habits at home. Nevertheless, the persistence of different food habits is striking and there have been a number of studies relating the contrasting pattern of disease with the differences in food, especially with the low fat intake of the immigrants.

Recent immigrants from the Yemen have a low incidence of diabetes and coronary heart disease, but there is a greater prevalence in Yemenites who have lived in Israel for 25 years or more (Cohen, Neumann, and Michaelson, 1960). The food habits of the old settlers and recent immigrants have been examined to find a possible explanation (Cohen, Bavly, and Poznanski, 1961). There was a larger calorie intake amongst the old settlers but the difference was not great, and the intake of fat in both groups was similar. There are many papers dealing with nutrition in Israel, including the results of the surveys carried out by Dr. Sarah Bavly and her colleagues in the College of Home Economics of the Ministry of Education and Culture (Bavly, 1960; Bavly, Mundel, Guggenheim, and Halevi, 1962). The nutrition of the Bedouin in the Negev has also recently been described (Groen, 1964).

Genetics. The interpretation of genetic studies in Israel depends in part on the history of the Jews. They were dispersed from Palestine first at the time of the Assyrian Exile, 721 B.C., again in the Babylonian Exile, 586 B.C., but the greatest dispersion was following the crushing of the Jewish revolt in A.D. 70. Although many Jews returned from the different exiles, and a small group probably remained permanently in Palestine, the majority of Jews after A.D. 70 were to be found in numerous colonies in Mesopotamia, around the Mediterranean, and central and western Europe. The last group were eventually described as Ashkenazi Jews.

There was some degree of contact between these widely scattered groups, but the next major disruption occurred with the expulsion of the Jews from Spain in 1492. The Sephardim, as they were termed, spread and settled in many countries, including the Netherlands, Britain, France, Italy, and the Balkans. Some also went to North Africa, Turkey, and Syria.

It is with this very brief background that the results of the genetic studies of the present population of Israel must be considered. The strong interest in genetics is based in part on the expectation that the findings might provide objective evidence of the common origin of the different Jewish communities. This expectation has not been completely realized. In the case of the blood groups, for example, there are striking differences between say Yemenite and European Jews. In general terms, there is a much closer resemblance between the Gentiles and Jews of each particular country than there is between the Jews from different countries. Nevertheless, there are some important similarities between Jews from many different regions as well as differences from the Gentiles of their own country of origin. These points are not only of interest to the Jewish people but are of fundamental importance to the student of human genetics. In the case of the Jews, their history stretches over thousands of years and is also very detailed, so historical facts can be used to interpret genetic findings as well as vice versa. The part played by the effects of environment and genetic drift has to be understood before conclusions can be drawn regarding the degree of similarity between two groups of mankind. As further details become available of the genetic composition of the Jewish people, it will be possible to evaluate more accurately these factors.

The widespread interest of geneticists in the Jewish people is illustrated by the contents of the book, edited by Dr. Elizabeth Goldschmidt (1963), entitled *The Genetics of Migrant and Isolate Populations*, which contains an account of the papers, demonstrations, and discussions given at a symposium held in Jerusalem. The material of the following section is drawn very largely from this book, which should be consulted by all those interested in South-West Asia.

Blood groups. The ABO blood group system has been widely studied and the world distribution has been described by Mourant, Kopec, and Domaniewsak-Sobczak (1958). Mourant (1959) has extracted all the material dealing with Jewish populations including the extensive investigations of Gurevitch and his colleagues (Gurevitch, Hasson, and Margolis, 1956; Gurevitch, Hasson, Margolis, and Poliakoff, 1955; Gurevitch, Hasson, Margolis, and Polishuk, 1955; Gurevitch, Hermoni, and Margolis, 1953; Gurevitch, Hermoni, and Polishuk, 1951; Gurevitch and Margolis, 1955; Margolis, Gurevitch, and Hasson, 1957). The latter collected blood group data from 3500 subjects who were members of ten different communities in Jerusalem. Yemenite and Cochin Jews have a frequency of O ranging from 72 to 73 per cent, whereas in the other eight communities the range was 51–63 per cent. In Jews from North Africa, including Tunisia, Algeria, Morocco, and Libya, all have similar percentages of B of about 16 per cent and A about 22 per cent. The Arab population have, on the other hand, much lower percentages of B, ranging from 9 to 12·5 per cent, and rather lower percentage of A, 19·5 to 21 per cent.

When the Jewish populations of Europe are compared with the Gentiles, there is an irregular relationship. In some cases the Jewish and non-Jewish population are very similar. The Roumanian and Lithuanian Jews have A and B frequencies which are almost identical with the gentile population. On the other hand, Jews from Georgia have markedly different ABO frequencies from the autochthonous population. However, Jews from a number of different European countries—Hungary, Poland, Ukraine, Russia, Germany, and Roumania—have fairly similar blood groups, approximately 28·5 per cent A and 12·5 per cent B, and these are about the same for the group of Ashkenazi Jews in Jerusalem, 26·2 per cent A and 12·2 per cent B. The Jews from Austria, Czeckoslovakia, and Lithuania have about 25 per cent A and 13 per cent B. In Amsterdam, the Sephardic Jews have a quite different blood group composition, A 26 per cent, B 9 per cent, and this is virtually identical with the Dutch population. In thirty-three surveys of different European Jewish communities, the percentage of B ranged from 8·5 to 19 per cent, and for A from 24 to 33 per cent. It is clear that the members of these different communities cannot be considered to be homogenous. Mourant concludes that although 'the average blood group gene frequency of all the Jews (of eastern Europe) are similar to the average frequencies of all the non-Jews of corresponding nationalities . . . the resemblances . . . are deceptive and probably accidental'.

The Asiatic Jews differ considerably from each other and also from European Jews. They also appear to differ considerably from the corresponding non-Jewish populations. In general, there are both higher A and B groups than in Europe, with the exception of the Yemenites A 17 per cent, B 9 per cent, and the Samaritans with 15·5 per cent A and 7 per cent B.

The Cochin Jews have an unusual distribution with a higher B than A, but in this they resemble the Indian population.

The Rh blood groups. There is considerable variation amongst the Jewish communities, with a range of 4–17 per cent of Rh-negative. The CDe or 'mediterranean' chromosome is relatively high in all groups, ranging from 41·5 to 60·5 per cent, with an average of 51 per cent. Of particular interest is the cDe chromosome, which is extremely high (50 per cent or more) in many African people and very low in Europe (2–3 per cent). This 'African' chromosome is present in the Jews of Israel in a range of 4·1–11·0 per cent, averaging 7 per cent. This is considerably higher than is found in Europeans or in the mediterranean basin. The Moslems of South-West Asia have from 10 to 20 per cent of this chromosome.

Blood groups in other regions of South-West Asia. Although there are blood group data from the non-Jewish populations of South-West Asia, these are still far from adequate. ABO studies in Turkey (Aksoy, Ikin, Mourant, and Lehmann, 1958) show that group A exceeds 30 per cent in most of the country but it falls somewhat in eastern Turkey. The Armenians have even higher frequencies of group A genes. The B gene in Turkey has a frequency of 10–15 per cent. In the Lebanon, Nassif (1953) found 31 per cent A and 8 per cent B, in a sample of 3600 which included most of the different religious communities. Mourant points out that in general the frequency of A falls steadily south of Turkey, and in Arabia it is about 15 per cent; the B gene is also very low in south Arabia, around 6–7 per cent.

Going east from Turkey into Iran, the A gene falls to 22 per cent, with the B gene increasing to 16–17 per cent. The Rh groups in Iran have been investigated by Boué and Boué (1956), who found relatively small differences between the different communities. The frequency of Rh-negative was very low.

Amongst other blood-group systems, the Duffy gene in Turks and Eli-Turks is similar to the upper European values (42–48 per cent). In Iran in the Moslem population of Teheran the value is higher, 58 per cent, and about midway between the European (40–43 per cent) and the Indian of 70 per cent.

Other gene systems and markers. The transferrins and hapto-globins have been studied in a sample of 1600 Jews in Israel, as well as 69 Israeli Arabs. All the transferrins were of group C. The frequency of the Hp^1 gene was 26·5 per cent in the Arabs and was between 25 and 30 per cent in the different Jewish communities, except for the Ashkenazi with 37·5 per cent. As far as neighbouring countries are concerned, in Iran there is 25 per cent, and in western Europe 38–42 per cent, with lower values in Italy of 34 per cent.

Deficiency of the enzyme glucose-6-phosphate-dehydrogenase (G6PD) has been investigated in the different Jewish and non-Jewish communities in Israel. There are very striking variations amongst the Jews, the percentage deficiency ranging from 0·4 per cent amongst Ashkenazi up to 58 per cent in Kurds. This latter figure is the highest so far recorded for any population. In one group of Kurds who came from the northern Iraq border with Turkey an incidence of 70 per cent deficiency was recorded. There was no deficiency found in 69 Samaritans, people who have lived in Palestine for 2800 years but who are considered to be of non-Jewish origin. In Ethiopia no deficiencies were found either in the Fallasha, a Jewish group, or in 1000 members of six different Ethiopian

25

tribes. The Arabs and Druze in Israel both had 4·4 per cent deficiency. A positive correlation between thalassaemia and G6PD deficiency has been demonstrated.

Colour blindness.—Data have been obtained on 7000 male Israelis, including 337 Druzes. The percentage of colour blindness varies from 3·9 to 10·1. The Ashkenazi Jews resemble Europeans with 8 per cent colour blindness, whereas the Iraqi and Yemenites had only 3·8 per cent and 4·7 per cent respectively. The Druzes have the highest colour blindness incidence with 10·1 per cent, and interestingly enough there is a tradition that this community absorbed some of the Crusader population. There is, unfortunately, no information available about other non-Jewish populations in South-West Asia.

Finger-print patterns. The finger-print patterns in 500 subjects in each of eight Jewish communities have been studied by Sachs and Bat-Miriam (1957). The communities were from Germany, Poland, Bulgaria, Turkey, Egypt, Morocco, Iraq, and Yemen. The results were expressed in terms of a pattern:

$$\text{intensity index} = \frac{\text{percentage loops} + 2 \times \text{percentage whorls}}{10}$$

This index was similar in all the Jewish communities and was considerably higher than in European gentiles. Israeli Arabs were similar to the Jewish communities with the highest index, which were the Iraqi and Yemenites. In Syria and the Lebanon even higher indices have been found.

Taste sensitivity. The ability to taste phenylthiourea has been examined in 1680 subjects of eight different Jewish communities. The proportion of non-tasters varied from 13 to 21·7 per cent, but these differences were not significant. A small group from Cochin and the Island of Gerba had much higher numbers of non-tasters, 31·7 and 41·4 per cent respectively. This corresponds to the 43 per cent of non-tasters in Bombay.

The proportion of non-tasters, apart from Cochin and Gerba, is much lower in Europe where it ranges from 25 to 43 per cent. In the Arab population of Egypt the percentage of non-tasters is 18 per cent, but information is lacking for the rest of South-West Asia.

Disease. The variation in the incidence of a number of diseases in the different Jewish communities has been examined. Owing to the very complete medical coverage in Israel, and the availability of medical care, it is unlikely that there is much differentiation between communities in the use made of hospital and other medical facilities. Comparisons are therefore probably valid. The diseases considered include some with a definite genetic basis and others with a less certain mode of inheritance, as well as a detailed study of arteriosclerosis and coronary heart disease.

Familial Mediterranean fever. The disease known as familial mediterranean fever is a genetic disorder characterized by fever, with pain in the joints and chest, and by amyloidosis. It is virtually confined to Jews and to Armenians. In 258 cases collected from the literature (Heller, Sohar, and Sherf, 1958), 133 were Jews and 76 Armenians. In Israel, a further 346 cases were ascertained by 1962. There were striking differences in the incidence among the Jewish communities. The Ashkenazi Jews only provided 6 out of 346. There were no cases amongst the Yemenite or Persian Jews. It is therefore essentially a disease of Jews from the mediterranean basin, i.e. Algeria, Morocco, Tripolitania, Egypt, Syria, Iraq, Turkey, and Greece. There is no difference between the Jewish and Armenian phenotype of FMF. At present, there is no explanation of the close similarity between Armenians and mediterranean Jews.

Tay-Sachs disease. Infantile amaurotic idiocy, or Tay-Sachs disease, which is due to a recessive gene, is not, as used to be thought, confined to Jews, but the majority of cases found in surveys in Europe and the U.S.A. were Jewish.

In Israel, the disease is almost confined to Ashkenazi. In 85,000 births of Ashkenazi origin there were 29 cases, whereas in 77,000 births of non-Ashkenazi origin there were only 2 cases.

Gaucher's disease. The main clinical feature of this disease is a gross enlargement of the spleen, often associated with an increased size of the liver. Of 23 cases identified in Jerusalem in 1957 all belonged to the Ashkenazi community. The current hypothesis is that Gaucher's disease is transmitted by a dominant gene with incomplete penetrance, but more studies are needed.

Fibrocystic disease. Mucoviscidosis or fibrocystic disease, which is hereditary, is characterized by abnormality of the exocrine glands. Although the disease is relatively rare amongst Jewish children, 24 confirmed cases occurred between 1955 and 1959; of these, 14 were born to Ashkenazi mothers out of 68,000 births, a frequency which is similar to that found in Ohio, U.S.A. (Steinberg, 1963). There were 10 cases born to non-Ashkenazi mothers out of approximately 136,000 births, so the gene is much rarer in this group.

Phenylketonuria. This condition, which leads to mental deficiency, is extremely rare amongst Jews, but 14 cases have been diagnosed in Israel, all in oriental Jews.

Essential pentosuria. This rare condition is almost completely confined to Jews, and a survey in Israel showed that all 18 cases found in a population of 180,000 were Ashkenazi.

Infantile pyloric stenosis. There are marked differences in the incidence of this condition in various countries, and in Israel it is much lower than that for northern Europe. However, the incidence is three times higher in Ashkenazi Jews than in the other Jewish communities.

Summary. The incidence of these various conditions shows considerable differences between the Ashkenazi and non-Ashkenazi Jews, as indicated in the following table.

	Ashkenazi	*Non-Ashkenazi*
Colour blindness	Higher incidence	
Taste sensitivity		No difference (except Cochin)
Finger-prints		No difference
G6PD	Rare	Variable; high incidence among Kurds
Familial Mediterranean fever	None	All cases reported
Tay–Sachs disease	29/85,000	2/77,000
Gaucher's disease	All cases reported	None
Fibrocystic disease	14/68,000	10/136,000
Phenylketonuria	None	All cases reported
Essential pentosuria	All cases reported	None
Pyloric stenosis	7·5/1000	2·5/1000

Atherosclerosis and coronary heart disease in Israel. A well-attested finding is the difference in the incidence of coronary heart disease in the various Jewish communities. Ashkenazi Jews have approximately three times as many cases as are found in non-Ashkenazi Jews. Even more striking is the virtual absence of this condition in Yemenite Jews (Dreyfuss, 1953; Dreyfuss, Toor, Agmon, and Zlotnik, 1957). It has also been shown that the blood lipid values of non-Ashkenazi Jews is lower than Jews from Europe (Brunner and Loebl, 1958). However, in Yemenites who had been settled in Israel for over 25 years blood lipid levels were more similar to values found in Ashkenazi Jews. The traditional diet of the Yemenites is low in fat, and Brunner (1963) in a survey found that for a group of 35 male agricultural workers aged 28–51, with an average weight of 58·7 kg and height of 168·2 cm, 21·5 per cent of the total intake of 2230 kcal was provided by fat. In Ashkenazi Jews the average fat intake provides approximately 35 per cent of total calories. The old settled Yemenites appear to have increased their fat intake, and with this dietary change blood lipid levels have increased. Nevertheless, this group still has a low level of mortality from coronary heart disease.

The results of a necropsy study of atherosclerosis in the aorta and in the coronary vessels has shown, however, remarkably little difference between Ashkenazi and non-Ashkenazi Jews (Ungar and Laufer, 1961; Ben-Ishay, Abramowitz, and Ungar, 1962). A total of 842 consecutive autopsies was carried out in patients aged 30 and over. They were divided into 568 Ashkenazi and 274 non-Ashkenazi. It was not possible to differentiate the latter more completely as the groups were too small for statistical analysis. There was a total of 20 per cent of acute myocardial infarction in the Ashkenazi group and 8 per cent in the non-Ashkenazi. As regards the degree of atherosclerosis of the aorta, this increased with age in both groups and there was no statistically significant ethnic difference. In spite of the similar degree of aortic athero-sclerosis, there was however the marked difference in the incidence of acute myocardial infarction. Ungar suggests that in the non-Ashkenazi Jews ischaemic heart disease might be due more to a gradual narrowing of the coronary vessels than to thrombosis, and that it would be of interest to investigate possible differences in blood clotting in the two groups. These findings by Professor Ungar and his colleagues throw some doubts on the relationship between blood lipid levels and the incidence of atherosclerosis, although its association with the incidence of coronary heart disease still remains to be explained.

Cohen, Neumann, and Michaelson (1963) examined all members of two communities of Yemenite Jews over the age of 30. One group had been settled in Israel for 25 years or more and the other had immigrated to Israel within 10 years. Hypertension was sig-nificantly greater in the 'old' Yemenites than in the newcomers and so was the incidence of sclerosis of the retinal vessels.

The difference in the blood lipid levels between Ashkenazi and Yemenite Jews has already been mentioned. Brunner, Manelis, and Loebl (1959) have shown that this is largely due to an absence of an age effect in the Yemenites. A rise in blood lipid levels with age has been frequently demonstrated, but when young and older Yemenites were compared no differences were found in any of the blood lipid fractions. Studies in progress in Israel will no doubt make the reasons for these differences clearer.

Diabetes. It is frequently reported that there is a high incidence of diabetes amongst the Jews. Cohen (1961) carried out a survey of over 15,000 subjects representing 90 per cent of the population in the area studied. They included 5000 recent Yemenite immigrants and 750 old settled Yemenites, 1000 recent and 500 old settled Kurds, 4300 Ashkenazi and 4150 non-Ashkenazi. There were no cases amongst the recent settlers from Kurdistan, and only 3 cases in the newcomers from the Yemen, whereas the old settlers in these two communities had an incidence of 2 per cent and 2·5 per cent respectively.

Amongst the Ashkenazi, the incidence of diabetes was 2·5 per cent, but the non-Ashkenazi had a significantly lower incidence of 1 per cent. Since the incidence in Germany, Australia, and New York of diabetes in non-Jewish population ranges from 1·5 to 3·2 per cent, it is unlikely that Jews are particularly at risk. How far the differences in the incidence of old and new settlers can be related to a changing diet is uncertain.

A frequent complication of diabetes is a degenerative vascular condition resembling or possibly identical with atherosclerosis. It has been shown that the incidence of vascular degeneration in Yemenite Jews with diabetes is extremely low, of the order of one-fifth or less of the incidence in comparable diabetics of other ethnic groups (Brunner, Altman, Loebl, Nelken, and Reider, 1964). It will be remembered that the blood lipid level of middle-aged Yemenites is the same as in young Yemenites. But Yemenites suffering from diabetes have raised blood lipids; in spite of this they are almost free of atherosclerosis.

Urolithiasis. An epidemiological survey of the incidence of kidney stones has revealed that this is ten times higher in Israel than in the United States. This is not a peculiar feature of Israel; probably the greater part of South-West Asia can be included in the 'stone' area (Frank, De Vries, Atsmon, Lazebnik, and Kochwa,

1959). The investigations of Professor De Vries, Dr. Frank, and their colleagues in Israel have shown that environmental and sociological factors are of great importance. There is a clear relationship with the climate; the incidence of urolithiasis is considerably higher in Eilat, on the Red Sea, than in the cooler north. There is also a difference between 'European' and 'Oriental' Jews, with the latter having a lower incidence. In the coastal area adjacent to Tel Aviv, the incidence varies from 4·1/1000 in Yemenites to 17·2/1000 for the 'European' Jews. However, in the hot dry climate of the southern part of the Negev, these differences disappear and all the communities represented have a high incidence of stone. Inquiries have shown that there are different attitudes to the need to maintain fluid balance which may be partly responsible for the higher incidence in the 'European' Jews, who have come from temperate countries where fluid requirements are relatively low, in contrast to the Yemenites who have lived for 2000 years in a hot climate. The difference in physiological acclimatization to heat could hardly account for the contrast, as one would expect the newcomers from temperate zones to adapt to the hot climate within a few weeks. Attitudes, however, may change much more slowly, and many prejudices against drinking large volumes of fluid were found amongst the Europeans, even after several years' residence. The fact that in Eilat all groups had a high incidence of urolithiasis was attributed to the large content of magnesium and calcium in the water.

There are also probable genetic factors in some forms of kidney stones and familial non-gouty uric acid urolithiasis has been demonstrated in a number of patients.

Incidence of malignancy. Mortality rates due to malignancy for European and Oriental Jews indicate a marked contrast, with the Europeans exhibiting a higher incidence for neoplasms at all sites except skin and larynx. Cancer of the uterine cervix is much lower in all Jewish communities than in European or American gentiles.

Other diseases. There is a preponderance of senile cataract and glaucoma in the non-Ashkenazi groups. Rheumatic heart disease is surprisingly common in Israel, particularly in the area of Jerusalem. The prevalence of multiple sclerosis differs amongst the immigrants to Israel according to their country of origin, with the highest number of cases in those from temperate countries and the lowest rate in immigrants from hot climates.

Marriage systems. There is a high rate of consanguineous marriages amongst certain Jewish communities. Even amongst the Ashkenazi Jews from Europe there is an average frequency of 1·5 per cent first-cousin marriages, which is higher than that observed in England or the U.S.A. Iraqi Jews have 16 per cent first-cousin marriages, as do Persian Jews, and most of the remaining non-Ashkenazi groups have percentages ranging from 5 to 10 per cent.

A group of particular interest is the Samaritan people, studied by Bonné (1963). The Samaritans are believed to be descended from settlers introduced into Palestine in 722 B.C. by the Assyrians. Originally numbering several thousands they dwindled to a total of about 150 in the nineteenth century. At present they number some 350, divided into two groups, one in Jordan and the other in Israel. In spite of the small size of the sect, the Samaritans are strictly endogenous and the proportion of first-cousin marriages is very high, of the order of 40 per cent. Further details of the demography of these remarkable people will be found in the paper by Bonné.

Consanguineous marriages are common amongst many people in South-West Asia, and there are studies by a number of authors. Grandquist (1931) found 37 per cent first-cousin marriages in an Arab village in Palestine. Barth (1954) in his work in Kurdistan discovered a tribal village with 57 per cent first-cousin marriages. Amongst the nomads of southern Persia, Barth (1961) ascertained a curious demographic pattern. The nomads had a relatively high standard of nutrition and hygiene in contrast to the villagers in the area, who were subject to recurrent epidemics and famine. The nomads had a high rate of increase of population but their total numbers remained relatively constant. The surplus nomads settled in the villages, whose population was in fact maintained in this way.

Physiology. The fields of special interest are those of human physiology, particularly the effects of environment on man and his adaptation to this environment. In addition, of particular importance to the IBP is the assessment of physical working capacity. Linked to the study of nutrition is the need to measure energy expenditure, water and electrolyte balance.

Outside Israel, a number of studies of the effects of the environment have been carried out in different regions of South-West Asia, but these have been made on Europeans living in the area. Ladell, Waterlow, and Hudson (1944) investigated heat illness amongst

British troops in Iraq during World War II, in particular the various forms of failure of sweating. Leithead and Pallister (1960) have investigated heat illness in the Persian Gulf area. A recent book, *Heat Stress and Heat Disorders* by Leithead and Lind (1964), includes a number of references to studies carried out in South-West Asia.

A comparison of the effects of heat on naturally and artificially acclimatized and unacclimatized British troops has been made in Aden. A complete account has been given in a report to the Army Personnel Research Committee of the Medical Research Council (Edholm, Adam, Cannon, Fox, Goldsmith, Shepherd, and Underwood, 1962), and a shorter version has been published (Edholm, Fox, Adam, and Goldsmith, 1963). There were marked differences between the three groups; the naturally acclimatized had far fewer ill effects than had the unacclimatized, and the artificially acclimatized were intermediate. Water intake was high, averaging 8·5 litres daily, but no significant differences between the three groups were found. There was a considerable fall in food intake in all subjects studied during the course of the investigation in Aden, which lasted for two weeks. A fall in food intake was also found in the group who were naturally acclimatized by a period of seven weeks in Aden. During this period food intake fell steadily as the environmental temperatures increased.

A second study has been made in Aden to investigate more fully changes in food intake in the heat (Edholm, Fox, Goldsmith, Hampton, Underwood, Ward, Wolff, Adam, and Allan, 1964). The subjects consisted of two groups of 24 men, one group acclimatized and the other unacclimatized to heat. The experiment was divided into three phases, each of 12 days' duration. In each phase the first 4 and last 4 days included moderately hard work, and during the intervening 4 days the men rested. The first phase was carried out in the U.K. with the unacclimatized men only; the second phase was in Aden with both groups, and the third phase was in the U.K. with both groups. The programme of activities in each phase was identical, and the estimated energy expenditure was similar in each phase. In spite of similar activities and energy expenditure, the food intake of both groups in Aden was approximately 25 per cent less than in the U.K. There were no significant differences in the proportion of calories derived from fat, protein, and carbohydrate taken in Aden and in the U.K.

TABLE 3
Anthropometric data

Region	Tribe	Number	Age (y) Av. and range	Height (m) Av. and range	Sitting height (m) Av. and range	Relative sitting height Av. and range	Weight (kg) Av. and range	Author	Remarks
N. Iraq	Turkoman	61 men	39.9 20–70	1·67 1·52–1·84	0·884 0·78–0·98	53 48–57		Field	
		29 women	26·7 17–44	1·56 1·46–1·66	0·815 0·72–0·89	52·2 48–55		Field	
Iran	Bakhdiari	149 men	40·5 18–83	1·62 1·44–1·80	0·855 0·76–0·99			Field	Infant mortality 400/1000
	Lurs	70 men	39·65 20–89	1·64 1·50–1·77			62·8 49·0–86·2	Field	
	Kurds	50 men	34·6 19–55	1·67 1·55–1·86			61·5 49·7–87·0	Field	
Kurdistan	Kurds I	133 men	35·4 18–70	1·66 1·49–1·81	0·873 0·75–0·98	52·54 46–67		Field	
	Kurds II	235 men	36·15 18–67	1·66 1·46–1·84	0·87 0·78–0·98	52·46 46–57		Field	
	Kurds III	230 men	34·25 17–70	1·66 1·49–1·81	0·867 0·75–0·98	52·18 46–59		Field	
		33 women	32·8 18–54	1·53 1·40–1·66	0·789 0·72–0·86	51·92 46–55		Field	
Kurdistan	Jews I	47 men	39·65 20–70	1·62 1·46–1·75	1·861 0·75–0·95	53·1 50–59		Field	
		23 women	38·95 15–75	1·51 1·40–1·65	0·785 0·68–0·83	51·64 50–55		Field	
	Jews II	59 men	36·30 19–65	1·66 1·55–1·78	0·882 0·81–0·98	53·38 50–55		Field	
		24 women	34·1 17–59	1·51 1·37–1·63	0·771 0·66–0·86	51·36 48–57		Field	

TABLE 3 (cont.)

Region	Tribe	Number	Age (y) Av. and range	Height (m) Av. and range	Sitting height (m) Av. and range	Relative sitting height Av. and range	Weight (kg) Av. and range	Author	Remarks
Iraq	Assyrian	360 men	28, 17–60	1·689, 1·52–1·88			64·8, 45·3–88·9 (416 subjects)	Field	
		126 women	37, 17–61	1·516, 1·42–1·66	0·777, 0·71–0·87	52·0, 49–50 (52 subjects)	57·5, 40·8–90·7	Field	
	Northern Shammar	273 men	41·65, 20–70	1·66, 1·52–1·87	0·888, 0·78–0·98	53·4, 48–61		Field	
		118 women	30·7, 17–70	1·54, 1·40–1·66	0·794, 0·69–0·86	51·74, 46–57		Field	
	Shammar	14 men	38·6	1·66	0·877	52·9		Field	
	Negroes	123 men	42·3, 20–50	1·54, 1·54–1·87	0·885, 0·83–0·93	53·0, 49–55		Field	
	Yezidi I, Jebel Sinjar	46 women	26·6, 20–70	1·67, 1·52–1·81	0·797, 0·78–0·98	51·2, 48–57		Field	
			18–54	1·56, 1·46–1·69	0·883, 0·72–0·86	53·14, 48–55		Field	
	Yezidi II,	101 men	40·5, 20–70	1·66, 1·49–1·81	0·796, 0·78–0·98	51·8, 48·6–51·8		Field	
	Sheikham	25 women	33·2, 18–64	1·54, 1·46–1·63				Field	
Kurdistan	Assyrian	106 men	29, 20–70	1·705, 1·52–1·90	0·856, 0·78–0·98	50·2, 46–55		Field	
		133 women	32·2, 18–69	1·523, 1·35–1·66	0·795, 0·72–0·89	51·98, 46·5–56·0		Field	
Iraq	Sububba (nomads but not Bedu)	38 men	37·6, 20–64	1·65, 1·49–1·78	0·86	52·9, 49–56		Field	Very high infant mortality, 400/1000
		10 women	25·5, 17–41	1·53, 1·46–1·66	0·802, 0·75–0·86	52·5, 50–55		Field	

TABLE 3 (cont.)

Region	Tribe	Number	Age (y) Av. and range	Height (m) Av. and range	Sitting height (m) Av. and range	Relative sitting height Av. and range	Weight (kg) Av. and range	Author	Remarks
Nomads of Arabia	Bekara	149 men	Adult	1·67	0·846			Shanklin	
	Alonite	309	Adult	1·52–1·82	0·766–0·926			Shanklin	
				1·68	0·86				
	Hamer	175	Adult	1·49–1·86	0·741–0·98			Shanklin	
				1·64	0·815				
	Mardeli	157		1·46–1·89	0·685–0·946			Shanklin	
				1·68					
	Hafar	93		1·49–1·84	0·769–0·942			Shanklin	
				1·68					
	Hijdarah	297		1·515–1·845	0·716–0·954			Shanklin	
				1·64					
	Manaly			1·49–1·84	0·759–0·955			Shanklin	
				1·70					
Bedouin	Revala	?		1·62				Shanklin	
Saudi Arabia		?	Adult	1·62				Lipsky	
Yemen		17	Adult	1·63				Seligman	
Muscat		31	Adult	1·65				Seligman	
Sheher		?	Adult	1·63				Seligman	
Eastern Arabia		?	Adult	1·66				Seligman	
Kardofan-Darfur border		15	Adult	1·70				Seligman	

Apart from Israel, no reports have been found which describe specific studies on the indigenous peoples of South-West Asia, and their response to heat. It will be an important objective of the IBP to fill this gap, and particularly to investigate the effects of dehydration. There are many travellers' tales describing the apparent tolerance of the desert Arabs for prolonged dehydration. Since current physiological doctrine emphasizes that there is no evidence that man can adapt to dehydration, it would be of great interest to study such people as the Bedouin.

In Israel, a number of studies have been carried out on man, and these are summarized in the proceedings of a symposium on 'Climate and Man in Israel' held in Beersheva in 1962.

Sohar and his colleagues (Sohar, Tennenbaum, and Yaski, 1962; Sohar, Tennenbaum, and Robinson, 1962; Sohar, Kaly, and Adar, 1963; Sohar and Adar, 1963) studied the reactions of a group of 19 healthy young men who marched the length of Israel from Eilat in the extreme south to Metulla in the north (370 miles) in 24 days during August, the hottest time of the year. Their daily sweat rate varied between 5 and 10 litres, but water balance was maintained and daily weight changes were small. Urine volumes were high, and, except for one day, ranged from 870 ml to 1770 ml. Salt balance was achieved on an average intake of 264 mE of sodium. A variety of drinks were available throughout the experiment, and the preferred one was cold water sweetened with a fruit flavour.

Toor and his colleagues (Toor, Masry, Katz, and Agmon, 1964; Toor, Masry, and Konfino, 1962) have studied salt and water balance and renal dynamics during work in the heat, and have shown the marked effects that can occur even in man well acclimatized to heat.

Givoni (1963) has developed a new thermal index called the Index of Thermal Stress, which takes into account the cooling efficiency of sweating.

Physical anthropometry. In this subject, the situation is different from all those described above in that little work appears to have been published in Israel, but there is considerable information from the rest of South-West Asia. This is largely due to the extensive studies of Henry Field and his colleagues, given in detail in volumes of the publications of the Field Museum and the Peabody Museum (1940–49, 1950, 1951–52, 1956). Only some of the mass of information contained in these publications can be given here. Indeed, even in these studies, in only a few were the body weights recorded, although very comprehensive measurements of the head are given. Extracts are given in Table 3. A number of other papers on anthropometry have been primarily concerned with skulls and head measurements.

Seligman (1917), in a paper on the physical character of Arabs, gives some figures for heights of Arabs, including 17 Yemenites, average 1·63 m, and 31 Muscat Arabs, 1·65 m. In the northern area of Saudi Arabia the Arabs were taller, with an average of 1·70 m. Lipsky (1959), in a study in Saudi Arabia, found an average height of 1·63 m. Shanklin (1936, 1938), who studied the Bedouin, obtained heights in different tribes, the averages of which ranged from 1·62 m to 1·70 m. Further details are given in Table 3.

In Turkey, a detailed anthropometric survey of 915 service personnel was carried out by Hertzberg, Churchill, Dupertuis, White, and Damon (1963). The average age of the subjects was 22·5 y, ranging from 17 to 45. Average weight was 64·6 kg$\pm$8·23 and height 1·69 m$\pm$5·73 per cent; sitting height was 0·897 m $\pm$3·15 per cent. Body fat was determined from skinfold thickness measurements and averaged 9·4$\pm$2·8 per cent of body weight. This is a low figure in comparison with similar subjects in Greece and Italy, whose body fat averaged 10·4 and 12·3 per cent respectively.

The heights and weights of recent immigrants to Israel from the Yemen were compared with those of Yemenites who had been settled in Israel for 20 years or more (Cohen, Bavly, and Poznanski, 1961). All subjects were over 30; in 100 male immigrants' average body weight was 56·5 kg and average height 1·62 m; in 110 male settlers average weight was 64·9 kg and average height 1·60 m. Amongst the women there was also an increased body weight in the settlers, 110 immigrants averaging 51·3 kg and the settlers 59·5 kg, their height being 1·48 m and 1·50 m respectively.

There is little information about the growth of children. Jager (1961) found in 9600 infants born in Baghdad that the growth curve was similar to that of German infants until the fourth month when the growth rate lagged. Mean weight at 1 year was 1625 g less than that of the German children. Amongst 9600 infants attending welfare clinics in Baghdad, the infant mortality was 135·5, and in the second year of life 39·4/1000.

Gounelle and Demarchi (1953) measured the weight of infants attending two clinics in Baghdad; their results are given in Table 4.

TABLE 4
Average weight of infants attending two ante-natal clinics in Baghdad (Gounelle and Demarchi, 1953)

Age (months)	No.	Weight (kg)	No.	Weight (kg)	Average
1	82	3·8	76	3·9	3·89
2	79	4·6	70	4·9	4·76
3	91	5·05	54	5·3	5·17
4	55	6·0	59	5·5	5·77
5	47	6·1	58	6·2	6·14
6	59	6·8	71	7·2	7·03
7	77	7·7	52	7·1	7·43
8	64	7·7	52	7·3	7·54
9	47	7·75	46	7·6	7·68
10	43	7·8	49	7·7	7·75
11	29	8·1	20	8·1	8·10
12	104	8·1	104	8·2	8·14
13	17	8·6	17	8·5	8·58
14	37	8·1	26	8·4	8·21
15	21	8·6	21	8·4	8·48
16	22	8·95	15	7·8	8·86
17	9	8·4	3	8·87	8·52
18	89	9·2	77	8·87	9·06

Proposals for research in Israel

The account given in the preceding pages of the work already carried out in South-West Asia relevant to the IBP on human adaptability has shown that there are very considerable gaps in knowledge for nearly the whole area, with the exception of Israel. It must be acknowledged that there are certainly papers which have been overlooked, but in view of the numerous comments in papers which have been read, testifying to the paucity of studies, it seems unlikely that the apparent gaps would be closed to any significant extent by material that has not been located.

It might seem illogical to propose plans for research in Israel, where already so much work has been done, rather than in other countries of this area where so much remains to be done. However, it will be argued that the situation in Israel is so unusual, and presents such exceptional conditions for IBP studies, that it would be folly not to take advantage of these opportunities. In essence, it is considered that Israel is particularly suitable for studies of the effect of climatic environment on man, and the problem to be studied is 'To identify and evaluate the relative role of environmental and genetic factors in determining the physiological status of the individual.'

This statement is too broad by itself, and specific questions are necessary before an evaluation can be made about the suitability or desirability of making studies in Israel. The questions which the environmental physiologist hopes may be solved by the IBP include the following:

(1) Are there significant physiological differences between the various groups of mankind; and, more specifically, are there physiological differences in the ability to tolerate or adapt to heat or cold or dehydration?

(2) If physiological differences are shown to exist, are these due to environmental or genetic factors, or both? Alternatively, a negative hypothesis can be proposed:

There are no demonstrable physiological differences between the various groups of mankind in their ability to tolerate or adapt to hot or cold environments or to dehydration.

On the basis of the present limited information, it can be stated that some differences have been demonstrated in the physiological responses to cold environments by various peoples living in cold climates, including the Australian Aborigine, the Alacaluf Indians of Terra del Fuego, the Bushmen of the Kalahari desert, Eskimoes and Indians living in the arctic and sub-arctic regions of Canada. However, the groups studied, including the controls, have been small in number and since the variability of response between individuals of the one group can be large, it can be argued that these physiological differences have not been demonstrated unequivocally.

In order to establish evidence of physiological differences between different groups, not only is it essential to study a considerable number of persons, it is also necessary to have detailed information about many other factors which may modify physiological responses. These factors include:

(1) *Environment.* The term 'environment' is considered to include:

A. (i) The physical or climatic environment, i.e. the temperature, humidity, radiation, and air movement.

   (ii) Modification of the environment by clothing, shelter, heating or cooling systems.

   (iii) Modification of the environment by physiological means, i.e. activity and posture.

B. Altitude or barometric pressure.

C. Composition of atmosphere, including presence of dust or gases other than those normally present in the atmosphere.

D. Composition of drinking water.

E. The social environment, which may influence the ways in which the physical environment is modified and may also affect the physiological responses by the effect of food habits, water intake habits, patterns of activity, &c.

(2) *Epidemiology*, or the pattern of disease. If anyone who is affected by, say, thalassaemia from which other groups are free, then the possible effects of such a condition on the physiological response to the environment has to be considered.

(3) *Anthropometry*. This should include detailed body measurements and, if possible, estimates of body composition.

4. *Demography*. Age and sex distribution, marriage patterns, size of families, &c.

(5) *Genetics*. Evaluation of all available genetic markers. The scale of study required is considerable, as it is evident that a multidisciplinary investigation is needed to evaluate all the factors involved. Although there are formidable problems of organization, these can be more clearly envisaged with the establishment of the IBP.

There are many reasons for making such a study in Israel. Although the country is small, there are at least three climatic zones: the semi-arid Negev, the Judean hills with an altitude up to 1000 metres near Jerusalem, and the Jordan valley with a semi-tropical climate. In addition, the coastal zone has a characteristic mediterranean climate. The great majority of the inhabitants have immigrated to Israel during the last fourteen years, coming from many different countries. In a number of cases, communities or villages have been formed of people coming from one particular country, and in some instances an entire village has moved *en bloc* from, e.g. Iraq to Israel.

There is a high standard of medical care for all inhabitants and

26

extensive demographic data are available. It is possible to select, in each of the three climatic zones, communities of similar origin who can be studied and compared to determine what effects of the environment can be demonstrated.

The plan of research

The outline of the plan as envisaged at present would be to study three communities in each of the three climatic zones, a total of nine communities. Three contrasting ethnic groups would be chosen, to include:

(a) European, Ashkenazi Jews, i.e. Poles, Roumanians, or Bulgarians;
(b) Oriental Jews, e.g. Yemenite or Iraqui;
(c) North African Jews, or groups such as Cochin Jews.

The final choice would depend on the communities to be found in the different climatic zones, so that three ethnic groups would be selected with representative communities in each of the three climatic zones. The size of the population to be studied is provisionally fixed at 1000 in each community in each zone, i.e., a total of 9000 (see following table):

	Desert	Hill	Jordan valley
European	1000	1000	1000
Yemenite	1000	1000	1000
North African	1000	1000	1000

In many cases the individual villages or settlements have populations much lower than 1000 so several villages in each zone may have to be included. The ideal would be to study all individuals in a specific community, although it may be necessary to have an upper age limit of about 70.

The specifications for any particular community include:

(1) rural, not urban;
(2) exclusively, or almost exclusively, of one ethnic group;
(3) situated in one of the three climatic zones;
(4) 'stable' community;
(5) immigrated since 1948.

The 1961 census shows that the age distribution of such rural communities is:

Years	%
0–4	17
5–14	27
15–29	25
30–44	15
45–64	12·5
65+	3·5

The population of the rural villages is approximately:

20·5 per cent European immigrated since 1948;
50·0 per cent Asia–Africa immigrated since 1948.

In all rural settlements there are:

10,000 from Egypt and Libya,
42,000 from Africa,
14,000 from Yemen,
13,000 from Iraq,
10,000 from Turkey and Iran,
3,000 from Bulgaria and Greece,
16,000 from Roumania,
9,000 from Czechoslovakia and Hungary,
9,000 from Austria and Germany,
30,000 from Poland and U.S.S.R.

In the Judean mountains there are:

1100 European,
3300 African,
3500 Asian.

In the Jordan valley:

6000 European,
6000 African,
2500 Asian.

In the Beersheva area and Negev:

1600 European,
9000 African,
2800 Asian.

The European group is relatively homogenous. If a particular national group were selected it would be difficult to get sufficient numbers in the Negev area or in the Judean mountain area.

The African group is of sufficient size in all three areas to make it possible to select groups of closely similar origin in all three areas.

In the Asian group are included Yemenites, Iraqui, Kurdish, Turkish, and Persian Jews. However, the distribution is very uneven in the three areas and it will be difficult to find sufficient numbers in each area if only one ethnic group is selected. There are considerable similarities between the Kurdish Jews from Iraq and the Kurdish Jews from Eastern Turkey, but the Kurdish Jews as a group are rather distinct from the Jews of Western Turkey (Istanbul) on one hand and from those of Central Iraq (Baghdad) on the other. Approximately 500 from each of these could be studied in each of the zones. Alternatively, 500 Yemenites in each area could be selected and either 500 Iraqui or 500 Kurdish Jews.

One reason for putting the desirable figure at 1000 is the likelihood of considerable wastage over the period of survey due to internal migration. It is difficult to make any precise estimate of losses due to this cause. There was much movement in the first years after immigration, with many leaving rural settlements for the towns. Although still continuing, the trend appears to be diminishing, especially with improvement in standards in the villages. A very tentative estimate of 30 per cent loss in 5 years has been made, based on past experience and estimates from studies of medical records. It is considered that deliberate selection of villages might yield more stable groups.

Organization. A provisional plan is set out below.

(1) Each aspect of study should be the responsibility of a specialized research team. The different aspects or disciplines are listed below, with details of facilities required, size of team, and length of work. Each team would have a high degree of autonomy. The emphasis is to be on a co-operative study in which the same subjects would be studied by different teams.

(2) Central planning and organization will be required for:
    (a) Selection of communities.
    (b) Phasing of work. Some studies, i.e. genetics, might only be required once in the survey; others, such as nutrition, would probably have to be repeated at different seasons of the year.

(c) Sampling. Although the aim would be to cover the whole population, this could probably only be achieved for certain aspects such as anthropology, epidemiology, demography, and vital statistics (birth rate, death rate, morbidity, marriage rate, &c.).

Nutritional studies may have to be done on a family basis, with smaller samples of individual studies.

Physiological studies, which are the most time-consuming and involve most interference with the subject, will have to be done on a sample of the population.

(d) Organization of facilities in or adjacent to each village; living accommodation for members of research teams, travel to and from regional laboratories, &c.

(e) Tabulation of data to be on an agreed basis for all teams. Data to be recorded in a form suitable for transfer to punch-cards or tape.

(f) Laboratory analyses; transport and storage of material (blood, urine, stools, &c.).

Facilities. Israel is unique, as there are both the opportunities for studies in human biology and the facilities available for carrying out these studies. There are already a number of research projects under way which are of related interest. Several of these have been mentioned in the account of research in Israel. In most fields, the laboratory facilities are excellent and there are, as is evident from the large volume of published work, active research groups of high standing.

Further details can be obtained from *Medical and Biological Research in Israel*, edited by M. Prywes; the *Handbook of the Hebrew University*, and the *Handbook of the Negev Institute*. Other advantages of Israel include the fact that it is geographically small with good communications, and that the problems of environment are of interest and concern to virtually all sections of the population, including Government departments, research institutes, and the medical services.

REFERENCES

ADOLPH, W. H., 1954. 'Nutrition in the Near East', *J. Am. diet. Ass.* **30**, 753–756.
—— SHAMMAS, E. I., and HALABY, S. H., 1955. 'The nutritive value of legume proteins and legume-wheat mixed proteins in Near East diets', *Food Res.* **20**, 31–34.
AKSOY, M., IKIN, E. W., MOURANT, A. E., and LEHMANN, H., 1958. 'Blood groups, Hp and thalassaemia in Turks in South Turkey— Eti-Turks', *Br. med. J.* **2**, 937–939.
AZIM, M. ABDEL and GISMANN, ANNE, 1956. 'Bilharziasis in South-West Asia', *Bull. Wld Hlth Org.* **14**, 403–456.
BAHADORI, A. and CLAUDIAN, J., 1957. 'Enquête sur l'alimentation et les budgets familiaux dans deux regions de l'Iran', *Bull. Inst. natn. Hyg.* **12**, 593–631.
BALTAZARD, M., BAHMANYAR, M., MOSTACHFI, P., EFTEKHARI, M., and MOFIDI, C. H., 1960. 'Recherches sur la Peste en Iran', *Bull. Wld Hlth Org.* **23**, 141–155.
BALTAZARD, M. and SEYDIAN, B., 1960. 'Recherches sur la Peste en Iran', *Bull. Wld. Hlth Org.* **23**, 157–167.
BARTH, F., 1954. 'Father's brother's daughter marriage in Kurdistan', *SWest J. Anthrop.* **10**, 164–171.
—— 1961. *Nomads of South Persia.* Oslo University Press; Allen & Unwin, London.
BAVLY, S., 1960. 'Food consumption and levels of nutrition of urban wage and salary earners' families in Israel (1956–1957)', *Central Bureau of Statistics, Special Series, No.* 101. Jerusalem.
—— MUNDEL, G., GUGGENHEIM, K., and HALEVI, H. S., 1962. *Survey on Food Consumption and Nutritional Status among the Rural Population in Israel 1959–60.* Ministry of Education and Culture, Jerusalem.
BEN-ISHAY, Z., ABRAMOWITZ, A., and UNGAR, H., 1962. 'Atherosclerosis and aging of the aorta in adult Jewish population of Israel', *Am. J. Cardiol.* **10**, 407–415.
BERRY, F. B. and SCHAEFER, A. E., 1958. 'Nutrition surveys in the Near and Far East', Report of the Interdepartmental Committee on Nutrition for National Defence, *U.S. arm. Forces med. J.* **9**, 91–106.
BONNÉ, B., 1963. 'The Samaritans: a demographic study', *Hum. Biol.* **35**, 61–89.
BOUÉ, A. and BOUÉ, J., 1956. 'Étude sur la répartition des groupes sanguins en Iran, ii', *Annls Inst. Pasteur, Paris* **91**, 898–911.
BROWE, J. H., 1961. 'A nutrition survey of the armed forces of Iran', *Am. J. clin. Nutr.* **9**, 478–514.
BRUNNER, D., 1963. 'A nutritional survey in Yemenite agricultural workers'. Preliminary Report, Cardiovascular Research Unit, Government Hospital 'Donolo', Tel Aviv-Jaffa.
—— ALTMAN, S., LOEBL, K., NELKEN, L., and REIDER, J., 1964. 'The relative absence of vascular disease in diabetic Yemenite Jews. I. A study of clinical findings', *Diabetes* **13**, 268–277.
—— and LOEBL, K., 1958. 'Serum cholesterol electrophoretic pattern, diet and coronary artery disease: a study in coronary patients and healthy men of different origin and occupations in Israel', *Ann. intern. Med.* **49**, 732–750.
—— MANELIS, G., and LOEBL, K., 1959. 'Influence of age and race on lipid levels in Israel', *Lancet* **1**, 1071–1073.

CHRISTIANSEN, S., 1954. 'A report on syphilis control in Turkey', *Bull. Wld Hlth Org.* 10, 627–690.

Climate and Man in Israel, Symposium held at Beersheva, 1962.

COHEN, A. M., 1961. 'Prevalence of diabetes among different ethnic Jewish groups in Israel', *Metabolism* 10, 50–58.

—— BAVLY, S., and POZNANSKI, R., 1961. 'Change of diet of Yemenite Jews in relation to diabetes and ischaemic heart disease', *Lancet* 2, 1399–1401.

—— NEUMANN, E., and MICHAELSON, I. C., 1960. 'Involutionary sclerosis and diastolic hypertension', *Lancet* 2, 1050–1051.

CORKHILL, N. L., 1951. 'Nutrition in Iraq, Lebanon and Syria in 1951', *WHO Report EM/NUT/1.*

COWAN, J. W., SABRY, Z. I., RINNU, F. J., and CAMPBELL, J. A., 1963. 'Evaluation of protein in Middle Eastern diets', *J. Nutr.* 81, 235–240.

DEMARCHI, M., HAMANDI, F., and ZAKI, L. S., 1961. 'A study on the evaluation of school meal supplement', *J. Fac. Med., Baghdad* 3, 12–16.

DREYFUSS, F., 1963. 'The incidence of myocardial infarctions in various communities in Israel', *Am. Heart J.* 45, 749–755.

—— TOOR, M., AGMON, J., and ZLOTNIK, A., 1957. 'Observations on myocardial infarctions in Israel', *Cardiologia* 6, 387–398.

EDHOLM, O. G., ADAM, J. M., CANNON, P., FOX, R. H., GOLDSMITH, R., SHEPHERD, R. D., and UNDERWOOD, C. R., 1962. 'Acclimatization to heat', *Army Personnel Research Committee, Med. Res. Coun., Lond., Report No. A.P.R.C.* 61/25.

—— FOX, R. H., ADAM, J. M., and GOLDSMITH, R., 1963. 'Comparison of artificial and natural acclimatization', *Fed. Proc.* 22, pt. i. 709–715.

—— —— GOLDSMITH, R., HAMPTON, I., UNDERWOOD, C. R., WARD, E. J., WOLFF, H. S., ADAM, J. M., and ALLAN, J. R., 1964. 'The effect of heat on food and water intake of acclimatized and unacclimatized men', *Army Personnel Research Committee, Med. Res. Coun., Lond., Report No. A.P.R.C.* 64/16.

FARID, M. A., 1954. 'Malaria in Jordan Valley', *Bull. Wld Hlth Org.* 11, 765–783.

—— 1956. 'Implications of the Mecca Pilgrimage for a regional malaria eradication programme', *Bull. Wld Hlth Org.* 15, 828–833.

FAWDRY, A. L., 1955. 'Splenomegaly, anaemia and hepatomegaly in S. Arabia', *Trans. Roy, Soc. Trop. Med. & Hyg.* 49, 387.

FIELD, H., 1940–49. 'Anthropology of Iraq. Part I', *Field Museum of Natural History, Anthropological series*, Vol. 30.

—— 1950. 'Anthropology of Iraq. Part II', *Field Museum of Natural History, Anthropological series*, Vol. 46.

—— 1951–52. 'The anthropology of Iraq and the Northern Jazira', *Papers of the Peabody Museum*, Vol. 46.

—— 1956. 'An anthropological reconnaissance in the Near East, 1950', *Papers of the Peabody Museum*, Vol. 48.

FRANK, M., DE VRIES, A., ATSMON, A., LAZEBNIK, J., and KOCHWA, S., 1959. 'Epidemiological investigation of urolithiasis in Israel', *J. Urol.* 81, 497–505.

GHOROURY, A. A. EL, 1954. 'Syphilis in Saudi Arabia', *Bull. Wld Hlth Org.* 10, 627–690.

GIVONI, B., 1963. 'Estimation of the effect of climate on man: development of a new thermal index'. Ph.D. Thesis. Building Research Station, Technion City, Israel.

GOLDSCHMIDT, ELISABETH (ed.), 1963. 'The genetics of migrant isolate populations', *Proceedings of a Conference on Human Population Genetics in Israel held at the Hebrew University, Jerusalem*. Williams & Wilkins, New York.

GOUNELLE, H. and DEMARCHI, M., 1953. 'Nutritional status of infants and very young children in Baghdad, Iraq', *J. Fac. Med., Baghdad* 17, 42–53.

—— —— RABII, H., RASHID, R., FINDAKLY, S., SELLOUMI, H. F., and COFMAN, S., 1956. 'Enquête de nutrition en Moyen-Orient de jeunes adultes', *Bull. Soc. scient. Hyg. aliment.* 44, 269–278.

GRANDQUIST, H., 1931. 'Marriage conditions in a Palestinian village', *Helsingfors Soc. Sci. Fdn* III, 8.

GROEN, J. J., 1964. 'Nutrition of the Bedouins in the Negev Desert', *Am. J. clin. Nutr.* 14, 37–46.

GUREVITCH, J., HASSON, E., and MARGOLIS, E., 1956. 'Blood groups in Persian Jews', *Ann. Eugen.* 18, 94–95.

—— —— —— and POLIAKHOFF, C., 1955. 'Blood groups in Jews from Tripolitania', *Ann. Eugen.* 19, 260–261.

—— —— —— and POLISHUK, Z., 1955. 'Blood groups in Jews from Cochin, India', *Ann. Eugen.* 19, 254–256.

—— HERMONI, D., and MARGOLIS, E., 1953. 'Blood groups in Kurdistani Jews', *Ann. Eugen.* 18, 94–95.

—— —— and POLISHUK, Z., 1951. 'Rh Blood Types in Jerusalem Jews', *Ann. Eugen.* 16, 129–130.

—— and MARGOLIS, E., 1955. 'Blood groups in Jews from Iraq', *Ann. hum. Genet.* 19, 257–259.

GÜRSON, C. T., NEYZI, O., and GEDIK, N., 1961. 'Infantile chronic malnutrition in Turkey', *Annls paediat.* 197, 256–266.

HALSTED, J. A., CARROLL, J., DEHGANI, A., LAGHMANI, M., and PRASAD, A. S., 1960. 'Serum vitamin B_{12} concentration in dietary deficiency (Iran)', *Am. J. clin. Nutr.* 8, 374–376.

HELLER, H., SOHAR, E., and SHERF, L., 1958. 'Familial mediterranean fever', *Archos intern. Med.* 102, 50–71.

HERTZBERG, H. T. E., CHURCHILL, E., DUPERTUIS, C. W., WHITE, R. M., and DAMON, A., 1963. *Anthropometric Survey of Turkey, Greece and Italy*. Pergamon Press, Oxford.

JAGER, S., 1961. 'Statistical information from a welfare clinic, in Baghdad, Iraq', *J. trop Med. Hyg.* 64, 212–216.

KELLY, F. C. and SNEDDEN, W. W., 1958. 'Prevalence and geographical distribution of endemic goitre', *Bull. Wld Hlth Org.* 18, 5–175.

LADELL, W. S. S., WATERLOW, J. C., and HUDSON, M. F., 1944. 'Desert climate: physiological and clinical observations', *Lancet* 2, 491–497, 527–531.

LEE, D. H. K., 1964. 'Terrestrial animals in dry heat: man in the desert', *Handbook of Physiology*, Sect. 4: Adaptation to the Environment. Am. Physiol. Soc., Washington.

LEITHEAD, C. S. and LIND, A. R., 1964. *Heat Stress and Heat Disorders*. Cassell, London.

—— and PALLISTER, M. A., 1960. 'Observations on dehydration and sweating', *Lancet* 2, 114.

LIPSKY, G. A., 1959. *Saudi Arabia, its People, its Society, its Culture*, pp. 269–270. Human Relations Area Files Press, New Haven.

MAY, J. M., 1961. *The Ecology of Malnutrition in the Far and Near East: Food Resources, Habits and Deficiencies*. Hafner, New York.

MARGOLIS, E., GUREVITCH, J., and HASSON, E., 1957. 'Blood groups in Jews from Morocco and Tunisia', *Ann. hum. Genet.* **22**, 65–68.

MOURANT, A. E., 1959. 'The blood groups of the Jews', *Jewish J. Sociol.* **1**, 155–176.

—— KOPEC, A. C., and DOMANIEWSKA-SOBCZAK, K., 1958. *The ABO Blood Groups: Comprehensive Tables and Maps of World Distribution*. Blackwell, Oxford.

NAJARIAN, H. H., ARAOZ, J. DE, KLIMT, C. R., AL ANI, K., and AZZANI, J., 1961. 'Studies in bilharziasis endemicity in the vicinity of Basra, Iraq', *Bull. Wld Hlth Org.* **25**, 467–478.

NASSIF, R. E., 1953. 'The incidence of blood groups in Lebanon', *J. méd. liban.* 346–349.

NEVITT, G. A., 1961. 'Dental health in the Middle East', *Bull. Wld Hlth Org.* **25**, 263–267.

SABRY, Z. I., 1961. 'Protein foods in Middle Eastern Diets', *Nat. Acad. Sci.–Nat. Res. Coun. Wash. Publ. No.* 843, 183–187.

SACHS, L. and BAT-MIRIAM, M., 1957. 'The genetics of Jewish populations. I. Finger-print patterns in Jewish populations in Israel', *Am. J. hum. Genet.* **9**, 117–126.

SELIGMAN, C. G., 1917. 'Physical character of Arabs', *Jl R. anthrop. Inst.* **XLVII**, 214–237.

SHAMMAS, E. I. and ADOLPH, W. H., 1954. 'Nutritive value of parboiled wheat used in the Near East', *J. Am. diet. Ass.* **30**, 982–983.

SHANKLIN, W. M., 1936. 'Anthropology of Akeydat and Manaly Bedouins and blood groups', *Am. J. phys. Anthr.* **XXI**, 217–252.

—— 1938. 'Anthropometry of Syrian males', *Jl R. anthrop. Inst.* **68**, 379–414.

SOHAR, E. and ADAR, R., 1964. 'Sodium requirements in Israel under conditions of work in hot climate', *Arid Zone Research XXIV, Environmental Physiology and Psychology in Arid Conditions*, pp. 55–62. UNESCO, Paris.

—— KALY, J., and ADAR, R., 1964. 'The prevention of voluntary dehydration', *Arid Zone Research XXIV, Environmental Physiology and Psychology in Arid Conditions*, pp. 129–135. UNESCO, Paris.

—— TENNENBAUM, J., and ROBINSON, N., 1962. 'A comparison of the cumulative discomfort index (Cum. D.I.) and cumulative effective temperature (Cum. E.T.) as obtained by meteorological data', *Biometeorology*, pp. 395–400. Pergamon Press, Oxford.

—— —— and YASKI, D., 1962. 'Estimation of daily water intake (to replace water loss) from the cumulative discomfort index (Cum. D.I.)', *Biometeorology*, pp. 401–405. Pergamon Press, Oxford.

STEINBERG, A. G., 1963. 'Dependence of the Phenotype on Environment and Heredity', *The Genetics of Migrant and Isolate Populations* (ed. E. GOLDSCHMIDT), pp. 133–143. Williams & Wilkins, New York.

STRAUSS, W., 1955. 'Continuation and Expansion of a Nutritional Survey within various Groups of the Population of Israel'. Report to the Ford Foundation, Sub. Project E. 4, Jerusalem (stencilled).
—— SHATAN-HERZBERG, M., and BORTEN, E., 1953. Nutritional survey in Israel, 2nd Interim Report, Surveys of 1951 and 1952/53, Hebrew University-Hadassah Medical School, Jerusalem (stencilled).
THOMSON, J. C. and MASHAYEKHI, M. B., 1962. 'Nutrition in Iran: report on a preliminary nutritional assessment survey of seven different geographical areas of Iran, April–June 1962', WHO Report EM/NUT/2, October.
—— BAHADORI, A., and MASHAYEKHI, M. B., 1957. 'Nutrition in Iran II: report on the food and nutrition situation in Iran', WHO Report EM/NUT/10, March.
TOOR, M., MASSRY, S., KATZ, I., and AGMON, J., 1964. 'The effect of fluid intake on the acidification of urine during rest and exercise in hot climate', Clin. Sci. 27, 259–270.
—— MATZRI, S., and KONFINO, D., 1962. 'Physiological aspects of work done by residents in a hot climate', Climate and Man in Israel, p. 13, a Symposium held at the Negev Institute for Arid Zone Research, Israel, 4–5 April, 1962. National Council for Research and Development, Jerusalem.
TROUPIN, J. L., 1955. 'Medical schools and physicians', Bull. Wld Hlth Org. 13, 345–361.
UNGAR, H. and LAUFER, A., 1961. 'Necropsy survey of atherosclerosis in the Jewish population of Israel', Path. Microbiol. 24, 711–717.
U.S. ARMY, 1959. 'South-West Asia: Environment and its relationship to military activities'. Quartermaster Res. and Engnr. Command. Tech. Rep. No. EP-118.
WINKLER, P. G., 1963. 'Trachoma in Hebron, Jordan', Bull. Wld Hlth Org. 28, 417–436.
WRAY, J. D., 1961. 'Kwashiorkor and marasmus in Turkey', Nat. Acad. Sci.–Nat. Res. Coun., Washington, Publ. No. 843, 189–195.

13

POPULATION GENETIC STUDIES IN AUSTRALIA AND NEW GUINEA

R. L. KIRK

CERTAIN areas of the world offer greater possibilities for seeking the solution to specific biological problems than do others. This is true particularly with respect to the study of human adaptability. Not every topic falling within the general schema outlined in the opening chapter can be studied profitably in a single geographic region or population group. Each region and each population within that region must be delineated first before the relevant topics can be chosen for more detailed analysis.

As a contribution towards this preliminary delineation the present chapter outlines the results of studies with a predominantly genetic bias among the indigenous populations of Australia and New Guinea and indicates where more intensive studies might be undertaken.

A. EXTENSIVE SURVEYS

The earliest studies of the distribution of genetic markers among the inhabitants of Australia and of New Guinea were carried out more than forty years ago (Tebbutt and McConnel, 1922; Heydon and Murphy, 1924). Before 1940, however, such studies were limited to the distribution of the ABO blood groups. They have been summarized by Boyd (1939).

During the past twenty years the range of such studies has been increased significantly. Simmons and his colleagues from Melbourne have published a large number of papers covering blood group studies in Australia and New Guinea, as well as in other parts of Oceania and South- and South-East Asia. Walsh and his colleagues from Sydney have added substantial blood group studies for New Guinea; Nijenhuis and his colleagues in Amsterdam performed a similar service for Netherlands New Guinea up to 1962 when the administration of this territory was taken over by Indonesia.

TABLE 1

*Range of gene frequencies and phenotype frequencies for blood group
systems by geographic regions in Australia*

Locality	p	q	r	Gene frequencies (*per cent*)				
				n	R_1	R_2	R_0	R_z
Cape York	4–22	0–14	74–96	66–88	66–79	6–8	4–25	1–11
South-East Queensland	18–25	2–4	71–80	72–79	66–67	11–12	13–16	6–8
Southern Gulf of Carpentaria	0–10	0–24	76–93	49–69	52–67	5–24	9–43	0–1
Northern Australia (including Bathurst and Melville Island)	8–23	?	77–92	66–73	64–69	7–25	6–29	0–2
Central Australia	22–46	0	54–78	61–87	56–57	25–41	1–12	0–7
Western Desert	31–50	0	50–69	90–100	51–57	38–44	2–3	2–3
Kimberleys	11–23	0	77–89	59–78	55–76	13–28	4–14	2–9
Western Central	35–46	0	54–65	68–78	57–62	27–29	0–9	2–13

Locality	Phenotypes (*per cent*)									
	Le(a+)	$P_1(+)$	Fy(a+)	Lu(a+)	K(+)	Di(a+)	Js(a+)	Jk(a+)	Wr(a+)	Wb(+)
Cape York	8–21	29–32	100	—	—	0	—	—	0	—
South-East Queensland	—	—	100	0	—	—	—	—	—	—
Southern Gulf of Carpentaria	0–9	9–27	—	—	—	—	—	61–69	—	0
Northern Australia (including Bathurst and Melville Island)	—	—	—	—	—	—	—	—	—	—
Central Australia	0–7	18–65	0	—	0	0	—	—	—	—
Western Desert	5	44–73	100	0	0	0	0	—	0	—
Kimberleys	0–19	24–61	100	—	0	0	—	—	0	—
Western Central	14–21	26–28	—	—	—	—	—	—	—	—

More recently several investigators have studied the distribution of various serum protein, haemoglobin, and enzyme variants in populations in Oceania. Kirk and his collaborators have been concerned chiefly with Australia, whilst Curtain and Kidson have been involved in similar detailed studies in New Guinea. Finally, Gajdusek and others and also Bennett have made studies in depth of special diseases in New Guinea which may have a genetic basis.

An overall review of genetic studies in Australia and New Guinea has been published recently by Kirk (1965*a*) and the same author has completed a comprehensive survey of all such studies in Australia (Kirk, 1965*b*).

1. *Blood group surveys in Australia*

More than 8000 of the estimated 50,000 full-blood Aborigines in Australia have been tested for the ABO blood groups, and over 6000 and 5000 respectively have been tested for the MN and Rh blood groups. Smaller numbers have been subjected to study for other blood group systems, but information is available for at least some of the known antigens belonging to the Lewis, P, Kell, Duffy, Lutheran, Diego, Sutter, Kidd, Wright, and Webb systems in addition to tests for the S and s antigens of the MNSs blood groups and variants in the Rh blood group system.

The available information for all blood group systems is summarized in Table 1. Where several independent investigations have been undertaken, or where several distinct groups have been sampled in one geographical region, the range of gene or phenotype frequencies is given.

(a) *The* ABO *blood groups.* Over the greater part of the continent only blood groups A_1 and O are present. The highest values of the blood group A gene are found in the desert areas south-west of Alice Springs and extending into Western Australia as far as Leonora. Values for gene *A* in this area range between 30 and 45 per cent. Peripheral to these desert areas the value of *A* falls, reaching values less than 25 per cent for almost the entire coastal area from Broome, in Western Australia, along the northern shores and down the east coast as far as New South Wales.

The *O* blood-group gene shows inverse variations in frequency to those shown by *A*, the highest values being found in coastal areas. The absolute highest value of *O*, 96 per cent, is found in

Aurukun in Cape York. Low values of O prevail throughout the desert areas.

Blood group B was detected in Aboriginal populations in Queensland in the earliest blood-group studies made in Australia. The presence of group B in Queensland has been confirmed in later investigations and the geographical limits for the spread of the B gene have been more precisely defined. The maximum frequency of the B gene of 14 per cent occurs at Mitchell River in Cape York, falling to a low value as one proceeds farther north. Recently, however, Simmons et al. (1962) found a highly aberrant population on Mornington Island in the Gulf of Carpentaria. Here only blood groups O and B are present, the value of B being 24 per cent. Simmons et al. (1964) have recently found a mainland group in the Barkly Tableland area where a similar high frequency of blood group B exists, and they suggest that this is the focus from which the B gene has spread in the Gulf of Carpentaria region.

(b) *The* MNSs *blood groups*. Australian Aborigines are characterized by the complete absence of the S antigen. Only two S-positive persons have been reported in over 3000 tests. One of these was thought to have been of mixed parentage, and the other was discounted since no repeat sample could be obtained.

More than 1400 persons from many parts of the continent have been tested with anti-s. All have been positive, so that no S—s— (U—) persons have been detected in Australia. No tests have been carried out, however, with specific anti-U sera from Negroes.

The blood-group N gene has a high frequency over the entire continent. With one exception the value of N exceeds 65 per cent and in the Western Desert area reaches a value of 95 per cent, and high values are found also in Cape York. But in both the desert areas and in Cape York values for N vary over a fairly wide range. For example $N = 70$ per cent at Hermannsburg and 100 per cent for a small sample of 56 persons at Cundeelee.

Variants of the M or N antigens have not been detected in Australia, possibly because they have not been looked for specifically. Simmons (1958) has tested thirty-four persons in Western Australia with anti-He. No Henshaw positive reactions were detected.

(c) *The* Rh *blood groups*. Four Rh genes, R_1, R_2, R_0, and R_Z, are present in all areas, but variations from region to region are marked. The frequency of R_1 ranges from 51 per cent at Cundeelee to 80 per cent at Mitchell River in Cape York. R_2 ranges from 6 per cent at Mitchell River to 44 per cent at Jigalong. In general R_1 values are low in desert areas, higher on the coast and tending to highest values in the north. The converse is true of R_2.

R_0 has a low value in most of the desert areas. It is zero at Jigalong and also at Yuendumu. In contrast R_z has its highest value in the desert areas but also has another focus of high frequency in Cape York, with highest values around the Mitchell River area.

No Rh-negative persons have been detected, although a number of persons failing to react with anti-D sera have been reported by Simmons both in Queensland and in Western Australia. Since such persons react with anti-C, Simmons considers that a fifth Rh gene, R', is also present in Australia. Vos and Kirk have found several persons in the Kimberley area of Western Australia who might be recorded as homozygous for the R' gene. They are, however, examples of an extreme form of D^u variant. The red cells from such persons fail to react with about 50 per cent of anti-D sera by the indirect antiglobulin reaction, but react normally with the remaining antisera. Careful testing with selected antisera has shown that similar cell types exist also in Cape York.

Recently Simmons (personal communication) has reported a single individual from La Grange in Western Australia whose cells consistently fail to be agglutinated in any test system with a battery of anti-D sera, but who is positive with anti-C and anti-e sera. Vos and Kirk have found a similar person at Sunday Island. These two persons suggest that the R' gene does occur, at least in this small area of north-west Australia, but that its frequency must be very low.

Variants of the Rh D antigen, both high grade and low grade D^u, occur in various parts of Australia.

A new variant of the E antigen was discovered by Vos and Kirk (1962) in the Western Desert area. The specific antibody reacted with all E-positive European bloods, but 35 per cent of Aborigines in the Western Desert who were E-positive failed to react with the new antibody. Surveys in other parts of Australia revealed that negative reactors were less frequent elsewhere, and in Cape York, where the frequency of E itself is low, only 1 per cent of E-positive samples failed to react.

Vos and Kirk suggested the term E^T for the antigen missing in the person who produced the antibody (anti-E^T). Recent work has shown that there is no relationship between E^T and E^u. Both variants exist in Aborigines. Nearly 100 samples from the Western Desert have been tested with anti-E^w. All were negative. Vos and Kirk have tested a large number of persons in Western Australia with anti-V. This antiserum reacts with 28 per cent of U.S. Negroes, in cases where the genes R_0 or r are present. Despite the presence of the R_0 gene among Aborigines, no positive reactor has been found.

The most remarkable phenomenon in the Rh blood-group system was the discovery by Vos, Vos, Kirk, and Sanger (1961) of red cells from a 37-year-old Aboriginal woman in the Western Desert which failed to react with all known Rh antisera. Tests on more than 500 persons belonging to the same population have failed to reveal anothere xample of Rh ---/---. Recently, Levine et al. (1964) have reported a person with similar blood in the United States.

(d) *Other blood group systems.* The phenotype frequencies for a number of other blood group systems are listed in Table 1. With the exception of the Lewis, P, Kell, and Duffy blood group results the figures are based on more limited series of observations. All of 272 persons were Lu (a—), all of 690 were Di (a—), and all of 124 and 36 were Js (a—) and Jk (a—) respectively.

More than 1300 persons have been tested with anti-K and anti-Fy^a. Hundred per cent were Fy(a)-positive and none were K-positive.† Among the 'private' antigens 93 persons have been tested with anti-Webb and 1019 with anti-Wr^a. All were negative.

No detailed and exhaustive studies of both the Lewis blood groups and of the secretion of ABH and Lewis blood group substances have been published for Australian Aborigines. In Table 1 the Le^a frequencies are based on a total of more than 3000 persons. The Le^a antigen is known to be labile, however, so that considerable uncertainty must be attached to the published figures.

Simmons et al. (1954) found 3 per cent of persons at Yuendumu to be non-secretors of ABH substances, whilst Vos and Kirk (unpublished) found 2 per cent non-secretors in Western Australia.

---

† Nicholls et al. (1965) report five Kell-positive individuals in Central Australia. Repeat tests on these persons have confirmed the original observations, and there is no indication of mixed blood parentage.

The P blood group system has been studied also with anti-P_1 sera. Frequencies of P_1 positive persons range from 18 to 73 per cent. The P_1 antigen is known also to be labile, and reactions are very variable, both between samples for the same anti-serum and between anti-sera for the same sample. The figures at present, therefore, should be interpreted with caution.

2. Blood-group surveys in New Guinea

The indigenous population of New Guinea approximates three million. Many of these persons have made contact with Europeans only within the last few decades, and there are areas in more inaccessible parts of the country where European contact is still virtually non-existent. The New Guinea population occupies a wide range of habitat. The lowland swampy coastal areas are hot and humid and malaria is holo-endemic. At the other extreme, two million people live in highland areas, often exceeding 5000 ft above sea level, with a more temperate climate and little or no malaria. Similar differences occur in the distribution of several other diseases.

(a) *The* ABO *blood groups.* Intensive blood grouping studies during the last two decades have provided observations covering the greater part of the Island. The most intensive investigations have occurred in the highland areas of the Australian Trust Territory, with less adequate coverage of the former Netherlands New Guinea and of Papua. These blood group studies have been summarized recently by Simmons *et al.* (1961).

Unlike Australia, blood groups A, B, and O are found in all populations in New Guinea. As is demonstrated by the range of gene frequencies in Table 2, based on a total of more than 16,000 persons, there is no consistent trend in the distribution of the ABO blood groups, and within any one area, where adequate sampling has occurred, significant differences in frequency between neighbouring linguistic groups, or even within a single linguistic group can be found.

The overall pattern is for the frequency of the blood group *A* gene to have values within the range of 10 to 30 per cent, for the frequency of the blood-group *B* gene to be within the range of 5 to 20 per cent, and with few exceptions to be lower than the frequency of *A* in the same population. The frequency of the *O* gene is moderately high, ranging from 50 to 80 per cent in most areas.

TABLE 2

Range of frequencies for various blood group systems in New Guinea.
The ABO, MNSs and Rh blood groups

Locality or population	Gene frequencies (per cent)										
	p	q	r	MS	Ms	NS	Ns	R_1	R_2	R_0	R_z
Coastal Gulf of Papua	18–25	11–20	62–67	0–5	4–23	8–10	71–86	95	2–4	1–2	0–2
Coastal Port Moresby area	10–13	16–18	69–72	0	18–24	6–9	70–73	86–94	6–14	0	0–0·1
Milne Bay	20	10	70	0	27	15	57	91	4	4	1
Bulolo Valley	27–32	16–17	51–57	0	10–16	10–12	72–80	87–94	4–13	0–2	0
Sepik River	20–45	4–26	41–66	0–6	3–18	6–17	70–75	81–94	4–15	0–4	0
Sarmi	27	12	61	0	28	0·5	71	95	4	1	0
Nimboran-Sentani-Sekori	19–30	8–10	60–72	0	3–11	0–2	87–97	80–96	4–12	0–8	0
Biak—Island of Schouten	10	12	78	0	27	4	69	93	6	1	0·3
Asmat	28–30	20–22	49–53	0	0–4	2–8	89–98	96–100	0·3–4	0–0·7	0
Coastal, near Merauke	18	9	73	0	6	10	84	88	8	1	2
Goloila	12	9	79	0	6	6	88	97	3	0·7	0
Kukukuku	14–34	2–13	60–74	0	8–10	4–8	83–86	76–85	7–21	3–7	0
Eastern Highlands†	11–32	5–22	50–77	0	1–15	0·4–11	82–97	85–98	4–12	0–8	0
Fore	29	10	61	0	3	5	93	93	4	3	0
Goroka‡	17–20	9–10	71–73	0–0·5	8–11	6–11	78–86	80–84	10–13	6–7	0
Chimbu	20–24	17–18	59–62	0–0·4	3	12–15	83–85	90	8	2–3	0
Western Highlands	15–37	7–22	56–70	0–6§	1–12	9–28	63–90	87–99	1–13	0–5	0
Telefolmin	20	10	70	0	4	1	95	87	6	7	0
Star Mountains	8	18	74	0	2	0	98	97	2	0·6	0·6
Djar, Mandobo, and Moejoe	7–19	5–12	73–83	0	4–6	10–28	64–85	86–95	3–10	2–9	0
Dani-Mulia	17–23	19–38	44–58	0	7–9	0	91–93	90–98	2–10	0–3	0
Wissel Lakes (Pygmies)	8	14	78	0	10	0·7	89	85	12	3	0
Enga	25	14	61	—	—	—	—	—	—	—	—

† Gimi, Keiagana, Kanite, Usurufa, Kamano, Auyana, Agarebi, Awa, Gadsup, Tairora, YarPavaian, Oiana.
‡ Mt. Hagen, Aiome, Chimbu to Mt. Hagen, Minji.
§ o except among fifty-four light-skinned natives.

The lowest A values, less than 10 per cent, are found in Netherlands New Guinea. The highest A frequency of 34 per cent has been recorded for one group of the Kukukuku sampled at Lae, but this extreme value is not found in other Kukukuku groups.

The blood group B achieves its highest frequency among the Dani-Mulia in the highlands of Netherlands New Guinea. Here gene B has a value of 38 per cent. This is in contrast to low values for B of 2 to 7 per cent in several linguistic groups of the Eastern Highlands.

The A group throughout New Guinea, with the exception of one family, belongs to subgroup A_1, and is similar to the A group of Australia and elsewhere in Oceania in this respect. In a recent report Simmons *et al.* (1961) record finding blood group A_2 in a father and three children of a family belonging to the Agarabi linguistic group of the Eastern Highlands. They believe this represents a recent mutation.

(b) *The* MNSs *blood groups.* In striking contrast to Australia, the S antigen is present in New Guinea, though frequently in low frequency. Among the Dani, in the Star Mountains and among the Nimboran and Sekori of Netherlands New Guinea there are population groups containing no S-positive individuals.

The frequency of S-positive persons in other parts of New Guinea varies widely. The highest value of 50 per cent occurs at Mandobo in Netherlands New Guinea, followed by 41 per cent among the Enga and a value of 37 per cent in the Western Highlands, and 35 per cent for Chimbu. These figures suggest a high focus for S in the centre of the Island with lower values peripherally, the general trend being subject to the marked fluctuations characteristic of gene frequencies in New Guinea.

New Guinea as a whole is characterized by extremely high values for the N blood-group gene. Its frequency ranges upwards from 70 per cent. In many areas, particularly in the Highlands, it exceeds 95 per cent, though similar high values have been reported from Daru Island and some areas bordering the Gulf of Papua. The lowest values of N are found on the Islands of Schouten, in northern Netherlands New Guinea, and also along the Gulf of Papua, east of the area of high N values.

(c) *The* Rh *blood-groups.* The Rh blood-group situation is even simpler than in Australia, with the three genes R_1, R_2, and R_0

satisfying the requirements for equilibrium in nearly all popu-lations. R_Z, which achieves relatively high values in parts of Australia, is found only in the coastal area in the western half of the Gulf of Papua, including Daru Island, and extending to the vicinity of Merauke, and in the Star Mountains area and on Biak, Isles of Schouten. Simmons et al. (1946) believe that the presence of R_Z on Daru Island and in neighbouring coastal areas is a result of Australian Aboriginal influence. Nijenhuis (1961b) doubts if the frequency of R_Z found in the south coastal area can be due solely to race mixing, and suggests that selective factors have been operative also.

R_O which is found, with two exceptions, throughout Australia has low frequencies in New Guinea, and is completely absent in some populations. In contrast, however, to R_Z some of the highest frequencies for R_O, ranging from 5 to 9 per cent, are found among Highland groups.

Throughout New Guinea the gene R_1 exceeds 85 per cent, with few exceptions, and in many populations it has a value around 95 per cent. R_2 generally ranges between 5 and 15 per cent. The frequencies for R_1 are among the highest in the world, though paralleled by the values for R_1 in a number of other Melanesian populations, and parts of Australia.

D^u variants appear to be highly localized. A small number have been found restricted to the Gadsup linguistic group in the Eastern Highlands (Watson et al., 1961; Simmons et al., 1961) and others have been reported from the Sentani and Nimboran groups in northern Netherlands New Guinea (de Vries and Nijenhuis, 1960; Nijenhuis and de Vries, 1962).

Elsewhere tests for both 'low-grade' and 'high-grade' D^u variants have failed to reveal their presence. E^u variants have been reported by Nijenhuis in Netherlands New Guinea, but have not been specifically sought elsewhere. A limited number of tests for C^w variants have been uniformly negative, and a small number of tests by Simmons et al. (1961) with anti-V have also been negative.

(d) *Other blood-group systems.* Table 3 records the range of phenotype frequencies for an additional nine blood group antigens. Most of these figures are based on a limited series of observations, but certain generalizations are permissible. The Fy^a antigen is present in all persons tested. The exceptional figure of 90 per cent $Fy(a+)$ persons among the Wissel Lakes pygmies is unreliable:

TABLE 3

Phenotype frequencies (per cent) for other blood group systems in New Guinea

Locality or population	P_1	Le(a+)	(LeB+)	Fy(a+)	K+	Lu(a+)	JK(a+)	Di(a+)	Js(a+)
Eastern Highlands	37	0	82	100	0	0	86	0	0
Fore	41	0	90	100	0	—	85	0	0
Goroka	57	0	—	100	2	—	—	—	—
Western Highlands	57	0	—	100	1	—	—	—	—
Asmat	58	—	—	100	—	—	—	—	—
Nimboran-Sentani-Sekori	49–66	3	—	100	0	—	—	0	—
Dani-Mulia	50	0	—	100	0	0	—	0	—
Wissel Lakes (Pygmies)	63	—	—	90†	—	—	—	—	—
Biak—Island of Schouten	43	—	—	100	0·6	0	—	—	—
Enga	43	0	59	100	0	0	92	0	0

† Tested after 6–9 months.

TABLE 4

Range of gene frequencies for serum protein groups by geographical region in Australia

Locality	Hp^1	Tf^D	Tf^B	Gc^1	Gc^{Ab}	Gm^a	Gm^{ax}	Gm^{ab}	$Inv(a+)$
Cape York	10–21	2–11	6	72–90	2–7	62–85	14–34	0–5	39–61
North Australia	—	—	—	87	2	—	—	—	—
Central Australia	13–29	5–10	0	86–94	1–5	62–70	29–37	0–1	37–47
Western Desert	15	20	0	92–98	0–1	73	27	0	49
Kimberleys	22–32	7–15	0	81–90	1	58	25	17	45
Western Central	25–39	10–16	0	91–93	2–3	—	—	—	—

the tests were carried out after the cells had been stored 6–9 months in a glucose-citrate solution. A few Kell positive persons have been reported in some surveys and these observations should be repeated. Elsewhere 100 per cent of all persons tested are negative with anti-K. Similarly no positive reactions have been reported with anti-Lu^a, anti-Js^a, and anti-Di^a. In the latter case Buettner-Janusch *et al.* (1960) found two Di(a+) persons among the Kapauke people of the highlands of Netherlands New Guinea. Several other anomalous results were present in the same report, and the observations on these people should be repeated. The P$_1$ frequency is remarkably uniform with a value around 50 ± 10 per cent for all those areas investigated. Another system which merits attention is the Kidd blood group system. Simmons *et al.* (1961) have tested 176 persons with anti-Jk^a and found nearly 90 per cent positive. Tests for the 'private' blood group antigen Wr^a as also for the Gr and Mg antigens were uniformly negative.

The Le^a antigen appears to be virtually absent. Simmons *et al.* (1961) found only one Le(a+) person in 740 tested from many parts of New Guinea, but in previous studies no Le(a+) persons were found. Nijenhuis (1961) found three Le(a+) persons in the Muyu and Star Mountain districts. A smaller number of persons have been tested for the presence of ABH substances in saliva: all were secretors.

Tests with anti-Le^b show variations in frequency from 59 per cent of Le(b+) in a small sample of Enga, to 90 per cent Le(b+) among the Fore. The difficulties of accurate Le^b typing under conditions of collection in the field and transportation to base laboratories are so great that at present the results must be treated with caution.

3. *Serum protein group surveys in Australia*

Studies of the distribution of the various serum protein group systems are not as extensive as for blood group systems. However, during the last five years Kirk's laboratory in Perth and that of Bennett in Adelaide have accumulated data for Aborigines from most parts of the continent.

(a) *Haptoglobin groups*. Three haptoglobin groups, Hp 1–1, Hp 2–1, and Hp 2–2 are found in all populations, and these are controlled by a pair of codominant alleles, *Hp*^{1} and *Hp*^{2}. A small percentage of persons are difficult to classify because of low haptoglobin concentration in the serum. These persons are referred to an ahaptoglobinemic, or more correctly hypohaptoglobinemic (Hp O). In African populations the proportion of Hp O persons may be as high as 30 per cent, and in African populations Hp O is associated with a high frequency of another haptoglobin phenotype, Hp 2–1 M. Elsewhere in the world examples of Hp 2–1 M are sporadic, as also is another rare phenotype, the 'Johnson' haptoglobin type.

The range of Hp^1 gene frequency in Australia is recorded in Table 4. Low values prevail in Cape York and in the Western Desert, with higher values peripherally. The highest value for Hp^1 is 39 per cent for a small group of 58 persons sampled at Nullagine in Western Australia, with a value of 32 per cent for 127 persons in the north Kimberleys.

Hp O frequencies are low, the highest mean frequency of 2 per cent occurring in Cape York. Elsewhere the frequency of Hp O ranges from zero to 3·6 per cent at Papunya in central Australia, with a mean frequency of approximately 1 per cent. No Hp 2–1M phenotypes have been found so far in Australia, but two examples of the 'Johnson' type have been reported at Papunya in central Australia (Nicholls *et al.*, 1965).

Only one study has been made of the distribution in Australia of the two subtypes of the Hp^1 gene, Hp^{1F}, and Hp^{1S} (Connell, Dixon, and Smithies, 1962). In north Queensland, Flory (1964) found two persons out of 102 with the Hp^{1F} gene, giving a total frequency of 1 per cent for Hp^{1F} in the whole sample. Further study of the distribution of Hp^{1F} and Hp^{1S} is needed.

(b) *Transferrins.* More than 2600 sera from Aborigines have been examined for transferrin type using starch gel electrophoresis. The range of frequencies for the genes controlling rarer transferrin phenotypes is given in Table 4. At the present time seventeen different human transferrin variants have been described. Fourteen of these have been summarized by Parker and Bearn (1962), the fifteenth, B_{Lae}, was observed in a single pedigree in New Guinea (Lai, 1963), the sixteenth, D_{Wigan}, in an English family (Robson *et al.*, 1964) and the seventeenth, $D_{Adelaide}$, in an Irish-Italian family in South Australia (Cooper *et al.*, 1964). Transferrin C is the commonest variant and is found in all populations. Variants with an electrophoretic mobility lower than transferrin C are called D variants; those with a mobility higher than transferrin C are called B variants. The current hypothesis is that all transferrin variants are under the control of codominant alleles at a single locus.

In Australia, the most striking fact is the presence of a slow-moving D transferrin, either in CD or DD combination, in all populations studied.

In Western Australia the frequency of the Tf^D gene is relatively high, ranging from 7 per cent at Kulumburu to 20 per cent in the Western Desert. Lower values prevail in Cape York where the mean Tf^D frequency is 6 per cent. A recent critical study (Kirk *et al.*, 1964) has failed to reveal any difference between the D transferrin in Australia and the D transferrin in New Guinea, or between either of these and the D_1 transferrin present in African Negroes. The Australian D variant, however, is detectably different from the D_{Chi} characteristic of the Mongoloid populations of South-East Asia.

Another transferrin variant has been found in one group at Edward River in Cape York (Kirk *et al.*, 1962). This is a B variant with a mobility intermediate between that of B_1 and B_2. It is not yet certain whether this corresponds to the B_{1-2} variant found in serum from a Venezuelan Indian (Arends *et al.*, 1962). Flory (1964) has reported also one sample with a B variant in a series from north Queensland.

(c) *The Gc groups.* Using the technique of immuno-electrophoresis in agar gels, Hirshfeld (1959) demonstrated a further polymorphism in human serum proteins, an α_2-globulin. Three phenotypes are present in all populations studied, Gc 1–1, the fastest moving component which gives a single smooth precipitin arc, Gc 2–2, the slowest moving component which gives also a single smooth precipitin arc, and Gc 2–1 which gives an extended precipitin arc with two components corresponding to the slower and faster arcs. These variations are controlled by a pair of codominant alleles, Gc^1 and Gc^2.

Recently other alleles have been described which appear to be restricted to specific populations. One of these, $Gc^{Chippewa}$, has been found only in Chippewa Indians, the other $Gc^{Aborigine}$, has been found so far only in populations in Australia and New Guinea (Cleve *et al.*, 1963).

The Gc^1 allele has a high frequency (Table 4) in all areas, exceeding 80 per cent except in Cape York. Here values lie between 70 and 80 per cent, except for one small sample at Weipa, with a value of 90 per cent. The Gc^{Ab} allele has its highest frequency in

Cape York (4 per cent) and with the exception of one group in central Australia, average values for Gc^{Ab} are in the range 1–2 per cent. In the Western Desert, however, the allele has disappeared almost completely.

(d) *The gamma globulin groups.* Two major non-allelic systems occur in the gamma-globulin groups, the so-called Gm and Inv systems. Both sets of phenotypes are demonstrated by an agglutination inhibition reaction. The phenotypes demonstrated in this way depend on several Gm alleles and a pair of Inv alleles, Inv^a and Inv^b. The main Gm alleles postulated at present are Gm^a, Gm^{ax}, Gm^b, Gm^c, and Gm^{ab}. Other alleles in the Gm system such as Gm^r have been incompletely studied as genetic markers in human populations.

Table 4 summarizes the gene frequency ranges for the Gm alleles and for the Inv(a) phenotype in Australia. In the desert areas of the centre only two alleles appear to be present, Gm^a and Gm^{ax}. The absence of Gm(b) in the Western Desert and in central Australia, confirmed in over 600 persons tested, is a unique property of these populations.† (In Cape York the frequency of Gm^{ab} is also low, ranging from zero to 5 per cent.) This result is in striking contrast to the 17 per cent frequency for the Gm^{ab} allele in the Kimberleys. It is of interest that Neel *et al.* (1964) have reported the absence of Gm(b) reactions in a small sample of Xavante Indians in Brazil.

The Gm(x) phenotype varies widely in frequency. It is lowest at Mitchell River (19 per cent) and highest at Papunya in central Australia (16 per cent). Gm(c) is absent in Australia. Inv(a) frequencies are relatively stable. In the Western Desert Inv(a+) is 49 per cent, in the Kimberleys 45 per cent, in Cape York values range between 32 and 61 per cent, and in central Australia between 37 and 47 per cent.

(e) *The Ag system.* Allison and Blumberg (1961) found that the sera of certain persons who have received a large number of blood transfusions can be used to discriminate two serum phenotypes in the population, those whose serum gives a precipitin reaction against the test serum on an agar diffusion plate, and those who do not. The system is called the Ag system, and those reacting are said to be Ag+ve.

† Nicholls *et al.* (1955) report the presence of two Gm(b+) individuals in central Australia.

Blumberg *et al.* (1962) found almost identical frequencies of Ag(+) persons among Whites and Negroes in the U.S. (54 and 55 per cent respectively). Allison and Blumberg had shown originally that for a small group of Micronesians the Ag(+) frequency was 98 per cent. No study on the Ag system for Australian Aborigines has been published so far. Blumberg has tested a number of sera from several localities and his results, which he has kindly made available, show a frequency of Ag(+) persons intermediate between that of U.S. Whites and Negroes and Micronesians. Approximately 84 per cent of Aborigines in Western Australia and central Australia are Ag(+). More extensive work using precipitin systems is under way.

(f) *Other systems.* There has been little or no study in Australia or New Guinea of several other recently discovered polymorphic systems. These include atypical pseudo-cholinesterase types, electrophoretic variants of serum cholinesterase, and serum alkaline phosphatase, red-cell esterase, and acid phosphatase variants, red-cell phosphogluconate dehydrogenase variants, and the Lp lipoprotein system. Our own laboratory in Perth is working with some of these systems, but results obtained so far are of a preliminary nature only. Horsfall *et al.* (1963) found no C_5 or atypical esterase variants among 104 samples from Queensland. Kirk (unpublished) has found less than 1 per cent C_5 esterase variants among Aborigines in Western Australia.

4. *Serum protein group surveys in New Guinea*

The amount of information on serum protein group distribution in New Guinea is still severely limited, and is confined almost entirely to haptoglobin and transferrin types. Haptoglobin and transferrin groups were studied by Curtain (1959), and Curtain *et al.* (1961) studied haptoglobin group distribution for a small series; Barnicot and Kariks (1960) gave both haptoglobin and transferrin results for several hundred persons in the highlands, and for a small group of coastal Papuans. Bennett *et al.* (1961) gave the same information for a small group belonging to the Fore linguistic group in the Eastern Highlands, and Lai (1962) gave haptoglobin and transferrin frequencies for small groups from a number of places. The only extensive study is that of Curtain *et al.* (1965). I am indebted to Dr. Curtain and his collaborators for making this information available before publication.

(a) *Haptoglobin groups.* The range of the haptoglobin gene Hp^1 frequencies given in Table 5 indicate that for all populations in New Guinea the Hp^1 frequencies are among the highest in the world. There is considerable overlap between Hp^1 frequencies in lowland and highland populations, but lowland populations on the average have higher Hp^1 frequencies, and in addition have a greater percentage of persons with no detectable haptoglobin by qualitative starch-gel techniques. Indeed, with one exception the highland groups have no, or a very small proportion of Hp O persons. The exception is a group of Chimbu sampled by Barnicot and Kariks (1960) who are recorded as having 23 per cent Hp O phenotypes. This area should certainly be resampled.

In the detailed study of Curtain et al. (1964) the Hp^1 frequency for the Eastern Highland populations is significantly lower, at the 1 per cent level, than the Hp^1 frequency in the Markham or Sepik River valleys. In the same study, no Hp O persons were found in nearly 1000 samples from highland areas, though Hp O frequency ranged from 2 to 13 per cent in the Markham and Sepik River valleys for nearly 900 samples.

The Hp 2-1M phenotype has a low frequency in New Guinea. Barnicot and Kariks (1960) found only one case in over 500 samples and Curtain et al. (1965) found only two cases in nearly 2000 samples. No 'Johnson' type haptoglobins have been reported.

TABLE 5
Range of frequencies for various genetic markers in New Guinea

Locality	Hp O (per cent)	Hp^1 (per cent)	Tf^D (per cent)	High HbA_2 (per cent)[†]	G-6-PD deficiency per cent (males)
Sepik River	4	70–76	12–14	0–25	1–8
Markham River	2–13	69–82	11–14	1–8	1–28
Eastern Highlands[‡]	0	59–71	6–14[§]	0	0–5
Eastern Highlands[¶]	0–23	53–72	6–11		
Southern Highlands	0	64–70	6–14	—	—
Western Highlands	0	75	14	2	—

† Exceeding 4 per cent of total Hb.
‡ Curtain et al. (1964).
§ Includes 1 transferrin BC out of 705.
¶ Barnicot and Kariks (1960).

(b) *The transferrin groups.* A slow moving transferrin variant is present in all New Guinea populations, and the Tf^D gene frequency (Table 5) is between 6 and 14 per cent. Kirk *et al.* (1964) have been unable to distinguish the New Guinea variant from the D variant in Australian Aborigines or from the D_1 variant of African Negroes.

Lai (1963) described a new transferrin variant, B_{Lae}, present in the serum of a person from a village near Lae. Curtain *et al.* (1965) have found two persons with this variant in the Bukawa linguistic population in the Markham River valley, and one further example in the Yagwoi of the Eastern Highlands. The same authors have found B_{Lae} in persons belonging to four linguistic groups in New Britain. They suggest that the existence of B_{Lae} in the Tolai people of New Britain suggests a link between these and the people of the Markham River valley, a suggestion which should be followed up with more detailed anthropological studies.

(c) and (d) *Gc and gamma globulin groups.* Information available at present on the distribution of phenotypes belonging to other serum protein group systems is extremely limited. The Gm and Inv groups have not been studied at all, and the only published investigation of the Gc groups has been by Kirk *et al.* (1963) for a small sample of forty-five persons from various places in New Guinea.

This study, which is of limited value because of the small number of persons examined suggests that the Gc^2 frequency (28 per cent) may be somewhat higher in New Guinea than in Australia (2–28 per cent). But it may be of significance that the highest value in Australia is in Cape York.

Of even greater interest is the fact that the small New Guinea series contained seven persons carrying the $Gc^{Aborigine}$ gene, two of these in homozygous form. New Guinea together with Australia and the New Hebrides therefore constitute the only places in the world so far where this particular gene has been detected.

Further examples of the Gc^{Ab} gene have been detected in an extensive survey of Gc groups in both lowland and highland groups carried out by Curtain and Baumgarten. Curtain (personal communication) reports a wide range of frequency for the Gc^1 allele ranging from 55 to 100 per cent.

Curtain (personal communication) has examined also nearly 2000 sera from various places in New Guinea for atypical cholinesterase variants. The frequency of heterozygotes varies from just under 1 per cent to 4 per cent. No case of a homozygous recessive person was detected.

No studies of the distribution of the Ag types have been published for New Guinea, nor of the more recently discovered polymorphisms mentioned in the section on Australia.

B. DISEASE AS A SELECTIVE AGENT

Since the discovery of the genetic basis of the haemoglobinopathies (Neel, 1949) and the selective advantage conferred on individuals in malarious areas by some of the genes controlling these (Allison, 1954) intensive surveys for the presence of sickling phenomena or abnormal haemoglobins have been made in many parts of the world. Linked with these have been studies of the distribution of thalassaemia, and more recently of deficiency of the red cell enzyme, glucose-6-phosphate dehydrogenase. Deficiency of this enzyme occurs in persons in many parts of the world, and is under the control of a sex-linked gene. Evidence is accumulating that the incidence of G-6-PD deficiency also is closely related to the endemicity of falciparum malaria (Motulsky, 1963).

Horsfall and Lehmann (1953) and Simmons (1958) found no case of sickling in 57 and 230 Aborigines respectively in Queensland and Western Australia. Horsfall and Lehmann (1956) examined a further 148 Aborigines from north Queensland by paper electrophoresis and found no evidence of abnormal haemoglobins. Similar negative results were obtained by Budtz-Olsen (1958) in Queensland and central Australia, and he also found no evidence of abnormally increased concentration of haemoglobin A_2. The latter is frequently taken as an indicator of thalassaemia. No reports of the presence of target cells in blood films made from Aborigines have been published, and the evidence to date suggests the complete absence of abnormal haemoglobins and thalassaemia in Australia.

There is also no evidence for the existence of G-6-PD deficiency in Australia. Budtz-Olsen and Kidson (1961) using a rapid screening method tested 435 males and 287 females without finding a single deficient person.

In contrast to Australia, haemoglobin variants, thalassaemia, and G-6-PD deficiency are present in New Guinea.

Initially, the search for haemoglobin variants or sickling produced negative results. Swindler (1955) examined for the sickling phenomenon blood films from persons in New Britain, and a very small number from New Guinea, without finding a single positive. Walsh and Cotter (1955) similarly obtained negative results in 161 specimens from Port Moresby and 280 from Chimbu in the Highlands. Simmons *et al.* (1961) tested 50 samples, likewise with negative results.

More recently, extensive surveys using electrophoretic methods have revealed the presence of haemoglobinopathies other than the sickle-cell anomaly. Ryan, Campbell, and Brain (1961) described a case of haemoglobin H disease from Kerema, and Neeb *et al.* (1961) reported Hb_{Lepore} from Hollandia in Netherlands New Guinea. Curtain *et al.* (1962) found a further case of Hb_{Lepore} in 354 persons of the Sause linguistic group in the Sepik River district. In the same paper the authors report finding an example of Hb E in a small group of samples from hospital patients in Port Moresby.

Despite these reports, it is clear that the frequency of abnormal haemoglobins is very low, even among coastal populations in New Guinea, with a frequency considerably less than 1 per cent. On the other hand, the evidence suggests that thalassaemia is more prevalent. Ryan (1961) reported the first clinically diagnosed case of thalassaemia and Ryan (1962) lists four cases of thalassaemia minor, in addition to the previously reported case of thalassaemia intermedia and of Haemoglobin H disease. Ryan (1963) has described three cases of chronic anaemia associated with bony changes suggestive of haemolytic anaemia.

Curtain and his colleagues (Curtain *et al.*, 1962) have surveyed the incidence of persons with elevated Hb A_2 fractions. An Hb A_2 fraction exceeding 4 per cent of the total Hb was taken as indicative of thalassaemia trait. No such cases were found among 238 Eastern Highlanders, but there were 2 out of 95 Western Highlanders (Enga) with elevated Hb A_2 levels. In the Sepik River valley district various villages within the Sause linguistic group showed variations from 0 to 25 per cent; in a smaller sample of the Abelam linguistic group in the Sepik River valley elevated Hb A_2 levels ranged from 1 to 8 per cent, the lower values occurring at the higher altitudes.

The incidence of G-6-PD deficiency varies even more widely than that of elevated Hb A_2 levels. Kidson (1961) found less than 1 per cent of 383 males in the Eastern Highlands were deficient, but in small samples from coastal areas the figures suggested higher values. This was borne out by Parsons and Ryan (1962) and by more extensive studies by Gorman and Kidson (1962). In the latter investigation the frequency of G-6-PD deficiency among males ranged from 3 to 29 per cent in the Markham River valley; it was 1 per cent in the Sause linguistic group of the Sepik River valley, although it was absent in many of the villages sampled, and it was 8 per cent among a much smaller sample of the Abelam linguistic group.

In the Eastern Highlands 1 per cent of males were deficient among the Tairora, 5 per cent among the Auyana and zero among the Gadsup, Awa, Kukukuku, Yate, and the north and south Fore. Small samples in West New Guinea gave frequencies of 0, 8, and 17 at Mulia, Merauke, and Asmat respectively.

The pattern of distribution of G-6-PD deficiency in New Guinea is of great interest in relation to the hypothesis that it is maintained by selection in populations where falciparum malaria is endemic. Malaria is holo-endemic in the coastal areas of New Guinea, decreasing in frequency with altitude and is generally absent in the highlands above 5000 feet. Occasional outbreaks of malaria occur among some highland populations, as in the case of the Enga in the Western Highlands.

Gorman and Kidson (1962) point out that a high incidence of G-6-PD deficiency may occur in coastal populations, but that high frequencies have not so far been observed in the highlands. Kidson and Gorman (1962a) show that in the Markham River valley there is a close correlation between altitude and decreasing G-6-PD deficiency, as one might expect on the basis of the malaria hypothesis. However, the authors point out that there are many exceptions to the generalization that a high frequency G-6-PD deficiency occurs in populations with a high incidence of malaria. The most striking case of this is among the Sause in the Sepik River district. Here only 3 out of 324 males tested were deficient, though these people live in a holo-endemic area. These authors question the validity of the malaria selection theory in relation to G-6-PD deficiency. They point out that the existence of a very large gene pool in populations around Lae, where the incidence of the deficiency among males approximates 30 per cent, may have resulted in slow diffusion of the trait along the Markham River valley among other linguistic groups, with dilution of the gene related roughly to distance. In this case, geographic distance along the valley would be correlated also with altitude.

It is of interest to note also that in the Eastern Highlands, G-6-PD deficiency has been found in two linguistic groups only, but that these two groups are not only adjacent geographically but also closely related linguistically. Kidson and Gorman point out that their data provides further evidence of the marked genetic heterogeneity of the Melanesian population in New Guinea.

One final aspect of the G-6-PD polymorphism is of genetic interest. Marks and Gross (1959) found two distinct types of G-6-PD deficiency. In one, characteristic of Negro populations, the enzyme activity of deficient males was 10–20 per cent of normal, whereas in the other, found in Caucasian populations, the activity was zero to 1 per cent of normal.

Parsons and Ryan (1962) found evidence to suggest that the two different forms of G-6-PD deficiency were present in New Guinea. Kidson and Gorman (1962b), however, found that the deficient males in New Guinea were all of the 'low' enzyme level type, and they suggest that the mutant gene in New Guinea may give rise to some kind of G-6-PD deficiency as in Caucasian populations. They point out, however, that the finding of a similar G-6-PD deficiency trait in two populations does not mean necessarily that this is proof that the gene spread in these populations from a single gene pool.

Kidson and Gorman believe that the higher enzyme levels reported in some New Guinea people by Parsons and Ryan may have been an artifact due to the presence of markedly anaemic patients among their 'deficient' series. It is known that during periods of acute haemolysis enzyme levels in deficient persons may rise due to the presence of young red cells, with higher G-6-PD content. It must be noted that Parsons and Ryan studied populations from areas not sampled by Kidson and Gorman, and, further, the latter authors must certainly have assayed blood from anaemic persons in their own studies. More detailed study of the different forms of G-6-PD deficiency in New Guinea including detailed analysis of the various electro-phoretic forms, is needed.

In addition to studies on the distribution of Hb variants, elevated Hb A_2 values, and of G-6-PD deficiency, the possibility exists that other genetic polymorphisms are held in balance by selective mechanisms involving common diseases. The haptoglobin and transferrin polymorphisms clearly are candidates for studies of this kind.

Quantitative serum haptoglobin determinations revealed significantly lower values in the lowland areas when compared with highland areas. Curtain and his colleagues suggest that the lowered serum haptoglobin levels and increased frequency of Hp O persons may be due to the removal of haptoglobin during intravascular haemolysis, for which malaria may be a major cause in the lowland areas of the Sepik and Markham River valleys. Lowering of haptoglobin levels will tend to increase the apparent frequency of Hp^1, which would explain the increased frequency of this gene in the lowlands compared with the highlands.

Another possibility discussed by the same authors is that there is a selective pressure favouring the Hp^1 gene in lowland areas. They state 'since sera of type 1–1 and type 2–1 individuals appear to bind more haemoglobin per 100 ml than does those of type 2–2, this could place the latter at a disadvantage in the maintenance of the delicate iron balance in the presence of haemolysis, intestinal iron loss due to parasitic infestation and dietary iron deficiency'. They point out, however, that although it is tempting to implicate malaria as a selective agent, more information is required on the possible role of factors such as filariasis, which is holo-endemic in the lowland areas, and on arbo-viruses, some of which are known to occur in lowland but not in highland populations, as well as the influence of social factors which may affect the distribution of haptoglobin genes.

In contrast to the Hp^1 gene frequencies, there is no marked difference in the distribution of the transferrin genes between highland and lowland populations, and the New Guinea area as a whole is one of relatively high frequency for a transferrin variant.

Curtain et al. (1964) have determined the total iron-binding capacity of the serum for all individuals studied, and they consider that this is a measure of transferrin level. They find no significant difference in iron-binding capacity between the various geographic or linguistic groups included in their survey, or between the sexes or various age groups. The serum iron levels, however, are significantly lower in lowland than in highland areas, and also significantly lower in the 0- to 10-year age group in males compared with the 11 to 20 and older age groups. Female values of course are lower in the older age groups.

C. SPECIFIC DISEASE SYNDROMES

In 1957 Zigas and Gajdusek described a new syndrome known as Kuru or 'trembling' disease which occurs with high frequency in parts of the Eastern Highlands of New Guinea. A number of characteristics of the disease have made it of extreme interest for students of population genetics, which in turn has resulted in intensive anthropological and epidemiological investigations throughout the entire region. Progress in the study of the disease has been reviewed by Bennett (1961) and Gajdusek (1961, 1963).

Kuru is restricted to persons belonging to the cultural and linguistic group known as Fore, or to a limited number of adjacent linguistic groups related to the Fore through intermarriage. Isolated cases elsewhere in New Guinea outside the Fore area have occurred always in Kuru region natives working away from home.

The disease accounts for the death of about 1 per cent of the population annually within the entire Kuru region, embracing a population of more than 35,000. There is an uneven spread of the disease throughout the region, however, so that in some small villages the annual death rate due to Kuru may be as high as 10 per cent.

Kuru mainly affects mature females, but about one-fourth of all cases occurs in children of both sexes. Adult males are rarely affected.

So far more than 1000 patients with the disease have been seen. It is an acute, degenerative disease of the central nervous system, which progresses rapidly after onset, and death ensues generally within one year. Recovery after the neurological signs have become established is rare.

Extensive and detailed studies of possible infectious or toxic factors in the environment have yielded no clue to the aetiology of Kuru. However, the restriction of the disease to one linguistic group and some of its immediate neighbours suggested to Zigas and Gajdusek in their initial investigation that genetic predisposing factors may be involved. Following this suggestion, Bennett, Rhodes, and Robson (1958, 1959) showed that there was a family pattern in the distribution of the disease which was consistent with a single gene model.

The striking difference in the sex and age incidence of the disease was accounted for by Bennett and his colleagues by the following hypothesis. Kuru is under the control of a single autosomal gene K, dominant to its allelomorph k in females and recessive in males; females of the genotype KK are potential victims of late onset, and of genotype Kk of early onset. Only males of genotype KK are potential victims, and these cases will be of the early onset type.

More detailed studies of the epidemiological and family pattern of the disease have been carried out by both Gajdusek and his collaborators and by Bennett and his colleagues. Gajdusek (1963) reviewing progress to that date, points out that the very high incidence of the disease in some of the South Fore villages raises serious doubts 'as to the possibility of a genetically determined lethal trait reaching such staggering frequency in a population where homozygous individuals are lost before reproductive age and heterozygous carriers, at least females, die earlier than their non-carrier age mates. The situation would seem to demand a remarkable genetic advantage associated with the Kuru trait, and the mechanism of random gene drift, as discussed by Sewell Wright, would be required to have played a very improbably intense role'.

Bennett (1962) referring to his own genetic hypothesis also indicates that Kuru could be maintained with high frequency only if there was a considerable selective advantage associated with the Kuru gene, but he adds that no such advantage has yet been demonstrated. He concludes 'from some points of view, then, the suggested possible genetic basis for Kuru appears rather improbable. But whatever the cause of this disease, there must surely be environmental factors playing a key role in its occurrence . . . environmental agents, maternal habits, and temporal variation in Kuru prevalence are some of the factors which may contribute to the family pattern and about whose role further information must be sought in the field'. In a detailed epidemiological study, McArthur (1964) also questions seriously the simple genetic model outlined above.

The possibility of the existence in New Guinea of other highly localized disease syndromes with genetic implications has been made clear by further survey work of Gajdusek and his collaborators. Wilson et al. (1959) described three cases of tremor syndromes in the Western Highlands of Australian New Guinea with similarities to Kuru, which they considered may be either new diseases or clinical variants of Kuru. More recently Gajdusek (1963) has found another motor-neuron disease, similar to amyotrophic lateral sclerosis with a focus of high incidence in the Jaqai and Awju linguistic groups on the coastal plain north-west of Merauke. Finally, Gajdusek (1962) has described among the Dani-speaking population of the Mulia region a highland group with a very high incidence of goitre and associated disorders among the females. In some villages the frequency of goitre among the females reaches 100 per cent. Central nervous system defects in this population range from slight mental subnormality to severe feeble-mindedness, often associated with deafness or deaf-mutism. Gajdusek points out that this population offers unique opportunities for studying the genetic and environmental factors involved in the pathogenesis of these disorders.

As a larger number of persons in New Guinea comes under adequate medical surveillance further instances of specific diseases with genetic backgrounds are likely to come to light.

D. REASSESSMENT

Early studies of the distribution of genetic markers in both Australia and New Guinea were concerned with the problem of racial classification and relationships. In common with investigators in many parts of the world the early worker believed that the genetic 'profile' of a population provided by the frequencies of genetic markers for a random sample of persons belonging to that population would provide information on its degree of identity as a separate race, sub-race, or caste, depending on the level of classification involved. The theoretical basis for such an assumption is the application of the Hardy-Weinberg equilibrium in large pan-mictic populations for genes not subject to selection. Under these restrictions, gene frequencies will remain stable in succeeding generations, and the problem of the origin of the different genetic profiles will be lost in the shades of the past.

The relatively recent discovery that certain genetic markers, such as the gene controlling the production of haemoglobin S, are subject to intensive selection has introduced a new concept. Mutations in the cistrons controlling the production of the α, β, γ, or δ haemoglobin polypeptides are random acts, relatively unlikely to occur in the same triplet, survive and become selected in two different populations. The existence of the same abnormal haemoglobin in two different populations, therefore, may be taken as strongly suggestive evidence of a genetic affinity between these two groups of people. The converse is not true necessarily, unless one equates the environment of the respective groups over a long period of time.

This argument can be extended to include certain other specific genetic markers for which there is, as yet, no evidence of selective advantage or disadvantage for the gene concerned. Examples of such markers are the transferrin and Gc variants and blood group antigens of localized distribution such as Di^a, Js^a, and He.

It is time to reassess the value of these concepts in current anthropological study. The wealth of detailed information on the distribution of genetic markers among the indigenous peoples of Australia and New Guinea helps to make such a reassessment possible.

Whatever the origin of the Australian Aborigines or the New Guinea Melanesians, and there is no dearth of speculation on this subject, their populations have become subdivided into small relatively non-interbreeding groups. This is attested to not only by the multiplicity of languages and dialects—several hundred in both Australia and New Guinea—but by the striking differences in the frequencies of genetic markers between many of these groups.

In some cases these groups have remained almost completely isolated from one another biologically. In Australia, for example, the existence of a whole complex of tribes in the Central and Western Desert areas without the Gm^b allele, or conversely the existence elsewhere in Australia of tribes with the Gm^b allele present in moderately high frequency, suggests that the rate of gene flow across at least some tribal boundaries has been low. Birdsell (1950) has made some ingenious calculations on the pattern of gene flow in Australian Aborigines based on the tribal distribution and making assumptions about the resistance to gene flow at each tribal boundary. But such patterns imply clines, and although many examples of apparent clines can be cited for the frequencies of genetic markers in Australia, there are also many examples of sharp discontinuities between geographically closely related groups.

The patterns in New Guinea are even more confusing. The most studied groups are in the Eastern Highlands, and in this area not only do we have a fairly detailed analysis of genetic markers of several linguistic groups, but there has been a beginning of a glotto-chronological analysis of the languages themselves. Watson *et al.* (1961) drawing on unpublished material of S. A. Wurm, attempted to relate the possible diffusion of the Rh variant D^u to the closeness of tribal relationship indicated by the glotto-chronology, and by the topography of the tribal areas. More recently, Livingstone (1963) has shown that in the same locality there is no correlation between the frequency of various genetic markers and degrees of relationship indicated by the percentage of cognates in the languages.

A number of other examples could be taken from New Guinea to illustrate the lack of correspondence between the distribution of genetic markers and language affinities. New Guinea languages fall into two main groups, Austronesian and non-Austronesian, and the distribution of these two quite distinctive groups is known in some detail (Capell, 1962). Though insufficient work has been done in some parts of New Guinea, the distribution of genetic markers does not seem to correspond with the pattern of language distribution, despite the efforts of some authors to prove that New Guinea is peopled by an older sub-stratum which has been submerged by more recent arrivals.

It may be argued that it is unreasonable to expect anything like genetic equilibrium and smooth gene frequency distribution in areas where the populations are broken into numerous small discrete groups. Such small groups may reflect the operation of genetic drift, and this has been cited with increasing frequency in recent years as a major cause of genetic differentiation in small human populations. A much larger part is likely to have been played by random events, both environmental and social. Epidemic disease, flood, hurricane, fire, and famine may all disturb the genetic structure of a small population by chance removal of unequal proportions of the genotypes represented in it. Similarly, war, marriage by capture, the possession of multiple wives, or the establishment of trading relations in certain directions but not in others may all lead to alterations in the genetic structure of the group.

Insufficient attention has been given in the past to co-ordination of genetic studies with detailed anthropological investigations which may reveal the nature of such disturbing factors. But the chance that such studies may do more than indicate the possibilities of disturbances is not great. Human memory is brief, and legend is sometimes a poor substitute for the truth. Whilst some clues may be obtained about events in recent generations, what happened in the distant past, say more than 100 years ago, must remain for preliterate populations largely a matter of conjecture.

Through the operation of the Founder Principle, what happens in small groups may reflect itself over multiple groups occupying a continental area. Australia and New Guinea may have been peopled by more than one wave of immigrants. But each such wave may have comprised no more than ten or twenty individuals. Birdsell (1957) has shown, making certain plausible assumptions, that from one such small group the entire continent of Australia could have been filled to the limits found at the time of the first European contact in as little as 800 years.

Finally, we do not know how important a role has been played by selection. Though the implication of selective agencies like malaria is suggestive for controlling the distribution of certain genetic markers such as thalassaemia and G-6-PD deficiency, there is not even a suggestion as yet for many of the other systems. One of the most pressing needs at the moment is the study of factors favouring the spread of alleles which may be of recent origin. Thus the Gc^{Ab} allele may well be spreading in Australia, having been introduced from New Guinea. Similarly, the B transferrin present only in Cape York may be destined to spread more widely in the next few generations, as has the transferrin B_{Lae} which has been found in New Britain and the neighbouring coastal area of New Guinea around Lae.

E. PROPOSALS FOR FURTHER STUDIES

The opportunities for further study in the Australian and New Guinea region are great, but they are also of considerable urgency. In Australia the breakdown of tribal boundaries is proceeding rapidly in all parts of the continent, and already it is impossible to study any group of significant size which still solely maintains a hunting and food-gathering economy. The rate of change in New Guinea is equally fast, but here the opportunities of finding groups still predominantly oriented towards their traditional culture are greater than in Australia.

In another publication, Kirk (1965*b*) has listed the topics of greatest importance for study in Australia. These are:

(a) The collection of anthropometric and genetic marker information for a series of tribes in Arnhem Land, all of which are still inadequately studied from the genetic point of view.

(b) The addition of further series to those already collected in Western Australia, Cape York, and the desert areas of the Northern Territory to bring the number of groups representative of individual tribes to a size suitable for meaningful statistical analysis.

(c) In all areas the collection of detailed information on fertility, actual mating patterns, and frequency of intertribal matings.

In New Guinea more detailed information on the distribution of genetic markers is required for:

(a) The Sepik River valley,

(b) The lowland areas around the Gulf of Papua and the lower reaches of the Fly River,

(c) The Western Highlands of New Guinea and the whole of the portion of the island at present controlled by Indonesia.

Information, similar to that outlined above for Australia, on fertility and mating patterns is important also for New Guinea. More detailed linguistic studies and analysis of social structure and mythology are necessary correlates to help in the interpretation of the genetic patterns.

In addition to the field studies outlined above, it will be useful to explore, through the use of computer techniques, the implications for change in the genetic structure of populations of certain assumptions about effective population size, selective values for certain genotypes and phenotypes and degree of isolation. A recent approach along these lines by Brues (1963) has demonstrated the value of such a technique for an understanding of the relative contributions of random genetic drift and selection on the spread of the world population values for the ABO blood group genes.

Both in Australia and New Guinea we need to know the likely effect on the change of gene frequencies of the preferred mating systems which exist in various tribes.

Finally, we need to develop computer programmes to give maximum likelihood estimates of gene frequencies and which allow for the varying degrees of relatedness of individuals in a sample. Since many tribal samples are small, and the individuals in the sample are interrelated, intertribal comparisons can become

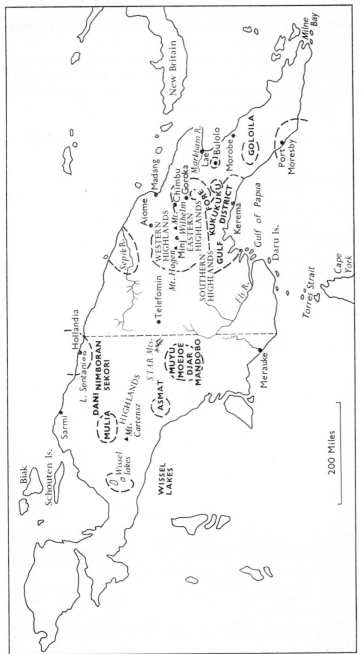

Fig. 1. New Guinea

meaningful only if we get the most efficient estimate of the genetic parameters concerned.

Whilst the solution of at least some of these problems may help to clarify still further the genetics of Australian and New Guinea populations, they may also throw light on the fund of speculation about the evolution of human populations in general.

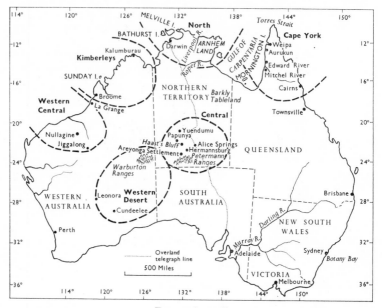

FIG. 2. Australia

REFERENCES

ALLISON, A. C., 1964. 'Protection afforded by sickle-cell trait against subtertian malarial infection', *Br. med. J.* **1**, 290–294.

—— and BLUMBERG, B. S., 1961. 'An iso-precipitin reaction distinguishing human serum-protein types', *Lancet*, **1**, 634–637.

ARENDS, T., GALLANGO, M. L., PARKER, W. C., and BEARN, A. G., 1962. 'A new variant of human transferrin in a Venezuelan family', *Nature, Lond.* **196**, 477–478.

BARNICOT, N. A. and KARIKS, J., 1960. 'Haptoglobin and transferrin variants in peoples of the New Guinea Highlands', *Med. J. Aust.* **2**, 859–861.

BENNETT, J. H., RHODES, F. A., and ROBSON, H. N., 1958. 'Observations on Kuru: a possible genetic basis', *Australas. Ann. Med.* **7**, 269–275.
—— —— —— 1959. 'A possible genetic basis for Kuru', *Am. J. hum. Genet.* **11**, 169–187.
—— 1961. 'Population and family studies on Kuru', *Eugen. Q.* **9**, 59–68.
—— AURICHT, C. O., GRAY, A. J., KIRK, R.L., and LAI, L. Y. C., 1961. 'Haptoglobin and transferrin types in the Kuru region of Australian New Guinea', *Nature, Lond.* **189**, 68–69.
—— 1962. 'Population studies in the Kuru region of New Guinea', *Oceania* **33**, 24–46.
BIRDSELL, J. B., 1950. 'Some implications of the genetical concept of race in terms of spatial analysis', *Cold Spring Harb. Symp. quant. Biol.* **15**, 259–311.
—— 1957. 'Some population problems involving Pleistocene Man', *Cold Spring Harb. Symp. quant. Biol.* **22**, 47–69.
BLUMBERG, B. S., BERNANKE, D., and ALLISON, A. C., 1962. 'A human lipoprotein polymorphism', *J. clin. Invest.* **41**, 1936–1944.
BOYD, W. C., 1939. 'Blood groups', *Tabul. biol.* **17**, ii, 113–240.
BRUES, A. M., 1963. 'Stochastic tests of selection in the ABO blood groups', *Am. J. phys. Anthrop.* **21**, 287–299.
BUDTZ-OLSEN, O. E., 1958. 'Haptoglobins and haemoglobins in Australian aborigines with a simple method for the estimation of haptoglobins', *Med. J. Aust.* **2**, 689–692.
—— and KIDSON, CHEV., 1961. 'Absence of red cell enzyme deficiency in Australian aborigines', *Nature, Lond.* **192**, 765.
BUETTNER-JANUSCH, J., GERSHOWITZ, H., POSPISIL, L. J., and WILSON, P., 1960. 'Blood groups of selected aboriginal and indigenous populations', *Nature, Lond.* **188**, 153–154.
CAPELL, A., 1962. 'Oceanic linguistics today', *Curr. Anthrop.* **3**, 371–428.
CLEVE, H., KIRK, R. L., PARKER, W. C., BEARN, A. G., SCHACHT, L. E., KLEINMAN, H., and HORSFALL, W. R., 1963. 'Two genetic variants of the group-specific component of human serum, Gc Chippewa and Gc aborigine', *Am. J. hum. Genet.* **15**, 368–379.
CONNELL, G. E., DIXON, G. H., and SMITHIES, O., 1962. 'Subdivision of the three common haptoglobin types based on "hidden differences"', *Nature, Lond.* **193**, 505–506.
COOPER, D. W., LANDER, H., and KIRK, R. L., 1964. '$D_{Adelaide}$—a new transferrin variant in man', *Nature, Lond.* **204**, 102.
CURTAIN, C. C., 1959. 'Starch-gel electrophoresis of Melanesian sera', *Aust. J. Sci.* **21**, 195–196.
—— GAJDUSEK, D. C., and ZIGAS, V., 1961. 'Studies on Kuru II. Serum proteins in natives from the Kuru region of New Guinea', *Am. J. Trop. Med. and Hyg.* **10**, 92–109.
—— KIDSON, CHEV, GAJDUSEK, D. C., and GORMAN, J. G., 1962. 'Distribution pattern, population genetics and anthropological significance of thalassemia and abnormal hemoglobins in Melanesia', *Am. J. phys. Anthrop.* **20**, 475–483.
—— GAJDUSEK, D. C., KIDSON, C., GORMAN, J., CHAMPNESS, L., and RODRIGUE, R., 1965. 'Haptoglobins and transferrins in Melanesia—their relation to hemoglobin, serum haptoglobin and serum iron levels in population groups in the territory of Papua and New Guinea', *Am. J. phys. Anthrop.* (In press)

428   POPULATION GENETIC STUDIES

DE VRIES, J. L. and NIJENHUIS, L. E., 1960. 'Blood group frequencies in New Guinea—I. The Sentani Papuans', *Am. J. phys. Anthrop.* **18**, 125–130.

FLORY, LYNN L., 1964. 'Serum factors of Australian aborigines from north Queensland', *Nature, Lond.* **201**, 508–509.

GAJDUSEK, D. C., 1961. 'Kuru: an appraisal of five years of investigation', *Eugen. Q.* **9**, 69–74.

—— 1962. 'Congenital defects of the central nervous system associated with hyperendemic goiter in a neolithic Highland society of Netherlands New Guinea', *Pediatrics* **29**, 345–363.

—— 1963. 'Motor-neuron disease in natives of New Guinea', *New Engl. J. Med.* **268**, 474–476.

—— 1963. 'Kuru', *Trans. R. Soc. trop. Med. Hyg.* **57**, 151–169.

GORMAN, J. G. and KIDSON, C., 1962. 'Distribution of an inherited trait, red cell enzyme deficiency in New Guinea and New Britain', *Am. J. phys. Anthrop.* **20**, 347–356.

HEYDON, G. M. and MURPHY, T. W., 1924. 'The biochemical index in the natives of the territory of New Guinea', *Med. J. Aust. Suppl.* 1, 235–237.

HIRSCHFELD, J., 1959. 'Immuno-electrophoretic demonstration of qualitative differences in human sera and their relation to the haptoglobins', *Acta path. microbiol. scand.* **47**, 160–168.

HORSFALL, W. R. and LEHMANN, H., 1953. 'Absence of sickle-cell trait in seventy-two Australian aboriginals', *Nature, Lond.* **172**, 638.

—— and LEHMANN, H., 1956. 'Absence of abnormal haemoglobins in some Australian aborigines', *Nature, Lond.* **177**, 41–42.

—— —— and DAVIES, D., 1963. 'Incidence of pseudo-cholinesterase variants in Australian aborigines', *Nature, Lond.* **199**, 1115.

KIDSON, CHEV, 1961. 'Deficiency of glucose-6-phosphate dehydrogenase: some aspects of the trait in people of Papua, New Guinea', *Med. J. Aust.* **2**, 506–509.

KIDSON, CHEV. and GORMAN, J. G., 1962a. 'A challenge to the concept of selection by malaria in glucose-6-phosphate dehydrogenase deficiency', *Nature, Lond.* **196**, 49–51.

—— —— 1962b. 'Contribution of red cell enzyme deficiency trait to an understanding of genetic relationships between Melanesian and other populations', *Am. J. phys. Anthrop.* **20**, 357–362.

KIRK, R. L., 1965a. 'Population genetic studies of the indigenous peoples of Australia and New Guinea', *Progress in Medical Genetics* IV, eds. A. G. STEINBERG and A. G. BEARN. Grune and Stratton, New York.

—— 1965b. 'The distribution of genetic markers in Australian aborigines', *Occasional Paper of the Australian Institute of Aboriginal Studies, Canberra.*

—— LAI, L. Y. C., and HORSFALL, W. R., 1962. 'The haptoglobin and transferrin groups among Australian aborigines from north Queensland', *Aust. J. Sci.* **24**, 486–488.

—— CLEVE, H., and BEARN, A. G., 1963. 'The distribution of group specific component (Gc) in selected populations in south and south east Asia and Oceania', *Acta genet. Statist. med.* **13**, 140–149.

KIRK, R. L., PARKER, W. C., and BEARN, A. G., 1964. 'The distribution of the transferrin variants D_1 and D^{Chi} in various populations', *Acta genet. Statist. med.* **14**, 41–51.

LAI, L. Y. C., 1962. 'Studies on inherited differences in serum proteins', Thesis, University of Western Australia.

—— 1963. 'A new transferrin in New Guinea', *Nature, Lond.* **198**, 589.

LEVINE, P., CELLANO, M. J., FALKOWSKI, F., CHAMBERS, J. W., HUNTER, O. B., and ENGLISH, C. T., 1964. 'A second example of ---/--- blood or Rh (null)', *Nature, Lond.* **204**, 892–893.

LIVINGSTONE, F. B., 1963. 'Blood groups and ancestry: a test case from the New Guinea Highlands', *Curr. Anthrop.* **4**, 541–542.

McARTHUR, NORMA, 1964. 'The age incidence of Kuru', *Am. J. hum. Genet.* **27**, 341–352.

MARKS, P. A. and GROSS, R. T., 1959. 'Erythrocyte glucose-6-phosphate dehydrogenase deficiency: evidence of differences between Negroes and Caucasians with respect to this genetically determined trait', *J. clin. Invest.* **38**, 2253–2262.

MOTULSKY, A. G., 1963. 'Pharmacogenetics' in *Progress in Medical Genetics*, (eds. A. G. STEINBERG and A. G. BEARN), Vol. III. Grune and Stratton, New York and London.

NEEB, H., BEIBOER, J. L., JONXIS, J. H. P., SIJPESTEIJN, J. A. K., and MULLER, C. J., 1961. 'Thalassemie met lepore hemoglobine bij twee Papoea-kinderen in Nederlands Nieuw Guinea', *Ned. Tijdschr. Geneesk.* **105**, 8–14.

NEEL, J. V., 1949. 'The inheritance of sickle-cell anaemia', *Science* **110**, 64–66.

—— SALZANO, F. M., JUNQUEIRA, P. C., KEITER, F., and MAYBURY-LEWIS, D., 1964. 'Studies on the Xavante Indians of the Brazilian Matto Grasso', *Am. J. hum. Genet.* **16**, 52–140.

NICHOLLS, E. M., LEWIS, H. B. M., COOPER, D. W., and BENNETT, J. H., 1965. 'Blood group and serum protein differences in some central Australian aborigines', *Am. J. hum. Genet.*, **17**, 293–307.

NIJENHUIS, L. E., 1961a. 'Blood group frequencies in the Netherlands, Curacao, Surinam and New Guinea—a study in "population genetics"'. Thesis, Amsterdam.

—— 1961b. 'Blood group frequencies in the upper Digul and Muyu district and in the Star Mountains of Netherlands New Guinea', *Nova Guinea*, n.s. **10**, (1) 1–14.

—— and DE VRIES, J. L., 1962. 'Blood group frequencies in New Guinea. III. Blood groups of the Nimboran Papuans', *Am. J. phys. Anthrop.* n.s. **18**, 193–196.

PARKER, W. C. and BEARN, A. G., 1962. 'Additional genetic variation of human serum transferrin', *Science* **137**, 854–856.

PARSONS, I. C. and RYAN, P. K., 1962. 'Observations on glucose-6-phosphate dehydrogenase deficiency in Papuans', *Med. J. Aust.* **2**, 585–587.

ROBSON, E. B., PARKER, W. C., BEARN, A. G., and HARRIS, H., 1964. 'A new transferrin variant D_{Wigan}'. In press.

RYAN, B. P., CAMPBELL, A. L., and BRAIN, P., 1961. 'Haemoglobin H disease in a Papuan', *Med. J. Aust.* **2**, 901–902.
—— 1961. 'Thalassemia, report of a case in Papua', *Med. J. Aust.* **1**, 128–129.
—— 1962. 'Thalassemia and anaemia of pregnancy in Papua', *Med. J. Aust.* **1**, 514–517.
—— 1963. 'Chronic anaemia with bony deformities in Papuan children', *Med. J. Aust.* **2**, 603.
SIMMONS, R. T., GRAYDON, J. J., and WOODS, E. F., 1946. 'Further observations on the Rh and Hr factors and the blood-group frequencies in Papuans', *Med. J. Aust.* **1**, 537–539.
—— —— and SEMPLE, N. M., 1954. 'A blood group genetical survey in Australian aborigines', *Am. J. phys. Anthrop.* n.s. **12**, 599–606.
—— 1958. 'A review of blood-group gene frequencies in aborigines of the various Australian states', *Proc. 7th Cong. Blood Trans., Rome*, pp. 287–292.
—— GRAYDON, J. J., ZIGAS, V., BAKER, LOIS, and GAJDUSEK, D. C., 1961. 'Studies on Kuru V. A blood group genetical survey of the Kuru region and other parts of Papua–New Guinea', *Am. J. trop. Med. Hyg.* **10**, 639–664.
—— TINDALE, N. B., and BIRDSELL, J. B., 1962. 'A blood group genetical survey in Australian aborigines of Bentinck, Mornington and Forsyth Islands, Gulf of Carpentaria', *Am. J. phys. Anthrop.* n.s. **20**, 303–320.
—— GRAYDON, J. J., and TINDALE, N. B., 1964. 'Further blood group genetical studies on Australian aborigines of Bentinck, Mornington and Forsyth Islands and the Mainland, Gulf of Carpentaria, together with frequencies for natives of the Western Desert, Western Australia'. *Oceania* **35**, 66–80.
SWINDLER, D. R., 1955. 'The absence of the sickle-cell gene in several Melanesian societies and its anthropological significance', *Hum. Biol.* **27**, 284–293.
TEBBUTT, A. H. and McCONNELL, S. V., 1922. 'On human iso-haemagglutininins with a note on their distribution amongst some Australian aborigines', *Med. J. Aust.* **1**, 201–209.
VOS, G. H., VOS, DELL, KIRK, R. L., and SANGER, R., 1961. 'A sample of blood with no detectable Rh antigens', *Lancet* **1**, 14–15.
—— and KIRK, R. L., 1962. 'A naturally-occurring anti-E which distinguishes a variant of the E antigen in Australian aborigines', *Vox Sang.* **7**, 22–32.
WALSH, R. J. and COTTER, H., 1955. 'Sicklemia in the Pacific', *Aust. J. Sci.* **17**, 175–176.
WATSON, J. B., ZIGAS, V., KOOPTZOFF, OLGA, and WALSH, R. J., 1961. 'The blood groups of natives in Kainantu, New Guinea', *Hum. Biol.* **33**, 25–41.
WILSON, K., ZIGAS, V., and GAJDUSEK, D. C., 1959. 'New tremor syndromes occurring sporadically in natives of the Wabag-Laiagam-Kundep region of the Western Highlands of Australian New Guinea', *Lancet* **2**, 699–702.
ZIGAS, V. and GAJDUSEK, D. C., 1957. 'Kuru: Clinical study of a new syndrome resembling paralysis agitans in natives of the Eastern Highlands of New Guinea', *Med. J. Aust.* **2**, 745–754.

14

PHYSIOLOGICAL ADAPTATION, FITNESS, AND NUTRITION IN THE PEOPLES OF THE AUSTRALIAN AND NEW GUINEA REGIONS†

R. K. MACPHERSON

School of Public Health and Tropical Medicine, The University of Sydney, Sydney, Australia

IT IS intended to restrict the scope of this paper in the greater part to a consideration of the aboriginal or indigenous inhabitants of Australia and New Guinea, but some attention must also be given to another group, the immigrant white or Caucasoid inhabitants, particularly those in Australia. White settlers have lived in Australia now for a period of almost 200 years, and fifth and even sixth generations of Australian-born Caucasoids must be commonplace. It might well be considered that these, living as they do in an environment which may be very different from that of their immediate ancestors, will have developed some measurable degree of physiological adaptation to their new situation.

In presenting any account of the native peoples of Australia and New Guinea an immediate dichotomy becomes necessary. The two peoples, the Australians and the New Guineans, must be considered separately. They are genetically distinct, their recent history differs, and their physical environments are dissimilar. Furthermore, before attempting any survey of their physiological adaptation, some attention must be given to the people themselves— their origins and their present status. It is only in the light of these facts that the desirable directions of research will become apparent, and an understanding of what investigations are feasible achieved.

† Paper presented at the Wenner-Gren Foundation for Anthropological Research Symposium No. 23, 'The Biology of Populations of Anthropological Importance', Burg Wartenstein, 29 June–12 July, 1964.

AUSTRALIAN REGION

The people

The surprising thing about this division of the human race, the Australoids, which ranks with the Negroids, Mongoloids, and Caucasoids, is how little is known of its origins and past history. At best it can be said that the hypothesis that these people migrated from eastern Asia by way of Indonesia, leaving behind them pockets of survivors, is the most likely of many, but whether they came as one migration to an empty continent, or as a succession of migratory waves, and whether they displaced pre-existing people, remain uncertain. The time of their intrusion into Australia has been variously set at from 1,000 to 150,000 years ago, but recent work using carbon-14 dating techniques does certainly seem to suggest that the most probable date is between 15,000 and 20,000 years B.P. The antiquity of man in Australia is, of course, a matter of fundamental importance to anthropologists and the topic has been discussed at length, especially with respect to the use of modern dating techniques, at a recent conference on aboriginal studies (Mulvaney, 1963; Browne, 1963). The now extinct Tasmanians—the last died nearly 100 years ago—were almost certainly a distinct group, but whether they were the original indigenes displaced towards the inhospitable south, or whether they arrived later, possibly by a sea journey along the eastern coast (Macintosh, 1949), must remain uncertain.

Australia was possibly a very different country when these people arrived, and it is also possible that their occupation played a part in changing it from a green and pleasant land to a country much of which is desert. Whatever date is ascribed to their coming, the country was already old geologically, its volcanoes extinct, and its mountains worn down. There are few places in which the altitude today exceeds 4000 feet.

Whenever they came to Australia, the aboriginals remained largely undisturbed until the coming of European settlement. There were, it is true, sporadic visitors, chiefly on the north and north-west coasts. Besides the occasional European there were, no doubt, visits either intentional, for purposes of trade, or accidental, as still happens when small boats are blown off their course from what is now Indonesia. Nevertheless, there was little change in their circumstances until 1788 when the First Fleet arrived in

Botany Bay. They were then, it is thought, about 300,000 in number, divided into 600 to 700 tribal groups speaking about 500 different, though on the whole related, languages. In the course of the next 100 years they were steadily displaced, as so many other primitive people have been, towards the more inhospitable parts of the country. Their numbers were reduced as their food supplies dwindled, a process hastened by exotic diseases and, in some cases, by deplorable barbarities on the part of the invaders.

This phase was succeeded by a period of benevolent paternalism, 'smoothing the pillow of a dying race', but of more recent years there has been a great awakening of the national conscience and successive governments have striven to pursue a more enlightened policy.

The results of the process just described can be best appreciated from a consideration of Table 1 (taken from *Year Book of the Commonwealth of Australia*, 1963). It will be seen that full-blooded indigenes have dwindled to 40,000 people of which the largest proportion is in the Northern Territory, with lesser numbers in Queensland and Western Australia and with negligible numbers in the southern and eastern States. Furthermore, only 4000 of these were so far out of touch with civilization that they were not enumerated on the census of 1961. This figure has probably been greatly reduced in the intervening three years.

TABLE 1

Commonwealth of Australia. Full-blooded aboriginal population,
30 June 1961

State or Territory	Enumerated June 1961	Not enumerated	Total
New South Wales	1,488	—	1,488
Victoria	253	—	253
Queensland	8,686	—	8,686
South Australia	2,147	—	2,147
Western Australia	8,121	2,000	10,121
Northern Territory	15,442	1,944	17,386
Tasmania	—	—	—
Total	36,137†	3,944	40,081

† Males 18,899; females 17,238.

29

Apart from these nomadic people, the remainder live either in the white community (sometimes still as fringe dwellers in country towns) or on sheep and cattle stations, but most are to be found in mission stations or Government settlements. In the Northern Territory there are at present thirteen settlements and fourteen mission stations, most of which are associated with aboriginal reserves of which there are seventeen of a total area of 95,000 square miles.

The conditions under which the aborigines live today and the provisions made for their welfare vary somewhat from State to State, but they are not so dissimilar that the description of the present situation in the Northern Territory (where they are the responsibility of the Commonwealth Government) cannot be applied to them as a group.

The present policy of the Australian Government is one of assimilation, and to that end sweeping changes have been made in their social position. The essence of these changes is this—previously an aboriginal was a ward of the State with restricted civil rights unless he could show cause why he should be granted full citizenship; now he has full citizenship by birth, and he only becomes a ward of the State if he can be shown to be, as in the case of all citizens, a person in need of care and protection. As a result, he has a right to vote and is eligible for all social services, old-age pensions, child endowment, maternity allowances, sickness benefits, and widows' pensions.

Furthermore, the country as a whole is extremely concerned for his welfare—his health, housing, nutrition, and the education of his children. In token of this the expenditure in the Northern Territory on aboriginal 'welfare' and education in 1962 was £A1,043,000 compared with £A133,000 in 1950. In addition, in 1962 he shared in the expenditure on health services of £A1,560,000.

The present policy towards the aborigines is, as it has been said, to achieve assimilation, but it is by no means clear just how this is to be achieved, or for that matter what is meant by the term. To the white Australian this may convey absorption of the aboriginal by repeated interbreeding until, by genetic dilution, he vanishes into the population as a whole. This may well be unacceptable to the aborigines, many of whom possess a very considerable pride of race, and who would prefer to see themselves persist as a recognizable part of the population. It is perhaps for this reason that some would substitute the word 'integration' for 'assimilation'. It is perhaps for this reason also that of recent years there have emerged some who assert their aboriginal or part-aboriginal origin. Cleland has recently published a paper (Cleland, 1960) outlining the problems of assimilation. This provoked considerable discussion (Abbie, 1960a; Duguid, 1960; Everingham, 1960; Hogg, 1960) which served to indicate the wide divergence of opinion which exists, and, more recently, Rowley (1962) has discussed the obscurity of the term 'assimilation' and has emphasized the repugnance the aboriginal may feel for turning into a white man and abandoning his ancestors.

That one type of assimilation is in progress is borne out by Table 2 (taken from *Year Book of the Commonwealth of Australia*, 1964) which shows that the number of enumerated half-castes is roughly equal to the number of aboriginals. How many more individuals there are with an inconspicuous aboriginal admixture it is impossible to say.

TABLE 2

Commonwealth of Australia. Full-blood and half-caste aboriginal population, 30 June 1961

State or Territory	Full-blood aborigines	Half-caste aborigines
New South Wales	1,488	13,228
Victoria	253	1,543
Queensland	8,686	11,010
South Australia	2,147	2,737
Western Australia	10,121	8,155
Tasmania	—	38
Northern Territory	17,386	2,318
Australian Capital Territory	—	143
Total	40,081	39,172

Most of the interbreeding which has occurred has been with Caucasoid stock, but, in addition to 'Malay' and other adventurers from the islands to the north of the continent who, from time to time, have landed on the north and north-western shores, there have been in recent times two substantial introductions of foreign genetic material into Australia—the Chinese and the 'Kanakas'.

The cessation of the transportation of convicts to New South Wales in 1840 led employers to seek some other source of cheap labour and Chinese labourers were introduced in large numbers until the discovery of gold in 1851 made this unprofitable—the Chinese deserted in large numbers to seek their fortunes mining for gold. In 1874 there was a further introduction of Chinese into the Northern Territory to assist in the construction of the Overland Telegraph Line. At its peak in the latter part of the nineteenth century there were some 50,000 Chinese in Australia. As they were an almost entirely male population living in rural areas interbreeding with the aborigines was inevitable. It was inevitable also that, with the cessation of immigration, their numbers should diminish rapidly by death or return to China, and the present Chinese population in Australia is small.

A further attempt to find a source of cheap labour, this time for the sugar-cane and cotton fields in Queensland and New South Wales, led to the recruitment of 'Kanaka' labour in the Pacific Islands, in circumstances often reminiscent of the African slave trade. Between 1847 and 1904 when the practice was abolished it is estimated that some 57,000 labourers were introduced. After December 1906, 3600 islanders were repatriated but some who had resided in Australia for many years, or who had acquired property, were allowed to remain, and a generation ago these and their descendants were recognizable among the population of the smaller towns of the north-east coast.

Physiological adaptation

Though the practical difficulties are great, the still nomadic remnant of the aboriginal population of central Australia provides the possibility of studying adaptation to extremes of temperature in a people living on a high protein diet who are exposed in an arid country, with little protection in the way of shelter or clothing, to the heat of a tropical sun by day and to the cold of the desert by night. Such opportunities are now rare, and, furthermore, the findings would provide a very necessary baseline from which to measure physiological adaptation to the changing way of life of their now non-nomadic kinsmen which, in itself, might provide an equally rewarding field of study.

Although the nomadic remnants of the central Australian aborigines now provide but meagre opportunities for the study of physiological adaptation to the climate to which they are exposed, the opportunities for the study of adaptation by the aborigines to a hot, moist environment are equally slender. It is true, of course, that substantial numbers of aborigines are to be found in Arnhem Land and along the coast of the Gulf of Carpentaria, but they are now, on the whole, far removed from their traditional way of life. Although the degree of westernization may vary from place to place, and even from mission station to mission station within 100 miles of one another, the traditional way of life has largely vanished. This state of affairs makes the necessity for well-organized studies extremely urgent. Indeed, it has been said that this generation provides the last opportunity for the study of the Australian aboriginal, particularly from the point of view of physiological adaptation, and this is the area in which knowledge is most scanty.

The study of the aborigines has been in progress for a long time. It began with the anecdotal observations of the early visitors and the first settlers in the country, but serious study may perhaps be considered to have begun at the turn of the century with the work of Spencer and Gillen, which culminated in the publication of *The Arunta* (Spencer and Gillen, 1927). For some reason or other, cultural anthropology has proved more attractive than physical anthropology and progress in the latter has been slow and much of what has been done directed towards aspects which we now consider of less importance, for example skeletal measurements in great detail. Indeed, it has been said (Abbie, 1951), 'Despite much intensive work, very little progress has been made towards settling quite a number of important problems posed by the Australian aborigine. There is still much controversy over his origin, ethnological affinities, physical characters, antiquity in Australia and relationship to the Tasmanian—to mention only some of the present uncertainties.'

The modern approach to the study of the aborigines in Australia perhaps may be dated from the end of the Second World War when, in addition to the characters formerly examined, blood pressures have been taken, samples of hair collected, fingerprints recorded, haematological studies initiated, urinary samples collected, and attention given to nutritional status by dietary studies and by the determination of skinfold thickness.

The work of Sir Stanton Hicks dating from 1929 stands in sharp contrast to the general lack of interest in the systematic observation of physiological adaptation which existed before 1940. The circumstances surrounding the initiation of these studies has recently been told (Hicks, 1964). Beginning with a study of the basal metabolism of the Australian aboriginal, instigated by Benedict, the work proceeded to embrace the whole problem of adaptation to cold.

In the Australian centre, though temperatures exceeding 100°F may occur during the daytime in summer, at night in the winter the air temperature may fall below freezing point, and even in the summer the nights are uncomfortably cold. The interesting problem is presented of how a race without clothing can survive these cold conditions at night. It was the aboriginal practice to build low windbreaks of bushes and lie close to small fires lit on the leeward side. This arrangement, as a defence against cold, would seem to be quite inadequate for those not specially acclimatized.

In his early observations Hicks and his co-workers (Hicks, Matters, and Mitchell, 1931; Hicks and Matters, 1933; Hicks, Moore, and Eldridge, 1934) were struck by the fact that the resting metabolism did not increase throughout the night, and in further studies (Hicks and O'Connor, 1938a, b; Goldby, Hicks, O'Connor, and Sinclair, 1938) they were able to confirm that body temperature, especially the skin temperature, of the aborigines fell to extremely low values. The aborigines could sleep with skin temperatures as low as 27–28°F. On the other hand, they did not appear to be 'insensitive to cold' in the ordinary sense of the phrase. It is clear that the ability to permit the body temperature to fall in this fashion reduces heat loss from the body and the absence of shivering permits sleep and conserves energy requirements. Such a physiological adaptation would be of great value.

The coming of the Second World War to Australia put an end to these studies, but the subject was re-opened later by Scholander and his co-workers (Scholander, Hammell, Hart, LeMessurier, and Steen, 1958). In their paper they describe experiments conducted at the Areyonga Settlement in central Australia on young men of the Pitjandjara tribe who, though they wore clothing during the daytime, habitually discarded it at night. They were able to show that the aboriginal method of sleeping 'proper bush', that is beside small fires behind a windbreak, provided conditions in which both white men and aborigines could sleep with comfort although the air temperature approached freezing point. When, however, the behaviour of whites and aboriginals protected only by a thin sleeping bag, such as was used in experiments on young Norwegian subjects (Scholander, Hammel, Andersen, and Løyning, 1958) was examined very different reactions were observed. The aboriginals slept soundly throughout the night with normal resting heat production, although their skin temperature fell markedly—the foot temperature dropping regularly to 12–15°C. The white controls, however, were unable to sleep, they shivered and thrashed about all night.

It was concluded that, whereas the white man achieves tolerance to cold by an increase in metabolism, the Australian aboriginal has resort to an increased insulation and is able to disregard the discomfort produced by the resultant fall in skin temperature, thus confirming the original work by Hicks and his colleagues.

These investigations were extended further the following summer (Hammel, Elsner, LeMessurier, Andersen, and Milan, 1959) when the cold conditions experienced during the winter were reproduced by the use of a refrigerated meat van. In addition to re-examining natives of the Pitjandjara tribe, the reactions of coastal aborigines living near Darwin, who, it could be safely presumed, had never been exposed to cold stress, were examined. The results showed that the differences between the central natives and the control whites existed in summer to the same extent as in winter. Without metabolic compensation body temperature of the aboriginals fell at a greater rate than that of the whites. The coastal aborigines behaved in a manner intermediate between the central natives and the control whites. Their metabolic heat production was 43 kcal/m²/hr compared with 49 for whites and 37 for central natives. In conclusion the authors suggest that the Australian aboriginal has an inborn ability to tolerate greater body cooling, without metabolic compensation, which can be increased by prolonged exposure to cold.

The adaptation of the Australian aboriginal to the hot, moist conditions which prevail in the coastal regions in the north of Australia has also recently been examined (Wyndham, Macpherson, and Munro, 1964). Two groups of aborigines, one of fourteen men from Weipa Mission Station and another of seventeen men from the Aurukun Mission Station, were exposed to hot, humid conditions in a portable climatic chamber for four hours, and their behaviour was compared with that of a small sample of seven

Europeans resident, at least temporarily, in the same area. There was little difference in the behaviour of the aboriginals and the Caucasians when the heart rates and rectal temperatures of the two groups were compared, but the amount of sweat produced by the aborigines (237 ml/m²/hr) was significantly less than that produced (384 ml/m²/hr) by the presumably naturally-acclimatized Caucasians.

Whatever conclusions may be drawn from these experiments concerning the acclimatization status of these aborigines, the fact remains that these natives were able to undertake exhausting day-long exercise, in hot conditions, in pursuit of game and to this extent were well adapted to their surroundings. It would seem that their lesser rate of sweating, which was noticeable during their daily activities, provides a considerable economy of water and salt and is thus an adaptation with considerable survival value. It is clear that these experiments should be repeated with great care, if only for the bearing they have upon the significance of the usually accepted criteria of acclimatization to heat.

One last remark may perhaps be made on the adaptation of the aborigines to their thermal environment. It would seem that, despite the careful work of Hicks, Scholander, Hammel, and their colleagues, the last word has not yet been said on the aborigines' adaptation to cold. Meggitt (1962), writing of the Walbiri people of central Australia, says 'In the couple of months that may be counted as winter, Europeans find the climate pleasant, but the aborigines detest the cold nights.' This accords well with my own views and it might be well to pursue the matter further.

The aborigines being a feral people were dependent much more than civilized man on the acuity of their special senses. Their ability to see, to hear, and even to smell, would be invoked in their search for food, the tracking of game, and protection from their enemies. Evidence that they possess unusual skill in these matters is amply demonstrated by the exploits of the 'black-trackers' widely employed in the police force in former times, and this skill is still used to good effect in the search for missing children and for those who have lost their way in the bush.

It might be rewarding, therefore, to investigate the visual acuity, colour discrimination, the acuity of hearing, and tonal and directional discrimination of aborigines. Even the study of their sense of smell might provide useful information. Though little seems to have been done in this direction of recent years, at the end of the last century the Cambridge Anthropological Expedition to Torres Straits investigated the vision (Rivers, 1901), hearing, smell, taste, reaction times (Myers, 1901), cutaneous sensations, and muscular sense (McDougall, 1901) of the inhabitants. All these things might well have survival value to native peoples. By way of interest, it might be added that the Cambridge Expedition also measured variations in blood pressure by means of the then recently-invented sphygmomanometer (McDougall, 1901).

As our opportunities to increase our knowledge of the aboriginal in his native environment dwindle, another problem presents itself with increasing importance—the effect of the impact of Western civilization on his culture and his physical characteristics.

Abbie (1960b) has summarized the physical changes in Australian aborigines consequent upon European contact (which might well be considered to constitute physiological adaptation to increasing civilization) as follows:

(1) an apparently rising level of immunity to many imported infectious diseases,

(2) a probable rise in such blood chemicals as cholesterol, phospholipids, and mucoprotein,

(3) a probable rise in mean blood pressure,

(4) a change in the menstrual pattern in women,

(5) a fading of skin pigment and the appearance of a suscepti-bility to sunburn,

(6) obvious dental deterioration, and

(7) the possibility of preserving undesirable genetic recessives and mutants in subsequent generations.

He considers that all these changes are purely physical and could be reversed if the natives reverted to their original habitat. Never-theless, Packer (1961), in a very thoughtful paper on the health of aborigines, points out that they have already gone so far along the road of adaptation to their changed environment that they cannot now turn back. It is noticeable that the aborigines having adopted clothing now show a marked reluctance to discard it. In physio-logical experiments aboriginal youths and men are often far more unwilling to work in the nude, or let others see them in the nude, than their European counterparts.

Physical fitness

Many people who are familiar with William Dampier's terse description (Dampier, 1729) of the Australian aborigines as 'the miserablest people in the world', are apt to apply it unheedingly to all aborigines, although it applied only to those on the north-west coast with whom Dampier came in contact. By far the greater number of the inhabitants of Australia at the time of the coming of the white man appear to have been good physical specimens, with sound dentition and a remarkable freedom from disease.

Disease does not seem to have provided any serious threat to the people in their primitive condition. For example, the position with respect to malaria today (Cilento, 1942), and presumably at times in the recent past, is that there is light endemicity with sporadic spread and very occasional rare epidemicity along the north coast from Broome in the west to Cairns in the east. Yaws and trachoma in the north and west probably antedated the white man, but, these apart, the aborigines seem to have been remarkably free from transmissable disease. Newcomers inevitably brought disease with them. With the Europeans came the infectious diseases common in the West which were disastrous to a population devoid of immunity. Leprosy was probably introduced with Chinese indentured labour in the north, and filariasis by coloured (Kanaka) labour recruited in the Pacific Islands for the cane fields of the east coast.

Today the health problems of the Northern Territory are leprosy, shigella infections, trachoma, and treponemal disease. There is a high incidence of positive treponemal serological tests, but it is attributed to yaws rather than syphilis. Syphilitic manifestations are uncommon.

A recent paper by Crotty and Webb (1960) has given a useful picture of the incidence of diseases causing death in the Northern Territory, but does not consider non-lethal disease which may be a major cause of incapacitation in a population. The people as a whole are remarkably free from cardiovascular disease, perhaps because, as Abbie and Schroder (1960) have shown in natives of Arnhem Land, although the blood pressure throughout life parallels the typical European pattern with age, it does so at a lower level.

In the past anaemia associated with a kwashiorkor-like nutritional disease was said (Crotty, 1958) to be common between the ages of 1 to 5 years. Hookworm was not apparently a principal factor in its development, but it seems rather to have been due to iron and protein deficiency in the late breast-feeding and weaning stage, owing to the absence of a suitable supplementary diet.

However, the disease pattern by itself is no measure of physical fitness, although it will be agreed that this term in itself is hard to define. Fitness, it would seem, is a measure of the extent to which an individual has adapted to his environment, so that much of what has been said under the heading of physiological adaptation is relevant here. In the commonly accepted meaning of the term, however, the aboriginals as a whole are extremely fit. Many have shown themselves capable of remarkable feats of physical endurance, but, as far as is known, there has been no investigation of their physical capacity by the application of formal tests of physical fitness such as the Harvard Pack Test. Whether the use of such tests would provide information on the capabilities of the people as a whole, as distinct from their relevance to the individuals tested, would depend upon the numbers examined and the sampling techniques employed.

Obesity is rare. Slenderness of the trunk, and especially of the limbs, is very characteristic. It is perhaps safe to say that the aboriginals exemplify the familiar Bergmann–Allen Rules (Bergmann, 1847; Allen, 1877). Abbie (1957, 1961a, b) has shown that the very young have physical proportions similar to European children of the same age, but a change occurs abruptly at 5 to 6 years, when there is a sudden extension of the lower extremities.

In view of the current trend of opinion, it is justifiable to include observations on blood pressure under the heading of physical fitness. Considering the facility with which the observations are made, there have been surprisingly few determinations of the blood pressure in Australian aborigines. Casley-Smith (1959), who states that only three previous series have been published, has analysed the blood pressure readings (which he derived from various sources) of about 2000 aborigines living in central Australia and northern Queensland. The values, especially the systolic, in central Australia were lower, and those in Queensland markedly higher, than in comparable Europeans. In both groups pressures rose more slowly with age than in the Europeans. The central Australian pressures increased with increasing European contact; the Queensland pressures diminished on such contact.

The following year Abbie and Schroder (1960) published their paper referred to previously which was based on recordings from 163 aborigines of all ages living in a Government settlement in Arnhem Land. In general, they found values comparable with those recorded in central Australia. The anomalous values found in Northern Queensland could perhaps be attributed to differences between observers or the conditions under which the measurements were made. There seems to be little doubt (Abbie, 1961a) that blood pressure in the aborigines rises in proportion to their association with Europeans. Urban aborigines have values closely corresponding to those for Europeans.

In this connexion also it is interesting to note that serum cholesterol levels in aborigines are significantly lower than for Australians of European descent. In reporting this Schwartz, Day, Peters, and Casley-Smith (1957) also add that, in contrast with control Europeans, there was no increase in serum cholesterol with ageing. In a later paper Schwartz and Casley-Smith (1958) also reported that the levels in tribal nomadic aborigines and in urban aborigines show a striking correlation with the levels of dietary fat intake in these groups.

Traditionally the splendid physique of native peoples is matched by their perfect teeth. This is, unfortunately, no longer true for the aboriginal people as a whole. As the result of a dental survey at Haast's Bluff in central Australia, Heithersay (1959) reported that the incidence of dental caries in all age groups was much greater than that for aborigines of the pre-European era, although still much lower than in civilized Europeans. The aborigines seemed to preserve some immunity to caries during adolescence, but once caries appeared deterioration was rapid. There were relatively few cases of periodontal disease. The subjects examined consumed a mixed diet of European and native foods, and this well-documented paper would indicate that part of the price which the aboriginal must pay for the privileges of civilization is a progressive deterioration in his dentition.

Nutrition

The pre-European Australian aboriginal was a nomad who neither tilled the soil nor husbanded any domestic animals, but lived by the chase. His diet, in consequence, was essentially meat (and fish in littoral communities), supplemented by what fruits or roots the womenfolk could gather. Indeed, nothing edible, animal or vegetable, was too insignificant to escape his attention.

It was inevitable, therefore, that the settling of the land by Europeans should deprive him of his major food supplies, and those in contact with white settlers had their diet supplemented by European foods, chiefly white flour, from the earliest times. Later the aggregation of natives on settlements and missions depleted the traditional foods in the area, so that he depended more and more on 'rations'. These, for a variety of reasons, were often ill-chosen, and undernutrition and malnutrition were undoubtedly commonplace. This state of affairs has, however, largely been remedied with time and the natural evolution of events. It is perhaps most convenient to consider the present position from the time of the Second World War onwards, as this event markedly disrupted the life of the aborigines in the Northern Territory, and later events were strongly influenced by the rapidly-increasing awareness in Australia, as elsewhere in the world at this time, of the importance of nutrition as a science.

In 1948 the American–Australian Scientific Expedition to Arnhem Land undertook a survey, that might well stand as a model for subsequent investigations, of the nutrition of the aboriginals living in that area. The food consumption and dietary levels were recorded; the health and nutritional status of the subjects was assessed; the dental and periodontal health of the population was recorded; biochemical assessments of the nutritional status of the population were made; the food consumption and dietary patterns of aborigines living on naturally occurring foods were investigated; analyses of native foods were carried out; and the report (Mountford, 1960), when it appeared, was rounded off with a section on conclusions and recommendations. This was, no doubt, the most exact and comprehensive survey of its nature ever undertaken in Australia, and it is considered that the findings would be applicable to similar groups of aborigines in any area in the Northern Territory today, when due allowance has been made for variations in local conditions.

In 1951 a survey was made, on behalf of the Government, of natives living on five Government settlements, six missions, and six cattle stations scattered throughout the Northern Territory, and since then dietary surveys have been undertaken as a routine procedure by the Commonwealth Department of Health. Though much of the information collected has remained unpublished, at least two very valuable papers have appeared (Kirk and Hipsley, 1961; Corden, 1962).

Early in the 1950's the Department of Health, aware of the shortcomings of the aboriginal dietary pattern, worked out a 'Ration Scale' as a guide to what was considered to be the minimum acceptable diet. Unfortunately, such difficulties as lack of transport facilities, especially for perishable foodstuffs, hindered its implementation, and the dietary pattern of non-nomadic aboriginals consisted of such unperishable foodstuffs as white flour, polished rice, sugar, and tea, with irregular and insufficient amounts of meat, fish, fruit, and vegetables. The tastes of the aborigines themselves often defeated attempts to improve their nutrition. For example, they failed to avail themselves of the supplies of dried milk provided, which would have been of immense value to children and pregnant and lactating women. The position was summarized in 1962 as follows (Corden, 1962), 'Aboriginal diets on the whole do not seem to be adequate and are apparently considerably inferior to what was available to them when living in small nomadic groups. Much education, wise leadership, finance and hard work in solving agricultural problems will be needed to enable these people to lead healthy, useful lives within the social and economic framework of our Australian community.'

Translated into other terms, we may say that, subject to inevitable climatic disasters and the varying productivity of different areas, the nomadic aboriginal of today, as did his ancestors before the coming of the white man, has a diet that is adequate in calories, high in animal protein, rich in iron and calcium, and more than adequate in Vitamin A, the Vitamin B complex, and Vitamin C. However, in times of drought and flood he inevitably suffers privation and hunger of varying extent. The aboriginal living in a community, on the other hand, though enjoying a diet high in calories, would be provided with insufficient high-class protein and inadequate calcium and iron and variable amounts of Vitamins A, B, and C, which might well be often below recommended values.

The Governments of the Commonwealth and the several States concerned have acted vigorously to remedy this situation in the past few years. Ration scales have been extensively revised to ensure they achieve an adequate nutritional level, intensive educational campaigns directed both to the aborigines themselves and those responsible for their care have been undertaken, and medical supervision has become more continuous and more effective. Improved communications, especially the increasing use of the aeroplane, has contributed materially to the implementation of these reforms. Moreover, a more fundamental approach to the whole problem of nutrition has been made in terms of research programmes in agriculture and animal husbandry, because any realistic and permanent solution to the problem of nutrition can only be achieved by the provision of a *milieu* in which the people themselves can, by their own efforts, attain an adequate standard of living.

NEW GUINEA REGION

The people

The country in which the New Guineans live is very different from the neighbouring continent of Australia. Australia extends over some 30° of latitude. The long bird-shaped island of New Guinea is almost all contained in the first 10° south of the equator. Australia is an old land, its hills worn down, but New Guinea is new, active volcanically, with a great backbone of mountains reaching 5000 metres in height. Mount Wilhelm, the highest mountain in the Territory of Papua and New Guinea, is 4700 metres, and in West Irian the highest, Mount Cartensz, is 5040 metres high. The snowline in this region is about 4500 metres. Much of Australia is desert. New Guinea, except for a relatively low rainfall area around Port Moresby, is a land of heavy rainfall, dense forests, great swamps, and many rivers. Temperature in Australia is largely determined by latitude, in New Guinea the only escape from the heat is provided by altitude. At least in the southern parts of Australia summer and winter are distinct. In New Guinea seasonal changes are minimal. Australia is, and always has been, scantily populated. New Guinea is by comparison densely populated. Malaria, it was noted, is of insignificant importance in Australia. In New Guinea it is of overwhelming importance, and to it, in certain areas, we must add scrub typhus and filaria.

The island of New Guinea remained relatively untouched by the Western world until very recent times. It is true that the Netherlands Government annexed that part of the island which lies to the west of 141°E in 1828, but little or no attempt was made to penetrate into the interior, and it remained as much undisturbed as the eastern half which was shared in 1884 between Germany and Great Britain, which latter country later transferred her share, Papua, to Australia. After the First World War, Australia also inherited the German share as a League of Nations mandate. It is now a United Nations Trust Territory and is administered jointly with Papua as the Territory of Papua and New Guinea.

Early explorations of the interior of the island were often individual forays, sometimes provocative, and ending all too often in tragedy. The coming of the Western Powers made for a much more peaceful and systematic penetration, but even after the First World War the *tempo* of development was not greatly increased. However, after the Second World War the winds of change blew with tornado force in New Guinea. The Netherlands New Guinea is now West Irian, and in the Territory of Papua and New Guinea in 1964 the first elections to the Legislature based on adult suffrage resulted in the returning of thirty-four indigenous candidates. As a measure of the increasing sophistication of the inhabitants, it may be added that the percentage of informal votes was negligible. All this in a land where, but a few short years ago, large areas were uncontrolled and patrols ventured into them only at the risk of their lives.

This lengthy excursion into geography and history may seem ectopic in a paper of this nature, but it is necessary as a background to any scientific work in New Guinea. It was the climate and the terrain—dense forest, swamps, and steep mountain ranges, which, by preventing any freedom of movement, hindered the development of the country in the Western sense. It is these same factors which provide conditions of intense anthropological and physiological interest in the country. They divided the population into discrete units, each restricted often to a single mountain ridge, having little or no dealings with its neighbours, except perhaps as trade or warfare, interbreeding within itself (with all the genetic consequences), and speaking its own special language. This last in itself, in its turn, has tended to perpetuate the isolation and hinder the emergence of larger units of population.

The coming of the aeroplane solved the problem of communication at a single stroke and made possible many advances. In one respect, however, the solution was incomplete. The aeroplane made possible contact with these peoples, the exploration of the country, and its effective pacification and administration, but aeroplanes are expensive and air travel is not freely available to native peoples, so the segregation of the separate racial communities was not greatly disturbed and they may still be studied as units. The sands of time, however, are fast running out. The building of roads is now proceeding apace—the bulldozer is completing the work begun by the aeroplane. Roads will immediately increase the mobility of the population, intermingling of the various groups will rapidly occur, and their genetic individuality vanish. Even the barrier of language is being broken down. In the Territory of Papua and New Guinea the official policy is to teach English as a second language, and, though Melanesian pidgin still remains the only *lingua franca* of the people in many areas, its replacement seems inevitable.

The native inhabitants of the island of New Guinea are Melanesians—the predominantly dark-skinned, woolly-haired people who occupy the greater part of the western Pacific. Based on physical differences in stature, hair texture, nose form, and other characteristics, they are often divided into a Papuan type and a Melanesian type proper. A second division is also sometimes made between those speaking Melanesian languages and those speaking non-Melanesian languages which are often grouped together as Papuan languages. But since the Papuan type inhabitants do not necessarily speak one of the Papuan languages all is confusion. To the uninstructed onlooker it seems that, as there is infinite diversity within both the ethnic and the language groups, it would be well to abandon these distinctions. In most cases each language is spoken by a comparatively small number of people. In the coastal districts this would seldom exceed 5000 people and often much fewer. In the Highlands, however, there are language groups which contain as many as 30,000 people.

The total indigenous population of the Territory of Papua is about 530,000 people and in the Trust Territory of New Guinea (both enumerated and estimated) 1,470,000, making a total for the Territory of Papua and New Guinea of some 2 million inhabitants. In The Netherlands New Guinea, as it then was at the end of 1961, the total enumerated and estimated population was 718,000 people.

Perhaps the easiest way to comprehend these figures is provided

30

by Scragg (1962)—'The native of Papua and New Guinea lives with his family in a village of 100 to 200 persons usually 5 to 10 miles from the next village. He is one of 1·8 million people. His family is one of about 350,000 and his village one of 11,000.' Scragg might have added that he speaks one of perhaps 400 languages. The corresponding figures for the West Irian native would be very similar. There would be 100 to 300 people in his village and he would speak one of 200 languages. It must, of course, be added and emphasized that in the larger towns, both in the eastern and in the western half of the island, there is an ever-growing body of urbanized indigenes in varying degrees of westernization living a completely urban existence, many of whom in dress, speech, and manners, are indistinguishable from the Caucasian population.

Physiological adaptation

In his paper on nutrition in New Guinea, Bailey (1963a) makes the very sound observation that, although malnutrition has been amply demonstrated in children and protein deficiency in pregnant and lactating women, and skinfold thickness measurements are low and there is a decline in the weight–height ratio with age and the serum albumin is low, both men and women perform physical feats and show sustained stamina that few of us could match. It could well be, as this writer suggests, that we are in fact dealing with a highly specialized adaptation to a particular way of life. Perhaps it is that we fall into the trap of thinking that because the natives differ from standards derived from Western peoples they are 'abnormal'. An average value for the protein in sweet potato, the chief article of diet of so many New Guineans (see p. 455), is 1·1 per cent, so that an adult who ate even 3 kg of sweet potato per day would obtain only 33 g of *vegetable* protein. This is far below the usually accepted daily protein requirements, certainly below the 1 g/kg recommended at one time, but does this mean that it is insufficient ? It could be that standards should be revised.

That the diet of the New Guinea natives is not without its special advantages has been amply substantiated by the work of Dr. H. M. Whyte and others at the Kanematsu Memorial Institute in Sydney on material from New Guinea. It has been concerned mainly with body build, blood pressure, blood lipids, and blood coagulation. These workers were particularly interested in the possible relationship of these factors to diet and the relative absence of cardiovascular disease in New Guinea, and in comparing the findings with the results of parallel studies among European (Caucasoid) men in Australia.

They were able to show (Whyte and Yee, 1958) that the serum cholesterol level was the same in new-born infants in both situations (70 mg/100 ml), it doubled in one year for both, and then rose steadily with age in Australians and fell to adult levels in the New Guineans. Values for adults, collected in a variety of situations in New Guinea (de Wolfe and Whyte, 1958), were found to be little more than half the Australian values, and this was, of course, associated with a great difference in the intake of fats. Studies of blood clotting and fibrinolysis (Goldrick and Whyte, 1959; Goldrick, 1961) showed that clotting times were shortest in natives but fibrinolysis was greatly increased. Increase of body bulk in Australians was associated with a decrease in fibrinolysis but the contrary held in natives, in whom muscle, not fat, was the chief contributor to body bulk. In yet another study on a similar topic (Whyte, 1963) it was shown that ageing was accompanied in Australians, but not in New Guineans, by increasing body bulk (obesity), blood pressure, and serum cholesterol levels. These findings provided confirmation of their earlier work (Whyte, Graham, and de Wolfe, 1958; Whyte, 1958) on Australian and New Guinea men, one of the principal conclusions of which was that the blood pressure of young adult male natives in New Guinea is not very different from what is found in Europeans. They differ, however, in not rising with age.

New Guinea, by virtue of the isolation of its population units and certain associated factors such as polygyny, provides unique opportunities for the study of genetics—opportunities which can be expected to vanish within the next generation. It is pleasing, therefore, to be able to record that much work has already been done on blood groups and other genetic markers in the New Guinea natives. This work is discussed at length by Dr. R. L. Kirk in Chapter 13.

One particularly active group of haematologists led by Dr. R. J. Walsh of the New South Wales Red Cross Blood Transfusion Service has studied populations in the Central Highlands (Ivinskis, Kooptzoff, Walsh, and Dunn, 1956), the Gulf District (Jüptner, Kooptzoff, and Walsh, 1958), Dutch New Guinea and the Solomon

Islands (Cotter and Walsh, 1958), the Goilala sub-district of Papua (Kariks, Kooptzoff, Cotter, and Walsh, 1958), the Western Highlands (Walsh, Cotter, and Macintosh, 1959), the Bulolo River Valley (Armytage, Kooptzoff, and Walsh, 1959), the Mount Hagen area (MacLennan, Kooptzoff, and Walsh, 1960a), the Sepik River district (MacLennan, Kooptzoff, and Walsh, 1960b), Minj (Walsh, Jameson, and Kooptzoff, 1960), Telefomin (Rieckmann, Kooptzoff, and Walsh, 1961), Goroka (Kariks, Kooptzoff, Steed, Cotter, and Walsh, 1960) and Aiome (Champness, Kooptzoff, and Walsh, 1960). The last-mentioned district is particularly interesting because of the small (pygmoid) stature of the people (see p. 454).

This work is of special value because the study of the blood groups has been accompanied in most cases by the collection of anthropometric data, and other haematological determinations such as haemoglobin values and serum protein levels have been made. From these last, a number of interesting facts emerge. One is the uniformly high values obtained for the γ-globulin fraction of the serum proteins. Furthermore, they provide convincing evidence of adaptation to altitude. At Mount Hagen (MacLennan, Kooptzoff, and Walsh, 1960a), for example, the altitude (6000–7000 ft) combines with an absence of malaria to give values for haemoglobin as high as 17 g/100 ml. In areas where malaria is present the haematopoietic effect of altitude is diminished.

An adaptation of great interest to climatic physiologists is that demonstrated by Highland natives on a high potassium, low sodium diet. This results not only from their vegetarian diet, but from lack of access to the sea. They are dependent for their supply of sodium chloride on salt traded by the maritime peoples. This is often largely adulterated with wood ash, partly by its method of preparation and partly, it is suspected, deliberately by unscrupulous vendors. Indeed, Wills (1958), who published analyses of a number of specimens of salt, has shown that some specimens are almost entirely wood ash. Recently Macfarlane, Howard, and Hipsley (1964) have investigated water and salt metabolism in a Highland people, the Chimbu. They have shown that in sweat, saliva, and milk the concentration of sodium was about only one-quarter, and in urine about one-half, of that found in Caucasians living in the same area. Another investigation of interest to climatologists, as well as geneticists, is the work of Walsh (1963) on variations in skin pigment in some Asian and Pacific people.

It will have been noted that as yet no reference has been made to work done west of 141°E. It is difficult to determine what research is being undertaken there at present, and it would be inadvisable to prophesy what may be done there in the immediate future. However, reference to a paper (de Bruijn, 1958) presented by Dr. J. V. de Bruijn to the North Pacific Science Congress at Bangkok in 1957, which summarizes the anthropological research done by, or with the co-operation of, the Bureau of Native Affairs at Hollandia, and which contains a valuable bibliography as an appendix, will serve to show that up to that time cultural anthropology had received the most attention in The Netherlands New Guinea. Nevertheless, a beginning had been made in physical anthropology and substantial work had been done in the field of nutrition (Voors, 1956; Luyken and Luyken-Koning, 1956; Luyken and Luyken-Koning, 1958). The findings were largely in agreement with those in the Territory of Papua and New Guinea. Good work had also been done in haematology, and again the results were much the same as in Papua–New Guinea. For example, it was found (Bakker, Bliek, and Luyken, 1957) that the serum proteins of malaria-free natives showed the same low levels of serum albumin and the high levels of γ-globulin described elsewhere. Of the work done subsequently, special mention must be made of the investigations of Luyken and his associates of serum cholesterol levels (Luyken and Jansen, 1960) and the composition of breast milk (Jansen, Luyken, Malcolm, and Willems, 1960). These workers have also shown (Couvée, Nugteren, and Luyken, 1962; Luyken, Luyken-Koning, and Pikaar, 1963) that, in people living on a sweet potato diet, the urea nitrogen of the urine is, as would be expected, very low but they excrete large quantities of hippuric acid (as much as 555 mg/g creatinine). The source of this hippuric acid is uncertain but it is clearly derived from some substance present in the sweet potato.

Finally it is perhaps permissible to consider kuru (Zigas and Gajdusek, 1957; Gajdusek and Zigas, 1959; Bennett, Gray, and Auricht, 1959; Fortune, 1960; Bennett, 1962) as a failure of adaptation. Kuru (trembling) is a rapidly progressive disorder of cerebellar function for which there is no effective treatment and which is uniformly fatal. It kills half the female population and one-tenth of the males, and the result is a great preponderance of males in the population. Not the least fascinating problem it poses is whether or not it represents genetic defect (see Chapter 13). A check of all movements into and out of the kuru area is now kept as well as a registry of marriages and births. It is confined at present to a restricted area in the Eastern Highlands.

Physical fitness

The New Guinean is small in stature by European standards, probably less than 66 inches tall. Seligman (1909) records a height of 71 inches as 'unusual for a Papuan'. Some could fairly be described as pygmies, for instance the people near Aiome where the average height for males is about 58 inches and females some 4 inches less (Champness, Kooptzoff, and Walsh, 1960). It would be of great interest to determine whether these pygmoid people are a racially distinct group. The continuous gradation that has been observed in the height of the natives in the western half of the island as one proceeds from the coast to the Highlands would seem, however, to be evidence against this hypothesis.

All shades of brown occur in the skin, and the typical New Guinean is spare, devoid of fat, but well-muscled. His wife will look, to European eyes, much older than her years. Apart from a variety of ornaments, his clothing will be scanty, perhaps an apron of sorts in front and a bunch of leaves (often *Dracaena sp.*) behind, or he may wear nothing more than a phallocrypt.

When met casually he may appear leisurely or even idle in his behaviour, but, of necessity probably, he usually proves to be extraordinarily fit. He has no means of transport except his legs, and to move from one place to another he has, in the Highlands, to ascend and descend hills of incredible steepness by seemingly impossible paths. His total energy expenditure per day might not be greater than that of the active European, but the pattern might be very different. It is tempting to speculate to what extent the rigours of his existence achieve this high standard of physical fitness by a process of natural selection.

Excluding accidental trauma, the most important threats to his health are malaria, pneumonia, infections of the intestinal tract, tuberculosis, and infections of the skin and subcutaneous tissue. Malaria is the most widespread disease and the greatest cause of morbidity, and a high priority is given by the health services to its control. Tuberculosis, while more common in the coastal areas than in the interior, is decreasing owing to modern methods of treatment including B.C.G. vaccine, case finding, and thoracic surgery. Infections of the skin and subcutaneous tissue are common. *Tinea imbricata* in particular is widespread. The incidence of venereal disease is very low. The incidence of leprosy is very high in some areas, but leprosy colonies have been established and treatment is given in Administration and mission hospitals. A long-range investigation to determine the efficiency of B.C.G. vaccination in the control of leprosy is in progress.

Having escaped the hazards of infancy and early childhood, his expectation of life as an adult must remain uncertain until more reliable vital statistics are available. His death when it comes will probably not be due to cardiovascular disease, which is relatively infrequent, but most likely to some disease of the respiratory system. Pneumonia, malaria, infections of the alimentary canal, and pulmonary tuberculosis are the chief causes of death, and of these pneumonia is by far the most frequent. In the Highlands, as might be expected, seasonal outbreaks of pneumonia occur leading to deaths chiefly in the very young and the very old.

Nutrition

The dominating practical problem facing New Guineans today is simply that of food, and it is not extravagant to say that, as the population may be expected to 'explode' in the next few years as a result of a reduction in infantile mortality and an increased expectation of life, a crisis of great magnitude is at hand. The problem in its simplest terms is one of protein deficiency.

The diet of the New Guinea native is substantially vegetarian. The only domestic animal, the pig, is seldom eaten except on festive occasions. At other times the diet consists of sweet potato (*Ipomea batatas*), taro (*Colocasia* spp.), yams (*Dioscorea* spp.), pit pit (*Saccharum edule* or *Setaria palmafolia*), together with several species of beans. In the coastal region fish is added, and sago (*Metroxylon sagu*) and coconuts may be substituted for the sweet potato. In some areas, for example the Markham Valley (Read, 1946, 1950), bananas are extensively cultivated. All these, with the exception of the fish and beans, are extremely low in protein. Kau-kau (sweet potato) varies widely in composition between varieties, but even the best are mostly water and a man may have to eat as much as 2 kg/day to obtain the necessary calories. It is estimated that kau-kau in Highland areas supplies at least 90 per cent of the total calories. The deficiencies of this diet are, as would be expected, especially apparent in children. Kwashiorkor and marasmus are common.

The health authorities are well aware of the problem. Indeed, as far back as 1936 Clements (1936), in a very comprehensive paper, showed that dietary deficiencies might play a part in the aetiology of tropical ulcer. Remedial action by the Government has taken several directions, the introduction of cattle and the improvement of the breed of pigs; the teaching of improved agricultural practices to replace the primitive methods in use today; the introduction of cash crops such as coffee, cocoa, rubber, and tea, to improve the economic status of the people; and the introduction of new crops, such as beans and peanuts which are rich in protein, in order to remedy, especially for the growing child, the absence of adequate supplies of milk and other sources of high grade protein in the Western diet.

Considerable research is being directed to the clinical aspects of nutrition and an extensive study of the diet of the Chimbu people has recently been published (Venkatachalam, 1962). It embraces a consideration of the adult diet, infant feeding, lactation, composition of breast milk, morbidity and mortality statistics, the birthweight and the growth of infants, biochemical investigations in the laboratory, and finally necropsy and histopathological studies. It could well be taken as a model for future surveys.

There has also recently been published a review of nutrition in the whole of the Territory of Papua and New Guinea (Bailey, 1963a) by the Specialist Medical Officer (Nutrition) with the Department of Public Health, and this should be consulted for an authoritative statement on the present position. In this review it is stated that, 'It is now well established that the main public health nutritional problem in the Territory is protein-calorie malnutrition in infants and toddlers.' At the same time he points out that the position can be emotionally exaggerated. The incidence of infantile malnutrition is high, but in a casual visit to a village one sees only an occasional malnourished child among hordes of healthy ones. In this paper also, the author considers at length the question of protein supplements for infants and toddlers and stresses the value of peanuts. This he also discusses elsewhere (Bailey, 1963b). Two other papers which may be consulted with advantage are those by Oomen and Malcolm (1958) on nutrition in

Papuan children and Ryan and Murrell (1964) on nutrition and infection in Papuan children. Ryan and Murrell advance the hypothesis that malnutrition plus infection produces the kwashiorkor syndrome. This is particularly interesting because it has been suggested in Africa that cold can precipitate kwashiorker in marasmic children (Lawless and Lawless, 1963).

Goitre is widespread in New Guinea, particularly in the Highlands. Experimental work, including the therapeutic effect of injections of iodized oil, has shown that the aetiological factor is iodine deficiency, and consideration has been given to the introduction of a public health programme of goitre prevention by wide-scale periodic injections of iodized oil (Hennessy, 1964).

The importance of diet in the physiological characteristics of New Guinea natives has been emphasized in a recent paper by Barnes (1965), who determined the height-weight ratio, arm circumference, blood pressure, blood cholesterol, and urinary chlorides in a group of Europeans and three groups of indigenes living in the Chimbu sub-district in the Eastern Highlands. The three native groups had respectively no access, very restricted, and considerable access to European articles of diet and a roughly comparable access to tobacco and alcohol. The results showed that the values for all the variables measured conformed strikingly closely to the degree of 'civilization' of the group concerned. The significance of this with respect to the present and future disease patterns of the native population is discussed.

This paper is important for another reason also. It indicates the growing attention being paid to comparative and multidisciplinary studies in New Guinea even though individual investigations may be on a comparatively modest scale.

THE CAUCASIAN IN THE AUSTRALIAN AND NEW GUINEA REGIONS

Some 11 million Caucasians live in the Australian and New Guinea regions and their number is growing both by natural increase and, as Table 3 (taken from *Year Book of the Commonwealth of Australia*, 1964) shows, by the prosecution of an energetic migration programme. In pursuance of established policy, the general practice is not to permit persons of non-European descent to enter Australia for the purpose of settling permanently and, although exceptions are made on a number of counts, the result is that the population of Australia proper is remarkably uniformly European in origin and as yet predominantly of British stock. Though there is some tendency for the segregation of national groups, for example the Italian communities in North Queensland, the immigrants as a whole are being assimilated to form a homogeneous population.

TABLE 3

Commonwealth of Australia. Arrivals of assisted migrants,
January 1947 to June 1963

Source	No. of migrants
Austria	17,122
Belgium	1,152
General Assisted Passage†	20,188
Germany	69,814
Greece	33,608
Italy	45,420
Malta	28,944
Netherlands	65,649
Refugee	202,871
Spain	7,880
United Kingdom	469,638
Other schemes	28,098
Total	990,384

† Mostly Scandinavians, U.S. Americans and British nationals from countries other than the United Kingdom.

It has been recognized from the earliest times that life in the hot northern regions and the arid centre of the continent might well require a considerable degree of physiological adaptation. The systematic study of possible adaptations may be considered to have begun with the establishment of the Australian Institute of Tropical Medicine at Townsville in 1909. The work done at this Institute until it was closed in 1930 was concerned chiefly with the general problems of acclimatization, including temperature regulation and the effects of heat on the cardiovascular system. Reference to much of this work will be found in Sundstroem (1926) and it has been reviewed by Macpherson (1949). The work at Townsville was later continued and extended at Brisbane by

Lee and his co-workers (Lee, 1940; Lee and Boissard, 1940; Lee, Murray, Simmonds, and Atherton, 1941). During the Second World War a study was made of the effects of service in New Guinea on Australian troops (Macpherson, 1949) which showed that any deterioration when present was largely psychological in nature, but that the climate did impose a severe stress particularly on the skin.

The increasing industrialization of the north and centre of Australia, much of which is concerned with mining, has focused attention on salt and water requirements. In this field Macfarlane and his co-workers have been particularly active and much of this work is conveniently summarized in a recent review article (Macfarlane, 1963).

At the invitation of the Commonwealth Government, a survey was made in 1956 of environmental problems in tropical Australia with special reference to the Northern Territory and New Guinea. The results of this survey have been published (Macpherson, 1956) and the author lists a considerable number of topics, mainly of a physiological nature, on which he considers further research is desirable for the proper understanding of the effects of a hot climate on man and the amelioration of the lot of those who have to live in such an environment.

Work to date in Australia has largely gone to show that for Europeans the hazards to life in the tropics, which were once thought to exist, are largely imaginary. For example, the work of Patrick (1951) and that of Refshauge (1955), on the heights and weights of schoolchildren in Queensland and New Guinea respectively, have shown that children grow and thrive in these environments. Perhaps as a result of the removal of these fears, or perhaps on account of the increasing sophistication of the community, there has been an increasing interest shown in the factors which determine thermal comfort.

The finding of Hindmarsh and Macpherson (1962) that the preferred environmental temperature in Sydney for indoor sedentary workers is 73°F has been confirmed by others elsewhere in Australia, and the interesting fact has emerged that effective acclimatization to heat does not raise to any great extent the level of the preferred temperature. Of equal importance in a sophisticated community is the level of environmental temperature at which sleep becomes disturbed. Studies in a community in the

Northern Territory (Macpherson and Muncey, 1962) showed that when the average night temperature exceeded 76°F there was a sharp increase in the disturbance of sleep by excessive warmth.

When it is said that fears for the effect of a tropical climate on health and well-being of a predominantly Caucasian population have proved to be ill-founded, it is not meant to imply that such environments are not without serious discomfort. Furthermore, extremes of environmental temperature do constitute a hazard to the vulnerable groups in the community—the sick, the very old, and the very young. During heat-waves, even in the southern parts of Australia, mortality among very young children can be high (Danks, Webb, and Allen, 1962). At the other end of the life scale, recent studies in a hospital for the aged and chronically ill have shown (Macpherson and Ofner, 1965) that the mean number of deaths per day during summer and autumn was 1·58 on days on which the maximum temperature was 80°F or more compared with 1·06 on days on which the maximum temperature was less than 80°F.

One hazard to health, if not to life (which as yet appears inevitable) in the northern parts of Australia is the danger of developing cancer of the skin. Europeans, especially blonde Europeans, in tropical Australia are particularly susceptible to cancer of the skin (Blum, 1940; Cooper, 1956; Carmichael, 1962), and, as Lancaster (1956) has shown, exhibit an increased incidence of melanoma. Pigmentation of the skin provides an important protection from skin cancer and this serves to emphasize the necessity for further work on the pigmentation of the skin. It is not without interest that Abbie (1960b) found that one of the results of the adoption of Western ways by the Australian aboriginal is a diminution in the pigmentation of his skin.

The Commonwealth of Australia and its territories stretch from the Equator to the South Pole—from Nauru Island (0° 32′ S) to the Australian Antarctic Territory. In Antarctica a number of stations are permanently manned, and at these stations active research on adaptation to cold has been conducted for some years past by medical officers of the Australian National Antarctic Research Expeditions in association with the School of Public Health and Tropical Medicine of the University of Sydney. This includes continuing studies of changes in the weight, skinfold thickness, blood pressure, body temperature, food intake, and thermal comfort standards of members of the expeditions through-out their stay in Antarctica. In addition, individual projects are undertaken—for example, studies of the dietary patterns at the base stations and in the field (especially in relation to the intake of fats), serum cholesterol studies, the effect of exposure to cold on blood-clotting time (Hicks, 1965), and the role of noradrenaline in acclimatization to cold. It would seem that there is unequivocal evidence that acclimatization to cold does occur (Budd, 1962, 1964).

SUGGESTIONS FOR FUTURE RESEARCH

The Australian Aborigines

The lacunae in our knowledge of the physiological adaptation of the Australian aborigines to their way of life should be evident from the account which has been given, but it is convenient to recapitulate them here as suggestions for future research.

Much remains to be learned concerning temperature regulation in the heat and in the cold, salt and water balance in arid regions, nutritional status and rate of growth, blood chemistry, blood pressure in relation to age and diet, the acuity of the special senses, and skin pigmentation. Although this work is especially important in relation to aborigines still living their traditional way of life, it should also embrace aborigines in progressive grades of Euro-peanization to detect the alterations which accompany this change, and part-aborigines to assess the results of interbreeding. Finally, studies in the aborigines should be correlated with similar investi-gations on possibly related peoples in neighbouring countries. All these, but particularly this last, will contribute to a solution of the greatest challenge offered by the aboriginal people—the riddle of their origin.

The New Guineans

It has been said of The Netherlands New Guinea (de Bruijn, 1958) that it '. . . is an earthly paradise for anthropological research. In this twentieth century with its rapidly disintegrating primitive culture the Territory still offers numerous opportunities for anthropological studies of cultures barely influenced or even untouched by Western culture.' This is in a large measure true for the island of New Guinea as a whole.

To list individual topics in any detail would be tedious, but it should be clear from what has been said that a vast amount of information, anthropometric, physiological and genetic, could readily be gathered. Opportunities for the study of adaptation to heat, and, in mountain communities, to cold, and to altitude exist. Fitness, growth, and physique can be studied against a varied background of race, nutrition, environment, and endemic disease. Energy expenditure, especially the pattern of energy expenditure, in native communities should be measured. The effect of urbanization and the adoption of Western patterns of diet and clothing deserves attention. Skin pigmentation, salt and water metabolism, mineral metabolism, including the relation between iodine intake and goitre, dental development, the composition of body fluids, saliva, sweat, urine, and milk, are all of interest. The country seems to be a geneticist's happy hunting ground, and the epidemiologist has splendid opportunities to study a community free from many of the diseases of civilized life, especially those of the cardiovascular system. It goes without saying that proper co-ordination would enhance the value of any studies which might be undertaken.

The Caucasians

Europeans in the Australian region provide excellent opportunities for the study of the effects of both heat and cold and any suggestions for future research can only be based on a personal judgement of their order of priority.

For the peoples occupying the continent of Australia the pressing problems would seem to be the special reactions to hot environments of infants, women, the aged, and the infirm; the effect of climate on fertility; the physiology of skin and of the sweating mechanism; skin tanning and protection from ultraviolet light; water and salt intake; renal function and water balance, especially in the arid zone. From a scientific point of view, perhaps the most attractive topic is the comparative study of adaptation to both heat and cold in the Australian population with the opportunities it would provide for a much-needed further elucidation of the underlying nervous and endocrine changes which control the mechanisms, both short- and long-term, of acclimatization.

Acknowledgements. It is a pleasant duty to acknowledge that assistance has been received from many sources in the preparation of this paper, but special help has been given by Dr. E. H. Hipsley of the Australian Institute of Anatomy, Canberra, Dr. W. A. Langsford, Commonwealth Director of Health, Darwin, Dr. R. J. Walsh of the New South Wales Red Cross Blood Transfusion Service, Sydney, and Dr. H. M. Whyte of the Kanematsu Memorial Institute, Sydney. It is also thought proper that attention might be drawn to the fact that a considerable body of the work to which reference has been made in this paper has been supported by the Wenner-Gren Foundation for Anthropological Research.

REFERENCES

ABBIE, A. A., 1951. 'The Australian aborigine', *Oceania* 22, 91–100.
—— 1957. 'Metrical characters of a Central Australian tribe', *Oceania* 27, 220–243.
—— 1960a. 'The future Australian aboriginal', *Med. J. Aust.* 1, 146.
—— 1960b. 'Physical changes in Australian aborigines consequent upon European contact', *Oceania* 31, 140–144.
—— 1961a. 'Recent field work on the physical anthropology of Australian aborigines', *Aust. J. Sci.* 23, 210–211.
—— 1961b. 'A preliminary survey of the growth pattern of central Australian aboriginal males', *Oceania* 31, 215–221.
—— and SCHRODER, JUDITH, 1960. 'Blood pressures in Arnhem Land aborigines', *Med. J. Aust.* 2, 493–496.
ALLEN, J. A., 1877. 'The influence of physical conditions in the genesis of species', *Radical Rev.* 1, 108–140.
ARMYTAGE, JEAN, KOOPTZOFF, OLGA, and WALSH, R. J., 1959. 'A study of the haemoglobin values and blood groups of some indigenous natives of the Bulolo River Valley, New Guinea', *Oceania* 29, 297–301.
BAILEY, K. V., 1963a. 'Nutrition in New Guinea', *Food Nutr. Notes Rev.* 20, 89–112.
—— 1963b. 'Malnutrition in New Guinea children and its treatment with solid peanut food', *J. trop. Pediat.* 9, 35–43.
BAKKER, ANNA W. I., BLIEK, A., and LUYKEN, R., 1957. 'The serum proteins of malaria-free inhabitants of Central Netherlands New-Guinea', *Documenta Med. geogr. trop.* 9, 1–8.
BARNES, R., 1965. 'Comparisons of blood pressures and blood cholesterol levels of New Guineans and Australians', *Med. J. Aust.* 1, 611–617.
BENNETT, J. H., 1962. 'Population studies in the kuru region of New Guinea', *Oceania* 33, 24–46.
—— GRAY, A. J., and AURICHT, C. O., 1959. 'The genetical study of kuru', *Med. J. Aust.* 2, 505–508.
BERGMANN, C., 1847. 'Über die Verhältnisse der Warmeökonomie des Thiere zu ihrer Grösse', *Gottinger Studien* 3, 595–708.
BLUM, H. F., 1940. 'Sunlight and cancer of the skin', *J. nat. Cancer Inst.* 1, 397–421.
BROWNE, W. R., 1963. 'Some problems of dating the past'. In *Australian Aboriginal Studies* (ed. HELEN SHIELS). Oxford University Press, Melbourne.

BUDD, G. M., 1962. 'Acclimatization to cold in Antarctica as shown by rectal temperature response to a standard cold stress', *Nature, Lond.* **193**, 886.

—— 1964. 'General acclimatization to cold in men studied before, during and after a year in Antarctica', *ANARE Reports, Series B,* **4**, *Publication No.* 70. Department of External Affairs, Melbourne.

CARMICHAEL, G. G., 1962. 'A survey of skin cancers and solar keratoses in country areas in Queensland', *Med. J. Aust.* **1**, 395–400.

CASLEY-SMITH, J. R., 1959. 'Blood pressures in Australian aborigines', *Med. J. Aust.* **1**, 627–633.

CHAMPNESS, L. T., KOOPTZOFF, OLGA, and WALSH, R. J., 1960. 'A study of the population near Aiome, New Guinea', *Oceania* **30**, 294–304.

CILENTO, R., 1942. *Tropical Diseases in Australia.* Smith and Paterson, Brisbane.

CLELAND, J. B., 1960. 'The future of the Australian aboriginal', *Med. J. Aust.* **1**, 28–29.

CLEMENTS, F. W., 1936. 'Tropical ulcer with special reference to its aetiology', *Med. J. Aust.* **2**, 615–644.

COOPER, A. G. S., 1956. 'Skin cancer', *Australian Academy of Science Symposium on Man and Animals in the Tropics,* p. 75. Australian Academy of Science, Canberra.

CORDEN, MARGARET, 1962. 'Observations on food habits of Europeans and aborigines in the Northern Territory', *Food Nutr. Notes Rev.* **19**, 3–8.

COTTER, HELEN and WALSH, R. J., 1958. 'Haemoglobin values in some Pacific native groups', *Med. J. Aust.* **2**, 603–604.

COUVÉE, L. M. J., NUGTEREN, D. H., and LUYKEN, R., 1962. 'The nutritional condition of the Kapaukus in the Central Highlands of Netherlands New Guinea. 1. Biochemical examinations', *Trop. geogr. Med.* **14**, 27–32.

CROTTY, J. M., 1958. 'Anaemia and nutritional disease in Northern Territory native children', *Med. J. Aust.* **2**, 322–325.

—— and WEBB, R. C., 1960. 'Mortality in Northern Territory aborigines', *Med. J. Aust.* **2**, 489–492.

DAMPIER, W., 1729. 'Voyages', *The Discovery of Australia* (WOOD, G. A., 1922). Macmillan ,London.

DANKS, D. M., WEBB, D. W., and ALLEN, JEAN, 1962. 'Heat illness in infants and young children. A study of 47 cases', *Brit. med. J.* **2**, 287–293.

DE BRUIJN, J. V., 1958. 'Anthropological research in Netherlands New Guinea since 1950', *Oceania* **29**, 132–163.

DE WOLFE, M. S. and WHYTE, H. M., 1958. 'Serum cholesterol and lipoproteins in natives of New Guinea and Australians', *Aust. Ann. Med.* **7**, 47–54.

DUGUID, C., 1960. 'The future of the Australian aboriginal', *Med. J. Aust.* **1**, 145–146.

EVERINGHAM, D., 1960. 'The future of the Australian aboriginal', *Med. J. Aust.* **1**, 146–147.

FORTUNE, R. F., 1960. 'Statistics of kuru', *Med. J. Aust.* **1**, 764–765.

GAJDUSEK, D. C. and ZIGAS, V. 1959. 'Kuru: Clinical, pathological and epidemiological study of an acute degenerative disease of the central nervous system among natives of the Eastern Highlands of New Guinea', *Am. J. Med.* **26**, 442–469.

GOLDBY, F., HICKS, C. S., O'CONNOR, W. J., and SINCLAIR, D. A., 1938. 'A comparison of the skin temperature and skin circulation of naked whites and Australian aboriginals exposed to similar environmental changes', *Aust. J. exp. Biol. med. Sci.* **16**, 29–37.

GOLDRICK, R. B., 1961. 'Fibrinolysis, blood clotting, serum lipids and body build in natives of New Guinea and Australians', *Aust. Ann. Med.* **10**, 20–28.

—— and WHYTE, H. M., 1959. 'A study of blood clotting and serum lipids in natives of New Guinea and Australians', *Aust. Ann. Med.* **8**, 238–244.

HAMMEL, H. T., ELSNER, R. W., LeMESSURIER, D. H., ANDERSEN, H. T., and MILAN, F. A., 1959. 'Thermal and metabolic responses of the Australian aborigine exposed to moderate cold in summer', *J. appl. Physiol.* **14**, 605–615.

HEITHERSAY, G., 1959. 'A dental survey of the aborigines at Haast's Bluff, Central Australia', *Med. J. Aust.* **1**, 721–729.

HENNESSY, W. B., 1964. 'Goitre prophylaxis in New Guinea with intramuscular injections of iodized oil', *Med. J. Aust.* **1**, 505–512.

HICKS, C. S., 1964. 'Terrestrial animals in cold: exploratory studies of primitive man', *Handbook of Physiology, Section 4, Adaptation to the Environment* (ed. D. B. DILL), Chap. 25. American Physiological Society, Washington.

—— and MATTERS, R. F., 1933. 'The standard metabolism of the Australian aborigines', *Aust. J. exp. Biol. med. Sci.* **11**, 177–183.

—— —— and MITCHELL, M. L., 1931. 'The standard metabolism of Australian aboriginals', *Aust. J. exp. Biol. med. Sci.* **8**, 69–82.

—— MOORE, H. O. and ELDRIDGE, E., 1934. 'The respiratory exchange of the Australian aborigine', *Aust. J. exp. Biol. med. Sci.* **12**, 79–89.

—— and O'CONNOR, W. J., 1938a. 'Skin temperature of Australian aboriginals under varying atmospheric conditions', *Aust. J. exp. Biol. med. Sci.* **16**, 1–18.

—— —— 1938b. 'The effect of changes of environmental temperature on the skin circulation of the naked Australian aboriginal, as measured by the Sahli-Jaquet Volumebolograph', *Aust. J. exp. Biol. med. Sci.* **16**, 19–28.

HICKS, K. E., 1965. 'Changes in blood-clotting time, serum-cholesterol level, and plasma-prothrombin index in Antarctica', *Lancet* **1**, 30–32.

HINDMARSH, Margaret E. and MACPHERSON, R. K., 1962. 'Thermal comfort in Australia', *Aust. J. Sci.* **24**, 335–339.

HOGG, J. B., 1960. 'The future of the Australian aboriginal', *Med. J. Aust.* **1**, 145.

IVINSKIS, V., KOOPTZOFF, OLGA, WALSH, R. J., and DUNN, DIANE, 1956. 'A medical and anthropological study of the Chimbu natives in the Central Highlands of New Guinea', *Oceania* **27**, 143–157.

JANSEN, A. A. J., LUYKEN, R., MALCOLM, S. H., and WILLEMS, J. J. L., 1960. 'Quantity and composition of breast milk in Biak Island (Neth. New Guinea)', *Trop. geogr. Med.* **2**, 138–144.

JÜPTNER, H., KOOPTZOFF, OLGA, and WALSH, R. J., 1958. 'The blood groups of some native inhabitants of the Gulf District, New Guinea', *Oceania* **29**, 123–126.

KARIKS, J., KOOPTZOFF, OLGA, COTTER, HELEN, and WALSH, R. J., 1958. 'A study of the heights, weights, haemoglobin values and blood groups of the natives of the Goilala Sub-district, Papua', *Oceania* **29**, 117–122.

—— —— STEED, MARGARET, COTTER, HELEN, and WALSH, R. J., 1960. 'A study of some physical characteristics of the Goroka natives, New Guinea', *Oceania* **30**, 225–236.

KIRK, NANCY E. and HIPSLEY, E. H., 1961. 'Review of progress in nutrition in Australia and the Territory of Papua–New Guinea', *Food Nutr. Notes Rev.* **18**, 66–87.

LANCASTER, H. O., 1956. 'Some geographical aspects of the mortality from melanoma in Europeans', *Med. J. Aust.* **1**, 1082–1087.

LAWLESS, J. and LAWLESS, MARGARET M., 1963. 'Kwashiorkor—The result of cold injury in a malnourished child', *Lancet* **2**, 972–974.

LEE, D. H. K., 1940. 'A basis for the study of man's reaction to tropical climates', *Univ. Qld. Pap. (Physiol.)* **1**, No. 5.

—— and BOISSARD, G. P. B., 1940. 'The effect of exercise in hot atmospheres upon the pulse rate', *Med. J. Aust.* **2**, 664–668.

—— MURRAY, R. E., SIMMONDS, W. J., and ATHERTON, R. G., 1941. 'The effect of exercise in hot atmospheres upon the salt-water balance of human subjects', *Med. J. Aust.* **2**, 249–258.

LUYKEN, R. and JANSEN, A. A. J., 1960. 'The cholesterol level in the blood serum of some population groups in New-Guinea', *Trop. geogr. Med.* **2**, 145–148.

—— and LUYKEN-KONING, F. W. M., 1956. 'Nutrition and nutritional status of urban and rural Papuans in Netherlands New-Guinea', *Documenta Med. geogr. trop.* **8**, 45–54.

—— —— 1958. 'Nutritional state of the Marind-anim tribe in South New Guinea', *Documenta Med. geogr. trop.* **7**, 315–339.

—— —— and PIKAAR, N. A., 1963. 'Nutritional studies in sweet potato areas of New Guinea. 2. The excretion of nitrogen compounds and sulphur in urine by Papuan children on sweet potato diets with and without supplements', *Central Institute for Nutrition and Food Research T.N.O., Utrecht, Report No. R 1620.*

MCDOUGALL, W., 1901. 'Cutaneous sensations', 'Muscular sense' and 'Variations of blood-pressure', *Reports of the Cambridge Anthropological Expedition to Torres Straits*, Vol. 2, Part 2. University Press, Cambridge.

MACFARLANE, W. V., 1963. 'Endocrine functions in hot environments', *Environmental Physiology and Psychology in Arid Conditions: Reviews of Research*, pp. 153–222. U.N.E.S.C.O., Paris.

—— HOWARD, BETH, and HIPSLEY, E., 1964. 'Water and salt metabolism of the Chimbu', *Proc. Aust. physiol. Soc.* 20–22 May 1964, p. 26.

MACINTOSH, N. W. G., 1949. 'A survey of possible sea routes available to the Tasmanian aborigines', *Rec. Queen Vict. Mus.* **2**, 123–144.

MACLENNAN, R., KOOPTZOFF, OLGA, and WALSH, R. J., 1960a. 'A survey of the blood groups and haemoglobin values of natives in the Mount Hagen area, New Guinea', *Oceania* **30**, 313–320.

—— —— —— 1960b. 'A survey of the blood groups and haemoglobin values in the Sepik River district', *Oceania* **30**, 305–312.

MACPHERSON, R. K., 1949, 'Tropical fatigue', *Univ. Qld. Pap. (Physiol.)* **1**, No. 10.

—— 1956. *Environmental Problems in Tropical Australia.* Commonwealth Government Printer, Canberra.

—— and MUNCEY, R. W., 1962. 'The disturbance of sleep by excessive warmth', *Aust. J. Sci.* **24**, 454–456.

—— and OFNER, F., 1965. 'Heat and the survival of the aged and chronically ill', *Med. J. Aust.* **1**, 292–295.

MEGGITT, M. J., 1962. *Desert People.* Angus and Robertson, Sydney.

MOUNTFORD, C. P. (ed.), 1960. *Records of the American–Australian Scientific Expedition to Arnhem Land*, Vol. 2, *Anthropology and Nutrition.* Melbourne University Press, Parkville.

MULVANEY, D. J., 1963. 'Prehistory'. In *Australian Aboriginal Studies* (ed. HELEN SHEILS). Oxford University Press, Melbourne.

MYERS, C. S., 1901. 'Hearing', 'smell', 'taste', and 'reaction-times', *Reports of the Cambridge Anthropological Expedition to Torres Straits*, Vol. 2, Part 2. University Press, Cambridge.

OOMEN, H. A. P. C. and MALCOLM, S. H., 1958. 'Nutrition and the Papuan child', *South Pacific Commission Technical Paper No.* 118.

PACKER, A. D., 1961. 'The health of the Australian native', *Oceania* **32**, 60–70.

PATRICK, P. R., 1951. 'Heights and weights of Queensland school children with particular reference to the tropics', *Med. J. Aust.* **2**, 324–331.

READ, K. E., 1946. 'Social organization in the Markham Valley, New Guinea', *Oceania* **17**, 93–118.

—— 1950. 'The political system of the Ngarawapum', *Oceania* **20**, 185–223.

REFSHAUGE, JOAN J., 1955. 'Heights and weights of Port Moresby European school children', *Papua New Guin. Med. J.* **1**, 41–48.

RIECKMANN, K. H., KOOPTZOFF, OLGA, and WALSH, R. J., 1961. 'Blood groups and haemoglobin values in the Telefomin area, New Guinea', *Oceania* **31**, 296–304.

RIVERS, W. H. R., 1901. 'Vision', *Reports of the Cambridge Anthropological Expedition to Torres Straits*, Vol. 2, Part 1. University Press, Cambridge.

ROWLEY, C. D., 1962. 'Aborigines and other Australians', *Oceania* **32**, 247–266.

RYAN, B. and MURRELL, T. G. C., 1964. 'Nutrition and infection in Papuan children', *Med. J. Aust.* **1**, 556–559.

SCHOLANDER, P. F., HAMMEL, H. T., ANDERSEN, K. L., and LØYNING, Y., 1958. 'Metabolic acclimation to cold in man', *J. appl. Physiol.* **12**, 1–8.

—— —— HART, J. S., LEMESSURIER, D. H., and STEEN, J., 1958. 'Cold adaptation in Australian aborigines', *J. appl. Physiol.* **13**, 211–218.

SCHWARTZ, C. J. and CASLEY-SMITH, J. R., 1958. 'Serum cholesterol levels in atherosclerotic subjects and in the Australian aborigines', *Med. J. Aust.* **2**, 84–86.

—— DAY, A. J., PETERS, J. A., and CASLEY-SMITH, J. R., 1957. 'Serum cholesterol and phospholipid levels of Australian aborigines', *Aust. J. exp. Biol. med. Sci.* **35**, 449–456.

SCRAGG, R. F. R., 1962. 'Health in the Papua and New Guinea village', *Med. J. Aust.* **1**, 389–395.

SELIGMANN, C. G., 1909. 'A classification of the natives of British New Guinea', *Jl R. anthrop. Inst.* **39**, 246–275.

SPENCER, B. and GILLEN, F. J., 1927. *The Arunta. A Study of a Stone Age People* (2 volumes). Macmillan, London.

SUNDSTROEM, E. S., 1926. 'Contributions to tropical physiology', *Univ. Calif. Publs Physiol.* **6**, 1–216.

VENKATACHALAM, P. S., 1962. 'A study of the diet, nutrition and health of the people of the Chimbu area (New Guinea Highlands)', *Territory of Papua and New Guinea Department of Public Health Monograph No. 4.*

VOORS, A. W., 1956. 'Growth curve in Papuans', *Documenta Med. geogr. trop.* **8**, 167–170.

WALSH, R. J., 1963. 'Variations of melanin pigmentation of the skin in some Asian and Pacific peoples', *Jl R. anthrop. Inst.* **93**, 126–133.

―― COTTER, HELEN, and MACINTOSH, N. W. G., 1959. 'Haemoglobin values of natives in the Western Highlands, New Guinea', *Med. J. Aust.* **1**, 834–836.

―― JAMESON, J. L., and KOOPTZOFF, OLGA, 1960. 'Blood groups and haemoglobin values of natives from Minj, New Guinea', *Oceania* **31**, 77–82.

WHYTE, H. M., 1958. 'Body fat and blood pressure of natives in New Guinea: Reflections on essential hypertension', *Aust. Ann. Med.* **7**, 36–46.

―― 1963. 'Body build and blood pressure of men in Australia and New Guinea', *Aust. J. exp. Biol. med. Sci.* **41**, 395–404.

―― GRAHAM, I. A. D., and DE WOLFE, M. S., 1958. 'Body fat, blood pressure and serum cholesterol of Australian men', *Aust. Ann. Med.* **7**, 328–335.

―― and YEE, IRIS L., 1958. 'Serum cholesterol levels of Australians and natives of New Guinea from birth to adulthood', *Aust. Ann. Med.* **7**, 336–339.

WILLS, PAMELA A., 1958. 'Salt consumption by natives of the Territory of Papua and New Guinea', *Philipp. J. Sci.* **87**, 169–177.

WYNDHAM, C. H., MACPHERSON, R. K., and MUNRO, A., 1964. 'Reactions to heat of aborigines and Caucasians', *J. appl. Physiol.* **19**, 1055–1058.

YEAR BOOK, 1963. *Official Year Book of the Commonwealth of Australia,* No. 49. Commonwealth Government Printer, Canberra.

YEAR BOOK, 1964. *Official Year Book of the Commonwealth of Australia,* No. 50. Commonwealth Government Printer, Canberra.

ZIGAS, V. and GAJDUSEK, D. C., 1957. 'Kuru: Clinical study of a new syndrome resembling paralysis agitans in natives of the Eastern Highlands of Australian New Guinea', *Med. J. Aust.* **2**, 745–754.

15

GENETICAL AND ANTHROPOLOGICAL CHARACTERISTICS OF ARCTIC POPULATIONS

W. S. LAUGHLIN

Department of Anthropology, University of Wisconsin

THE genetically diverse populations inhabiting similar Arctic habitats, together with the genetically similar populations inhabiting more diverse Arctic habitats constitute in themselves a comparison matrix in which generalizations can be formulated and tested. Another basis for testing generalizations is that provided by well-preserved skeletal populations that are demonstrably ancestral to living populations and not simply earlier populations who preceded them in the same place. By strict definition only a minority of populations commonly labelled 'Arctic' live inside the Arctic Circle. The majority of Eskimos and Aleuts live south of the Arctic Circle in Greenland, Canada, and Alaska. It is fortunate for research purposes that the same people are distributed continuously from the high Arctic to the sub-Arctic and it is unnecessary to be concerned with artificial boundaries. Viewed with reference to circumpolar distribution, populations of the Mongoloid division of our species are clearly the dominant occupants of northern regions with few but important exceptions. The Lapps of Norway, Sweden, Finland, and Russia represent a clearly defined White group (European or Caucasian) who are well-established. The Medieval Norse colonies of south-west Greenland represent an informative experiment by another White group that did not succeed in establishing a continuing population. The principal aim of this paper will be to discuss variation primarily among the Eskimos and Aleuts of the New World and Siberia, and among Siberian Mongoloids, with comparative references to the intrusive White groups and to the closely related American Indians. The sibling Eskimos and Aleuts span the longest linear area in the world, extending from the Aleutian Islands and Chukchi Peninsula in the west, across the North American continent to the east coast of Greenland. Though not numerous, except in their more southern areas, they have occupied a variety of ecological zones ranging from the most northerly position permanently occupied by any human group, the Thule District of northern Greenland, to the sub-Arctic area of Alaska.

The large number of studies performed on arctic peoples is not yet commensurate with the analytical possibilities, and there are many gaps in the data as well as in the analysis of the data. The remarkable tenacity of arctic populations in accommodating to changes and the general populations increase, much in hybrid populations, gives assurance of their importance for scientific studies in the future, though the strategy of studies must include several new methods.

Serological characterization

The blood groups provide an efficient method of characterizing the principal peoples under discussion. Among the Eskimos and Aleuts A_1, M, R_1, R_2, are high in their frequencies, B is low but variable, Kell and Diego are absent, and all are Duffy positive. The latter three have not been tested in Aleuts. Within the Eskimo distribution the central Arctic departs markedly from the values for Alaska and for Greenland. This is particularly noticeable in the low values for A_1 and for B, and for the lower R_1 and R_2, which tend to approximate each other. In distinction to this the R_1 gene is substantially higher in the East and in the West. Thus, there is not a cline but rather a central block which departs from the isolates on either side. Early studies of Heinbecker and Pauli (1927) which included some Polar Eskimos indicated a very low A and B frequency. This appears to be confirmed by the recent studies of Gürtler and colleagues (personal communication). Incompletely analysed morphological data of Jørgensen, Laughlin, and Gilberg, personal communication (study conducted 1963) on the Polar Eskimos suggests that they may prove to be more similar to Canadian Eskimos than to other Greenlandic Eskimos and this suggestion is in keeping with their low A and B frequency. Their high degree of isolation and their proximity to Canadian Eskimos are relevant geographical factors.

Within the Eskimo–Aleut area, and likely Siberia and among the

Indians, the genes for A_2, K, C^w, r, and Fy^b may be reliably attributed to White contact. A distinct rise in the N gene is common and a depression of A_1 where the frequency was high. Diego may be introduced by either Indians or Japanese and R_0 has been introduced by Negro admixture. The relatively high frequency of A_2 in a Koniag isolate or deme is attributable to economic success and not to selective advantage nor to heterosis. The effects of White admixture are also detectable in baldness, increased amount of hair, pigmentation, nose form, and other morphological characters but not reliably in stature increase, for which the data, generally inadequate, suggests the possibility that hybrid statures are below expectation. Russian admixture must have included many Siberian Mongoloids who differed little from the western Alaskan populations. Similarly, Chinese admixture made possible by the presence of several hundreds of Chinese working in canneries on Kodiak Island, would not be detectable except for Diego or R_z.

An explanation for the depressed A and B frequencies and the lowered R_1 in the central Arctic area cannot yet be provided though possible explanations may be highly illuminating and lead to some useful analysis. One suggestion is that of genetic drift (Laughlin, 1950). This area had low population density, the total number likely being no more than 7000 or 8000 which is approximately the number of Koniag Eskimos alone, the greater number of whom occupied Kodiak Island. Further, these Eskimos lived in small groups that were separated by considerable distances and were frequently subjected to complete extinction, as in the case of the Sadlermiut Eskimos of Southampton Island who became extinct in 1903. The Polar Eskimos were convinced that they were the only people in the world at the time of their discovery in 1818. Many of these groups were highly mobile and had difficulty in finding suitable mates. While the ecological and demographic features are prominently involved and contributed to some true inbreeding, inbreeding as such does not appear to have been common, and it may properly be considered rare for the entire area. Inbreeding effect, on the other hand, which is found among isolates of a population which are small in size and does contribute to a change in gene frequencies, is akin to genetic drift and should be considered as a possible factor in utilizing an explanation involving genetic drift. A discussion of inbreeding not present, and of inbreeding effect, clearly present, has been utilized in the analysis of the blood groups of three Koniag Eskimo isolates (Denniston, 1964).

Another explanation has been advanced by Chown and Lewis (1959). They have suggested the possibility of an earlier substratum population, the archaeologically known Dorset Eskimos, which differed as much from contemporary Eskimos as they in turn differ from Indians. Such a Dorset residuum would be expected to differ in frequencies rather than presence or absence of particular genes. This explanation is not incompatible with that of drift including inbreeding effect, for an earlier population is most likely to be detectable in an area where the hybridizing and replacing population is not large in proportion to the earlier residents. In any event homogeneity for a large area in earlier times should not be assumed in making reconstructions. In this respect the skeletal information does indicate a lack of homogeneity in western Alaska and in Greenland and a number of secular changes. Strict comparison between morphological and serological data cannot be made but a uniform homogeneity for any large area can probably be ruled out for any period. Selection by disease does not appear to offer an avenue to explanation of this interesting distributional pattern.

Possible hybridization with Indians can be ruled out on two grounds—there is no serological evidence and the behavioural evidence in the form of known matings and cultural inhibitions maximizes the distinction between the Mongoloid Eskimos and the quasi-Mongoloid Indians. In general, the Indians of North America are characterized by low to zero frequencies of the A_1 gene, ranging to the world's highest frequency among the Blood and Blackfoot Indians of Montana and Alberta, and by an absence of the B gene. In addition the R_2 gene is generally higher. Other differences are found in the presence of Diego among Indians and a low frequency of non-tasters. The Eskimos have low BAIB excretion rates whereas Alaskan Athabaskan and Apache Indians show similarly high rates (Allison, Blumberg, and Gartler, 1959). Eskimos have a low incidence of haptoglobin type, 1–1 in contrast to Alaskan Indians who show an incidence similar to that of Europeans (Blumberg, Allison, and Garry, 1959). The moderate anaemia which occurs in Alaskan Eskimos over a considerable area may prove to have an hereditary basis which will provide another distinction from Indians (Scott *et al.*, 1955). Important to a consideration of Eskimo-Indian relationships is the fact that contiguous groups of Indians show marked differences, in Alaska and Canada. The village of Allakaket recently studied by Merbs and Meier (1963), personal communication, provided a typical western Alaskan ABO profile and a typical absence of B and low A_1 among the Indians who share various services but apparently insufficient genes to provide detectable evidence of mixture.

An extremely informative analysis by Chown and Lewis (1959) reveals a cline running from north-west to south-east with MS being replaced by Ns. The closer the Eskimos are to Indians geographically, the more distant they are genetically. Differences in morphology and physiological adaptation seem consonant with the pronounced genetic differences between Eskimos and Indians (Milan, 1963).

Turning to the blood groups of Siberian Mongoloids, Eskimos, Chukchi, and Lamut, for whom recent data on the ABO and MN systems are now available (Levin, 1958, 1959; Zolotareva, 1964) the essential affinity of the Eskimo–Aleut stock with Asiatic Mongoloids, rather than with American Indians, is well attested. Two hundred and fifty-six Chukchi show a phenotypic frequency of 12·5 per cent B and 3·5–45·3 per cent B, and one group of 53 Lamut show 20·8 per cent B and 13·2 per cent AB.

The high frequency of B in central Asia is well known for both Mongoloid and Indo-European groups. It is likely that there is a cline extending from central Asia into the North American Eskimos, comparable to that extending into Europe. Important changes in slope may however be apparent when intervening areas have been typed. The N frequencies appear to be slightly higher in Siberia except for the Lamut for whom the data is limited to only fifty-three persons.

The Lapps may be dismissed from consideration in the predominantly Mongoloid circumpolar area because of their uniquely high A_2 frequency and also their unusually high NS frequency which is comparable only in the Ainu of Japan. The medieval Norse of Greenland may be presumed to have frequencies similar to the Icelanders (Steffensen, 1953).

In retrospect it is interesting that although the Eskimos originated in western Alaska and spread from there eastward to Greenland, there is no perceptible cline from west to east but rather a unique partitioning of three zones with the central zone departing from the eastern and western zones.

Morphological aspects

An overall characterization of Arctic Mongoloids benefits from the totally large number of metrical studies and from the skeletal studies of directly antecedent populations. Summaries and original studies are found in the works of Debets, 1959; Levin, 1963; Michael, 1962; Hrdlicka, 1944, 1945; Gessain, 1960; Jørgensen, 1953; Laughlin, 1950, 1963; Furst and Hansen, 1951; Moorrees, 1957; Pedersen, 1949; Skeller, 1954; Seltzer, 1933; Stewart, 1939; Dahlberg, 1963. The extent of information for Siberia and the New World is of greater value because of the skeletal antecedents and because of successive studies on the same groups as most precisely shown in the Angmagssalik Eskimos. This in turn is a result of early interest in Eskimos as evidenced by the fact that the first anthropological description of a human skull was given for a west Greenland specimen by Winslow in 1722.

In spite of the wealth of material several misconceptions still prevail and they should be specifically challenged. The most common misconceptions are that Eskimos are fat, that they are homogeneous, and that they provide evidence of morphological adaptation to cold stress. The first is palpably fallacious—Eskimos, Aleuts, and Siberian Mongoloids are lean. The second requires serious qualification and depends upon the scale used for comparison. Ideas of homogeneity have been most often founded upon the minority of Arctic Eskimos and have omitted the middle and sub-Arctic majority. The relation of the morphological characteristics to cold adaptation has not been experimentally verified and the assumption that whatever characterizes people in a cold area is tangibly related to that cold is an inadequate assumption, even for preliminary research. Eskimo adaptation to cold stress appears to be primarily physiological and cultural. The genetics of the physiological adaptation are not yet known and essentially the same morphology is found in Mongoloids living in temperate zones.

The Arctic Mongoloids for whom the best data exist and for whom the original populations at the time of European contact were of considerable size (16,000 Aleuts, 70,000 Eskimos and 12,000 Chukchi) are characterized by medium to sub-medium statures, with notable exceptions, long trunks and short legs yielding a high relative sitting height index, short lower leg and often a short forearm, large heads, large faces, straight nasal profiles with small tips, and high frequencies of epicanthic folds. The males display much muscle relief and both sexes are lean as shown in low skinfold measurements. Beard and body hair are scant and balding is rare except in the presence of White admixture. In pigmentation they range from dark to light with many individuals clearly ruddy in facial complexion. Tanning is apparent for all exposed areas. The sacral spot is of high frequency and individually may be remarkably extensive in its distribution over the trunk, shoulders, and buttocks.

The fingerprint patterns can be epitomized by reference to the index of pattern intensity (Meier, 1964). A pattern of 14 is representative of most Eskimo groups, with a range from 13·5 in Karluk, Kodiak Island (affected by a relatively few related males with a large per cent of arctics, thus reducing the intensity index) to 17·3 for east Greenland. The lowest frequency of whorls is found in the east central Arctic and the highest frequency in east Greenland. European and Negro populations have lower pattern intensity values, whereas North American Indians and some Asiatic groups have higher values. Newman (1958) has called attention to the reduced pattern intensity running from North America into South America and reiterates the suggestion of Cummins and Midlo (1943) that higher finger pattern intensities are apparently a Mongoloid trait. A study in progress by Gilberg and his colleagues will provide detailed information on the Polar Eskimos.

Head form as reflected in cephalic index has low values in Greenland and the central Arctic, and higher values in western Alaska with the most pronounced brachycephaly in south-western Alaska. Gessain (1960) has discussed the distribution of stature and head form most recently and noted an interesting qualification on clines which had previously been postulated. Two groups of tall Eskimos differ significantly in head form. The interior Eskimos of the Brooks Range, the Nunatagmiut, are brachycephalic (C.I. 81) but otherwise are in the central area of above average stature. The coastal Mackenzie Eskimos, geographically not far from them are dolichocephalic (C.I. 74) and similarly are tall. Thus, at the highest level of generalization there are two zones for head form with the boundary falling between these two groups in eastern

Alaska; but for stature there is again a central area that departs from the values for western Alaska and for Greenland and eastern Canada with similarity to the blood group picture. Both the genealogies and archaeological researches suggest that the interior Eskimos of Alaska are comparatively recent occupants, that they do not have much if any connexion with earlier remains in that area, and that the occupants of this area have had to move to and from the coast in response to the fluctuations of the caribou herds. That the interior Eskimos are above mean in stature yet serologically and genealogically allied with the coastal Eskimos of Alaska constitutes an interesting puzzle. However, the small size of the isolate and its recency deprives it of the significance it might otherwise contain.

The eyefold deserves mention in relation to its putative function in protecting the eye from cold and from glare. Though there is no experimental evidence on the insulating function of the fat about the eyeball, nor on the value of a reduced exposure of the eyeball, it is clear that 'snowblindness' and excessive glare reflected on the water constitute real problems to Eskimos travelling by sled or by kayak. The high development of slit goggles, primarily for travel on ice and snow, and of visors, primarily for kayak travel, provide cultural evidence of inadequate protection of the eye by the eyefold.

Decomposition and testing of clinical distributions

Any corporation of related peoples such as those contained within the Aleut–Eskimo stock that is spread over a long linear distribution, will necessarily provide many correlations between physical characteristics and external environmental variables, but will not automatically provide evidence therewith of significant variables or of causal relationships nor provide critical tests of hypotheses. Clines constitute a useful way of mapping inter-group variation and their correlations provide a useful departure point for beginning inquiry. They must, however, be decomposed for critical testing of their evolutionary significance.

It has been observed for well over a century that the Aleuts and Eskimos who made extensive use of kayaks were small in stature and had short legs. Some observers attempted to relate the especially short legs of the kayakers to their use of kayaks, though none apparently related the taller stature of the more northerly Eskimos to their use of sleds. Kayaks are obviously maximized in those areas with more open water, southern Greenland, southern Alaska, and the Aleutian Islands. Kayak use and technical elaboration of kayaks (one and two hatches, three-piece keelsons, &c.) reached their highest development in the Aleutian Islands and the Kodiak Archipelago where there is no winter ice. There is a patent correlation between the use of boats and the availability of open water and this has been of crucial significance in the distribution of the members of this stock, their ecology, population density, and composition. The number of correlates is indeed very high. Stature is higher in the colder regions where sled travel is more common (North Alaska and Siberia, the central Arctic, and polar Greenland), and these are the same regions where the amount of winter light is small and of summer light is large. I wish to point out that there is no better evidence for a causal correlation between physique and temperature than there is between physique and light, or between physique and kayaks or sleds. Plausibility of such correlations should serve as a stimulus to the formulation of critical tests, and the collection of the necessary physiological data and family data and for tests of differential survival.

In his sophisticated and useful study of the possible nature of the factors involved in the inverse correlation between mean body weights and mean environmental temperatures in native people of the Americas, Newman has called attention to the correspondence in ten samples of Eskimos and Aleuts, 'This close approximation of observed and calculated weights makes it clear that on the average the Eskimo conform to the New World weight–temperature regression equation developed in this paper' (Newman, 1960). I should like to demonstrate that even though two of the constituent samples in this series are very similar, the Aleuts and the south-west Greenland Eskimos, and do conform and thereby contributed substantially to the conformity for the entire series, the meaning of this fit is both obscure and even incompatible with a clinal distribution employing temperature as a significant causal variable. They are similar to each other in spite of adapting to different conditions.

The two major invalidating factors are, first, the pronounced differences in temperatures and second, the length of time the people have been adapting to their external environments. There are three kinds of temperatures in which arctic coastal peoples must operate; household temperature, outside-air temperature, and sea-water temperature. Household temperatures, in which over one-third of their lives was spent, was traditionally hot in Greenland, and conversely cool in the Aleutians. The Greenlanders heated their houses and often went about without clothes inside them. The Aleuts did not heat their houses and never went about without clothes inside them. Outside air temperatures were very cold in winter and ascended to warm in the summer in all Greenland. Air temperature in the Aleutians was cool, moist, and stable throughout the year, and over the entire length of the island chain. The water temperature, in which both people occasionally froze and drowned, was essentially the same, especially from the standpoint of heat loss with total immersion, though there was no winter ice in the Aleutians. Finally, a fourth temperature is relevant because both people wore tailored clothing superbly designed to

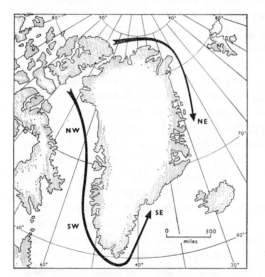
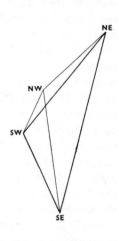

FIG. 1. Migration of the Eskimos about Greenland. The migration was confined to the coasts because of the inland ice. It moved in two directions, with the result that the terminal isolates (the north-east and the south-east), separated for the longest period, show the greatest morphological differences.

FIG. 2. Geometric representation of the relative degrees of similarity between the four Greenlandic Eskimo isolates. The difference between the north-east and the south-east isolates is greater than the difference between any other two contiguous isolates. Though geographically as far apart as the north-east and south-east isolates, the north-west and south-west isolates exchanged mates more frequently and are much more similar to each other.

maintain a warm micro-climate so that a man could sit in a kayak for hours at a time or lie on the ice while hunting. In addition to the clothing they had many behavioural practices whereby they avoided excessive sweating on the one hand and becoming too cold on the other. The mean cold-month temperature has little comparative value in these two regions, the people have adjusted to two quite different environments in spite of the latitudinal similarity and their common use of kayaks.

The second point concerns the historical time depth, and the population history. The Aleuts have occupied their territory for a period at least sixteen times greater than the south-west Greenland people have occupied theirs. There is excellent proof (skeletons and radiocarbon dates) that the Aleuts have occupied the Aleutians for over 4000 years (Laughlin and Reeder, 1962), there is good proof that they have occupied it over 8000 years (Black and Laughlin, 1964), and there is presumptive proof that they walked into their present location some 12,000 years ago when the Bering Land Bridge was intact. In marked contrast the south-west Greenlanders have been in their present location only since the demise of the Medieval Norse, some 500 years. Prior to that time they were part of a population living under even colder conditions farther to the north. Continued gene flow from the north has meant that not only had the original body of migrants adapted to conditions further north, but they have been receiving a continuous supply of genotypes from an area of greater cold stress (Figs. 1 and 2).

Still another point related to the composition of these samples is that the Aleutian sample represents the genetic experience of a people distributed longitudinally over a relative homogeneous area 1250 miles in length. It is composed of two isolate samples, an eastern Aleutian and a western Aleutian which differ more from each other in stature and weight than do the south-west Greenland Eskimos from the east coast Angmagssalik Eskimos further to the north. The reduced size of the western Aleuts can most economically be attributed to the original establishment of a size difference contained in the first migrant samples to move into the western portions. Gene flow can only move west and east, and historically it is known that most movement has been from east to west. There is no selection gradient in temperature or light that could plausibly be offered to explain the longitudinal Aleutian cline. The south-west Greenland sample is drawn from a more restricted area, a part of an essentially linear and latitudinal distribution. The Angmagssalik Eskimoes represent a sample drawn from the southwest coast of Greenland some 500 years ago. An apparent sampling accident (drift) is reflected in their frequency for blood group B, the highest in Greenland.

In summary, the differences in temperature that actually affected these people are substantially different in the two areas, and the period in which these people have been living in these two areas is substantially different. Any linear occupational area such as the Aleutians or coastal Greenland in which the people have been migrating in one direction and in which gene flow has moved primarily in the same direction will automatically provide correlations with environmental variables, and no correlations if the environment is relatively stable. Arctic peoples are ideal for the study of clinal variation because severally restricted distributions running both latitudinally and longitudinally can be used for comparison. A large portion of the variation can be attributed to migration and gene flow, with gene drift an important accessory in the introduction or establishment of extreme values in small and isolated groups. While cold stress provided an important form of external selection its effects were skilfully buffered. Superbly designed clothing, efficient housing, an elevated basal metabolism in some, a remarkably good state of physical fitness maintained throughout life, and judicious habits appear to be the major factors involved in thermal adaptation of the Eskimos that can be validated at the present. Certainly the old paradigm that clinal variation over distance when correlated with an external environmental variable automatically added up to evidence of selection is fallacious for Arctic peoples. No possibilities can be overlooked in future researches and the possibility of a significant variation in light stimulus and growth deserves careful attention. I think that here, as elsewhere in the world, the population history preceding the end-point at which the people are measured contains necessary clues to some of the many processes which have simultaneously operated upon the populations or, intrinsically, within the populations.

Secular change among living people. There are many indications of continuing change within isolates. Some of these appear well marked when skeletal populations are utilized. However, they can be demonstrated for living people by recourse to the studies of Gessain (1960) and Skeller (1954) on the Angmagssalik Eskimos. The interval between their measurements of these people was sixteen years. The stature and cephalic index are nearly identical for both males and females. However, the minimum frontal diameter and the bigonial diameter are much reduced in the latter study (Gessain, 1950). The probable explanation for this reduction in facial diameters lies in the reduced use of the jaws which in turn is related to the increasing assumption of a European diet and diminishing use of the jaws for fabricational purposes.

Evidence of change over longer periods. The most obvious evidence of changes taking place within Eskimo or Aleut populations is seen in the trend toward brachycephaly. Invariably where earlier skeletal populations are compared with later series, and later series with living peoples there has been an increase in the index, usually attributable to increase in the breadth of the head (Laughlin, 1958). Beginning with 1884–5 the east Greenland Eskimos have been measured on four occasions. The differences have been trivial. The males have a cephalic index of 76·5. However, the skeletal series shows an index of 70·9 for males. This is too great a difference to attribute to soft part tissues. Continuity between living and dead is well documented and European admixture has been minor.

Substantial differences in head form are well documented for western Alaska, especially the Aleutians and Kodiak Island. These are so great (73 for early skeletons at Nikolski and 85 in the people living there now, an index of 83 if two units are subtracted for tissue differences) that the possibility of population replacement, possibly an immigration from the east, has been considered. The absence of significant differences in the dentition (Turner, 1964) and in other traits, although the earlier and later skeletons can be sorted out visually, leaves the likelihood of evolutionary change within the populations as the best explanation at present. The best estimate for time, derived from radiocarbon dates, is somewhere in the order of 1500 years for such a change. Such internal change must remain an estimate with a low or medium probability rather than an established fact, for the present. Brachycephalization is not unique to Mongoloids by any means but the examples seem well-founded and the possibility of replacement rather than internal change seems small (Suzuki, 1958; Levin and Sergeyev,

1964). Like many other traits used for study head form is of greatest utility over short distances within populations known to be related. Changes in head form do reflect changes in growth and may provide a cue to other more significant changes. In spite of the frequency of references to a typical head form for Eskimos (dolichocephalic with keel) it obviously varies greatly in both its geographical and temporal distribution.

The epicentre for brachycephaly which I earlier indicated for Kodiak Island, based upon Hrdlicka's measurements of eleven living Koniags, for which he secured an index of 87·0, must be qualified. For three Koniag isolates the male index is respectively: Kaguyak 81, Old Harbor 83, and Karluk 81. These are the same isolates for whom the blood groups are known and previously referred to. In spite of European admixture there has been little if any response in stature (mean of 161 cm). It is entirely possible that Hrdlicka inadvertently picked old Koniags whose heads had been artificially deformed, in his attempt to secure 'purebloods'. The later skeletal series show substantially higher values. Kodiak was likely an epicentre but the skeletal measurements and not the living provide the better evidence.

Inter-individual variation over distance

A method for studying the distribution of continuous morphological traits over distance consists of plotting the individual values of members of isolates rather than the mean values of isolates within a population. This method of studying intra-group variation in the strict sense, therefore inter-individual variation, may be of special value in linear, narrow file distributions about the world, such as those of various people inhabiting coastlines, rivers, or island chains. The evolutionary effectiveness of isolation by distance is handsomely demonstrated in the pinnipeds who in broad terms have inhabited a generally monotonous environment but owing in large part to their breeding on ice fronts or on land fronts and having followed separate, linear, diverging pathways, have evolved into twenty genera (Scheffer, 1958). Genetical aspects of isolation by distance are found in the papers of Wright (1955). Previous studies of variation in the Aleutian Islands had made use of the east and west isolates (Moorrees, 1957; Laughlin, 1951). In order to retrieve information either minimized or discarded by comparisons between isolates—the traditional method of describing clines—Laughlin, Gilbert, and Peterson (1965) plotted the island distribution of several cranial dimensions, indices, sex, and age. The sample consisted of 168 crania from 14 islands over a distance of 1250 miles, the maximum range of the Aleut population. Plotting of the metrical data shows a size reduction from east to west. This accords with the size reduction seen in the living Aleut isolates but reveals undulations or departures unnoticeable in a cline based on isolates. The one significant correlation is between age and distance, significant at the 1 per cent level. Age at death is higher in the eastern area than in the western. This is in the area with greater population density. Partitioned into three dialectical or geographical divisions, the estimated population figures are approximately 10,000 in the eastern, 4000 in the central, and 2000 in the western division. These figures then indicate the potential population pressure for gene flow to the west. Though the Aleutians are relatively homogeneous in terms of external environment, sea and air temperatures, cloud cover, wind velocities, small annual fluctuation in temperatures, and in the kinds of faunal resources with the exception of the far-eastern end where the walrus and some land mammals enriched the diet, they interestingly are separated by increasing distances between the islands progressing to the west. Contact with other people— Eskimos—was possible only at the eastern end. Thus, the conditions for isolation by distance are ideally represented and presumably played a major role in the frequency and the distribution of traits.

Skeletal evidence: dentition, discrete traits, and pathologies

Preoccupation with continuous measurements and with problems of affinity have tended to deprive skeletal studies of their other uses involving discontinuous distributions, growth information, and pathologies.

The Eskimos can be equally well characterized by noting the high frequency of metopic sutures; dehiscences of the tympanic plate, mandibular, and palatine torii; numerous large cranial foramina; missing third molars; spinal defects; persistence of the ilio-public union; spondolysthesis; and arthritis of the elbow. For the frequencies of some of these traits see the accompanying article, 'Eskimos and Aleuts: their origins and evolution'.

Moorrees has recently shown that it is possible to define a basic

GENETICAL AND ANTHROPOLOGICAL

pattern for the dentition and jaws of Mongoloids consisting of marked shovel-shape of the incisors, relatively small differences between the mesiodistal crown diameters of the maxillary central and lateral incisors, a very low incidence of Carabelli's cusp, and a relatively high frequency of the marked forms of the mandibular torus. The dentition of any Mongoloid population can therefore be defined by a specific modification of the master pattern and by the incidence of other dental traits. Intensification of basic characteristics is more pronounced, for example, in Eastern than in the Western Aleuts as evidenced in the greater frequency of marked shovel-shaped incisors and of marked mandibular tori. 'The retention of a "Y" grove pattern in the first molars, of five cusps in the other two mandibular molars, and of four cusps in the maxillary second molars is likewise greater in the eastern Aleuts. Simplification in the morphology of their dentition is shown only by the greater prevalence of the bicuspal form of the mandibular second premolar and of the tricuspal form of the maxillary third molar' (Moorrees, 1962). These observations are currently being extended on skeletal populations by Turner.

TABLE 1
Arthritis in Eskimo elbows

	Arthritic		Non-arthritic	
	Trochlea	Capitulum	None	Total
Male	3	19	32	54
Female	13	1	61	75
				(chi square $=28.7$)

Owing to the fact that the mandibular torus, shovel-shaped incisors, and other such traits have been used as evidence for identification of *Sinanthropus* as a fossil form ancestral to contemporary Mongoloids, it is of special interest to note that the mandibular torus occurs in *Australopithecus*. It is clearly present, bilaterally, in Sts 52 and also in the adolescent from Makapan. In the latter it is less pronounced (Robinson, personal communication). Any theory concerning the evolutionary aetiology of this trait and its function will have to consider its appearance in the line leading to the erectus phase but clearly occurring before this phase. Mongoloids are probably a comparatively recent development, possibly of no more than 10,000 or 20,000 years. In no way does the occurrence of such traits in early forms, either in the *Australopithecus* or in the erectus phase, indicate that Mongoloids can be traced back to those forms.

There are some interesting pathological patterns more easily observed in the dry skeleton than in the living person. Eskimos have achieved the world's highest frequencies of neural-arch defects (Merbs and Anderson, 1962; Merbs, 1963; Stewart, 1953). An unusual sex-and-site distribution for arthritis is found among the skeletons of the extinct Sadlermiut Eskimos, and tabulated by Merbs (Table 1).

Though skeletal anomalies occur in high frequency there is little evidence of trauma except for compression fractures and dental ablation. The latter appears to correlate with dog traction. It is possible that the use of the jaws to hold lines and untie frozen traces while working the dogs, explains in large part the loss of the incisors.

Ecology, population composition, size, and distribution

The problems of comparing population size for different zones, or of discussing population density stem from the necessity of comparing land areas which differ in all their important facies and which do not possess boundaries of the sort found in terrestrial areas and of utilizing linear coastline measures that are not comparable for islands and mainland. Nevertheless some generalizations are possible and some marked contrasts and their consequences can be illustrated. In all cases the technological aspects of the culture are especially prominent.

The most relevant factor for analysis is differential accessibility. Harsh conditions in the Arctic area are imposed most directly on the very young and the very old. These segments of the population have least direct assess to the food supply. In the case of the older and often infirm segments the direct genetic consequences are mitigated by the fact that the females have often completed their reproductive activity. They do, however, have an extremely important role in delivering and caring for the newborn and tending children as well as educating them. Where the populations are large, and the distance between demes is small the proportion of infants and old people is much larger than in those places where the total population is small and demes are separated by many miles. A large number of correlates, causes, and consequences can be partially delineated. In a real sense the sampling error between generations must be considerably reduced in the dense areas, and gene flow between demes and populations considerably greater.

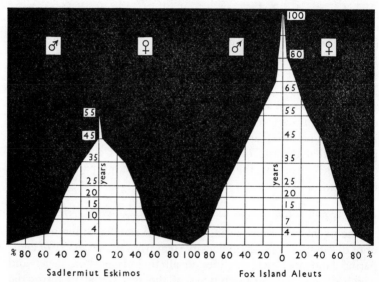

Sadlermiut Eskimos   Fox Island Aleuts

FIG. 3. Data on age at death of the Sadlermiut Eskimos of Southampton Island, Canadian Arctic, and Aleuts of the Fox Island district in the eastern Aleutians. The Sadlermiut Eskimos died relatively early in life as compared with these Aleuts. Infant mortality was also greater under the more stringent conditions of the Arctic environment.

For examples of harsh conditions we may use the Polar Eskimos of north Greenland (250–400 persons) and the extinct Sadlermiut Eskimos of Southampton Island in Hudson Bay (80–300 persons) (Fig. 3). For examples of more luxuriant conditions we may use the Aleuts of Umnak Island (2000 persons) in the eastern Aleutians, and the Koniag Eskimos of Kodiak Island (16,000 Koniags on Kodiak). In terms of differential accessibility there are fewer ecological niches directly available to children and to old people in the high and middle Arctic zones represented by Thule and Southampton. This is most quickly seen in the adaptations to hunting on the winter sea ice. Where the ice is present for eight or nine months a large per cent of the food supply has to be secured on it. This involves hunting on the edge of the ice or punching holes in the ice to secure narwhal, seal, or fish. The reward for punching a hole in two feet of ice is often insufficient to compensate for the energy consumed. Further, it is often necessary to employ a dog team to reach a suitable spot and the dogs require feeding. Children, pregnant women, old women, arthritic men, and several related kinds simply cannot secure their own food under such conditions, much less collect a surplus for others. Infanticide and exposure of old persons was accordingly more common in such areas.

By contrast, in the Aleutians and Kodiak Island the disadvantaged segments of the population could more often collect their own food and they had more ecological niches within their reach. An appreciation of their considerably improved position can be most quickly gained from a view of the correlative benefits of open water the year round. An intertidal zone rich in edible algae and invertebrates was immediately accessible to young children, encumbered women, and relatively immobile old people. Sea urchins, molluscs, and *Ulva* could be collected with ease and safety. Annual runs of salmon were regularly caught and dried by children, women, and old men.

The most obvious factors in the Aleutians are fresh-water lakes (salmon and birds), streams (salmon trapping, gaffing), protected bays (hand-line fishing, seining, boat-launching), reefs (shell-fish, kelp fish, octopus, algae), beaches (stranded whales, sea lions and seals, clams, driftwood), off-shore island (birds, eggs, sea-mammal rookeries), soil cover (plant foods, basketry grass), cliffs (cliff birds), and open water (sea mammals and fish, resident and transient). Those animals which live in rookeries the entire year (sea lion and to a lesser extent hair seal) or in highly localized clusters (sea otter) are more important than large numbers of migrating animals, caribou or whale, in terms of population subsistence. To these factors must be added the complexity of coastline, and the strength of tides and currents. In addition to providing a richer environment complex coastlines are more efficiently scanned by hunters, especially those in kayaks. It should be noted that a major aspect of hunting is the scanning and stalking which precedes the more dramatic aspect of harpooning or shooting. The genius of the kayak lies as much in providing a means of scanning large areas, in pursuit and in retrieval of game, as in its manœuvrability for the actual harpooning or lancing operations.

As an ecological adaptation the kayak requires more study than it has received. Old men and children can use kayaks for hand-line fishing in which case the length of the line determines in large part the faunal types they will sample. At the other extreme whales or pelagic forms such as fur seal on their annual movements to the breeding grounds can be hunted from kayaks. Whole demes can travel in the larger open boats (umiaks) and thus take advantage of seasonal fluctuations in food supply.

Individually there appears to be selection against certain kinds of men which is expressed in the disease termed 'kayak fear'. These persons, apparently concentrated on the west coast of Greenland, may suffer an attack at sea in which case they may become giddy, begin sweating, even become nauseated, and typically lose their orientation. They may become immobilized after experiencing sensations of sinking or rising and generally losing their horizon. To the extent that this may have a partially hereditary basis, its localization in Greenland suggests a population difference. Paucity of references in the early literature suggests that it may have been maximized appreciably in two centuries. Men who suffer from this disease often never go to sea again. Nevertheless they may have already fathered children and can continue an economically useful existence on shore and thus continue to be important genetic contributors to their demes. The apparent absence of this disease in the Alaskan sub-Arctic where use of kayaks is more extensive and probably much older suggest that if the genes for this condition were present they may have been reduced or eliminated sometime in the past. The elucidation of such behavioural problems is an important research goal which will require extensive interdisciplinary co-operation (Laughlin and Taylor, 1963).

Viewed from the standpoint of nutrition the more luxuriant areas are those in which children can secure a significant proportion of their own food and thus enjoy a more sustained and diverse diet. The cultural system for environmental exploitation requires an intensive utilization of each mammal for both dietary and fabricational purposes. Intestines, stomach contents, internal organs, brains, and marrow are extensively used by Arctic peoples. Citation of a single example illustrates these nutritional and environmental protection aspects. The sea lion of southern Alaska (*Eumetopias jubata*) may be partitioned for the following uses: stomach—storage of dried fish; hide—skins for kayaks and umiaks; oesophagus—clothing, boot leggings, pants, and waterproof parkas; intestines—waterproof parkas, &c., and food; pericardium—bags and water bottles; flippers—boot soles; flesh—food; teeth and whiskers—decorative purposes; skeleton—fabricational purposes. Thus, quantitative nutritional studies related to particular population cohorts become extremely complex.

In retrospect the correlation between infant mortality; longevity; complex coastlines; winter-ice or open water; number, kind, and accessibility of various ecological niches; population size and distribution; intervillage relations; and extinction by starvation, is complex but comprehensible. A single point of focus such as the kayak contrasted with the sled epitomizes these relations. Dogs represent an economic drain and an important source of infection or transmitting agency for trichinosis. Further, they require extensive training and cannot be handled by children and women, much less the infirm individuals. There is further feedback in the real sense that they occasionally eat the Eskimos. In marked contrast kayaks do not need to be fed, at most they take a little water. They can be used by boys of ten and over in protected waters and they can be used for hand-line fishing by old men. Drowning of course is a hazard associated with their use and this may be a prominent feature in the sex ratio favouring an excess of women (Mikkelsen, 1944). One other kind of circular relationship of importance is that provided by old people who possess effective esoteric knowledge of parturition and disease control. The development of empirically derived scientific knowledge correlates with the high density area of the Aleutian–Kodiak area (Marsh and Laughlin, 1956; Laughlin, 1961).

Suggestions for research

Repetitive and long-term studies are clearly of utility in studying human growth, the succeeding generations of the offspring of hybrid matings and such things as seasonal variations in antibody titres. Genetical, anthropometric, and physiological observations have rarely been made on the same persons, and even more rarely have they been repeated on successive generations of the same populations. A practical problem is that of finding groups that are relatively stable and which will likely remain constant for some generations in the future. The Russians installed a population of Aleuts on the Pribiloff Islands to exploit the fur-seal herds that breed there. There are some indications that Aleuts had been there previously but they were unoccupied at the time of their discovery in 1787. Assuming constancy of breeding habits on the part of the fur seal, and continuation of existing international agreements, the isolates of these two islands might well justify intensive, long-range biological studies. A second highly-comparable population and situation is found on the Kommandorski Islands off the Kamchatka Peninsula of Siberia. These two islands, Bering and Medni, were unoccupied by humans at the time of their discovery in 1741. They were the home of the unique Steller's sea cow, the spectacled cormorant, and of fur seals, hair seals, and sea otters. Aleuts from Attu and Atka were settled on Medni and Bering Islands respectively in 1826. Their numbers are roughly equivalent to those of the Pribiloff Islands. They have prospered and will likely constitute a stable population for many generations to come. Villages such as Wainwright are ideal for study. The rewards for participation in the form of information from laboratory tests which are ordinarily inaccessible or expensive, the establishment of walking blood-banks, growth norms, guidance on orthodontic treatment, treatment of eye diseases, &c., are appreciable for each individual and when properly articulated with existing health facilities of the State and Federal Government can ensure wholehearted co-operation.

The solution of various genetic-environmental interaction problems requires three generations or more with detailed knowledge of individual genotypes, mating, and pregnancy records with known genealogical relationships between members of the isolates. Sites similar to the Pribiloff Islands in Alaska, Arctic Canada, Labrador, and Greenland as well as Siberia are feasible. Programming of studies so that maximum utilization of each blood specimen by judicious sharing of specimens between laboratories and maintenance of frozen specimens in anticipation of new antisera or serum protein factors is desirable for the maximum extraction of information with the least intrusion into the activities and time of the people being studied.

The recommendations of the World Health Organization's Scientific Group on Research in Population Genetics of Primitive

Groups (1964) and those contained in the International Biological Programme (Section D, Human Adaptability), are both realistic and comprehensive. Applied to local regions and to specific populations they can be adapted with attention to utilization of the advantages of the particular groups to special research problems. Two specific recommendations should be considered. First, skeletal populations related to living populations should be studied for the dental, growth, and pathological information contained in them, as well as for refining estimates of the length of time the people have lived in the area and of their affinities. Secondly, contiguous isolates should be studied simultaneously if possible. Problems of gene flow depending upon mixture with other groups are necessary to estimates of selection intensity and effects of selection as opposed to genetic drift and mutation. Attention to inbreeding effect which results from the partitioning of a population into small demes obviously depends upon the study of contiguous related isolates. Few breeding isolates are geographically or culturally highly isolated. The degree of gene flow across successive isolates is crucial to our analysis of human evolution.

Conclusions

(1) The Chukchi, Eskimos, and Aleuts appear to be the terminal populations in the radial flow of the gene for blood group B from Central Asia. After introduction into these large, corporate populations, the frequencies of B have likely been affected by variations in interdemic and intrademic selection values, including random drift.

(2) The fact that the *B* gene has not yet penetrated into contiguous groups of North American Indians suggests the interesting possibility that the earlier Aleuts and Eskimos of 4000–5000 years ago had little or no *B*, and that existing Eskimo frequencies are not yet high enough, given the low frequency of Eskimo–Indian crosses, to penetrate remaining dispersal barriers.

(3) Longevity is significantly correlated with longitude in the Aleutians, being greater in the eastern than in the western islands. Population density is substantially greater in the eastern islands. Head form, as seen in the cranial index, varies over distance (1250 miles) in the same direction with larger and broader heads in the east. The common evolutionary trend towards brachycephalization in Aleuts and Eskimos may importantly reflect changing growth patterns partially contingent upon longevity and population density.

(4) The appreciable amount of both morphological and serological variation arranged in distributions that are linear and longitudinal, and the apparent absence of external selection gradients such as temperature, light, altitude, and disease, suggests that migration and mixture, gene flow, accidents of sampling in founding groups, and various intrinsic forms of selection, are important factors in the distribution of variation. Conversely, latitudinal north–south clines may include adventitious correlates with external stress gradients that do not bear genetic or physiological validity.

(5) European–Eskimo hybrids do not regularly show the expected influence of European contributions in such things as stature. There may well be buffered systems present in the Eskimos which afford some degree of protection from variations that might prove disadvantageous.

(6) Different patterns of physiological adaptation to cold stress may be anticipated in arctic peoples for it is already apparent that Eskimos and Indians differ in this respect. These patterns may prove to have a high element of heritability but this has not yet been demonstrated. Certainly a complex of factors are involved— elevated basal metabolism, good state of physical fitness, adaptive behaviour, excellent clothing, efficient housing, and effective treatment of frostbite after it occurs. The role of body size and proportions as such in their thermal adaptation has not been established.

Acknowledgements. National Institutes of Health, Rockefeller Foundation, National Science Foundation, Wenner-Gren Foundation for Anthropological Research, World Health Organization, Graduate School, University of Wisconsin, Alaska Native Service, Alaska Department of Health, Mrs. Dora Kramer. Research Assistants: Charles F. Merbs, Robert Meier, Christy Turner, Carter Denniston, Kenneth I. Taylor, Lois Lippold, William Stini. Colleagues: Dr. Bruce Chown and Marion Lewis, Dr. J. Balslev Jørgensen, Dr. F. A. Milan, Dr. Albert A. Dahlberg, Dr. W. G. Reeder, Dr. A. Gilberg.

REFERENCES

ALLISON, A. C., BLUMBERG, B. S., and GARTLER, S. M., 1959. 'Urinary excretion of B-amino-isobutyric acid and Eskimo and Indian populations of Alaska', *Nature, Lond.* **183**, 118–119.

BLACK, R. and LAUGHLIN, W. S., 1964. 'Anangula: A geological interpretation of the oldest archaeological site in the Aleutians', *Science* **143**, 1321–1322.

BLUMBERG, B. S., ALLISON, A. C., and GARRY, BARBARA, 1959. 'The haptoglobins and haemoglobins of Alaskan Eskimos and Indians', *Ann. hum. Genet.* **23**, 349–356.

CHOWN, BRUCE and LEWIS, MARION, 1959. 'The blood group genes of the copper Eskimo', *Am. J. phys. Anthrop.* **17**, 13–18.

CUMMINS, HAROLD and CHARLES, MIDLO, 1943. *Finger Prints, Palms and Soles*, an *Introduction to Dermatoglyphics*. Blakiston, Philadelphia.

DAHLBERG, ALBERT A., 1963. 'Analysis of the American Indian dentition', *Dental Anthropology* (ed. D. R. BROTHWELL), pp. 149–177. Macmillan. New York.

DEBETS, G., 1959. 'The skeletal remains of the Ipiutak cemetery', *Actas Del XXXIII, Congreso Internacional De Americanistas*, Vol. II, pp. 57–64. San Jose, Costa Rica.

DENNISTON, CARTER, 1964. 'The blood groups of three Koniag isolates', A thesis submitted in partial fulfillment of the requirements for the degree of Master of Science (Anthropology) University of Wisconsin.

FURST, CARL M. and HANSEN, FR. C. C., 1915. *Crania Groenlandica*. Copenhagen.

GESSAIN, ROBERT, 1960. 'Contribution à l'anthropologie des Eskimo d'Angmagssalik', *Medd. Grønland* **161**, 128–134.

GÜRTLER, H., *et al.*, 1900. Personal communication.

HEINBECKER, P. and PAULI, R. H., 1927. 'Blood grouping of the Polar Eskimo', *J. Immun.* **XIII**, 279–283.

HRDLICKA, ALES, 1944. *The Anthropology of Kodiak Island*. Wistar Institute, Philadelphia.

—— 1945. *The Aleutian and Commander Islands*. Wistar Institute, Philadelphia.

JØRGENSEN, JORGEN BALSLEV, 1953. 'The Eskimo skeleton', *Medd. Grønland* **146**, 1–154.

LAUGHLIN, W. S., 1950. 'Blood groups morphology and population size of the Eskimos', *Cold Spring Harb. Symp. quant. Biol.* **XV**, 165–173.

—— 1958. 'Neo-Aleut and Oaleo-Aleut prehistory', *Proc. 32nd International Congress of Americanists, Copenhagen*, 1956, pp. 516–530. Munksgaard, 1958.

—— 1961. 'Acquisition of anatomical knowledge by ancient Man', *The Social Life of Early Man* (ed. S. L. WASHBURN), pp. 150–175. Viking Fund Publications in Anthropology, No. 31.

—— 1963. 'Eskimos and Aleuts: Their Origins and Evolution', *Science* **142**, 633–645.

—— and REEDER, W. G., 1962. 'Rationale for the collaborative investigation of Aleut–Konyag prehistory and ecology.' *Arctic Anthropology*, **1**, 104–108.

LAUGHLIN, W. S., GILBERT, J. P., and PETERSON, M. Q., 1965. 'Longitudinal variation reflected in Aleutian crania.' *In press.*
—— and TAYLOR, K. I., 1963. *Sub-Arctic Kayak Commitment and 'Kayak Fear'*. Department of Anthropology, University of Wisonsin.
LEVIN, M. G., 1958. 'Blood groups among the Chukchee and Eskimos', *Soviet Ethnography*, No. 5, pp. 113–116.
—— 1959. 'New material on the blood groups of the Eskimos and Lamuts', *Soviet Ethnography*, No. 3, p. 98.
—— 1963. 'Ethnic origins of the peoples of northeastern Asia', Arctic Institute of North America, *Anthropology of the North*, Translations from Russian Sources, No. 3 (ed. HENRY N. MICHAEL). University of Toronto Press.
—— and SERGEYEV, D. A., 1964. 'Ancient cemeteries in the Chukotsky Peninsular and some aspects of the Eskimo problem'. *VII International, Congress of Anthropological and Ethnological Sciences, Moscow* 1964. Nanka Publishing House Moscow.
MARSH, GORDON H. and LAUGHLIN, WILLIAM S., 1956. 'Human Anatomical knowledge among the Aleutian Islanders', *SWest. J. Anthrop.* **12**, 38–78.
MEIER, ROBERT, 1964. 'Fingerprint patterns from Karluk Village, Kodiak Island'. In preparation.
MERBS, CHARLES FRANCIS, 1963. 'The sadlermiut Eskimo Vertebral Column'. A thesis submitted in partial fulfillment of the requirements for the degree of Master of Science (Anthropology), University of Wisconsin.
—— and ANDERSON, JAMES E., 1962. 'A contribution to the human ostology of the Canadian Arctic', *Occ. Pap. R. Ont. Mus. Art Archaeol.*
MICHAEL, H. N., 1962. 'Studies in Siberian ethnogenesis', Arctic Institute of North America, *Anthropology of the North*, Translations from Russian Sources, No. 2. University of Toronto Press.
MIKKELSEN, EINAR, 1944. 'The East Greenlanders possibilities of existence, their production and consumption', *Medd. Grønland* **134**.
MILAN, FREDERICK ARTHUR, 1963. 'An experimental study of thermoregulation in two arctic races'. A thesis submitted in partial fulfillment of the requirements for the degree of Doctor of Philosophy (Anthropology), University of Wisconsin.
MOORREES, COENRAAD, F. A., 1957. *The Aleut Dentition*. Harvard University Press.
—— 1962. 'Genetic considerations in dental anthropology, *Genetics and Dental Health* (ed. CARL J. WITKOP, JR.), pp. 101–112. McGraw-Hill.
NEWMAN, MARSHALL T., 1958. 'A trial formulation presenting evidence from physical anthropology for migrations from Mexico to South America, *Migrations in New World Culture History*, pp. 33–40. University of Arizona Press.
—— 1960. 'Adaptations in the physique of American aborigines to nutritional factors'. *Human Biology*, **32**, 288–313.
PEDERSON, P. O., 1949. 'The East Greenland Eskimo dentition', *Medd. Grønland* **142**, 1–256.
SCHEFFER, V. B., 1958. *Seals, Sea Lions and Walruses: A Review of the Pinnepeda*. Stanford: Stanford University Press.

Scott, E. M., Wright, Rita C., and Hanan, Barbara T., 1955. 'Anaemia in Alaskan Eskimos', *J. Nutr.* **55**, 137–149.
Seltzer, Carl C., 1933. 'The anthropometry of the western and copper Eskimos, based on data of Vilhjalmun Stefansson', *Hum. Biol.* **V**, 313–370.
Skeller, Erik, 1954. 'Anthropological and ophthalmological studies on the Angmagssalik Eskimos', *Medd. Grønland* **4**.
Steffensen, Jon, 1953. 'The physical anthropology of the Vikings', *Jl R. anthrop. Inst.* **8B**, 85–97.
Stewart, T. Dale, 1939. 'Anthropometric observations on the Eskimos and Indians of Labrador', *Anthropological Series, Field Museum of National History* **31**.
—— 1953. 'The age incidence of neural-arch defects in Alaskan natives, considered from the standpoint of etiology, *J. Bone Jt Surg.* **35**A, 937–950.
Suzuki, Hisashi, 1958. 'Changes in the skull features of the Japanese people from ancient to modern times', *Sel. Pap. 5th Int. Cong. anthropol. ethnol. Sci. Philadelphia*, 1956, pp. 717–724.
Zolotareva, I. M., 1964. 'Blood Group Distribution of the Peoples of Northern Siberia'. *Arctic Anthropology*, **III**, 26–33.

16

THE CIRCUMPOLAR PEOPLE—HEALTH AND PHYSIOLOGICAL ADAPTATIONS[†]

J. A. HILDES

*Department of Medicine, University of Manitoba,
Winnipeg, Canada*

Introduction

THE people inhabiting the circumpolar regions do so only through the development of technologies to protect them particularly from the extreme cold of winter. In the north this has been accomplished by a number of indigenous races as well as by relatively recent settlers and explorers from the temperate regions. The habitation of the Antarctic has been achieved only in very recent years by heavily supported expeditions—so far composed only of male personnel. Nevertheless, it is of interest to consider the biological factors which may contribute to the success of both indigenous and immigrant groups, or which may develop as a consequence of polar habitation.

Climate and geography

There are many definitions and descriptive phrases applied to the parts of the world under consideration. These are variously based on environmental temperature, hours of sunlight, the nature of the vegetation, the latitude, or even on social considerations. The important characteristics of these regions have been listed in the Conference on Medicine and Public Health in the Arctic and Antarctic (1963):

(1) low temperature;
(2) snow-covered and/or frozen soil for long periods;
(3) prolonged darkness and prolonged light;

† Presented at the Wenner-Gren Symposium No. 23, The Biology of Populations of Anthropological Importance 29 June–12 July, 1964, Burg Wartenstein.

33

(4) special features of flora and fauna making agriculture very difficult;

(5) low density of population;

(6) communication difficulties;

(7) low economic strength.

The people and their living conditions

The world's population of Eskimos, numbering 50,000–60,000, occupy the North American coast and the Arctic Islands from Greenland to arctic Alaska and across the Bering Strait to Asia. The Aleuts—approximately 6000—are related to the Eskimos and occupy the Aleutian chain of islands. The North American Indians of arctic Alaska and Canada are indigenous arctic people who blend into the Indian populations of the forested sub-arctic regions. The Lapps occupy northern Scandinavia and number 33,000. Other groups about which less is known in America and Europe are the indigenous people of Asia. The Ainu of northern Japan may also be included as an indigenous northern population.

Non-indigenous European people in the Arctic include such groups as Icelanders, and northern Scandinavians who have lived in the Arctic for many generations as well as more recent 'immigrant' groups and transient populations.

The indigenous populations have developed diverse native cultures which still exist but it is unrealistic to think of them without considering the major effects which contact with 'southern' or 'European' cultures have had. This contact has been of variable duration and intensity for the different indigenous groups but all have experienced it to some degree. Nevertheless, there still exists groups of Eskimos (Hart *et al.*, 1962), Arctic Indians (Irving *et al.*, 1960), and shepherd Lapps (Andersen *et al.*, 1960), whose manner of living still provides the opportunity to study the physiological situation as it probably existed before modification by outside influences.

The conditions of life in the Arctic have obvious bearing on physiological requirements. The arctic coastal Eskimos lived in small nomadic or semi-nomadic groups—sometimes family size—dependent to a large extent on sea mammals, not only for food but also for clothing and fuel. Fish, birds, and land animals, and in some situations, berries and other vegetations contributed to the diet. Inland Eskimos relied to a greater extent on the migrating caribou but also moved to the coast and to inland water for sea mammals and fish. Dogs were the only domesticated animals and were widely used for travelling or as beasts of burden. Snow for building shelters was used in many areas and provided relatively good but temporary housing. Skin tents provided shelter in seasons when snow was not available (Jeness, 1958; Birket-Smith, 1959).

This manner of living required long periods of exposure to the environment for the hunters, but perhaps under ordinary circumstances, with significant cold exposure only to the extremities and the face. A high degree of physical endurance is required for travelling and hunting. Accidental death by injury or drowning was a frequent threat and failure of the hunt could lead to starvation since the establishment of large food stores was not well-developed.

The influence of European contact was to convert a hunting way of life to a trapping one based on the sale of furs. This created a dependence on the trading post for imported food, clothing, and fuel. The trading post thus became the focal point of settlement so that communities became larger and more fixed, but not necessarily better adapted to the climate or the terrain. This tendency to more permanent settlements has continued and has been further emphasized by the more recent provision of health and welfare services including education, religion, financial support to families with children, pensions for the aged and the disabled, and relief rations when food or money is scarce. When trapping is poor or the price of furs low, or when other temporary industries such as whaling factories, mining, or defence establishments close down, the transition back to a hunting way of life is very difficult. In some areas these changes have had a profound effect on diet, nutrition, and disease, as well as on social order. However, as indicated above, the influence of 'European' culture has not always been drastic. Where dependence on a money economy has not been complete, hunting for food and the old ways of life have been preserved although modified.

Health of arctic populations of North America

Mortality and morbidity are high in the indigenous populations of arctic North America, particularly in infancy, but also in the elderly, although there is wide variability from community to community (Hildes *et al.*, 1959; Hildes, 1960; Lederman *et al.*,

1962). Major causes of mortality and morbidity are infectious diseases, and accidental death. There is no evidence to date of diseases specific to the arctic regions: the problems lie mainly in the field of social and preventive medicine and are related to the features of arctic living outlined earlier. These factors also pose problems for the establishment of health services comparable to those found in the temperate area adjacent to the Arctic.

Infectious disease. The nature of the terrain and the presence of permafrost pose difficulties for safe water-supply and for sewage disposal even when the limitations imposed by the low economic level prevalent in the indigenous populations are not operative. The trend to larger and more permanent settlements enhance the difficulties. As one would expect, enteric infections are important. Viral, bacterial, protozoal, and parasitic enteric infections are known to exist (Hildes *et al.*, 1959; Schaefer, 1959; Hildes, 1960) and many are probably endemic.

Other infections are also related to the living conditions. Regular ablutions are difficult, and lice infestation, impetigo, and other skin infections are common. Tuberculosis remains a major problem in spite of the intensified efforts for prevention and treatment, and occasionally this disease may still cause local epidemics (Moore, 1964). This disease is probably mainly responsible for the high incidence of corneal scarring and other eye disease common in the Eskimo populations (Reed and Hildes, 1959).

Respiratory virus diseases such as measles and influenza may cause epidemics with a high attack rate if all age groups in an isolated population are susceptible. Such an occurrence may be devastating in the winter if reserves of food and fuel are low (Sabean, 1954). However, antibody surveys indicate that some respiratory virus diseases are endemic in arctic communities (Hildes *et al.*, 1958; Wilt *et al.*, 1961; Hildes *et al.*, 1965). In the case of psittacosis a higher incidence of antibodies is found in the Arctic than in temperate regions (Wilt *et al.*, 1959; Hildes *et al.*, 1965).

Diet and nutrition. In their native state the indigenous arctic populations lived on a diet almost entirely composed of animal protein and animal fat. Why then do Eskimos not suffer from arteriosclerosis? This question cannot be answered at the present time since the two premises on which it is based are by no means established. Arteriosclerosis does occur in Eskimos but there is insufficient evidence to assess its severity (Lederman *et al.*, 1962).

What dietary evidence is available suggests that the fat content of the Eskimo diet is probably little different from that of the average North American diet, although the protein content is higher (Conference on Medicine and Public Health, 1963). All Eskimos and Arctic Indian groups depend to a greater or less degree on the import of food: in the Cumberland Sound area of Baffin Island—a relatively large and stable community of 700 Eskimos where the major activity is the hunting of seal both for food and trade—over 20 tons of refined carbohydrate and 35 tons of flour were imported in one year. The calculated *per capita* consumption of flour was approximately two-thirds of the average Canadian consumption (Lederman *et al.*, 1962).

Where imported foods account for a high proportion of the diet iron deficiency anaemia occurs in both women and children (Sellers *et al.*, 1959; Scott and Heller, 1964).

On the other hand higher resting metabolic rates have been found in Eskimos compared to Whites (Rodahl, 1952; Irving *et al.*, 1960; Hart *et al.*, 1962). This has been attributed to a high dietary protein intake although the evidence is conflicting (Hammel, 1964).

Neoplasms. Autopsy studies (Gottman, 1960; Lederman *et al.*, 1962) show that a variety of neoplasms occur in Eskimos but quantitative data are not available to determine if the incidence is unusual, except in the case of an unusual type of salivary gland malignancy with a relatively high incidence in Canadian Eskimos (Wallace *et al.*, 1963). The report of Fibiger (1923) suggests that the same situation may have existed in Greenland forty years ago.

Physiological studies

It is not surprising that there has been considerable interest in the physiological responses to cold of Arctic people and other primitive groups exposed to cold. These have been recently reviewed by Hammel (1964). Concepts of mechanisms of cold adaptation in humans have been developed on the basis of extensive animal studies where two distinctive mechanisms have been demonstrated.

Insulative adaptation. Scholander *et al.* (1950) showed that arctic mammals had a great tolerance to cold which was achieved through insulation, mainly by the furry coats. The environmental temperature below which a metabolic response is brought into play—the critical temperature—is far below the body temperature. A similar finding has been reported for a land mammal with bare skin (Irving, 1956) and for aquatic arctic mammals (Hart and Irving, 1959). In these cases the required insulation is effected by a cooling of the peripheral tissues and the deep body temperature is maintained without increase in metabolic rate. Cooling of the skin and superficial tissues through vasoconstriction alone has a limited usefulness and in some animals peripheral heat exchanger mechanisms are present which allows for circulation of cooled blood to the peripheral insulative layer of tissue.

It is well known that in man vasoconstriction and pilo-erection in the skin occur in response to cold. This offers sufficient insulation for mild cold conditions. The critical temperature of humans is considered to be approximately 27°C which is in the range of tropical animals. Man (and some other animals with high critical temperatures) uses behavioural means of increasing insulation by wearing clothes or building shelters. Without such measures the circumpolar peoples could not survive the degree of environmental cold to which they are exposed even though large fur-bearing arctic mammals have achieved success in this direction. We are concerned with the possibility that some human populations, through physiological adaptations, have developed their insulative capacities to allow a significant lowering of critical temperature. The results of studies of moderate night-long cold exposure of Australian Aboriginals (Scholander et al., 1958) suggest this possibility. These observations form part of a series of studies concerned with metabolic as well as thermal responses to cold and are considered again later. The insulative mechanisms in bare-skinned animals including man are dependent on responses of the peripheral circulatory system to environmental temperature either directly, or through the controlling action of peripheral nerves. Therefore, adaptive changes in both animals and humans have been looked for in peripheral blood-vessels and nerves. Some evidence has been found in animals of special tolerance of peripheral nerves to cooling (Chatfield et al., 1953). Changes in sensation in the cold and in cold numbness in the hands and feet of humans repeatedly exposed to cold have been investigated with suggestive but inconclusive evidence that adaptation of nerve function may occur in humans (Mackworth, 1953; Hildes, unpublished).

The peripheral circulation in cold-adapted humans has been the subject of numerous studies, most of which indicate enhanced blood flow in the appendages and consequently an increase in heat loss from the skin (Page and Brown, 1953; Le Blanc et al., 1960; Hildes et al., 1961; Eagan, 1963). However, it is difficult to know if these local changes are dependent on local causes or whether they represent systemic circulatory adjustments secondary to increased metabolic activity (Brown et al., 1954) or a change in blood volume (Bazett et al., 1940; Brown et al., 1954; Doupe et al., 1957). If such circulatory adjustments occur without changes in metabolic rate a loss of stored heat and a redistribution of heat is implied. The 'core' and 'shell' concept of heat distribution was put forward by Carlson (1954). As will be indicated later the fluctuations in human deep body temperature, or rectal temperature at any rate, may be greater than has been hitherto considered to be physiological. (Elsner and Bolstad, 1964).

Bazett et al. (1948) described the pre-cooling of arterial blood in humans with hands in cold water—a mechanism for heat exchange between the peripheral tissues and the body.

Metabolic adaptation. Animals which are adapted to cold by an insulative mechanism may have some metabolic or hormonal process to account for changes in fur growth and the deposition of subcutaneous fat. What is well-documented is that small laboratory animals, and perhaps some small animals in the natural state, develop a metabolic adaptation which affords them protection when tested with a severe cold stress. This response is developed gradually during exposure to continuous cold reaching its maximum in four to six weeks and persisting for some weeks after return to a warm environment.

Although in a warm environment the metabolic rate of cold acclimated animals is close to but somewhat higher than the 'warm acclimated' controls, when they are placed in the cold they have the ability, even when curarized, to increase metabolism and maintain body temperature. 'Warm-adapted' control animals, under these conditions, do not increase their metabolism to the same extent and body temperature falls (Cottle and Carlson, 1956). When not curarized the cold-adapted animals in the cold preferentially use this non-shivering thermogenesis but the warm acclimated animals shiver in the cold (Hart et al., 1956). Although practically all tissues of cold-acclimated animals have an increased metabolic rate, major non-shivering thermogenesis goes on in the muscles. Therefore non-shivering thermogenesis as well as heat developed by muscle contraction is related to muscle mass.

Metabolic cold adaptation in man. With the above considerations in mind we may consider the human studies which have been carried out on various populations and which is the special subject of Hammel's review (1964). A common technique of whole-body, night-long moderate cold exposure introduced in the study by Scholander *et al.* (1958) on Norwegian students has been used to study the responses of Australian Aborigines, Lapps, Arctic fishermen, Arctic Indians, Eskimos, Andean Indians, Alacaluf Indians of Southern Chile, and Kalahari Bushmen. Hammel classifies the reactions of the Eskimos and Arctic Indians to this type of cold exposure as a metabolic acclimatization intermediate between the well-developed response in the Alacaluf Indians and that of un-acclimatized urban White, but which is different from the insulative type of adaptation best seen in the Australian Aborigines and also demonstrated to a lesser degree by Kalahari Bushmen.

In those studies in which shivering was objectively assessed (Arctic Indians (Irving *et al.*, 1960), Eskimos (Hart *et al.*, 1962), Kalahari Bushmen (Hammel *et al.*, 1962), and the Caucasians used as controls in these studies) good correlation was found between increases in metabolic rate and electrical activity in muscle.

However, the suggestion that Scholander's Norwegian students (1958) had developed a metabolic adaptation to cold during their weeks of exposure receives support from the reports of Davis (1963) that human subjects repeatedly exposed to cold in a chamber (or by moving to Greenland), shift from a shivering to a non-shivering heat production on exposure to a standard cold stress of short duration. Also the metabolic rate of the Alacaluf Indians was high in the warm and this was noted to a lesser extent in Eskimos and Arctic Indians. Whether these are entirely attributable to differences in diet or physical fitness as opposed to an adaptation to cold is difficult to assess, although as Hammel points out they do influence the responses to cold whatever their origin. The most recent study of Andersen (1964) on two groups of young Norwegians, both exposed to a programme of physical training and work, but only one group exposed to cold, tends to support the concept that physical fitness plays an important part in changing tolerance to cold, under the conditions of exposure and diet and exercise experienced by their subjects. The conditions under which other groups experience cold exposure may be important to the pattern of response to cold which develops in the different groups (Hammel, 1964).

From these considerations it is obvious that the study of physical fitness assumes considerable importance. Such studies have been carried out on a very limited number of Canadian Eskimos and Arctic Indians, by K. Lange Andersen and also some studies have been made on Alaskan Eskimos (Andersen *et al.*, 1960; Andersen, 1964).

The hormonal and biochemical mechanisms associated with increased tolerance to cold in man have not been investigated systematically although a considerable body of knowledge is being accumulated in animal studies. Davis (1963) has reported some preliminary results on man indicating an increased metabolic response to nor-adrenaline in his subjects. Such observations should be extended to the indigenous populations which show such a wide range of thermal and metabolic responses to a standard cold exposure.

Changes in thyroid function have been considered in some studies. Brown *et al.* considered that the Eskimos studied had many features of increased thyroid activity (1954). Others have indicated that the increased basal metabolic rate in Eskimos was due to diet (Rodahl, 1952). Although Hart *et al.* (1962) found Eskimos in hospital to have a lower metabolic rate than Eskimos in Baffin Island they had no evidence on which to assign the difference to the diet, the degree of physical fitness or to other reasons. Bass (1960) reported an increased turnover of thyroid hormone in subjects exposed continuously to cold in a chamber. The methods of assessing thyroid activity in humans are not easily carried out in the field but further studies would seem profitable.

Areas of ignorance

Although scientific interest in the circumpolar people has existed for a long time and has been particularly active in recent years there remain large gaps in our knowledge concerning the micro-climate of the people of all ages and both sexes, their level of activity, details of the diet, physical fitness, and cold tolerance, not to mention the underlying biochemical and hormonal basis of their physiological responses.

It would be informative to compare Arctic populations of the same racial background living under different environmental and cultural conditions as well as to further study the differences between races living under similar conditions.

Other areas of environmental factors which may have bearing on the adaptation of circumpolar people but which have not been studied are geomagnetism and photo-periodicity.

The special situation of expeditions particularly those wintering over one or two years in the Antarctic pose special problems related to periods of inactivity and isolation.

The experience which has been accumulated through field biological studies in the polar regions provides assurance that intensive studies of selected Arctic populations by multi-disciplinary teams can be carried out, and would provide new information on the role of genetic and environmental factors in adaptation to circumpolar living.

REFERENCES

ANDERSEN, K. L., BOLSTAD, A., LØYNING, Y., and IRVING, L., 1960. 'Physical fitness of Arctic Indians', *J. appl. Physiol.* **15**, 645–648.
—— LØYNING, Y., NELMS, J. D., WILSON, O., FOX, R. H., and BOLSTAD, A., 1960. 'Metabolic and thermal responses to a moderate cold exposure in nomadic Lapps', *J. appl. Physiol.* **15**, 649–653.
—— 1964. 'Interaction of chronic cold exposure and physical training upon human bodily tolerance to cold', *Report on Contract AF 61 (052)–758 Arctic Aero-Medical Laboratory.*

BASS, D. E., 1960. *Cold Injury* (ed. S. M. HORVATH). Josiah Macy Jr. Foundation, Capital City Press, Montpelier, Vermont.

BAZETT, H. C., SUNDERMAN, F. W., DOUPE, J., and SCOTT, J. C., 1940. 'Climatic effects on the volume and composition of blood in man', *Am. J. Physiol.* **129**, 69–83.
—— LOVE, L., NEWTON, M., EISENBERG, L., DAY, R., and FORSTER II, R., 1948. 'Temperature changes in blood flowing in arteries and veins in man', *J. appl. Physiol.* **1**, 3–19.

BIRKET-SMITH, K., 1959. *The Eskimos.* Methuen, London.

BROWN, G. M., BIRD, G. S., BOAR, T. J., BOAG, L. M., DELAHAYE, J. D., GREEN, J. E., HATCHER, J. D., and PAGE, J., 1954. 'The circulation in cold acclimatization', *Circulation* **9**, 813–822.

CARLSON, L. D., 1954. *Man in Cold Environment.* Arctic Aeromedical Laboratory, Ladd Airforce Base, Alaska.

CHATFIELD, P. O., LYMAN, C. P., and IRVING, L., 1953. 'Physiological adaptation to cold of peripheral nerves in the leg of the herring gull (*Larus argentatus*)', *Am. J. Physiol.* **172**, 639–644.

CONFERENCE ON MEDICINE AND PUBLIC HEALTH IN THE ARCTIC AND ANTARCTIC, 1963. *Tech. Rep. Ser. Wld Hlth Org.* 1–29, 253.

COTTLE, W. H. and CARLSON, L. D., 1956. 'Regulation of heat production in cold adapted rats', *Proc. Soc. exp. Biol. Med.* **92**, 845–849.

DAVIS, T. R. A., 1963. 'Non-shivering thermogenesis', *Fed. Proc.* **22**, 777–782.

DOUPE, J., FERGUSON, M. H., and HILDES, J. A., 1957. 'Seasonal fluctuations in blood volume', *Can. J. Biochem. Physiol.* **35**, 203–213.

EAGAN, C. J., 1963. 'Local vascular adaptation to cold in man', *Fed. Proc.* **22**, 947–952.

ELSNER, R. W. and BOLSTAD, A., quoted by HAMMEL, 1964. 'Adaptation to the environment', *Handbook of Physiology*. Am. Physiol. Soc., Washington.

FIBIGER, J., 1923. 'Über das Vorkommen von Krebs und Geschwulsten in Gronland; Ergebnisse der vom danischen Cancerkomitee bewerkstelligten. Untersuchungen', *Z. Krebsforsch.* **20**, 148–187.

GOTTMAN, A. W., 1960. 'A report of one hundred and three autopsies on Alaskan natives', *A.M.A. Archs Pathol.* **70**, 117–124.

HAMMEL, H. T., HILDES, J. A., JACKSON, D. C., and ANDERSEN, H. T., 1962. 'Thermal and metabolic response of the Kalahari Bushmen to moderate cold exposure at night', *Tech. Rep. No.* 62–44 *Arctic Aero-Medical Laboratory, Ladd Airforce Base.*

—— 1964. 'Adaptation to the environment', *Handbook of Physiology* (eds. D. B. DILL, E. F. ADOLPH, and C. G. WILBER). Am. Physiol. Soc., Washington.

HART, J. S., HEROUX, O., and DEPOCAS, F., 1956. 'Cold acclimatization and the electromyogram of unanesthetized rats', *J. appl. Physiol.* **9**, 404–408.

—— and IRVING, L., 1959. 'The energetics of harbour seals in air and in water with special consideration of seasonal changes', *Can. J. Zool.* **37**, 447–457.

—— SABEAN, H. B., HILDES, J. A., DEPOCAS, F., HAMMEL, H. T., ANDERSEN, K. L., IRVING, L., and FOY, G., 1962. 'Thermal and metabolic responses of coastal Eskimos during a cold night', *J. appl. Physiol.* **17**, 953–960.

HILDES, J. A., WILT, J. C., and STANFIELD, F. J., 1958. 'Antibodies to Adenovirus and to Psittacosis in Eastern Arctic Eskimos', *Can. J. publ. Hlth* **49**, 230–231.

—— WHALEY, R. D., WHALEY, H., and IRVING, L., 1959. 'Old Crow—a healthy Indian community', *Can. med. Ass. J.* **81**, 837–841.

—— WILT, J. C., and STACKIW, W., 1959. 'Neutralizing viral antibodies in Eastern Arctic Eskimos', *Can. J. publ. Hlth* **50**, 148–151.

—— 1960. 'Health Problems in the Arctic', *Can. med. Ass. J.* **83** 1255–1257.

—— IRVING, L., and HART, J. S., 1961. 'Estimation of heat flow from hands of Eskimos by calorimetry', *J. appl. Physiol.* **16**, 617–623.

—— WILT, J. C., PARKER, W. L., STACKIW, W., and DELAAT, A., 1965. 'Surveys of respiratory virus antibodies in an Arctic Indian village', *Can. med. Ass. J.* **93**, 1015–1018.

—— PARKER, W. L., DELAAT, A., STACKIW, W., and WILT, J. C., 1965. 'The elusive source of psittacosis antibodies in the Arctic', *Can. med. Ass. J.* **93**, 1154–1155.

—— 'Adaptation to cold numbness in the fingers', unpublished data.

IRVING, L., 1956. 'Physiological insulation of swine as bare-skinned mammals', *J. appl. Physiol.* **9**, 414–420.

—— ANDERSEN, K. L., BOLSTAD, A., ELSNER, R., HILDES, J. A., LØYNING, Y., NELMS, J. D., PEYTON, L. P., and WHALEY, R. D., 1960. 'Metabolism and temperature of Arctic Indian men during a cold night', *J. appl. Physiol.* **15**, 635–644.

JENESS, DIAMOND, 1958. *Indians of Canada*, 4th ed. National Museum of Canada, Bulletin 65, Anthropological Series No. 15, Ottawa.

LEBLANC, J., HILDES, J. A., and HEROUX, O., 1960. 'Tolerance of Gaspe fishermen to cold water', *J. appl. Physiol.* **15**, 1031–1034.

LEDERMAN, J. M., WALLACE, A. C., and HILDES, J. A., 1962. 'Biological aspects of aging', *Proc. 5th Int. Congr. Geront.*, pp. 201–207. Columbia University Press, New York, N.Y.

MACKWORTH, N. H., 1953. 'Finger numbness in very cold hands', *J. appl. Physiol.* **5**, 533–543.

MOORE, P. E., 1964. 'Puvalluttig—an epidemic of tuberculosis at Eskimo Point, N.W.T., *Can. med. Ass. J.* **90**, 1193–1202.

PAGE, J. and BROWN, G. M., 1953. 'Effect of heating and cooling the legs on hand and forearm blood flow in the Eskimo', *J. appl. Physiol.* **5**, 753–758.

REED, H. and HILDES, J. A., 1959. 'Corneal scarring in Canadian Eskimos', *Can. med. Ass. J.* **81**, 364–366.

RODAHL, K., 1952. 'Basal metabolism of the Eskimo', *J. Nutr.* **48**, 359–368.

SABEAN, H. B., 1954. 'Observations regarding medical care for the Eskimo', *Dalhousie med. J.* **7**, 10–13.

SCHAEFER, O., 1959. 'Medical observations and problems in the Canadian Arctic', *Can. med. Ass. J.* **81**, 248–253, 386–392.

SCHOLANDER, P. F., WATERS, V., HOCK, R., and IRVING, L., 1950. 'Body insulation of some arctic and tropical mammals and birds', *Biol. Bull.* **99**, 225–236.

—— HAMMEL, H. T., HART, J. S., LEMESSURIER, D. H., and STEEN, J., 1958. 'Cold adaptation in Australian Aborigines', *J. appl. Physiol.* **13**, 211–213.

—— —— ANDERSEN, K. L., and LØYNING, Y., 1958. 'Metabolic acclimation to cold in man', *J. appl. Physiol.* **12**, 1–8.

SCOTT, E. M. and HELLER, C. A., 1964. 'Iron deficiency in Alaskan Eskimos', *Am. J. clin. Nutr.* **15**, 282–286.

SELLERS, F. J., WOOD, W. J., and HILDES, J. A., 1959. 'The incidence of anaemia in infancy and early childhood among Central Arctic Eskimos', *Can. med. Ass. J.* **81**, 656–657.

WALLACE, A. C., MACDOUGALL, J. T., HILDES, J. A., and LEDERMAN, J. M., 1963. 'Salivary gland tumours in Canadian Eskimos', *Cancer* **16**, 1338–1353.

WILT, J. C., HILDES, J. A., and STANFIELD, F. J., 1959. 'The prevalence of complement-fixing antibodies against psittacosis in the Canadian Arctic', *Can. med. Ass. J.* **81**, 731–733.

—— —— PARKER, W. L., and DELAAT, A., 1961. 'Sendai virus antibodies in the Arctic', *Can. med. Ass. J.* **84**, 319–321.

17

HUMAN ADAPTABILITY WITH REFERENCE TO THE IBP PROPOSALS FOR HIGH ALTITUDE RESEARCH

G. AINSWORTH HARRISON

Anthropology Laboratory, Department of Human Anatomy, University of Oxford

THE study of human adaptability, which forms one of the major sections of the proposed International Biological Programme, is beset with innumerable conceptual and methodological difficulties. In this paper, I should like to consider some of these problems, in relation to the proposals which are developing under IBP auspices, to investigate the biological effects of high altitudes on man.

First the word 'adaptability' itself; this has been used in a number of different ways. What is usually meant is the capacity of the individual to respond to changes in the environment in ways which facilitate survival and this is the sense in which I will use the term. However, in the title of the IBP section, it is being used in a much wider sense, to cover all the ways in which man is fitted to his environment and includes genetic and cultural, as well as so-called 'phenotypic' responses. I shall take this wider definition as my terms of reference.

Perhaps the most important aspect of the problem is that it is concerned with the totality of the human response—at the level of both the individual and the population—to the totality of the environment. Of course, one is inevitably limited, by lack of basic knowledge about the natures of the individuals, the population, and the environment, but the important point is that one is dealing with complex interactions, and any study must be as fully integrated as possible. In the past most biological studies of human populations have been concerned solely with some particular parameter, such as genetic variation, temperature acclimatization, or physical fitness. The majority indeed have been much more limited than this. Further, the orientation of these studies has rarely been towards general ecology. Physiologists have largely been interested in the nature of adaptive mechanisms, rather than in their effects, and practically no attention has been given to recording and analysing inter-individual variations in response. Anthropological geneticists, have, until quite recently anyway, been more concerned in tracing the movements of, and relationships between, populations, than in analysing the selective forces which produce diversification. Thus, even when, as has sometimes happened, physiologists and anthropologists have chosen the same population for study, rarely if ever does the data obtained throw much light on the ecological complex. One of the great possibilities offered by the IBP programme is the opportunity to undertake, on the same people at the same time, as fully integrated studies as are now possible. To plan such work with respect to the Himalayas has been the object of a working group of British human biologists, and I will summarize these plans later.

Adaptive mechanisms

As is now well recognized, the capacity to survive in any environment is determined in many different ways. In the first place, there is the adaptability of the individual, which itself is made up of innumerable physiological, behavioural, and developmental components. These can rather broadly be divided into (1) reversible mechanisms, mainly physiological and behavioural, whose state is changeable at least to some extent throughout the life of the individual, and (2) irreversible mechanisms, which are only environmentally labile during the period of growth and development. Obviously, these latter mechanisms are more difficult to recognize than reversible responses. Further, not all environmentally determined responses facilitate survival. If the adaptive mechanisms are inadequate to maintain homeostatis and homeorhesis in some environment, the consequent changes in state, some of which may involve the homeostatic mechanisms themselves, will represent loss of adaptation. The changes which occur at extremes of altitude even in the fully acclimatized individual, are a case in point. Often one of the major problems in considering environmental lability is to determine whether some particular change is adaptive, rather than indicating a breakdown of fitness.

The second major component in adaptation—genetic adaptation—involves the environment as the selecting agent. Selection of course operates in a number of ways and is as much concerned with maintaining genetic stability, as in producing genetic change and diversity. Thus for instance, it not only increases the frequency of genes, and gene combinations, which facilitate survival, but is responsible for constancy of gene frequencies in a polymorphic situation. It is also convenient to distinguish between selective forces which are operating universally and those which are related to some particular environment. The existence of an ABO blood group polymorphism would seem to be the result of a universal selection, but the level at which it is set probably depends upon particular ecological conditions. Further, whilst it is often necessary to consider selection in some particular genetic system, it is now widely appreciated that in doing this one is usually abstracting an idealized system. Invariably there is interaction within the genetic system; one knows already, for instance, that ABO blood group status is important in considering selection in the Rh system (Stern *et al.*, 1956; Race and Sangar, 1958; Kirk, 1961). In fact selection operates ultimately on the overall phenotype of the individual, and every component of the environment determines the nature and intensity of the selection. In this connexion, it may be noted that environmentally determined adaptability must itself have a genetic basis produced by selection, and that this adaptability will interact with the environmentally rigid genetic adaptations. Thus, for instance, quantitative variation in some environmentally determined response may represent different genetically determined capacities to respond, but it may also indicate different 'needs', since the magnitude of a response will also depend upon the extent by which the individual, as a result of the rest of his genotype, departs from the optimal phenotype. It is known that some indigenous tropical peoples sweat less than fully acclimatized Europeans (Weiner and Lee, unpublished) and this could well be due to their better genetic adaptations. This type of interaction implies that even amongst individuals who have apparently successfully adapted to some environmental components, there is variation in their 'reserves' for homeostatis, and, in the whole ecological complex this would no doubt lead to differential selection. Such variability may only be recognizable directly during times of environmental crises, when homeostatic capacities are at their limits. It may well be, however, that the crisis situation has been particularly important in determining the course of human evolution.

In somewhat broader terms, the nature of the gene pool is an important aspect of genetic adaptation since it determines the likelihood of persistence of the population. Except in the most general way, however, this parameter is impossible to measure. What is important is the mating structure of the population, since this will affect selection, and studies of human adaptation must be concerned with analysing the variety of complex mating patterns practised by human societies.

The third major component in human adaptation, is the cultural-technological one. Whilst much of this originates in behavioural adaptability, it is essentially distinct from the other mechanisms, being a function of the population, rather than of the individual, but with a much more flexible transmission than genetic inheritance. In many ways, also, it is the most important, since the biological success of the human species is directly dependent upon its unique capacity for culture. Further, this success has depended on a quite advanced technological and social level and not until the neolithic revolution did man become a dominant mammalian species. Many habitats, particularly those in the colder regions, could not be occupied at all by man without the aid of technological invention. From the biological point of view, however, the principal importance of cultural adaptation, is that it modifies the nature of the natural environment in which man is living and therefore the selective forces operating. In considering the adaptation of the Eskimo to the Arctic it is important to take into consideration the fact that for most of the arctic winter, he is living at a temperature of about 70°F (Wulsin, 1949). In the series of environmental envelopes with which the individual is surrounded, that closest to him is usually determined mainly by his technology. These cultural environments, of course, often confuse the study of biological adaptations, and one of the advantages of a study of high altitude adaptation, is that, at the moment, mountain peoples have no methods of artificially changing the most critical factor in their environment—barometric pressure.

Identifying adaptations

Since all these different adaptive mechanisms are interacting in a complex way, unravelling any particular situation raises extremely difficult methodological problems. In principle, the most easy to identify are the reversible changes involved in adaptability, since they will concomitantly change with change of environment. Much has been learned of physiological acclimatization to high altitudes by Europeans from observations on mountaineers as they change environment (Hurtado and Clark, 1960; Weihe, 1964). The main deficiency in this data is that it relates almost exclusively to the young healthy adult male and practically no attention has been given to individual variation. Further, it is extremely dangerous to extrapolate from the responses made by Europeans to those made by peoples drawn from a different gene pool.

Whilst it is obviously preferable to study reversible responses by observations on the same individuals in different environments, it would also seem reasonable to suppose that differences between populations with a recent common ancestry but living in these different environments include these reversible responses along with the irreversible ones. Thus for instance, comparison of Indians of the lowlands with recent migrants to high altitude might well reveal their total adaptability to both environments, and if the changes in a group of adult Indians as they moved from one environment to the other were also investigated, then one might be able to partition the adaptability into reversible and irreversible responses. The main difficulty in doing this is in recognizing how recent a common ancestry must be before selective changes have made the populations uncomparable in these terms. On this point we have no information, and it will obviously depend upon the magnitude of the environmental change. However, one may expect that selection will operate very strongly to produce genetic change when a population moves from one environment to a totally different one, and even the composition of the migrants themselves may be affected by it. Also to be considered, of course, are the possible effects of selective migration, and miscegenation with neighbouring populations after separation.

As has already been mentioned, the possibility that some responses represent changes in fitness has to be taken into account too. It may generally be expected that individuals have their maximum fitness in their habitual environment and that a radical change of environment will typically lower both somatic and reproductive fitness. One would, therefore, expect that characters which to some extent reflect somatic fitness such as growth rate and body weight will change, solely as a result of this. The situation may be even more specific. It is deductively evident that most of

34

physiological response to high altitudes represent adaptations and one can turn directly to determining their efficacy. But, so far as I know, the significance in the change in eosinophil count for instance, cannot be so deduced, and it has itself to be tested.

In rather general terms, there would seem to be two ways in which the biological significance might be resolved (Harrison, 1963). In the first place, one would expect that both the inter- and intra-variability of an individual adaptable mechanism, would be lowered in a new, i.e. non-habitual, environment, whereas the variability of a fitness indicator would rise. Since a population cannot immediately have full genetic adaptation to a new environment, the homeostatic reserve must be less, and fewer states are compatible with survival. Hence one would expect lowered variability in adaptable mechanisms. On the other hand, since the efficacy of these mechanisms in maintaining homeostasis cannot be greater and most probably will be less than in the habitual environment, the individual will tend to be less well buffered against the effects of environmental variation, and fitness indicators will therefore show greater variation. One should, therefore, be able to gain some insight into the significance of a character change by comparing the variability of the character in the habitual environment and in the new environment.

The second method involves comparing migrants to a new environment with the indigenous peoples for whom the environment is habitual. The latter should obviously have the greater fitness, and, therefore, not show, or show to a lesser extent, the responses in the migrants which were associated with loss of fitness. One would also expect that the growth rate in the indigenes would be faster, except in so far as growth rate is determined by ultimate size, and that the variability in fitness indicators would be less. On the other hand, the variability in the adaptable mechanisms themselves might be higher, since the presence of the presumed genetic adaptations increases the reserve of homeostasis, and more states are compatible with survival. However, there is an inherent danger in confusing genetic adaptations with adaptability in this case, and it is more than possible that a character representing an adaptable mechanism in the migrants is genetically fixed in the indigenes. Differences in variability, then, might well arise from differences in the relative contributions of the two mechanisms.

When one comes to the genetic mechanisms themselves, and the detection of selection, the problem is equally complex. Sometimes it is possible from knowledge of physiological function, or from the close association between the geographical distribution of a character and an environmental variable to deduce the nature of a selective force. Thus without clear-cut experimental proof, one can feel fairly sure that skin colour is determined, at least in part, by ultraviolet radiation (Harrison, 1961), and body build is related to thermal regulation (Roberts, 1953). However, since in both of these cases the genetics is not fully understood, and there is certainly some environmental lability, we do not know how much of the association is due to adaptable responses. This is particularly so in the case of body build which may well show considerable developmental adaptability, though study of migrants suggests that it is not a major factor in the association.

Other indirect evidence can come from experimental investigations such as for instance on the antigenic overlap between a pathogen and a blood group, or on the comparative performance of peoples of different physiques in hot-room tests, but in the final analysis the best demonstration that selection is operating, depends upon showing a differential net fertility of different genotypes. This is certainly the only way of measuring the intensity of the selection. Because of the advent of medical science, one cannot evaluate in this way the many associations which have now been found in advanced societies between blood groups and various diseases. Certainly the selection we know of is operating now with neither the intensity nor in the direction to maintain these polymorphisms (Sheppard, 1959) and it is generally recognized that the factors which originally set at least the level of these polymorphisms are probably no longer acting in these societies. One of course has to turn to populations in which the gene markers we know are still likely to be determined by the natural environment. Even the nature of the selection operating on sickle-cell haemoglobin would never have been established from studies of the American Negro, and perhaps could never have been discovered at all twenty years hence. The point is mentioned because even in less advanced societies, it is as possible that changes in gene frequency are occurring as much because an old selective force has disappeared, as because a new one is acting. Both processes will occur following a change of environment, and while this does not matter in determining the overall effects of selection, it is important in tying the selection to particular ecological factors.

Unless a population is very large, or there is a high mortality rate as a result of an environmental crisis such as a disease epidemic, or the investigator can spend a long time in the field, one is unlikely to be able to measure differential mortality directly in primitive communities. Differential fertility is somewhat easier, if relationships can be established and reported information about family size, miscarriage rates, &c., relied upon. In the main, however, one will only be able to detect changes in genotype or gene frequencies indirectly, by significant departures from the frequencies expected in the absence of selection. If selection is actually affecting gene frequency, then, of course, a longitudinal study over a number of generations is theoretically the best way to detect it. However, such studies are rarely practicable, and anyway would not detect the selection maintaining a balanced polymorphism at equilibrium. On the other hand, looking for departures in a single generation will usually necessitate very large samples. The numbers required, of course, depend not only on the magnitude of the selection coefficients, but also on the frequency of the genes involved and must be estimated for each system. Another difficulty arises when, as is usual, gene frequencies have to be estimated on the assumption of random mating. In the mating systems of many societies the degree of departure from randomness may well more profoundly disturb expected genotype frequencies than any likely selection coefficient. In part, this difficulty can be avoided by comparing phenotype frequencies in different age groups, since unless the mating system has recently changed, the effects of this system will be the same in each age-group. Further a trend with age may well be significant, when departure from expectation within any one age-group is not. However, using this approach involves the collection of yet more data, and if the main selection operates very early in life, it would still go undetected. It is, of course, also possible that a particular selective factor not only tends to operate at one age but is also intermittent, so that the population at the time of observation has not been exposed to it. Studies of selection at high altitude are likely to be particularly free of this difficulty, since at least the low tension of atmospheric oxygen is more or less constant, and any selection that it imposes is unlikely to be intermittent.

Plan of a Himalayan study

One of the most important reasons for proposing IBP studies of the effects of altitude, is that in general terms one is more likely to be able to detect selective effects and recognize the significance of adaptable responses to high altitude than any other type of environment. In addition to the advantages already mentioned, there is the most crucial of all—very great changes of environment in comparatively short distances. This not only facilitates study, but also means that some of the peoples in these different environments are often recently related to one another. The great value of such groups in detecting both adaptability and selection has already been considered. On the other hand the difficulty of the terrain—though of great practical difficulty to investigators—means that the complicating factors of gene flow are probably at a minimum except along mountain passes.

The design for the Himalayan study, which the British IBP high-altitude working party has put up for discussion is essentially one of a comparison between two populations, one of which (A) is indigenous to high altitudes (AH), but with recent migrants to lower levels (AL), whilst the other (B) is basically a lowland population (BL), but with some sub-groups at high altitudes. With regard to the various difficulties discussed, the unique similarities between (AH) and (BH), and between (AL) and (BL) should represent the adaptable responses to the two environments, whilst the differences must be genetic, and include, if not exclusively so, the effects of genetic selection for high altitude on A and for low altitude on B. By contrast the similarities between (AH) and (AL), and between (BH) and (BL) are either genetic or due to an environmental factor which is not varying with altitude, whilst differences are 'phenotypic' adaptations.

One of the practical difficulties, of course, is to recognize living populations which correspond to these ideals. In Nepal it would seem that the Sherpa populations of the Sola Khumbu will afford a co-operative sample of (AH) whilst the migrant Sherpas in Darjeeling can be considered to be (AL). Various North Indian populations are (BL) and it is possible, though not yet clear, whether there are adequate (BH) representatives of some of these. There is also the possibility that comparisons of the people of the Marsyanda Khola, with those of the Chaka region in Central Nepal will afford another (BL) (BH) contrast. These possibilities are now being investigated, and the intention is that, once the IBP has been successfully launched, a pilot study of the Chaka region will be undertaken with the view to subsequently sending an expedition there, as well as to Sola Khumbu.

Since a series of handbooks about IBP investigations will soon be appearing, it seems unnecessary to specify in detail the nature of the biological information it is intended to collect. This would obviously be as complete as possible and, in summary, would include, (1) detailed medical examination along with the special study of blood samples for bacterial and viral antibodies, blood parasites, haemoglobin concentration, M.C.V., P.C.V., M.C.H.C., plasma proteins, plasma lipids, creatinine, Vitamin A, and carotene, (2) as much demographic information as possible, especially on pregnancy histories and neonatal mortality, (3) nutritional data which on Sherpas, at least, should be comparatively easy to obtain, (4) genetic studies, on an age basis, using as many systems as possible, (5) anthropometric and anthroposcopic observations, and (6) physiological studies, including respiratory capacity and related observations, working capacity, and tests for cold and heat tolerance. It is really in this last section that the uniqueness of the proposed investigations is most evident. The large-scale screening of a population in physiological terms has rarely been attempted before.

REFERENCES

HARRISON, G. A., 1961. *Pigmentation in Genetical Variation in Human Populations*. Pergamon Press, Oxford.
—— 1963. 'Temperature adaptation as evidenced by growth of mice', *Fed. Proc.* **22**, 691.
HURTADO, A., and CLARK, R. T., 1960. *Parameters of Human Adaptation to Altitude, in Physics and Medicine of the Atmosphere and Space* (eds. O. O. BENSON and H. STROGHOLD), pp. 352–369. Wiley, New York.
KIRK, R. L., 1961. 'Blood-group interaction, and the world distribution of ABO gene p^2 and the Rh gene r (*cde*)', *Am. J. hum. Genet.* **13**, 224.
RACE, R. R. and SANGER, R., 1958. *Blood Groups in Man*, 3rd ed. Blackwell, Oxford.
ROBERTS, D. F., 1953. 'Body weight, race, and climate', *Am. J. phys. Anthrop.* **11**, 533.
SHEPPARD, P. M., 1959. 'Natural selection and some polymorphic characters in man', *Natural Selection in Human Populations*. Pergamon Press, Oxford.

STERN, K., DAVIDSON, I., and MASAITIS, L., 1956. 'Experimental studies on Rh immunization', *Am. J. clin. Path.* **26**, 833.

WEIHE, W. H. (ed.), 1964. *The Physiological Effects of High Altitude.* Pergamon Press, Oxford.

WEINER, J. S. and LEE, D. H. K. Unpublished, see WEINER, J. S., in HARRISON, G. A., WEINER, J. S., TANNER, J. M., and BERNICOT, N. A., *Human Biology* (1964). Oxford University Press.

WULSIN, F. R., 1949. 'Adaptations to climate among non-European peoples', *Physiology of Heat Regulation and the Science of Clothing*, (ed. L. H. NEWBURGH). Saunders, Philadelphia.

18

A PROGRAMME FOR PHYSIOLOGICAL STUDIES OF HIGH-ALTITUDE PEOPLES†

L. G. C. PUGH

Division of Human Physiology, National Institute for Medical Research, London

PHYSIOLOGISTS are accustomed to thinking of acclimatization to altitude in terms of physiological adjustments to hypoxia, and most of our physiological knowledge of high-altitude peoples at present relates to this aspect of their environment. There are of course other elements of the high-altitude environment which are equally, if not more, important for man's survival and development. The most obvious of these relate to:

(1) *Climate.* Because of the lapse of temperature with altitude and the intensity of solar radiation at altitude, the high-altitude dweller is likely to be exposed to a very wide range of thermal stresses, and IBP expeditions may expect to find evidence of unusual tolerance of both cold and heat among high-altitude peoples.

It is perhaps worth while remarking here that the Incas and Spanish settlers in South America found the cold at high altitude a greater problem than the 'thin air' (Monge, 1948).

(2) *Physiology.* Most high-altitude regions are either mountainous or barren (or both). In either case, survival demands a high degree of physical endurance, probably also a high physical working capacity. Comparisons between mountain dwellers and plainsmen at high and low altitudes would be rewarding from this point of view.

(3) *Isolation.* Isolation from neighbouring peoples, both friendly and hostile, may be expected to have had important cultural and genetic effects on high-altitude peoples.

(4) *Nutrition.* The severe climate at high altitude, as well as the

† Paper prepared in advance for participants in Symposium No. 23, 'The Biology of Populations of Anthropological Importance', 29 June–12 July 1964.

leeching of trace elements such as iodine from the soil, has had important nutritional influences on high-altitude peoples, and one suspects that neglect of such factors may at times have misled physiologists in interpreting their findings on the results of investigation of acclimatization.

BRITISH PROJECT FOR HIMALAYAN STUDIES

The research proposal put forward by the British IBP Working Party on the adaptation of populations to high altitude consists of a multidisclipine study of:

(1) the Sherpa inhabitants of the Sola Khumbu district of Nepal who live mainly at altitudes of 3000–4500 m (11,000–14,000 ft);

(2) the Sherpa population of the Indian town of Darjeeling 1500 m (5000 ft) in collaboration with Indian physiologists;

(3) the inhabitants of the Chaka region (3000–4500 m) 5 days' journey north of Katmandu;

(4) a special high-altitude physiological expedition to study the adjustment of Sherpas to 6000 m (20,000 ft) along the lines followed by the Himalayan Scientific and Mountaineering Expedition 1960–61.

Before going further it is well to describe briefly what is already known of these peoples.

Chaka population

These people have been visited by Professor C. von Furer Haimendorf, who has described them as living in approximately the same altitude range as the Sherpas of Sola Khumbu, but in a wide valley. No physiological observations have been made on them. They are assumed to be of Tibetan origin.

The Sherpas

The Sherpas of Sola Khumbu occupy some of the most rugged terrain in the world where it is impossible to move more than a short distance without going up or down hill and there is no animal transport of any kind.

According to local tradition they migrated from Northern Tibet about 200 years ago. They did not settle at first, but travelled annually over the Nang Pa La Pass, 5800 m (19,000 ft), to the grazing ground of Sola Khumbu. It may have been the introduction of the potato about 100 years ago that enabled them to settle permanently in Sola Khumbu. Their principal villages lie on or near a trade route connecting Tibet with India and Nepal and they live partly off this trade; otherwise their chief occupations are yak and sheep breeding and the cultivation of potatoes and barley.

Climate

The climate at 3500–4500 m (12,000–14,000 ft) is characterized by intense solar radiation by day and high long-wave radiation loss at night. Bishop in 1961 (Pugh, 1962a) observed values of total hemispheric radiation as high as $1 \cdot 7$ gcal cm^{-2} min^{-1} on clear days in May 1961, which is 50 per cent more than the highest values observed at Kew, London. Precipitation is more or less confined to the monsoon period between April and September and amounts to about 38 cm (15 in.) a year. The region is therefore classified as semi-arid. The temperatures during the winter months are always below freezing point at night, with a low limit in the region of $-10°C$ to $-15°C$ at 3500 m (12,000 ft). The meteorology of the region was studied by the 1960–61 Himalayan Scientific and Mountaineering Expedition and by previous Swiss expeditions, but further studies will be necessary before the climate can be adequately described.

Clothing

In contrast to their neighbours at heights below 2500 m (9000 ft) the Sherpas are clad to withstand a cold climate. The clothing is of the Tibetan type. The men wear either sheepskin or woollen clothing; the women wear woollen dresses and undergarments of wool, with skirts reaching to the ankles and multi-coloured aprons. When travelling the women, in particular, show little readiness to adapt their clothing to the climate. In summer they carry loads to the relatively hot climate of the Katmandu plain still wearing their heavy native dress.

Dwellings

The two-storey Sherpa houses are similar to those seen in other parts of Nepal. They are built of stone with slatted wooden roofs and unglazed windows. The family live on the upper floor and the animals underneath. Chimneys are unknown; the smoke from the hearth escapes from a hole in the roof and as a result the rooms are filled with smoke for much of the day.

Nutrition

The staple Sherpa diet consists of potatoes and tsampa (flour made from roasted barley). Tsampa is used almost exclusively for travelling and porters have told me that they allow themselves 1 seer (3 lb) a day, i.e. about 3500 cal. Being Buddhists the Sherpas do not slaughter animals themselves but this is done seasonally by hired butchers; the meat is kept for long periods hung up in their houses. Milk, eggs, and butter are also available in small quantities and I have heard that the yaks are occasionally bled for food. There are two local alcoholic beverages, *rakshi* distilled from potatoes, and *chung*, a kind of beer, brewed from fermented millet.

Health

The most obvious medical disorder among the Sherpas is endemic goitre. On my first visit to the district in 1952 I recorded that nearly all the women, half the men and about 20 per cent of the children suffered from it, but I saw only two cretins. Chronic respiratory disease, including tuberculosis, is very prevalent. Doctors on expeditions have reported rheumatic heart disease, rheumatoid arthritis, ankylosing spondylitis, syphilis, and a high incidence of infective skin and eye disease among children. Malaria is common among porters, being presumably contracted during visits to low altitudes.

Porterage

I made a study of porters on Shipton's expedition to Cho Oyu in 1952. The body weights of the porters ranged from 43 to 57 kg (95–125 lb) and their height from 147 to 160 cm (58–63 in.). Below 1800 m (6000 ft) they carried loads of 63 kg (140 lb) and from 1800 to 3600 m (6000–12,000 ft) they carried loads of 36 kg (80 lb). They marched 10 to 12 hours a day covering 10 to 12 miles. Some of the marches included ascents and descents of 1200 m (4000 ft). At above 3600 m (12,000 ft) the porters' loads were reduced to 27 kg (60 lb) but on occasions they carried 32–36 kg (70–80 lb) to 5800–6000 m (19,000–20,000 ft). On

Mount Everest in 1963 the porters carried 18 kg (40 lb) up to 8000 m (26,000 ft).

Where possible, loads are carried in conical carrying baskets with head bands. Mechanically this is an extremely efficient method since the centre of gravity is brought close to the vertical line

TABLE 1

Haemoglobin level in Sherpas, Europeans, and South Americans resident at high altitude

	No. of subjects	Haemoglobin (g/100 ml)	
Mount Cho Oyu 1952			Before expedition
Europeans	8	20·3 (18·3–22·0)	14·9 (14·1–15·5)
Sherpas	6	19·0 (17·6–20·0)	13·6 (11·6–15·5)
Mount Everest 1953			
Europeans	12	20·9 (19·3–23·3)	
Sherpas	18	19·3 (15·1–23·6)	
Ming Bo 1960–61			
Sherpas resident at 3800–4300 m	22	17·1 (14·5–21·3)	
Sherpas living temporarily at 5800 m	10	17·9 (15·8–22·7)	
Europeans living temporarily at 5800 m	8	19·6 (18·9–21·2)	
South America			
Native miners resident at 5300–5800 m ('Quilcha)	6	22·9 (18·4–25·6)	
Native miners resident at 4500 m (Morococha)	32	20·76	

passing through the centre of the pelvis and the greater part of the weight is transmitted straight to the skeleton and not through the muscles of the shoulder girdle. When carrying heavy loads or ascending steep slopes the porters work intermittently resting for ½ min every 2 to 3 min. At 2000–3000 m (6500–10,000 ft), their pulse rates were 140–160 beats/min on steep paths, 100–124 beats/min on level ground, and 84–104 beats/min going downhill.

Physiology

Tables 1, 2, 3, and 4 summarize data so far collected on Sherpas by British expeditions.

Haemoglobin. Haemoglobin levels are lower than those of South American native populations living at comparable altitude and the haemoglobin levels in high-altitude porters tend to be lower than those of European visitors. No correlation has been found between the haemoglobin concentration and physical performance.

TABLE 2

O_2 uptake in steady climbing at maximum pace at 13,200 ft (4000 m)

	$\dot{V}_{O_2}$ kg/l./min	Ventilation equivalent l./l.O_2 (STPD)
Sherpas		
Tensing	41·4	20·5
Ang Temba	45·1	24·4
Da Namgyal	48·3	19·5
European		
E. P. Hillary	43·6	28·1

Physical endurance. The physical endurance of Sherpas at high altitude is greater than that of European visitors. Climbing parties ascending to great heights have depended on Sherpa porters to carry their loads and have often owed their lives to them when accidents have happened. The 1960–61 Expedition reported that their Sherpa porters regularly carried loads of 30 kg (66 lb) up to 6000 m (20,000 ft) at approximately the same speed as white men climbing without loads. Table 2 shows some measurements of maximum uptake of oxygen in Sherpas compared with E. P. Hillary at the time of the ascent of Mount Everest in 1953. Judging by the ventilation equivalent for oxygen Hillary was working at maximal capacity but the Sherpas were not.

Tables 3 and 4 show some results obtained during ergometer exercise at 5800 m (19,000 ft) by the 1960–61 Himalayan Expedition. The white subject was one of the fittest members of the scientific party and the Sherpa was a high-altitude porter who had carried loads to 8000 m (26,000 ft) on previous expeditions. The differences in performance were very striking. At the 900 kg-m/min work load the Sherpa had a higher oxygen intake, heart rate, and cardiac output, but lower ventilation and normal blood pH. Because of the normal blood pH the Sherpas arterial P_O was the

TABLE 3

Results from the 1960–61 Himalayan Scientific and Mountaineering Expedition of simultaneous blood and respiratory measurements at 5800 m (19,000 ft) (bar. 380 mm Hg): (a) in the European with the highest work capacity (JBW), and (b) in one of the strongest Sherpas (DT)

Subject	Work rate (kg-m/min)	Arterialized venous blood					$\dot{V}_E$ (l./min) (BTPS)	$F_E\,CO_2$ (%)	$F_E\,O_2$ (%)	f (per min)	$\dot{V}_{O_2}$ (l. min) (BTPS)	$P_A\,CO_2$ (mm Hg) (calc.)	$P_A\,O_2$ (mm Hg) (calc.)	$P_a\,O_2$ (mm Hg)	$P_A\,O_2$—$P_a\,O_2$ (mm Hg)	R	Heart rate (beats/min)
		HbO_2 content (vols. %)	CO_2 content (vols. %)	HbO_2 capacity (vols. %)	HbO_2 % sat.	pHs (Henderson–Hasselbalch)											
JBW (64 kg)	Rest	19·3	28·6	26·4	73	7·44						21†					114
	300	20·2	29·0	27·6	73	7·50	45·2	5·25	15·42	25	0·98	22	47	35	12	0·93	125
	600	16·5	28·8	26·4	62	7·51	69·2	5·19	15·45	25	1·49	19	50	29	20	0·93	122
	900	17·6	23·3	28·1	62	7·52	115·4	4·57	16·36	35	2·04	17	53	29	24	0·99	140
	1200	12·2	25·0	27·6	44	7·57	179·3	3·94	17·49	50	2·30	15	57	20	37	1·17	125
DT Sherpa (63 kg)	300	17·1	27·3	27·3	62	7·40	37·2	6·13	14·14	25	1·01	25	42	32	9	0·87	120
	600	16·3	23·5	27·3	59	7·35	53·5	7·01	13·48	25	1·56	26	42	32	10	0·92	146
	900	14·7	24·2	28·0	52	7·35	81·9	6·90	14·04	25	2·28	26	44	29	15	0·96	162
	1200						113·5	6·29	14·98	—	2·70	23	48			1·02	186
	1400						118·5	5·43	16·36	—	2·39	20	53			1·24	186

† From CO_2 dissociation curve.

same as that of the white subject although his O_2 saturation was lower. In 3 to 4 minutes' maximum exercise, the Sherpa worked at 1400 kg-m/min compared with 1200 kg-m/min, and his maximum O_2 intake was 2·70 l./min compared with 2·30 l./min for the white man. This high O_2 intake was achieved with a maximum work ventilation of only 119 l.BTPS/min compared with 180 l.BTPS/min and a heart rate of 186 beats/min compared with 125–140 beats/min for the white man. Calculations based on other data

TABLE 4

Data from the Himalayan Scientific and Mountaineering Expedition 1960/61 on a high altitude porter and the fittest member of the scientific party, based on simultaneous blood and respiratory measurements during ergometer exercise at 5800 m (19,000 ft)

	DT Sherpa	JBW
Body weight (kg)	63	64 (normal 74 at sea level)
Maximum 3–4 min exercise (kg-m/min)	1400	1200
Maximum O_2 intake (l./min)	2·70	2·30
Maximum work ventilation (l.BTPS/min)	119	180–200
Maximum work heart rate (beats/min)	186	140–125
Cardiac output (l./min)	23 (calculated)	17
Results at 900 kg-m/min		
O_2 intake (l./min)	2·28	2·04
Ventilation (l.BTPS/min)	82	115
Diffusing capacity for O_2 (ml/min/mm Hg)	97	60
Alveolar P_{O_2} (mm Hg)	44	53
Blood pH	7·35	7·52
Arterial P_{O_2} (mm Hg)	29	29
Arterial saturation (%)	52	62

suggested a D_{O_2} of about 95 ml/min/mm Hg for the Sherpa compared with 60 ml/min/mm Hg, and a maximum cardiac output of about 23, compared with 17 l./min. This finding suggests that the high-altitude Sherpa owed his superior performance primarily to a high pulmonary diffusing capacity and greater cardiac output. There was also evidence of marked difference in respiratory control.

The findings on the Sherpas are qualitatively similar to those of

Theilen, Gregg, and Rotta (1955) on South American miners at 4500 m (15,000 ft) compared with visitors. But the physical working capacity both in the white men and in the Sherpas on Himalayan expeditions appears to be very much greater than values reported from South America and one is led to wonder whether the South American miner's performance is affected by factors other than altitude, such as nutrition, dust disease, coca chewing, &c.

Preparatory expeditions

A pilot expedition will be an essential preliminary to investigations in Chaka, but may not be necessary in the case of the Sherpas since we have contact with them in various ways. Such an expedition could be carried out by one or two trained observers who would investigate the size and distribution of the population, their attitude to visitors, and logistic matters.

Readers wishing to compare these data with findings on South American natives are referred to Hurtado's review (1964) and the Proceedings of a Symposium at Interlaken in September 1962.

Full-scale expeditions

A complete biological survey will require successive expeditions extending over a period of several years with further expeditions in the more distant future. The choice of subjects for study, and success in carrying out such studies, will of course depend on the personality and skills of the leaders of the expeditions and their teams. Such people tend to be individualists and not to take too kindly to planning from above. It is suggested therefore that potential expedition leaders and their teams should be sought at an early stage while plans are still fluid and that efforts should be made to find workers who will be prepared to take part in successive expeditions.

It is a matter for discussion whether such expeditions should be composed of workers from one or several disciplines. For this reason, it is useful at this stage to consider physiological plans under two headings:

(a) investigations on large numbers not requiring special physiological training, and

(b) investigations, requiring special physiological training, to be carried out on a limited number of subjects.

35

Investigations on large numbers. Investigations of this type come under the heading of 'Background Population Characteristics' in the project of the Royal Society Working Party. They include:
anthropometric measurements,
fat thickness at selected sites,
chest X-ray,
E.C.G.,
haemoglobin concentration,
resting blood pressure and heart rate, and
simple lung function tests.

Investigations on restricted numbers. These would be carried out by a physiological team of four to six investigators which would require hutted accommodation. Subjects could be engaged for the duration of the expedition and act as porters as well as subjects for physiological studies. The programme would include, in addition to items under heading (a) above, measurements of:
basal metabolism,
food and energy balance,
aerobic capacity,
lung volume,
diffusing capacity for CO,
blood volume,
heart rate, ventilation and O_2 intake and cardiac output at 4 work rates on a bicycle ergometer,
blood gases and blood pH:
respiratory response to gas mixtures containing varying mixtures of O_2 and CO_2,
heat and cold tolerance, and
thyroid function.
The procedure and methods of analysis will follow the lines laid down in the projected IBP handbooks.

Special high-altitude expedition

British physiologists have expressed interest in a physiological expedition to 6000 m (20,000 ft) to study the adaptation of Sherpas to very high altitudes along the lines of the 1960–61 Expedition. The programme would include many of the items under the previous headings with the addition of endocrine studies similar to those carried out in 1960–61 (Pugh, 1962b) as well as studies of fat metabolism.

Additional suggestions

1. *Nutritional survey.* This will be simplified by the fact that the Sherpas have so few items of diet. It might even be possible to weigh the entire food supply of a village.

2. *Physical working capacity.* There will be no difficulty in using the bicycle ergometer provided the subjects are taken on as porters and stay with expeditions throughout. I have also used walking uphill and step tests in the Himalaya. In my opinion walking uphill is a good method for large-scale application as there is no learning to be done.

Gas sampling is always essential and I am in favour of gas analysis on the spot as well as storage of samples in sealed ampoules.

3. *Strength tests.* Generally speaking, Sherpas have weak arms and strong legs. I should have thought that a simple battery of tests such as those used by the U.S. Navy (1961 and 1962) would yield as much useful comparative information as complex dynamometric tests. We already know the number of pull-ups, press-ups, single leg deep knees bends, &c., that athletes and other fit European and American adults can perform.

4. *Pulmonary function.* In the light of the results of the 1960–61 Himalayan Scientific and Mountaineering Expedition, I propose that maximum exercise D_{CO} and lung volume would be the most useful measurements. The question whether the large thorax seen in Sherpas is a developmental characteristic like the large chest of the asthmatic or whether it is inherited, is worthy of study.

5. *Laboratory facilities.* Having carried out studies in tents in the Himalaya and also experienced the advantages of a hut at 5800 m (19,000 ft) I should say that while good work can be done in tents, the amount of work accomplished in a given period will be two to three times greater if a hut is provided. I have not found Sherpa houses suitable for use as a laboratory because of poor lighting, draughts and dust, and the difficulty of temperature control.

The design and production of a laboratory hut suitable for use on IBP expeditions would be a useful subject for discussion.

6. *Transport and packaging.* Expeditions will need expert advice on packaging techniques. My personal experience has been that the only way to make quite certain that a delicate piece of apparatus will arrive undamaged is to carry it yourself. This is surely an

absurd state of affairs. We in Britain have much to learn from the United States in this respect. Consideration might usefully be given to the compilation of a handbook on packaging of equipment, or inclusion of a section on this subject in the handbook on the storage and transport of samples.

REFERENCES

HURTADO, A., 1964. *Handbook of Physiology*, Sect. 4, Adaptation to Environment (eds. D. B. DILL, E. F. ADOLPH, and C. G. WILBER), p. 843. Am. Physiol. Soc., Washington.

MONGE, C., 1948. *Acclimatization in the Andes: Historical Confirmation of 'Climatic Aggression' in the Development of Andean Man* (translated from Spanish by D. F. BROWN). Johns Hopkins Press, Baltimore.

Proceedings of a Symposium on the Physiological Effects of High Altitude, Interlaken, 1964. Pergamon Press, Oxford.

PUGH, L. G. C., 1962a. *Geogr. J.* **128**, 447–456.

—— 1962b. *Br. med. J.* **ii**, 621–627.

THEILEN, E. O., GREGG, D. E., and ROTTA, A., 1955. *Circulation* **12**, 383.

U.S. NAVY, 1961. *Sec. Nav.* 6100. 1 *pers. G.*11 *Kap.* 14 *August.*

—— 1962. *Buprs.* 6100. 2a *pers. G.*111 *Kap.* 18 *September.*

INDEX